SCANDINAVIAN LANDS

SCANDINAVIAN LANDS

BY

ROY MILLWARD

Lecturer in Historical Geography
University of Leicester

LONDON
MACMILLAN & CO LTD
NEW YORK · ST MARTIN'S PRESS
1964

MACMILLAN AND COMPANY LIMITED
St Martin's Street London WC 2
also Bombay Calcutta Madras Melbourne

THE MACMILLAN COMPANY OF CANADA LIMITED
70 Bond Street Toronto 2

ST MARTIN'S PRESS INC
175 Fifth Avenue New York 10 NY

PRINTED IN GREAT BRITAIN

TO

CHARLOTTE, HELEN, AND TIM

companions on this intellectual journey
through Scandinavia and along many
miles in Northern Europe

CONTENTS

	PAGE
LIST OF ILLUSTRATIONS	ix
LIST OF MAPS	xi
PREFACE	xv

CHAPTER

1. WHAT IS SCANDINAVIA?   I

PART I

THE REGIONAL GEOGRAPHY OF SCANDINAVIA

2. NORWAY   11
3. SWEDEN   44
4. DENMARK   80
5. FINLAND   107

PART II

SOME FACETS OF SCANDINAVIAN GEOGRAPHY

6. SCANDINAVIAN LANDSCAPES AND CLIMATES   143
7. THE HISTORICAL DEVELOPMENT OF SCANDINAVIA   172
8. THE AGRICULTURAL GEOGRAPHY OF SCANDINAVIA   221
9. THE GROWTH OF SCANDINAVIAN INDUSTRIES   260
10. HYDRO-ELECTRIC POWER IN SCANDINAVIA   280
11. MERCHANT NAVIES AND FISHING FLEETS   305
12. FORESTRY AND TIMBER INDUSTRIES   333
13. IRON AND STEEL IN SCANDINAVIA   376
14. THE ENGINEERING INDUSTRIES OF SCANDINAVIA   405
15. THE ELECTRO-CHEMICAL AND ELECTRO-METALLURGICAL INDUSTRIES   427
16. SCANDINAVIA TODAY   446
NOTES   461
BIBLIOGRAPHY   465
INDEX   473

LIST OF ILLUSTRATIONS

PLATE

1 The Town Hall, Oslo
2 Kristiansand
3 Lake Mjøsa
4 Gudbrandsdal
5 Røros
6 Bergen
7 The Bremanger metal refinery, Svelgen
8 The skerry-guard
9 Fjord settlement in Vestlandet
10 Jotunheimen
11 Trondheim
12 Mosjøen
13 Traena
14 Solsöm on the island of Leka, north Norway
15 Vaerøy, Lofoten islands
16 Svartisen
17 Old Uppsala
18 Uppsala
19 Latorpsbruk iron mine, Bergslagen
20 Landscape in Södermanland
21 The Göta canal
22 The Göta river near Trollhättan
23 Smögen, a fishing village in Bohuslän

BETWEEN
PAGES
144-145

24 Göteborg
25 Scene in Norrland
26 The Ljusnan valley, Hälsingland, northern Sweden
27 The Indals river
28 A fäbod in the forests of Dalarna, Sweden
29 Areskutan mountain, Jämtland, Sweden
30 Kalmar castle, Sweden
31 Visby, Gotland
32 Island of Ven
33 Helsinki in the grip of winter

BETWEEN
PAGES
304-305

ix

Scandinavian Lands

PLATE

34 Tampere

35 Melavesi, Finnish lakes plateau

36 Punkaharju

37 Kaukopää sulphate pulp mill, Finland

38 Savonlinna

39 Lake Päijänne

40 Rovaniemi

41 Pallastunturi

42 Ahvenanmaa (Åland) isles

43 The Little Belt bridge

44 The chalk cliffs of Møn

45 Helsingør, Denmark

46 Esbjerg

47 Roskilde, Denmark

48 Copenhagen

BETWEEN
PAGES
304-305

LIST OF MAPS

FIGURE   PAGE

1   Viking settlements in western Europe   3
2   Racial characteristics in northern Europe   6
3   Norway — distribution of lowland   12
4   Norway — densely populated areas (1950)   15
5   South Norway — provinces and counties   17
6   South Norway — geology   21
7   North Norway — provinces and counties   38
8   North Norway — geology   39
9   Norway — population of urban centres (1950)   42
10   Sweden — densely populated areas (1950)   45
11   Sweden — provinces   47
12   The political evolution of Sweden   49
13   Sweden, Norway, Denmark — eskers   52
14   City plan of Stockholm   58
15   The political geography of the Göta valley in the seventeenth century   65
16   Geology of Skåne   68
17   Norrland — geology   74
18   Denmark — solid geology   81
19   Denmark — geomorphology   82
20   Denmark — density of population (1950)   85
21   Westward growth of Copenhagen   89
22   The growth of Copenhagen   90
23   Copenhagen and a future conurbation of the Øresund   91
24   Bornholm — solid geology   94
25   Denmark — distribution of clayey and sandy soils   97
26   Finland — distribution of recent sands and clays   111
27   Finland — cultivated and improved land in 1943   113
28   Finland — abandoned settlements of the Åland isles, 1900–1950   123
29   Finland — forests   132
30   Caledonian elements in northern Europe   144
31   Geology of the Oslo area   148
32   Scandinavia — chief stages of ice retreat   152
33   Scandinavia — changes in sea level in late glacial and post-glacial times   154
34   South Norway — areas that emerged from the sea in post-glacial times   159
35   Thin-butted flint axes in southern Norway   160
36   Scandinavia — annual precipitation   164
37   Scandinavia — mean temperatures for January and July   166

FIGURE   PAGE
38 Length of vegetative period and length of snow cover   168
39 Denmark — Neolithic chambered tombs   174
40 The heaths of Jutland   176
41 Expansion of *seter* settlement in the parish of Orsa, 1663–1918   184
42 The foundation of Swedish towns in the seventeenth century   187
43 Extent of post-glacial submergence in Norrbotten   189
44 Abandonment of *seters* in Dalarna, 1900–1958   191
45 Summer and winter pastures of reindeer herds in Norway   201
46 Evidence of hunting and fishing communities in stone-age
      Finland, 7000–1800 B.C.   204
47 Prehistoric sites and the recession of the Finnish shoreline   207
48 Settlements of the Baltic Finns at the end of the prehistoric period
      (A.D. 1200)   208
49 The Swedish-speaking population of Finland, 1950   213
50 Finland — routes to medieval hunting and fishing grounds   216
51 Areas of settlement in medieval Finland (A.D. 1200–1400)   217
52 Denmark — agricultural yields   229
53 Denmark — sugar beet   231
54 Denmark — agricultural regions   232
55 Sweden — length of farming year   237
56 Land redistribution in the village of Vattnäs, Mora parish   238
57 Sugar-beet factories in Sweden   245
58 Norway — arable land   250
59 Finland — the northern limit of spring wheat   252
60 Finland — displaced rural population, 1947   255
61 Post-war settlement areas in Finland   256
62 Freshly reclaimed land at Jukajoki, northern Karelia   258
63 Length of railways in northern Europe, 1847–1959   271
64 Scandinavia — hydro-electric power, 1960   283
65 Power stations of Indalsälven   285
66 Finland — power stations in the Oulu basin   287
67 Finland — the Kemi river hydro-electric project   288
68 Norway — water power resources, 1950   291
69 Norway — hydro-electric power, 1960   293
70 Norway — electricity transmission lines, 1955   295
71 Norway — Abjøra power station   299
72 Pirttikoski — Finland. Underground power station   301
73 Sweden — main electricity transmission lines, 1958   303
74 The development of Norway's merchant navy   310
75 Development of merchant fleets, 1900–1955   311
76 Positions of Norwegian ships on one day in 1959   314
77 Norway — fishing grounds   316
78 Landings and number of fishermen in the Lofoten cod fisheries,
      1930–1959   318
79 Norway — quantity of catch from the main fishing districts, 1955–
      1956   321
80 Total yield of Norwegian fisheries, 1900–1960   322

List of Maps

FIGURE   PAGE

81   Fishermen in Bohuslän, Sweden, 1955   324

82   Vestvågøy — Lofoten islands. Areas reserved for different types of fishing gear   328

83   Norway — forests   334

84   Forests in northern Europe   337

85   Forest types in Finland   339

86   Finland — annual growth of timber   341

87   Finland — state forests and company forests   344

88   Sweden — ownership of forest and woodland   346

89   Categories of timber consumption in Sweden, 1851–1955   350

90   Timber floatways in Finland   352

91   Timber industries in Sweden   355

92   Finland — sawmills, 1959   357

93   Finland — the Kemi valley   362

94   Finland — pulp mills, 1959   371

95   Norway — manufacture of mechanical and chemical pulp in the Oslo region   372

96   Sweden — mining, 1954   377

97   Iron ore mines and iron and steel works in northern Europe   379

98   Norway — minerals, 1957   381

99   Bergslagen — iron ore mines   384

100   Export of Swedish iron ore   386

101   Sweden — iron and steel works and base metal plants   387

102   Concentration of iron industry in the Bergslagen region, 1860–1950   390

103   Industrial interests of the Uddeholm group in Värmland   391

104   Sweden — engineering industry, 1954   406

105   Activities of A.S.E.A. in Sweden   408

106   Output of the Swedish shipbuilding industry   412

107   Chief suppliers to Volvo factory, Göteborg   414

108   Shipbuilding in Norway, 1957   421

109   Finland — engineering, 1958   425

110   Norway — electro-chemical industries   429

111   Norway — electro-metallurgical industries   435

112   Sweden — chemical industry   443

PREFACE

In writing this geography of Scandinavia I have confined my field of study to the four countries that belong to the mainland of northern Europe, excluding Iceland and Greenland which normally belong to regional studies of the Scandinavian world. The history of the ninth and tenth centuries joined this volcanic island and the remoter, ice-covered Greenland to the communities of northern Europe. Although race, language, and, in the case of Greenland, political affiliations still provide close links with the Scandinavian countries, the economic evolution of Norway and the Baltic countries since the middle of the nineteenth century and the power relationships that have developed in our own times in northern Europe have practically removed these tiny Atlantic settlements from the sphere of Scandinavian affairs. In the realm of physical geography, too, it is possible to isolate Iceland and Greenland from a study of Scandinavia. The smoking volcanoes, immense basalt plateaus, and the cold, dusty deserts of Iceland's interior find no parallel in Scandinavian Europe. Likewise, the immense high ice-plateau of Greenland where glaciers calve each summer in the quiet fjords presents an image of northern Europe in the Ice Age rather than an analogue of the Scandinavian peninsula today. The first section of the book sketches the regional geography of the four Scandinavian countries. The small region — the *pays* of the French geographer — is the key to the understanding of the geography of the wide area that we call Scandinavia, an area ranging from Arctic Norway's bleak fjords to the forested shores of the Gulf of Finland and the prosperous farmlands of southern Denmark. The regional unit is often dominated by a morphological or geological feature. History, too, has contributed to the character of the minor region. Through the centuries peasant cultures have evolved slowly in the Scandinavian lands, shaping and shaped by their environment. The industrial revolution that has transformed the geography of western Europe, obliterating the old regional differences and creating new contrasts, has only reached the northlands in the past few decades. In all the Scandinavian countries there is still a sense of the primitive, the wild and the untamed, of a geography whose elements go back to the beginning of time.

The second part of the book attempts a study of Scandinavia as it is today after showing the relevance of physique and history to an understanding of contemporary geography. The chief sectors of the economy of the northern countries are analysed in the terms of their history and their present functions, and Scandinavia is seen to be in the throes of an industrial revolution, a change that is transforming the societies of these northern states. Lastly, the political problems of the north are set against the economies of the Scandinavian countries. Here the pace of change is greatest and least predictable. Even before this chapter appears in print much of its content could seem as faded and irrelevant as the pages of ancient history, especially in these months when the rest of western Europe is debating whether to be at ' Sixes ' or ' Sevens '.

In the writing of this book I am deeply indebted to Terence Garfield and his cartographic assistants in the Department of Geography at the University of Leicester, whose skill has gone into the preparation of all the maps. I wish to thank E. C. Marchant and W. A. G. Pace who read an early version of the manuscript and offered valuable criticisms, also J. H. McD. Whitaker who gave of his knowledge of Norwegian geology. For the photographs in the text I wish to acknowledge the following sources : Aerofilms and Aero Pictorial Ltd., Widerøe's Flyveselskap og Polarfly A/S of Oslo, the libraries of the Finnish Travel Information Centre and the Finnish Embassy, the Bremanger Smelteverk, and the manager of the Pyhäkoski power station in Finland. I have received valuable help from several officials of the embassies of the Scandinavian countries and not least from the countless people in those northern lands who have talked of places and problems on journeys into this ever fascinating part of Europe.

R. M.

CHAPTER 1

What is Scandinavia?

WHEN a Swede leaves his native country to visit some other part of Europe, he describes his trip as 'a journey to the continent'. This phrase reveals the inner thought that Scandinavia, like the British Isles, stands somewhat remote from the main trunk of Europe. But this major region of northern Europe may be described in more precise terms than the colloquial remarks of a Scandinavian traveller making his way to central Europe across the complicated chain of train ferries between the stepping-stones of the Danish archipelago.

There are many definitions of Scandinavia. In the mind of a geologist Scandinavia largely belongs to the outcrop of the Baltic Shield, composed of the oldest rocks on the face of the continent, that were folded and peneplained several times during the Archaean period [Fig. 30]. Again, the climatologist seems able to offer a satisfactory definition of this region in the terms of a climate that swings between the extremes of a summer of almost perpetual light and a long, dark winter, when the curtains of the aurora borealis hang in the northern sky. Here perhaps lies one of the clues to the character of Scandinavian Europe. Are not the vast tracts of coniferous forest and the immense northern tundras a living expression of this seasonal rhythm? And is it not possible to imagine the national temperaments of Norway and Sweden as a subtle reflection of the harsh climate of these lands that stretch far beyond the Arctic Circle? Their solid, reliable, and outwardly unexpressive peoples seem to be the proper counterpart of a climate that has barely tolerated the presence of men during the few thousand years since the waning of the Ice Age. In no other part of the world are cities to be found in such high latitudes. Greenland's ice-mantled plateau lies on the same latitude as Oslo, Stockholm, and Helsinki, and the equivalent latitudes of North America are occupied by the scarcely inhabited wastes of tundra at the mouth of Hudson Bay and the bleak shores of Alaska.

In trying to define the main areas of the European continent it

B   I

is not possible to limit oneself to the facts of the physical environment. The landscapes of Europe and the societies of the various nation-states are as much a product of their history as a reflection of their physical setting. Therefore, to make a definition of Scandinavia, one must take into account the history of the peopling of this area from the south and east as the Quaternary ice-sheet rapidly melted away in the centuries after 12,000 B.C. This vast region, with its focal point in the basin of the Baltic Sea, was isolated from many of the main currents of European history. Scandinavia never felt the direct impact of Roman civilization, though the hoards of coins and drinking-vessels of Roman origin that have been found in Danish bogs and on the island of Gotland show that the north was in contact with the Roman world.[1] There was a gap of a thousand years before the seeds of Christianity took root in northern Europe. Likewise, the industrial revolution that transformed the economy of the coalfields of western Europe about 1800 only began to make its mark on the Baltic area in the first decade of the twentieth century, after the harnessing of water-power for the production of electricity.

Scandinavia remained apart from the main stream of Europe's settlement history. She was not deeply affected by the great migrations of peoples in central and western Europe that followed the crumbling of Roman power north of the Alps after the fourth century A.D. In fact, it has been suggested that a worsening of the climate of northern Europe late in the Iron Age made this remote fringe of the continent less habitable in the first centuries of the Christian era.[2] The peoples of Scandinavia migrated southwards from the Baltic area to make their own contribution to the barbarian folk movements. In the third century, the Goths sent out settlers from their homeland in east Sweden and the isle of Gotland to colonize the Dnieper valley and the shores of the Black Sea. From this area of south-eastern Europe the Goths migrated westward through central Europe, their name becoming the ultimate symbol of the culture that flowered on the Atlantic margins in the early Middle Ages.

It is fatally easy to see the rôle of Scandinavia as one isolated from the main currents of political, social, and economic life in the European continent. In truth, this area was scarcely affected by the great movements of peoples in the dark ages and it played an insignificant part in the imperial and colonial history that took European culture and techniques to the other four continents.

2

What is Scandinavia?

But one must not be tempted to sketch the character of Scandinavia simply as a group of lonely communities on the polar fringe practising a European way of life. In certain phases of Europe's history the lands of the north acted with striking effect. Viking

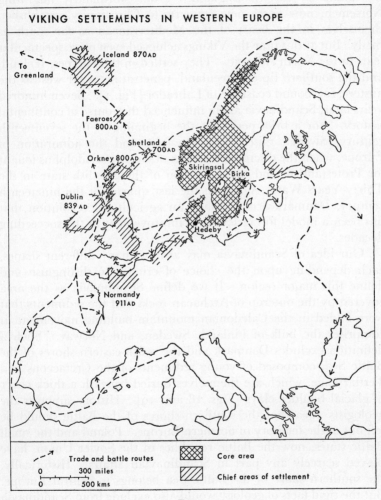

VIKING SETTLEMENTS IN WESTERN EUROPE

Iceland 870 AD

To Greenland

Faeroes 800 AD

Shetland 700 AD

Orkney 800 AD

Skiringsal

Birka

Dublin 839 AD

Hedeby

Normandy 911 AD

Trade and battle routes

0   300 miles

0   500 kms

Core area

Chief areas of settlement

FIG. 1

During the ninth and tenth centuries A.D. the peoples of Scandinavia expanded by trade, warfare, and settlement from the core area in the southern half of the peninsula and the Danish archipelago. They made their deepest mark on the North Sea basin and the islands of the North Atlantic, but Viking raiders and traders reached the western basin of the Mediterranean and Constantinople, the metropolis of the Byzantine Empire.

3

raiders and settlers profoundly influenced the margin of Atlantic Europe in the ninth and tenth centuries A.D. Apart from the devastating, though temporary, economic damage, the Norsemen established kingdoms such as Normandy and settled heavily on the plains of eastern England. From Normandy, migrating Norsemen, now fierce new converts to Christianity, established themselves in the heart of the Mediterranean as far south as Sicily. But at this time the Vikings achieved even more spectacular feats in the North Atlantic. They settled in the Faeroes, Iceland, and the southern tip of Greenland, penetrating as far west as the austere, fog-bound coastline of Labrador [Fig. 1]. Seven hundred years later, Scandinavia again influenced the course of continental history. For a brief period at the beginning of the seventeenth century, Sweden raised both the fears and the admiration of Europe, when the disciplined armies of Gustavus Adolphus fought for Protestantism and the expansion of the Swedish state in the Thirty Years War. Again, in the last quarter of the nineteenth century, Denmark accomplished an agricultural revolution that has been a model for agricultural improvement in the succeeding decades.

Our idea of Scandinavia may assume many different shapes, each depending upon the choice of criteria to distinguish and define this major region. If we define Scandinavia as the area covered by the outcrop of Archaean rocks and the sediments that were folded in the Caledonian mountain-building movement, it comprises the bulk of Finland, Sweden, and Norway. Such a definition excludes Denmark and the south-eastern shores of the Baltic Sea, composed of young sediments of the Cretaceous and Tertiary age, which are themselves buried beneath a thick cover of glacial boulder clays [Figs. 18 and 19]. History supports the geologists' idea that the southern shores of the Baltic should be left out of the territory of northern Europe. Poland and the small Baltic states, now the Baltic republics of the Soviet Union, have played scarcely any part in Scandinavian affairs. Historically, the southern shore of the Baltic Sea belongs to central Europe. But the rigid facts of geology would also exclude from Scandinavia the Jutland peninsula and the Danish archipelago. Physically, Denmark is a projection of the German plain. The same floor of Tertiary clays and Cretaceous limestones is largely masked by the waste of the last Ice Age. The physique of Denmark is scarcely distinguishable from that of northern Germany, but historically

the country has always belonged to Scandinavia. Until the late
Middle Ages her kings ruled over territories in southern Sweden,
and Denmark retained control of Norway until the end of the
Napoleonic Wars. Apart from a powerful political influence on the
affairs of northern Europe in distant medieval times, Denmark
today displays close affinities with her neighbours Norway and
Sweden. The Danish, Swedish, and Norwegian languages are
closely related to each other and seem to spring from a common
tongue that was spoken in Scandinavia more than a thousand
years ago. In the past century, the life of the Danish people
evolved a pattern that closely resembles the way of life in Norway,
Sweden, and Finland. Like her Scandinavian neighbours, Denmark has adopted the ideal of a society with comfortable middle-
class standards. Government proceeds through a parliamentary
system that is crowned with a constitutional monarchy, a feature
also of Norway and Sweden. Danish politics have been comparatively placid for the past century and a half — a sharp
contrast indeed with the violence and turmoil of many parts of
Europe since the beginning of the nineteenth century. The
Danish economy rests upon the steady export of agricultural products to maintain a high internal standard of life. Although not
leaning upon dairy farming, the other Scandinavian countries are
equally dependent upon primary products for their national
survival. Sweden sells her rich iron ores, timber, and wood-pulp
overseas. Finland lives by the natural wealth of her vast tracts
of softwood forest. Norway reaps the harvest of the North
Atlantic's fishing-grounds, scours the Southern Ocean with her
whaling factories, and her tramp steamers act as carriers between
the ports of the five continents. The health of each of these states
depends upon a vigorous international trade. Although Denmark's topography, geology, and climate make her indistinguishable from central Europe, her history and economic development
have joined her to Scandinavian Europe.

The regional unity of Scandinavia seems to lie as much in the
facts of human geography as in the physical features of her landscapes, but even within this realm of knowledge a single clear-cut
definition is hard to reach. The physical characteristics of the
peoples of northern Europe suggest that the region might be
sketched in terms of the distribution of the Nordic race [Fig. 2].
Scandinavian people, tall and blonde with fair skin and blue eyes,
often conform to the accepted description of the Nordic race.

5

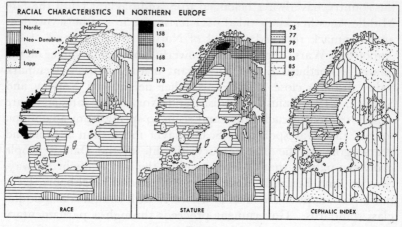

RACIAL CHARACTERISTICS IN NORTHERN EUROPE

Nordic	Neo-Danubian	Alpine	Lapp

cm
158
163
168
173
178

75
77
79
81
83
85
87

RACE · STATURE · CEPHALIC INDEX

FIG. 2

The Nordic race dominates the coastlands of the Baltic Sea. Eastward, in central Finland, Nordic types give way to the Neo-Danubian race, derived from Nordic roots and now predominant among the Slavs in Poland and Russia. The Lapps, descendants of Upper Palaeolithic hunting peoples with a distinct Mongoloid element' prevail in northern Scandinavia and along the mountain divide of Sweden and Norway. The distinctive broad-headed Alpine element in western Norway may represent a survival of pre-Iron Age folk migrations. The map showing average stature marks out the Nordic area as one of tall people and, likewise, the Nordic sector of central Scandinavia stands out on the third map as a region of long-headed characteristics.

This dominant physical type is partly explained by the remoteness of Scandinavia from the great movements of peoples that affected Europe in the first ten centuries of the Christian era. The basic stock of the north European people was established two thousand years earlier by the waves of settlement in the Bronze Age. But the tenuous facts of racial geography and its artificial classifications of mankind cannot give unity to Scandinavia. Disconcerting contradictions stand forth clearly in the very heart of this major European province. For instance, the Lapps, small groups of reindeer-herders who follow a decaying, nomadic way of life on the tundras of northern Scandinavia, possess distinct physical characteristics that link them with the peoples of Arctic Asia.

Again two distinct stocks compose the Finnish nation; they even reveal their diverse origins in their spoken language. The population of south-western Finland contains a strong Swedish element, a result of migration across the Gulf of Bothnia that started as long ago as the sixth century A.D. [Fig. 49]. It only

6

came to an end when Finland passed from Swedish to Russian control in the Napoleonic Wars. But the bulk of the Finnish population was born of a folk movement that started on the Russian steppes in the late Iron Age. They probably moved north-westwards along that ancient route of barbarian traders and migrant peoples — the Dnieper valley [Fig. 48]. The exotic origin of the Finns is evident in their language, which, apart from a number of words borrowed from Swedish, has no affinities with the other tongues of Scandinavia. The only other relatives of Finnish in Europe are the languages of the Baltic republics on the southern shore of the Gulf of Finland. Far to the south, on the middle Danube plains, the language of Hungary belongs to this same group, and it is thought that the Magyars were a branch of the same Asiatic people who moved directly westward from the Ukrainian steppe to split the Slavs and settle the region between the Carpathians and the northern foothills of the Balkans.[3]

No satisfactory single criterion can be found to distinguish Scandinavia, either in the realms of physical or human geography. As a physical region its history begins more than two hundred million years ago, and features of these earliest landscapes still belong to the scenery of modern Scandinavia. Man came to the task of shaping this ancient landscape a mere four thousand years ago, but within this brief span his influence has been profound.

Today we may pick upon many disparate facts, from both the long geological history and man's brief tenancy of this region, as distinctive of Scandinavia. The primeval shaggy hummocks of red granite in the Swedish province of Bohuslän, the patternless maze of eskers and lakes that characterize the scenery of the Finnish plateau, the deep, glassy fjords penetrating for scores of miles the plateaus of western Norway — all these are essential elements in a definition of Scandinavia. Likewise one might point to the hygienic austerity of Scandinavian cities as a characteristic sign of this region. Again, the peasant society that has survived in the recesses of the long valleys of south-eastern Norway might be chosen as a true symbol of this huge province of the European continent. Its elaborate wooden buildings, displaying great skills in carving, and its folk songs and archaic costumes are unique, even in northern Europe. For some, the quintessence of Scandinavia exists on a less tangible plane — in the curious remoteness

7

of the music of Sibelius or the gloomy introspection of the characters in a play by Ibsen or Strindberg. But with the long argument about the nature of Scandinavian Europe unsettled, we may say that it is composed of the states of Denmark, Finland, Norway, and Sweden. With all their internal diversity, as described in the following chapters, these nations have much in common — sufficient to form one of the major regions of our continent.

PART I

THE REGIONAL GEOGRAPHY
OF SCANDINAVIA

CHAPTER 2

Norway

POVERTY is the hallmark of Scandinavia's physical environment. Denmark alone is excluded from this generalization, because she consists of a peninsula of central Europe and an archipelago of low islands blocking the gateway to the Baltic Sea. Her soils are deep and fertile when compared with those of the rest of Scandinavia. Likewise, Denmark's summers seem warm, sunny, and bountifully prolonged into the autumn when compared with those of the more northern countries. Finland, Sweden, and Norway suffer common physical handicaps. Each stretches far beyond the Arctic Circle. In all three countries, and especially in Norway, farmers and fishing communities have penetrated the polar region more deeply than anywhere else on the face of the earth.

High latitude forms but one element in the physical poverty of these countries. The outcrop of Europe's oldest rocks over vast areas of Norway, Sweden, and Finland adds another intractable item to the economy of the northern states. Again, Scandinavia acted as the gathering ground of Europe's greatest ice-sheets in the Quaternary period, ice-sheets that removed all trace of the soils that must have accumulated under the warmer climates of late Tertiary times in northern Europe. The Quaternary Ice Age impoverished the agricultural development of the Scandinavian countries to an extent that cannot be calculated.

THE NORWEGIAN NATION IN ITS PHYSICAL SETTING

Norway ranks with Finland as the poorest among the Scandinavian states. Her northern territories reach further into the Arctic than the 'northlands' of either of her neighbours. In the south she has nothing to match Sweden's fertile plains in the rich province of Skåne. Norway's disadvantages are exaggerated because she contains the biggest tract of highland in northern Europe. Much of south-western Norway lies above three

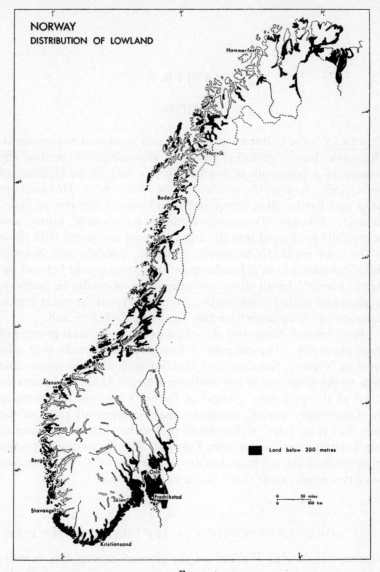

FIG. 3

Lowland is severely limited in Norway. It is most extensive in the south-east, facing
the Skagerrak and the shores of Oslo fjord. Another tract of lowland centres on
Trondheim fjord. These regions form two of the chief cores of settlement and economic
development in the country. In the far north there are considerable tracts of land
below the 200-metre contour, but here climate precludes any thorough settlement
and economic growth.

thousand feet, and an even greater area of the country stands above fifteen hundred feet, the uttermost limit of permanent settlement in these northern latitudes. It seems ironical that the forces responsible for the shaping of Europe since mid-Tertiary times have given to Norway the highest land in northern Europe, while at the same time she has been blessed with an abnormally mild climate for such high latitudes. The enveloping warm waters of the North Atlantic, combined with the frequent invasion of warm air masses from the south, give the coastline of western Norway a climate that is almost a freak in the grand scheme of world climates. Yet any advantage to be gained from a climate whose mean January temperatures stand forty degrees above the average for their latitude, is largely cancelled out by the height of the land in western and central Norway [Fig. 3].

Norway is not a large country. With an area of nearly 125,000 square miles she is slightly larger than the British Isles. Sweden is half as big again and France is nearly twice the size of Norway. But a cold statistic of area is far from telling us everything about a country. The shape and extent of a nation's territory, the distribution of her mountains, plains, and rivers, and her endowment of mineral resources are more important to the understanding of the evolution of a state and the development of its economy.

Norway stretches for hundreds of miles from south to north. Thirteen degrees of latitude separate the white wooden villages of her southern coastline from the bleak North Cape. Northward of Trondheim, Arctic Norway presents a severe façade to the Atlantic Ocean. In parts, the Swedish frontier lies scarcely fifty miles from the sea, and at one point only five miles from the head of a deeply penetrating fjord. Through this region of grey fjords, bare, dull landscapes, and harsh glacier-ribbed mountains, a road runs like a long ribbon for 1250 miles from Trondheim to Kirkenes at the Russian frontier. Southward of Trondheim fjord, Norway becomes broader, but the backbone of mountains grows bolder as well. A high, empty wilderness formed by the massive rounded summits of the Dovrefjell, the snowfields of the Jotunheimen [Plate 10], and the lonely moors of the Hardangervidda, divides the fjords of the Atlantic coast from the open valleys leading down to Oslo fjord. Norway lacks physical unity. She suffers from the fact that her physical territory stretches northwards for hundreds of miles into the Arctic, a narrow corridor poised between the sea and a barren mountain backbone. Her physical incoherence is emphasized again on a local scale. Each of the many fjords along her western coast stands isolated from its neighbours by difficult upland country. Likewise, the long, forest-filled valleys of eastern Norway are separated from each other by an empty wilderness [Plate 4]. Even today, relics of peasant cultures survive in these valleys, cultures whose roots lie deep in the Viking period and the late Iron Age.

Norway's population statistics underline the problem of achieving political and economic coherence in this difficult environment. In 1961 her total population was 3,596,211 ; much less than half the number of Greater London, spread over an area slightly larger than that of the British Isles. It is hard for a nation to bring coherence to its territory when there are so few to accomplish the task. For centuries Norway has harboured distinctive and isolated cultural groups. The peoples of the western fjords have always looked out to the Atlantic, their lives brought to a focus in the activities of the towns of Bergen, Trondheim, and Stavanger. In contrast, the long valleys that drain to the Skagerrak are the home of peasant farmers and timber-cutters, who have created one of the loneliest and most individual cultures of the European continent.

The last years of the nineteenth century first saw the creation of a coherent Norwegian state, a product of the expanding railway network, the development of hydro-electric power, the spread of industry into the rugged interior, and the growth of Oslo as a capital city drawing its members from every province, and today housing one-sixth of the nation's total population. The late date of Norway's achievement of complete political independence, 1905, speaks of the difficulty of state-making in this harsh environment. It is interesting, too, that so many Norwegians see in their national character a reflection of the physique of their homeland. Brøgger, the famous historian of Norway, has written : 'there is probably no nation in the world whose character and development owe so much to the physical structure and characteristics of the country'.[1] In the more sophisticated parts of Europe this reads like a naïve determinism, but in Norway the struggle against a primitive environment is far from finished and the nation is still young.

Norway

REGIONAL CORES IN NORWAY

Every country contains some vital region that has performed an important rôle in the political and economic growth of the state. One remembers the parts played by the lower Thames Valley or the heart of the Paris basin in the national histories of England and France. Norway possesses three 'core' regions — the valleys

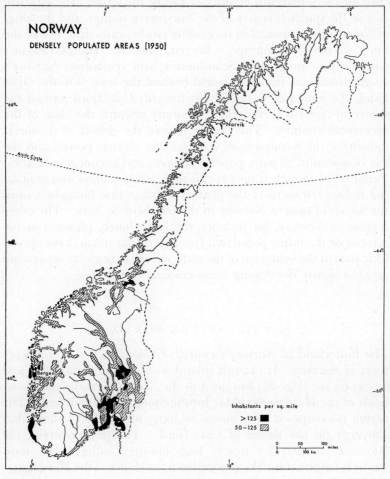

FIG. 4

Three main cores of settlement appear on the population map of Norway. The largest centres on Oslo and the valley-corridors of the south-east. Two smaller cores of settlement, historic nuclei, belong to Trondheim fjord and the islands and fjords of Vestlandet around Bergen.

15

of the south-east centred upon Oslo, the western fjords that turn towards Bergen as their capital, and the fertile plains and hills fringing the little island sea of Trondheim fjord [Fig. 4]. Each region played a decisive rôle at different times in Norwegian history; each forms a focusing point in Norwegian life at the present day. Trondheim acted as capital of medieval Norway before her crown passed to the royal house of Denmark at the close of the fourteenth century. Today this quiet little city still acts as the spiritual centre of the Norwegian nation, and the kings of Norway are crowned in its gloomy Gothic cathedral, one of the finest in northern Europe. Bergen, once the Hansa League's chief outpost in western Scandinavia, still symbolizes Norway's connections with the great world beyond the seas. On the other hand, the long valleys that drain towards Oslo fjord formed the centre of Norway's expanding economy towards the close of the nineteenth century. This area witnessed the growth of the forest industries, the harnessing of waterfalls for electric power, and the rise of sawmills, of pulp, paper, cellulose, and chemical industries. Paradoxical though it may seem, the eastern valleys also contain the richest remnants of the peasant cultures that flourished amid the forests of eastern Norway in the late Middle Ages. The other regions of Norway, for instance the high, lonely plateaus in the interior or the thinly populated fjords of the far north, have played little part in the evolution of the state, except as negative separating areas or slowly developing 'semi-colonial' territories.

SOUTH-EASTERN NORWAY

The hinterland of Norway's capital, Oslo, stretches over a wide tract of country. It extends inland from the pleasant fields and forests on the edge of Oslo fjord to the barren plateaus and snow-fields of the Hardangervidda, Jotunheimen, and Dovrefjell. The region is composed of a bunch of long, forest-filled valleys that converge on the shores of Oslo fjord. The most easterly, the Glomma, reaches for nearly four hundred miles. The most westerly empties into Skien fjord from the slopes of the Hardangervidda. This major region, composed of many minor and distinctive geographical tracts, now contains half the population of the country, much of its finest agricultural land, and most of Norway's important industries.

The very heart of this wide region — an area holding much forested and empty country — lies along the western and eastern shores of Oslo fjord. Here are two of Norway's traditional provinces, *pays* in the sense of the term used by French geographers.

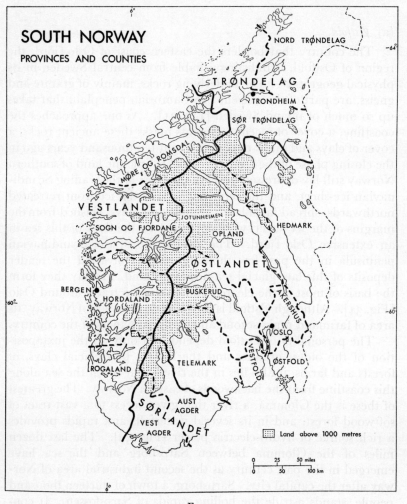

SOUTH NORWAY
PROVINCES AND COUNTIES

NORD TRØNDELAG

TRØNDELAG

TRONDHEIM

SØR TRØNDELAG

MØRE OG ROMSDAL

VESTLANDET

JOTUNHEIMEN

SOGN OG FJORDANE

OPLAND

HEDMARK

ØSTLANDET

BERGEN

HORDALAND

BUSKERUD

AKERSHUS

OSLO

VESTFOLD

ROGALAND

TELEMARK

ØSTFOLD

SØRLANDET

AUST AGDER

VEST AGDER

Land above 1000 metres

0   25   50 miles
0   50   100 km

FIG. 5

Norway's two chief provinces, Ostlandet and Vestlandet, are isolated from each other by a broad, empty tract of highland that reaches to more than nine thousand feet above sea level and scarcely ever descends below three thousand feet. In the east the counties coincide with the major valleys. In the west the county axis is usually a fjord. Rogaland, for instance, focuses on Bokn fjord and Hordaland takes Hardanger fjord as its spinal cord.

The Vestfold occupies the western shoreline, while the Østfold forms the tract of country to the east of the fjord. They stand out as distinct geographical entities, joined together by the capital city that has grown at the head of the fjord [Fig. 5].

(a) *Østfold*

The country that borders the eastern coast of Oslo fjord, the region of Østfold, is indistinguishable from central Sweden in its physical geography. The underlying rocks, mainly of granite and gneiss, are part of the ancient Pre-Cambrian peneplain that takes up so much of inland Sweden [Fig. 31]. As one approaches the coastline, a cover of recent sediments masks these ancient rocks, a cover of clays and sands deposited about ten thousand years ago in the closing phase of the Ice Age. At this time the land of southern Norway still lay depressed beneath the mass of the waning Scandinavian ice-sheet, and the returning sea, as the ice-front retreated northwards, spread far inland. Sands and clays, washed from the margins of the ice-sheet, were deposited on the floor of this sea in an extensive Oslo fjord. The steady rise of the Scandinavian peninsula in the past few thousand years converted the tender deposits of this late glacial sea-floor into land. Today they form the basis of most of the cleared and cultivated tracts around Oslo [Fig. 34]. Although Østfold is the smallest province of Norway, its area of farmland ranks second among the provinces of the country.

The personality of Østfold depends not only on the juxtaposition of the oldest granites and the newest post-glacial clays, of forests and farms, it also lies in the rivers that reach the sea along this coastline from the backwoods of eastern Norway. The greatest of these is the Glomma, a river that gives access to a vast tract of softwood forest, and in its several waterfalls and rapids provides a rich source of hydro-electric power [Fig. 39]. The last dozen miles of the Glomma between Sarpsborg and the sea have emerged in the past century as the second industrial area of Norway after the capital city. Sarpsborg, a town of thirteen thousand people, stands astride the boiling rapids of Sarpsfossen. It contains the largest pulp and paper factory in Norway, a hydro-electric station that supplies power to much of eastern Norway, and a carbide and fertilizer plant. Along the last reach of the Glomma, from Sarpsborg to the old fortress town of Fredrikstad at the river's mouth, lies a string of sawmills and pulp and paper factories.

(b) *Vestfold*

On the western shore of Oslo fjord lies Vestfold, a more varied region than its eastern neighbour, the Østfold. Sediments of Cambrian and Silurian age form much of the underlying geology. They appear in the landscape as corridors of shales, limestones, and sandstones that sometimes give rise to fertile soils rich in lime from the fossil shells which they contain. Amid this complex of fertile corridors rises a tumbled line of hills, composed of granites and lavas that were injected and poured out in Permian times [Fig. 31]. In parts, this zone of upland reaches two thousand feet above sea level and stands out as a tract of barren and thinly populated country. It is dark with a mantle of forest, broken by wastes of peat-bog. North-west of Oslo, this upland of igneous rocks achieves its greatest extent in the Nordmarka, a wilderness that forms a natural playground at the very fringe of the city. Here the precipices of the Kolsaas escarpment, formed by a lava of Permian age, act as a weekend climbing ground for young Norwegian mountaineers who later graduate to the fiercer, frost-shattered ridges of the lonely, unnamed peaks of the Arctic. And in winter, the forest trails of Nordmarka are cut by the ski-tracks of the hundreds who pursue this national sport within a stone's throw of the suburbs of their capital.

The coastline of the Vestfold seems even more favoured than that of its neighbour across Oslo fjord. Facing south and east across the sheltered waters of the fjord, it has earned the nickname of 'the Norwegian riviera'. Perhaps in the subtle nuances of microclimatology there is some justification for this title. At least it enjoys some of the warmest summers in Norway, spring comes noticeably earlier, and the mellow days of autumn seem to stay longest on this narrow, protected strip of coast. Deciduous trees are common in this favoured coastal fringe, and the little port of Larvik claims that it possesses on its outskirts the only beech forest in the whole of Norway, a not unusual parochial exaggeration in Scandinavia. Agriculture is certainly richer in Vestfold than elsewhere in Norway [Fig. 58]. Its orchards of apples, plums, and cherries rival in importance those of mild, sheltered sites along the western fjords.

Part of Vestfold's individuality as a region belongs to the chain of small ports and industrial towns that stretches along the coast between Drammen and Skien. Drammen, a town of nearly thirty thousand people, is one of the biggest industrial centres in Norway, apart from Oslo and Bergen. For more than a century Drammen has been famous for its exports of sawn timber. Today, its industrial structure is more elaborate with pulp and paper factories and a glass works. Drammen's close links with the timber industry result from the fact that the Dramselv, a river that taps the extensive softwood resources of Hallingdal, is the most important floatway for timber in Norway, after the Glomma. The overwhelming importance of the timber industries brings Drammen into the same class as Sarpsborg and the other industrial towns of Østfold [Fig. 95].

South of Drammen, Vestfold reveals the individual economic character of its towns. Holmestrand has an aluminium plant, while Tønsberg, Sandefjord, and Larvik all have a direct interest in the sea, a fact that connects them in the economic geography of Norway with the fishing ports lying along the west coast between Stavanger and Trondheim. Tønsberg was a port in the ninth century and proudly claims to be the oldest town in Norway. Today it is a prosperous whaling and shipbuilding centre. Sandefjord is the capital of the Norwegian whaling industry. There the international commission that attempts to control the exploitation of whales in all the world's oceans, fixing the amount of the annual catch, has its permanent headquarters. And there the successors of Melville's Captain Ahab live in their neat villas, when they are not ranging the wild, grey seas of Antarctica in their floating factories.

A few miles south-west of Larvik, the quiet waters of Skien fjord lead inland from the Skagerrak. Here stands another group of small industrial towns with a total population of just over forty thousand. Their activities seem uncommonly varied for Norway. Porsgrunn possesses the only porcelain works in the country. Close by at Herøya, the great Norwegian chemical corporation — Norsk Hydro — has assembled an industrial complex that concentrates on fertilizers [Fig. 110]. Along the shores of the fjord a string of small industrial towns — Brevik, Langesund, Stathelle — combine fishing, sawing timber, and wood-working as their main occupations. Two low waterfalls, now a source of hydro-electric power, mark the site of Skien at the head of the fjord.

Vestfold and Østfold combine with Oslo and its population of half a million to form the core of modern Norway. Many of Norway's basic industries are concentrated in this small strip of country, and most of her best farmland occupies the small, discontinuous plains on either side of Oslo fjord. This same area possesses Norway's closest network of roads and railways.

The integration of the economy achieved in the Oslo region is best illustrated by the contrast presented by southern Norway, an area that has escaped many of the changes of the past hundred years. It is one of the most beautiful parts of the country, if one is

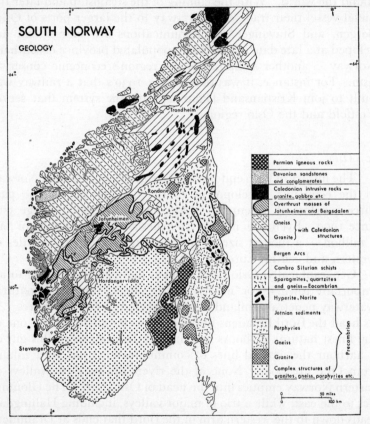

Fig. 6

Southern Norway divides into two geological provinces. The north and west is composed of rocks ranging from the Eocambrian to the Devonian and this is the zone of Caledonian structures. South and east of the front of the overthrust masses are the pre-Cambrian gneisses, granites, and porphyries that represent the extension of the Baltic shield into southern Norway. Distinctive features of this map are the vast belt of gneisses within the Caledonian structures that compose the barren mountains and plateaus northward of Bergen, the wide zone of Cambro-Silurian schists that underlie the softer scenery around Trondheim, the outcrop of similar rocks along the pleasanter Hardanger and Bokn fjords, and the tract of Permian lavas westward of Oslo.

21

not searching for the travel-brochure pictures of a Norway with steel-blue fjords and waterfalls that tumble out of the sky. Along this indented, forested coastline of low islands and narrow sounds stand small, white-painted wooden towns, such as Grimstad, Lillesand, and Arendal. They enjoyed a boom period during the nineteenth century when they built sailing frigates and sent them round the world. With the coming of the steamship and later the diesel vessel their trade drained away to the larger ports of Oslo, Bergen, and Stavanger. Communications are sparse, and developed at a late date in this thinly populated province of southern Norway — another symptom of the region's economic conservatism. For instance, it was only in the 1930's that a railway was built to join Kristiansand [Plate 2] with the system that serves Vestfold and the Oslo region.

(c) *Oslo*

The history of Oslo epitomizes the rôle of south-eastern Norway in the economic development of the country during the past three-quarters of a century. Oslo has grown into a large city since 1900. Even now it barely reaches a total population of half a million — a modest size in comparison with the great cities of western and central Europe.

Geographically, Oslo fjord seemed destined to give rise to an important town. For nearly seventy miles this deep, natural waterway penetrates inland between sheltered wooded shores. At its head the fjord broadens into a deep-water anchorage — one of the finest natural harbours in Europe. In contrast to this gift of a harbour the natural lines of communication that lead inland from Oslo are poor. None of the rivers draining the valleys of eastern Norway empties into the head of Oslo fjord. The Glomma lies to the east, while a trio of major valleys, including Hallingdal, leads down to the western arm of the fjord that ends at Drammen. In fact, if physical geography alone determined the siting of towns, their growth and their prosperity, then Drammen ought to have emerged as the capital of Norway.

Inland, the horizontal skyline of the Permian lava plateau of Nordmarka forms the background to the site of Oslo [Fig. 31]. This untamed wilderness that reaches down into the suburbs of the capital city stands as a symbol of the whole of Scandinavia, where men have carried the European way of life to its furthest frontier.

To the east of Oslo, an important gap through the flat-topped hills provides a route to Lillestrøm in the Glomma valley — a gap that has played a vital rôle in the economic history of Norway. Before the lower part of the Glomma river was developed as a floatway, much of the timber trade from Lillestrøm passed westward through this gap to the wharves at Oslo. Again, this break in the hills played a crucial part in the growth of the Norwegian railway network. The first railway, opened in 1854, followed this natural feature on its way to Eidsvoll. Later, in 1865, it carried the main line to Kongsvinger and thence to the Swedish frontier and Stockholm.

Oslo's growth towards the close of the last century is closely related to the further expansion of the Norwegian railway system. In 1872, a line ran westward joining Oslo to Drammen, and, at the end of the same decade, railway links were made with Göteborg in Sweden. While the railway network of western and central Europe was complete by the end of the Victorian era, it is interesting to note the amount of construction carried out by Norwegians in the twentieth century. In fact, the system of long main lines that has done so much to establish Oslo as the capital of Norway belongs entirely to the last fifty years. The Bergen railway penetrated Hallingdal and crossed the Hardangervidda at more than four thousand feet above sea level in 1909. Trondheim was reached by two routes, one following the long corridor of the upper Glomma and the other lying to the west across the lonely heights of the Dovrefjell. The main line into southern Norway was only finished in the 1930's, and today the railway engineer still pioneers a line into the Arctic north [Plate 12]. For the nineteenth-century statesman the railway was a symbol of power, both economic and political. In Norway today, it is regarded as an instrument to bring greater coherence to a nation divided in itself by fjord, *fjell*, and snowfield.

Oslo expanded not only under the influence of a growing railway system, but also as the first centre of the industrial revolution in south-eastern Norway. Along an insignificant river, the Akerselv, that foams its way to the sea through a score of small waterfalls, factory industries took root about a century ago. Today the parts of Oslo flanking this river still form the main industrial suburb — a district that employs more than a quarter of the industrial workers of the whole country. It contains foundries and small engineering shops, flour mills, and printing presses. Almost the whole of Norway's textile industry is concentrated in this single quarter of the capital city where small cotton mills work entirely for the home market.

Oslo's other activities are focused on the waterfront, where she handles much of the import trade of the country, an even greater proportion than Bergen. She imports foodstuffs, the raw materials for industry and, from the North Sea countries, the many manufactured goods that Norway is unable to produce herself. The quays and docks of Oslo are the scene, too, of Norway's largest shipbuilding and repairing industry.

In many ways Oslo is a microcosm of Norway. With the rapid growth of her population in the past few decades she has attracted immigrants from every Norwegian province. On national holidays her citizens come out in the folk-costumes of their native western fjords and quiet eastern valleys to remind this brash capital of her peasant background. The gaunt rectangular towers of Oslo's City Hall stand for the new Norway of the twentieth century, but in the topography of the city the past still lives [Plate 1]. At the western edge of the modern town stands the old farm of Frogner, a memorial to the peasant farmers who first settled this rim of fertile land at the head of Oslo fjord. Today the farm contains Oslo's municipal museum, and its fields and meadows have been transformed into the public park that houses Gustav Vigeland's grotesque and beautiful collection of statues whose theme is mankind in all its aspects. Six miles north of the city, on the hills that look down Oslo Fjord, stands Frognerseter, the summer pastures where the farmers of Frogner drove their cattle. Today it is a famous weekend resort for skiers, at the terminus of an electric tramway that climbs out from the main streets of the city. Bigger European cities such as Paris, Brussels, or Cologne have lost all trace of their rural past, but in Oslo an urban society and an urban scene have not yet reached their full development.

(d) *The South-Eastern Valleys*

The regional geography of south-eastern Norway would be unfinished without some reference to the long valleys draining towards Oslo fjord. As a home of Norway's peasant culture — the Norway that evolved slowly through the Middle Ages — they are as important as the western fjords. The roots of contemporary Norwegian nationalism lie in the Old Norse language that is still spoken by the country folk of these remote inland valleys.

From the Glomma corridor in the east to the bunch of western valleys that make up the core of Telemark province each river forms a single unit with some distinguishing individual features. Yet some major traits are common to each member. The lower reaches of each main valley contain lowlands that are limited in area but of considerable fertility [Fig. 34]. They consist of clays and sands laid down at the close of the Ice Age when the sea flooded far inland for a few brief centuries as the Norwegian glaciers retreated. Another cause of fertility in the lower sections of Norway's eastern valleys is the presence in the Caledonian structures of limestones of Cambrian and Silurian age. These rocks are especially valuable around Lake Mjøsa where they weather into a good soil and also form a rich element in the ground moraine that is wide-spread over this district.

These small fertile lowlands lie in a discontinuous arc around Oslo. For more than a millennium they have formed cores of settlement separated from each other by unpopulated forested uplands. One of the most famous of these tiny lowlands fringes the upper part of Lake Mjøsa, stretching northwards to Lille-hammer. Another, the Romerike, lies closer to Oslo and finds its regional capital in Lillestrøm. Another small area that is closely farmed and densely settled bears the traditional name of Ringerike and stretches down to the shores of Tyrifjord, with Hønefoss as its organizing town. Each of these cells of comparatively dense settlement is distinguished by farming of a 'lowland' type. Arable crops are important. Barley, oats, and even wheat prosper on the good soils and in the sunny summers of these eastern valleys. Root crops, too, are valuable. For instance, the eastern shore of Lake Mjøsa produces one of the heaviest potato harvests in Norway and here the surplus of milk from the dairy herds goes to butter and cheese factories that have grown up near the railway stations.

The landscapes of these regions look as though they have been shaped down the centuries by the hand of man. In the well-kept countryside at the head of Lake Mjøsa there are twenty parish churches of medieval date, a sign of intensive settlement scarcely to be matched elsewhere in Norway except along the coast line of the Vestfold [Plate 3]. Again, these are the only parts of inland Norway where towns were founded centuries ago. Hamar is nine hundred years old and was the home of bishops in the eleventh century. It drew its life as a town not only from the farms of the neighbouring lowland, but also from a forested hinterland in the lonely valleys of Gudbrandsdal and the upper Glomma.

If one excludes the sparsely populated shores of Lake Femunden close to the Swedish frontier, the most easterly of Norway's great valleys is the Østerdal, the upper course of the Glomma that runs in a deep trough for a hundred and fifty miles — a slit in the dull and boundless plateau of eastern Norway. There are dense forests of spruce and pine, the tall dark trees often filling the whole valley to the banks of the river. Upwards, the conifers become sparser and stunted through exposure to severe winds and heavy snow. Finally, they give way to an open screen of birch forest before the timber line and the frontier of the open tundra is reached at about three thousand feet above sea level [Fig. 83]. Forestry overshadows the whole economy of the Østerdal and many of the small farmers gain their chief source of income from timber cutting. Farms lie scattered along the valley, sometimes far apart from each other. Up above, in the birch-forest belt or out on the treeless plateau, stand the *seters* where the herds of cattle are driven in summer. This is not the sort of economy that generates towns and there are no towns in Østerdal apart from Røros, a copper-mining settlement that came into being in the seventeenth century [Plate 5]. It lies in a wide bleak basin close to the source of the Glomma, where the forest is open and stunted and the bare hillsides stand flecked with snow deep into the summer. Its wooden houses flank a street that climbs a long hill to a curious baroque-looking church, a reminder that the miner came as an intruder among these peasant-farmers whose ancestors reached a summit of architectural achievement in their wooden churches of the thirteenth century.

Gudbrandsdal runs nearly parallel to the Glomma valley. Its river, fed by the melting snows of the Jotunheimen, flows as a dark green band through the meadows of the valley floor. A succession of terraces and abandoned deltas of late glacial times provide good soils in this valley. Agriculture is the chief source of livelihood with forestry less important. Gudbrandsdal formed an early centre of settlement in the interior of Norway, and some families can trace back to the ninth century their occupation of sheltered sites halfway up the long slopes between the fertile river terraces and the summer pastures [Plate 4].

The next main valley to the west, Hallingdal, contains many features in common with Gudbrandsdal. It has a stable pastoral economy and a succession of fine farms and parishes with wooden churches. The railway from Oslo to Bergen uses this valley to climb to the high wilderness of the Hardangervidda. Other valleys have escaped the direct effects of the railway age. The Valdres valley, for instance, was used by an old and now abandoned track across the Filjefellto Sogne fjord. However, the mid-twentieth century has brought a further reassessment of values in the terms of transport with the motor-car, the heavy milk-lorry, and the network of summer bus services that extends to the loneliest parts of interior Norway.

The valleys to the west of Oslo are different again. Numedal suffered heavily from migration to the United States in the early years of the twentieth century. Its only town, Kongsberg, came into existence in 1624 as a silver-mining centre. The shorter valleys of Telemark, on the other hand, have been deeply influenced by the electro-chemical industries and the construction of massive hydro-electric stations [Fig. 69].

These long-settled lowlands and deep valleys are the home of a stable peasant society that has survived with few disturbances for a thousand years and more. Its disruption began only at the close of the nineteenth century, with the building of railways and the expansion of the timber trade as the rivers were transformed into floatways leading to the sawmills and pulp factories on the shores of Oslo fjord. Perhaps an even stronger force in the erosion of the old ways of life has been the continuous drift of young people to the rising industrial towns and, above all, the magnetic attraction of the capital city. Even so, much survives from the past. These valleys possess some of Norway's finest examples of architecture in wood. There are several wooden churches of medieval date, whose runic carvings with stories from the sagas remind one that Christianity came late to Norway, penetrating a mature pagan society and in part suffering absorption into that society. Gudbrandsdal, the valley that leads from the shores of Lake Mjøsa to the shapeless flat-topped mountains of the Dovrefjell, contains a fine succession of wooden churches or *stavkirken*. Likewise the old farms of these valleys are composed of a large number of wooden outbuildings, each serving a particular purpose as a storehouse or cattle shed. Sometimes the *stabbur* stands on pillars, raised from the ground to protect its contents from rats and mice — a practice that recurs in parts of the Alps where building in wood is again a medium through which a peasant culture receives its chief expression. In these lonely valleys, peasant costumes may still be seen whose designs have scarcely changed for three thousand years. On feast days in Hallingdal the women put on a dress that stretches down to the ankle and is made up of a number of rectangular panels — a pattern that has been handed down from the Bronze Age.

THE WESTERN FJORDS

The fjord coastline of south-western Norway forms a second core in the regional geography of the country. Down the centuries the fjords have displayed two opposing characteristics. While they have been open to many influences from across the sea, they have also sheltered culture traits from Norway's remotest past. Along their shores, peasant communities survive with farming methods that have sometimes changed little since the Middle Ages. Each fjord tends to act as an independent unit, and Norwegian history illustrates the difficulties of achieving the political cohesion of this area of branching waterways and mist-shrouded mountains. For instance, in the remote period at the close of the ninth century, when Harald Haarfarge created the first Norway out of many small kingdoms, the greatest opposition to this political process came from the chieftains of the western fjords. Their stubborn independence was one of the factors in the emigration of warlords and farmers to Shetland, Orkney, Ireland, the Isle of Man, and Iceland [Fig. 1].

The outlook of western Norway to the Atlantic Ocean and the North Sea lands forms another strand in the history of this region. The sea has opened Norway to influences from outside. For example, despite the forbidding nature of much of this coastline, prehistoric colonists penetrated to the inner recesses of the fjords in the Neolithic and Bronze Ages. Again, settlers from the Rhineland moved into south-western Norway at the time when the Anglo-Saxons were founding their villages beside the rivers of eastern England. By contrast, the lonely valleys of eastern Norway resisted settlement for another five hundred years until the beginning of the Viking Age. The medieval wooden houses built by German merchants along the quay in Bergen remind one that for four centuries this city was an important outpost of the Hanseatic League, and about six miles south of Bergen stands the ruin of a Cistercian monastery, another memorial to the foreign influences that have reached western Norway from across the sea.

Today, south-western Norway displays the sharpest contrasts in the nation's economy. Along the fjords villages nestle amid their apple orchards on tiny delta fans [Plate 9], and the farmers still follow the cattle up the age-old tracks to the high *seter* at the beginning of summer. On the other hand, the merchants and ship-owners of Stavanger and Bergen pursue a trade that reaches nearly every port on the world's oceans, securing to Norway her present high standard of life through their earnings in foreign currencies.

Each Norwegian fjord is an individual region. Even within a single fjord the differences between the outer seaward parts and the deep, sheltered, inner reaches are often so great as to merit their treatment as separate regions. Down to its smallest details the landscape of the fjords seems to be composed out of extremes. Opposite the gentle, cultivated slopes of a delta, thick with orchards and rich meadows, stands a barren rocky cliff that plunges for hundreds of feet to the depths of the fjord, hostile to settlement. But it is the heightening of contrasts, the mingling of opposites, that make the fjords of Norway one of the finest tourist districts in Europe.

(a) *Hardanger and Bokn Fjords*

South of Bergen two large fjords, Hardanger and Bokn fjord, have several features in common. Their main axes both run from south-west to north-east, a fact determined by the main trend-lines of the Caledonian folds. Again, both fjords coincide with synclines filled with schists of Cambrian and Silurian age. These rocks are more tender than the harsh granites, gneisses, and gabbros that occupy so much of the landscape of western Norway [Fig. 6]. Consequently, the lower parts of Hardanger and Bokn fjord contain greater tracts of farmland than elsewhere in western Norway. They are composed of seemingly innumerable branching arms and projecting peninsulas, and as they look south-westward to the open Atlantic they feel the full force of the mild westerly winds that form one of the chief elements in the weather pattern of this part of Norway. Hardanger fjord is famous for the extent of its agricultural land and its startling emerald-green meadows. The communities that live on the shores of these wide, complex south-western fjords are more deeply concerned with farming than fishing. Perhaps it is also significant that on the south shore of Hardanger fjord stands a large and handsome manor house, the centre of the barony of Rosendal. This feudal estate of the Osnes family was created by the fusion of nearly a hundred separate farms. The country house set in its park is an alien feature in the Norwegian landscape, especially among the western fjords where each peasant is an independent freeholder and the land systems of feudal Europe are unknown. It is interesting that Hardanger fjord contains a larger and richer tract of lowland than is usual in western Norway, a fact not unconnected with the rise of a powerful land-owning family.

Winding shorelines, low islands, and fertile soils form one of the chief traits of both Hardanger and Bokn fjord, but their inner parts contain features that belong to the conventional picture of fjord Norway. Sørfjord extends from Hardanger fjord as a deep, narrow cul-de-sac, its walls rising giddily to the enclosing plateau more than three thousand feet above the blue-grey ribbon at sea level. Here are Tyssedal, Eitrheim, and Odda with their power stations, metal-refining and chemical plants. Lysefjord, a branch of the expansive Bokn fjord, likewise forms a deep, unfriendly slit in the surrounding plateau.

(b) *Sogne and Nord Fjords*

The great fjords to the north of Bergen differ from those to the south. Instead of following the trend-lines of the Caledonian structures, Sogne fjord and Nord fjord bite deeply into the plateau of western Norway, their main axes running from east to west. Sogne fjord stretches inland for almost two hundred miles, traversing the Pre-Cambrian gneiss of the coastal plateau to reach the schists and gabbros of the Caledonian zone. Sogne fjord is a monumental feature of the Norwegian landscape. It lies almost four thousand feet below the high *seters* of the enclosing plateau, and the floor of the fjord reaches more than three thousand feet below sea level. With the long tributary fjords that converge on its upper section Sogne forms a world of its own, a region that typifies the most characteristic features of western Norway. In many parts cultivated land is scarce and bare walls of rock fall abruptly to the fjord. Settlements gather on delta fans, narrow terraces, or level alluvial flats at the heads of tributary fjords. With their fruit orchards, racks of drying hay, and wooden churches, they form pleasant oases amid this scenery of savage landforms, dark forests, and the glittering rim of distant snow fields [Plate 9]. But Sogne fjord not only represents the romantic ideal of the Norwegian landscape, it also contains at Høyanger and Årdal two of the country's biggest power stations and aluminium plants.

Nord fjord penetrates inland for less than half the distance of Sogne fjord and contains several individual features. It is much narrower and only half as deep as its great neighbour. It lacks the long tributary fjords that make up the inner world of Sogne. Instead, a number of severely glaciated valleys run down to the shores of Nord fjord, each containing a string of green lakes fed by ice-cold rivers draining from the plateau glacier of the Jostedal. Terraces, too, are better developed along the shores of Nord fjord and help to make it an important farming district.

(c) *The Fjord Provinces of Sunnmøre and Nordmøre*

Further north the landscapes of fjord Norway change again, another variation on the theme of this high and heavily glaciated plateau that projects south-westwards into the Atlantic. Here the deep trough of Romsdal separates the provinces of Sunnmøre and Nordmøre. In many senses this region is transitional to the area around Trondheim fjord. For instance, the speech of the country folk to the north of Romsdal possesses the tones and colours of the dialects spoken in the Trøndelag, the regional name of Trondheim's province. Again, the styles of farm building belong to the north rather than to the fjords that lie further south.

Many features of physical geography also distinguish this as a separate region. Here the fjords wind through a chaos of mountains and there is little sign of the high plateaus that dominate the coastal region of south-western Norway. Striking conical- and pyramid-shaped peaks, and ragged, harshly weathered ridges remind one of the mountain landscapes of the far north. Fifty miles inland, the alpine-like peaks and ridges give way to the dull massif of the Dovre, a high plateau with a summit at more than six thousand feet that today carries no glacier ice. This significant fact probably goes a long way towards explaining the distinctive scenery of this part of western Norway. The absence of ice on the Dovrefjell at the present time suggests that the snowfall is less than further south. If the precipitation of the Ice Age was similarly less than in the more exposed parts of Norway to the south and west, the overriding ice-sheet that ground its way towards the Atlantic was probably thinner. A maze of mountains and ridges might have projected above the broad glaciers in the valleys, to be exposed to the severe weathering of frost and temperature changes that have produced the 'alpine' landforms of today.

A complex chain of large and small islands is another distinctive feature of the coastal fringe in Nordmøre and Sunnmøre. In Sogne fjord life tends to focus on the little farming settlements in the inner fjord, a hundred miles from the open sea. Here, however, the chief centres have developed at Ålesund and Kristiansund in the island fringe. Ålesund, with a population of twenty thousand, stands amid a group of small islands made of soft, but comparatively fertile, boulder clays. They form the broken surface of a submerged bank, a terminal moraine deposited in a still-stand period by the ice from the interior during the Quaternary glaciation. Today, Ålesund is one of the chief centres of cod fishing and the main base for the sealing fleet that ranges the waters of the Arctic Ocean. Ålesund is the regional capital of Sunnmøre, while Kristiansund acts as the centre for the country to the north of Romsdal. With a population of only 13,000, Kristiansund occupies a site on three tiny bare islands and was founded in the middle of the eighteenth century. Its chief industry is the preparation of *klipfisk*, the split and dried codfish that can be seen in the summer months spread out upon the naked rocks around the town. Again, the growth of towns on the island skerries and their preoccupation with fishing reminds one of the economic pattern prevailing in the Arctic north of Norway.

The transitional character of Sunnmøre and Nordmøre is apparent in the climate of this region. This coastal strip enjoys uncommonly high winter temperatures — a feature, too, of the seaward parts of the more southerly fjords [Fig. 37]. For instance, the mean temperature of January at Ålesund is 2° centigrade (36° F.). But the change in the general trend of this coastline seems to bring a marked reduction in the rainfall of these provinces. Many parts of Sunnmøre and Nordmøre receive about fifty inches of rainfall a year, while further south the more exposed parts of Vestlandet are drenched with as much as two hundred inches of rain and snow. These lower figures of precipitation relate the area to Arctic Norway rather than the south [Fig. 36].

Again, the economy of the region contains other distinctive

traits. There is less cultivable land along the shores of these north-western fjords than further south in Hardanger or Bokn fjord. Pastoralism plays an even greater part in the agriculture of the region. The poverty of this area of alpine scenery, where the snow lies in the sunless cirques far into the summer, is more clearly reflected in the importance of fishing as a subsidiary occupation to farming. Most of the farmers along the fjords are fishermen as well, a way of life that is met again in Arctic Norway [Fig. 79].

Møre's outlook to the sea and the exploitation of the teeming wealth of her shallow off-shore banks has affected the population history of this region in the past three-quarters of a century. Population has shown a slight and steady increase since the 1870's, even among the remote, dispersed communities of the inner parts of the fjords. By contrast, elsewhere in Norway, especially in the long eastern valleys and in Sogne fjord, there has been a sharp decline of population.

(d) *Bergen*

Along the immense length of coastline between Stavanger and Trondheim it is hard to find any natural centre that would serve as a focal point. Each fjord is a distinct entity, and geography seems to have given the advantage to no particular place. Yet Bergen has emerged as a city that represents Vestlandet — the inchoate region of the fjords — as truly as Oslo is the regional capital of Østlandet [Plate 6].

The explanation of Bergen's importance among the towns of western Norway lies in the late medieval history of this region. Founded soon after A.D. 1070, Bergen only started to acquire its dominating position in the Norwegian economy when the Hansa merchants established a base there at the start of the fourteenth century. In the next three hundred years, under the direction of the Hanseatic League, Bergen came to monopolize the whole of the trade in dried fish from the ports of western and northern Norway. By 1600 she was one of the biggest towns in northern Europe and, with a population of fifteen thousand, was larger than Copenhagen. Bergen's pre-eminence today as a regional centre in western Norway is largely due to the economic and political policies of her medieval German merchants.

A closer examination of Bergen's physical setting also suggests that geography has played some part in the rise of this city.

D

Bergen lies mid-way between Nord fjord and the broad mouth of Bokn fjord — a site well placed to act as a regional centre for the western fjords. She also stands in the midst of a complex archipelago that stretches southwards from the mouth of Sogne fjord to the precincts of Stavanger. For a thousand years and more this chain of islands has formed a centre of denser population in western Norway. Northwards and southwards of Bergen, the large islands, separated from the mainland by deep calm channels, contain some of the widest benches of the 'strandflat' in Norway. Large parts of these islands lie at less than two hundred feet above sea level. Again, the seas that lapped round Norway in the few brief centuries at the close of the Ice Age left behind a veneer of fertile clays that largely determines the layout of cultivated land in the archipelago today. These low islands, exposed to the Atlantic and screened by the empty forbidding plateau behind Bergen, enjoy one of the mildest and wettest of Norwegian climates. This coastal territory adjacent to Bergen has long borne the name of Hordaland, a name that dates back to the migrant peoples who entered this region in the dark ages before the Vikings. It is a region of well-populated islands, small green plains, and harsh grey mountains. As long ago as Viking times this archipelago was a distinct region in the terms of human geography — a district set apart from the isolated wilderness of Sogne fjord.

Today, the life of Hordaland is strongly coloured by the commercial city that grew in its midst. Of late, industry has penetrated farming communities on the islands and peninsulas around Bergen. Sometimes the presence of a single factory — a cotton mill, a flour mill, or an engineering plant — is sufficient to divert the main interest of a settlement from agriculture to industry. For example, in the rural district of Haus manufacturing has now dislodged farming as the main occupation. But nowhere has industry appeared on a large scale. Vast industrial conurbations are unknown to Norway. The small settlement of yt Arna, with a population of about a thousand, typifies the scale of industry in western Norway. It has a large modern factory that produces both woollen and cotton goods.

In the suburbs of Bergen and in the outlying settlements on its tributary islands and fjords, textiles, flour-milling, and engineering form the chief occupations. As an industrial region this is as old as the manufacturing district of Oslo along the Akerselv, dating back to the middle of the nineteenth century. Once again the influence of a port, a window on the world outside, is apparent in the foundation of modern industries in Norway.

TRØNDELAG — THE REGION OF TRONDHEIM FJORD

A third province of Norway, Trøndelag, has contributed much to the making of the nation. The coherence of this region is explicable partly by its physical geography and partly by the formative events in Norwegian history that were enacted there.

The life of Trøndelag gathers around the shores of Trondheim fjord, an extensive sheet of inland water that differs profoundly from the mountain-enclosed trenches of Vestlandet's fjords. Its main axis follows the Caledonian grain of the country [Fig. 6], running from south-west to north-east, a structural feature that is matched in the wide south-western fjords of Hardanger and Bokn. From the shores of Trondheim fjord rise hummocky, glaciated hills. Extensive tracts are covered with the sands and clays laid down in transient post-glacial seas [Fig. 34].

Trøndelag repeats in miniature the agricultural economy of south-eastern Norway. Her prosperous farms, ranged along the billowy shore of this inland sea, produce good harvests of barley, turnips, potatoes, and swedes. Even fruit trees grow in these far northern latitudes. Apples, plums, and cherries are able to ripen in the most sheltered sites, huddled close to the white wooden farmhouses. Only wheat is unimportant, a result of the uncertain summers with their long hours of pale sunshine and the risk of killing frosts in the early autumn. Cattle-rearing forms the other branch of the farm economy, and the Red Trøndelag cows are famous among the breeds of Norway [Fig. 58].

Trøndelag mirrors the economy of south-eastern Norway in still another way. Forestry dominates the livelihood of the broad valleys that lead eastward to the Swedish frontier, and timber carried down to the wharves of Trondheim forms an important item in the port's trade.

The unity of Trøndelag lies deep in its physical make-up and in history. Several important valleys converge on the pleasant shores of Trondheim fjord, turning this miniature inland sea into a focal zone for a far wider region. Northwards, Namdal and the long corridor containing the Snåsa lake lead into Arctic Norway. To the east, Verdal and Stjørdal are two depressions, rich with forests, that provide ways through the uplands into Sweden. These natural links between the shores of the Atlantic and the Baltic have been used from the beginning of history when Bronze Age settlers first reached Trondheim fjord from sites on the lakes of Swedish Jämtland. Today a motor road follows Verdal across the frontier into Sweden, and in this valley lies Stiklestad, one of the sacred places of Norwegian nationalism, where King Olav II, the patron saint of Norway, was killed in battle nearly a thousand years ago. The more southerly valley of Stjørdal carries the railway from Trondheim to Östersund in Sweden, where there is a junction with the interior trunk-line that leads to the iron-mining districts of Swedish Lapland. This railway, constructed in 1881, was the first line to be opened in northern Norway. From the farms and forests of the lower Stjørdal it climbs above the tree line to the open tundras, crossing the frontier into Sweden at nearly two thousand feet above sea level. After its opening this railway stretched the hinterland of Trondheim beyond the Swedish frontier to the lake region of Jämtland, reinforcing geographical relationships that date back to prehistory. The growth of timber cutting along the railway stimulated a rise of population in Stjørdal, while the more northerly Verdal, forsaken by the transfrontier traffic, witnessed a shrinkage of population.

The valleys that enter Trondheim fjord from the south — the Nid, Orkla, and Gaula — played an even greater part in the evolution of this region. They provide ways across the Dovre massif towards the upper Glomma valley and the Gudbrandsdal. The Dovre railway, now the main route to Oslo, was completed only in 1921. The older Røros line that follows the Glomma valley was hindered by breaks of gauge until it was converted to standard track in 1940. Thus Trondheim fjord, a region already possessing a life of its own, is joined by nature and the improving arts of man with both northern and south-eastern Norway as well as Sweden. In contrast, the great fjords of the south-west stand separate from each other, hemmed-in by bleak plateaus, their blind valley-heads overlooked by the glittering white cover of a suspended snowfield.

Trondheim

Norway's third regional core, centred on Trondheim fjord, contains, in Trondheim, the country's third largest town. With a population of 58,000, Trondheim stands in a loop of the River Nid not far from where it empties into the fjord [Plate 11]. King Olav Tryggveson founded this city nearly a thousand years ago in the year A.D. 998 and it has always symbolized the spirit of the Norwegian nation.

Trondheim, an outpost of Europe on the edge of the empty Arctic, is a spacious little city with large squares and wide streets laid out on a rectangular plan. This formal pattern is the handiwork of the town-planners who reshaped the city after the numerous fires that swept through its wooden buildings down the centuries. Today, Trondheim is mainly an uninspiring, stone-built place, apart from a cathedral that is one of the glories of northern Europe and the line of coloured wooden warehouses that survives along the Nid.

Trondheim, perhaps even more than Bergen, has lived by the trade of the far north. Her medieval archbishops paid for the great cathedral from the profits of the trade in furs, fish, and whalebone drawn from their dim, northern territories. Even today the exports of fish, timber, and wood-products dominate her commercial life. A few industries have appeared in the suburbs that climb the low hills on either side of the natural moat formed by the bend in the Nid that contains the old core of Trondheim. It is interesting to remember that industry first took root in Trondheim in the 1840's, about the same time as the opening of the first textile mills along the banks of the Akerselv in Oslo and in the suburbs of Bergen. Like the other coastal cities of Norway, Trondheim was sensitive to the economic changes going on around the North Sea in the early nineteenth century, but in her remote northern position she was unable to build on the advantage of her first industrial experiments. Above all, Trondheim has remained a regional capital, trading on the products of its hinterland — the prolific wealth of her coastal fishing banks, the copper and iron ores of the valleys draining from the Dovre massif, and the timber of the country that lies eastward towards the Swedish frontier [Fig. 83].

NORWAY'S EMPTY REGIONS

The populated regions of Norway, her chief centres of economic activity, stand separated from each other by large expanses of empty or thinly-peopled country. These negative regions lie along a belt of high plateaus and savage mountains that stretch from the coast of Sørlandet to the bleak promontories projecting their crumbling cliffs of ancient sandstones into the Arctic Ocean at seventy degrees latitude north. Much of this belt, particularly in Arctic Norway, coincides with the structures of the Caledonian mountain system. These dull, high plateaus and complex massifs, bedecked with glaciers, are carved from the roots of that ancient Palaeozoic mountain system that has long since been erased from the scenery of the world [Figs. 7 and 8].

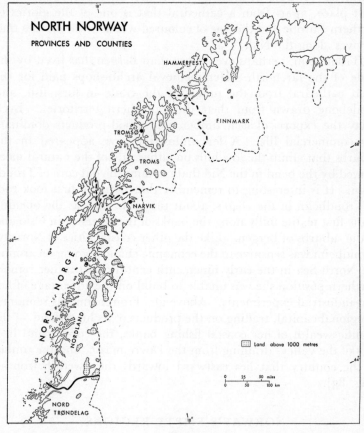

FIG. 7

Three counties, Finnmark, Troms, and Nordland, make up the province of North Norway. Along this narrow Atlantic façade the Swedish frontier often lies within a few miles of the head of an ice-free fjord.

Norway

Pre-eminent among the thinly peopled regions of Norway stands the extensive territory that stretches northwards from Trondheim fjord to the frontier with the Soviet Union. Half of Norway belongs to this 'northland', and four-fifths of this territory lies within the Arctic Circle. In itself this large territory contains

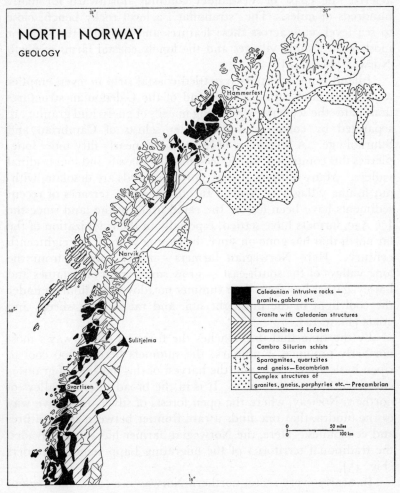

FIG. 8

The chief geological contrast lies between the complex Pre-Cambrian structures that underlie the dull plateaus of Arctic Norway and the landscapes to the south of Narvik where ragged ice-covered coastal mountains coincide with intrusive granites and gabbros of Caledonian date, while softer Cambro-Silurian schists belong to the inland longitudinal valleys.

39

much regional variety, but throughout its length, at least as far as the most northerly province of Finnmark, Arctic Norway displays two salient features. One of the most complex coastlines in the world faces the grey Atlantic. Here the islands, submerged reefs, sheltered channels, and deeply penetrating fjords that characterize the coast of Vestlandet continue northward for many hundreds of miles. The 'strandflat', a level rocky bench, close to sea level, cuts across these features and provides the sites for most of the fishing villages and the lonely coastal farms of north Norway [Plate 14].

Inland from this sparsely-settled coastal strip lie even emptier and wilder landscapes. The trend of the Caledonian structures dominates the scenery, where long massifs of gneiss and granite are separated by corridors in the softer schists of Cambrian and Silurian age. A succession of fjords, some nearly fifty miles long, pierces this complex of harsh, ice-chiselled massifs and longitudinal valleys. Many of these gloomy northern fjords are desolate, without fishing villages or farms. In others, where terraces of recent sediments have been left by the rapid uplift of the land since the Ice Age, farmers have settled, especially in the colonization of the far north that has gone on since the closing years of the eighteenth century. Here Norwegian farmers — many coming from the long valleys of the south-east — grow small crops of potatoes and barley, gather hay from their summer meadows that flourish under the cool light of the midnight sun, and raise cattle, sheep, and goats [Plate 12].

By the time that one reaches the frontiers of Norway's most northerly province, Finnmark, the summers become too cool to ripen barley effectively and the harvest of this hardiest of grains is cut green for use as fodder. It is in the broad interior valleys of northern Norway, where the open forests of silver birch give way to the tundra, that one finds a rare frontier between two cultures and economies. Here, the Norwegian farmer has slowly invaded the traditional territories of the migrating Lapp reindeer-herders [Fig. 45].

In nearly every sense, northern Norway is a 'colonial' region, a thinly-peopled territory depending on the crude exploitation of her natural resources, the chief of which are the fisheries of the submerged parts of the strandflat and the Arctic Ocean. In the interior, lonely mining settlements, working lodes of iron-ore and copper, tell of the same primitive status of this region in the

Norwegian economy, but the towns of the coastal belt, small as they are, represent an occupation of the polar world by a civilized society that cannot be matched elsewhere in such high latitudes.

Southward from the shores of Trondheim fjord stretches a succession of high plateaus, from which rise a number of ragged massifs reaching heights of more than eight thousand feet above the sea. Among these the Hardangervidda presents some of the most monotonous landscapes in Norway. Its rolling surface reaches to almost four thousand feet. Probably it preserves a fragment of the primordial peneplain of Scandinavia — that earliest morphological feature created at the beginning of recorded geological time, before the Cambrian sediments were deposited. Tracts of this ancient erosion surface are still intact in the Hardangervidda, as yet out of reach of the vigorous cycle of erosion initiated in late Tertiary times. Here and there, upstanding masses of metamorphosed sediments interrupt the monotony of Hardangervidda. Most notable among these is the ragged rock wall of the Hallingskarvet that looks down on the thin, steel thread of the Bergen-Oslo railway as it winds through the hummocky, ice-scarred pass at Finse.

North of the Hardangervidda, the empty region that forms the backbone of western Norway rises to heights of more than six thousand feet in the isolated massifs of the Jotunheimen, Jostedalsbre, the spectacular mountains of Rondane, and the ponderous summits of the Dovrefjell. The first two of these mountain groups carry extensive snow fields that shed off glaciers westward into the deep troughs of the fjords.

This great tract of high and empty country that separates the fjords of Vestlandet from the forested valleys of the east contributes many features to the personality of Norway. Its historic rôle is that of a divide separating the three chief centres of population — Vestlandet, Trøndelag, and Østlandet [Fig. 9]. In this negative way it has helped to preserve their individual qualities. For instance, in the popular speech of Norway the Dovre massif has long been recognized as a natural frontier. Trøndelag and Nordmøre are described as 'north-of-the-mountains', *nordenfjellske*, while Østlandet, south-east Norway, is known as *søndenfjellske*, 'south-of-the-mountains'.

These lonely plateaus perform more than this negative function of an empty frontier-zone between populous regions. For at least a thousand years they have provided summer grazing grounds for cattle, sheep, and goats from the surrounding valleys. Today the little clusters of wooden huts with their attractive grass-grown roofs — *seters* or summer farms — show the parts that have been used for centuries by farmers from both the fjords and the dry eastern valleys. It is possible, too, that the grazing of these uplands has contributed to their desolate appearance today. Predatory goats and the heavy cutting of timber for building and fuel

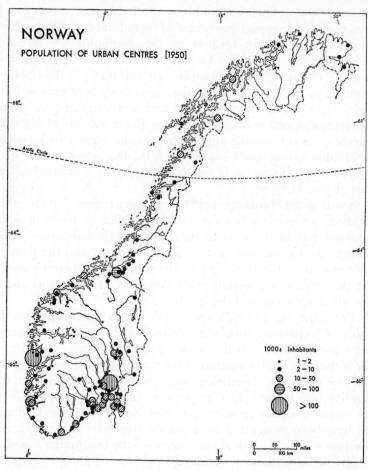

NORWAY
POPULATION OF URBAN CENTRES [1950]

1000s inhabitants
- · 1 – 2
- ● 2 – 10
- ◎ 10 – 50
- ⊜ 50 – 100
- ⊕ > 100

Fig. 9

The distribution of towns reveals the three chief cores of settlement and economic development in Norway — along the shores of the Skagerrak and Oslo fjord, in the coastline and fjords of Vestlandet, and centred upon Trondheim fjord. In northern Norway, almost without exception, towns have coastal sites on islands or peninsulas.

helped to depress the forest line on the fringes of these high plateaus. Today, fragments of pine and birch forest survive at more than three thousand feet on the edge of the Jotunheimen. They probably stand as relics of the high timber line of the Bronze Age, suggesting that summer grazing as well as climatic change has helped to clear much of the timber from these uplands.

As well as being a barrier, this spine of snowfields and tundras has been forced to act as a link between the main centres of population in Norway. Well-trodden and established tracks have connected the western fjords and the inland valleys since the early Middle Ages. For instance, an old pack-horse track runs across Sognfjell from the head of Sogne fjord to Lom in the Otta valley. In the past, the corn grown in the dry and sunny eastern valleys was carried westward over the mountains and exchanged for salt, produced along the coastline by the boiling of sea water. One of Norway's great triumphs of this century is the conquest of the high barrier of the *fjell* by modern means of communication. The Bergen-Oslo railway, now proudly flaunted in the travel-brochures as the highest standard-gauge line in Europe, was finished in 1909. Its construction was an immensely difficult task. For instance, the Gravehalsen tunnel, just over three miles long, took twelve years to cut. In the 1920's, a railway from Oslo to Trondheim was completed across the Dovre massif and a branch line reached the west coast through Romsdal. Since 1930 the road network has steadily grown across the empty plateaus that separate the east from the west in Norway. Summer bus services now follow the lines of some of the medieval pack-horse trails.

Railways and roads are opening up the empty areas of western Norway, especially for tourists in summer and the crowds of skiers in winter and spring, but nevertheless this region maintains its character as a 'backland'. In the mentality of the Norwegian people it stands for something as valuable as the historic events associated with Trondheim. This is one of the few parts of Europe where nature remains untamed, and the crude wilderness is an essential element in Norwegian life. One of the catch phrases of Norwegian nationalism says '*enig og tro til Dovre fallet*' — united we stand till the Dovre mountain falls. And what seems more permanent than these grey uplands whose very rocks have been in existence since the beginning of geological time?

CHAPTER 3

Sweden

SWEDEN is the biggest of the Scandinavian states, with one and a half times the area of Norway. Twice the size of the United Kingdom, she has a total population of 7,495,129 (1960) — a sum less than that of Greater London.

In almost every sense Sweden is the strongest and the biggest of the Scandinavian states. She has a larger population and greater area than any of her three neighbours, Denmark, Norway, and Finland. But these bare statistics are implicit in other more potent facts. For instance, Sweden is the greatest industrial power in northern Europe. Scores of small manufacturing centres lie along the belt of lake-filled lowland stretching between her capital city, Stockholm, and her chief port, Göteborg [Fig. 10]. Industry has a long and famous history in Sweden. In the later Middle Ages, Sweden became the world's greatest producer of copper and for several centuries, too, she held a high reputation as an exporter of bar-iron. Towards the close of the nineteenth century, Sweden developed one of the world's most skilled and specialized engineering industries. Its foundations lay in the older tradition of smelting and forging, and its raw materials came from the vast supplies of iron ore among the forested hills northward of Lake Mälaren.

Today, Sweden is noted for the variety and high quality of the goods made by her engineering industry. The list is a long one, containing turbines for hydro-electric stations, electric locomotives and railway gear, precision instruments, cameras, dairy equipment, telephones, machinery for pulp mills, armaments, and high-grade cutlery. Sweden holds a unique position among the Scandinavian countries in having a world-wide market for the products of her engineering shops.

To a large extent, the economies of Finland, Denmark, and Norway rest on primary products such as fish, timber, butter, bacon, or else the unseen income of tramp steamers that fly their national flag in every port of the world. Sweden possesses these primary resources as well. Her iron ores are the richest and most

44

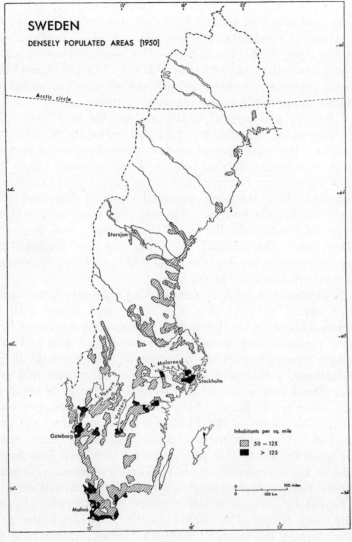

FIG. 10

The main areas of population lie in the south-west, around Malmö, and in the mid-lands between Göteborg and Stockholm. In central Sweden the shores of each of the great lakes form a focal area of settlement. The chief population centres of Norrland gather where major rivers empty into the Gulf of Bothnia. The only important inland settlement-area of the north is on the shores of Lake Stor.

extensive in Europe. Northwards from the Dal river stretch the greatest pine and spruce forests in Scandinavia [Fig. 84]. Each spring, two hundred million logs drift down the floatways and long rivers of Norrland to the pulp mills, cellulose, and hardboard factories along the Baltic coastline. The Swedish economy is more broadly based than any of her neighbours'. To the export of her natural resources in minerals and timber she has added the valuable things made by her ingenious people.

Mere size and natural wealth are not the only factors that contribute to the individuality of Sweden among the Scandinavian countries. Her geographical position amid the states of northern Europe matches the internal balance of her economy. More than half of her territory occupies the eastern part of the Scandinavian peninsula, where the long, powerful rivers of Norrland drain towards the Gulf of Bothnia. The rest of Sweden, a blunt peninsula poised between the Baltic and the Kattegat, looks southward to Denmark. The landscape of Skåne, her most southerly province, already has much of the quality of the scenery of Denmark and northern Germany [Plate 32].

If Norway is an Atlantic state looking outwards to the world's busiest ocean, then Sweden is a continental power with her interests focused on the Baltic Sea. Geography has given her a central position in the Scandinavian world, and time and again Sweden's history reveals the influence of this geographical fact. For instance, a thousand years ago Swedish traders and colonizers spread both eastward and westward from their homeland in the heart of the Baltic. Some penetrated the Dnieper valley to reach the shores of the Black Sea; others joined the great stream of Viking migrants who moved across the North Sea to settle amid the gentle clay hills and open valleys of East Anglia. Again in the seventeenth century, Sweden's central position in northern Europe asserted itself in a most spectacular fashion when her formidable peasant armies extended Swedish political power to the whole length of the Baltic coastline. Sweden is the 'great power' among the states of northern Europe, and part of this greatness she owes to her size, superiority of resources, and central position among her smaller neighbours.

The main regions of Sweden fall into two clear types, fertile clay plains that have acted as centres of settlement over many centuries, and, in sharp contrast, the forests and tundras where the struggle between man and crude nature scarcely seems to be

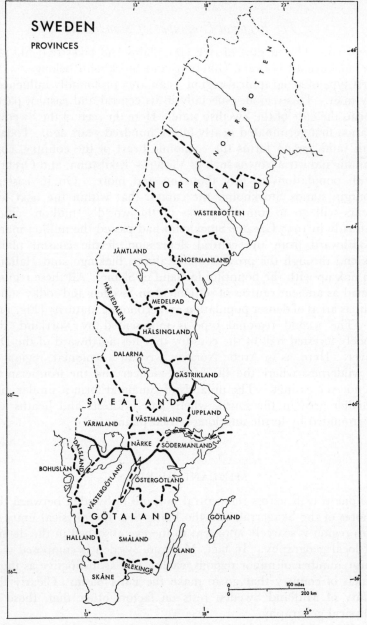

FIG. 11

The oldest provinces of central Sweden are centred on the shores of the great lakes. Uppland turns to the northern shore of Lake Mälaren and Västergötland looks towards the fertile southern coastal plain of Lake Vänern. The large northern provinces of recent colonization tend to coincide with axes of the major river valleys. In the south and west Skåne, Halland, and Bohuslän were wrested from Danish control in the seventeenth century, while the large province of Småland grew in the former no-man's-land between the territories of the medieval states of Denmark and Sweden.

resolved. The medley of rich clay plains and lakes that fills the broad lowland between Göteborg and Stockholm belongs to the first type of geographical region — an area profoundly influenced by man. This region, especially in its central and eastern parts, forms the core of the Swedish state. Here the seed of the Swedish nation first germinated nearly fifteen hundred years ago. Today, this same region forms the economic heart of the country, containing industrial towns such as Västerås, Eskilstuna, and Örebro, with populations of fifty thousand and more. On its eastern margin stands Stockholm, the capital that within the next few years will go to join the ranks of the world's 'million' cities. Already in 1955 Greater Stockholm had passed the million mark. Southward from the central depression, fertile coastal plains extend through the provinces of Kalmar, Blekinge, and Halland to link up with the bountiful lowland of Skåne. All these regions acted as ancient centres of settlement in Sweden and today stand out as areas of denser population and economic maturity [Fig. 11].

The second regional type is represented by Norrland, the lonely forested half of the country that lies northward of the Dal river. Here, as in Arctic Norway, we find a 'colonial' region — a wilderness where the life of the pioneer and the frontiersman is not yet extinct. The uplands of Småland form a similar and smaller area in the south, where lonely forests and heaths are surrounded by fertile and long-settled plains.

MIDLAND SWEDEN

As one travels across the central lowland of Sweden between the shores of the Skagerrak and the Baltic Sea, the physical unity of this region is scarcely apparent to the eye absorbed in the details of local geography. In fact, Midland Sweden is composed of a large number of minor regions, each a *pays* as distinctive as those tracts of country that go to make the Paris Basin. Clearly the unity of Midland Sweden rests on factors other than those of physical geography.

Eastward of Stockholm, central Sweden fades into the Baltic Sea in a confusion of small islands, the Stockholm archipelago. On the inner isles, pine and spruce forests alternate with jungles of wild raspberries and guelder roses that in turn give way to rich meadows in the flat-floored valleys. The small outer skerries,

Sweden

treeless and bleak under grey Baltic skies, lie separated from each other by wide stretches of sea. Many are now desolate and abandoned to the sea birds. By contrast, some of the plains flanking the great lakes are fertile and well cultivated. There the red-painted farms stand amid fields of oats and wheat and fat herds of dairy cows. But nowhere is prosperity continuous over many square miles of country. Even in this central lowland harsh blocks of the primitive gneiss rise up clothed with dark forests, symbols of the untamed landscapes that take up so much of

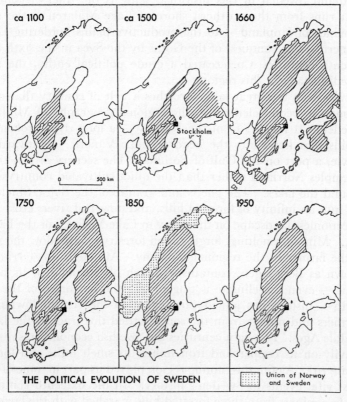

FIG. 12

Medieval Sweden was a Baltic power expanding eastward into Finland. The map of 1660 shows the climax of these centuries of Swedish history. Her control stretches eastward into the borderland of Karelia; Swedish Norrland is in the process of colonization; the Danes have been driven from western Sweden and she holds substantial territories on the southern shore of the Baltic Sea. The maps from 1750 to 1850 illustrate the loss of Finland.

northern Europe. Again, to the south of Lake Mälaren another kind of physical poverty makes itself felt. There lies a tract of country plastered with poor morainic material and vast spreads of granite boulders [Plate 20].

Through more than four thousand years of history, the inhabitants of Midland Sweden have shaped a unit from this disparate collection of natural regions between the Baltic and the North Seas. Today, this unit contains many of the elements belonging to the essential Sweden. This historic region results from the welding together of three groups of *pays*. The oldest part of Midland Sweden in this historical sense is the tract of country that runs from the northern shore of Lake Mälaren — the rich province of Uppland — to the productive plains bordering Lake Vänern. The conquest of the Goths by the Svea in the sixth and seventh centuries A.D. created a crude political entity, the first Swedish state, in this region.

North of the great lakes stretches a belt of country that contributes a second element to the regional geography of Midland Sweden. It reaches from the Klarälv — a long river broken by rapids that flows into the head of Lake Vänern — eastward to Gävle, a port on the Gulf of Bothnia. The scenery of this tract resembles Norrland rather than the quiet cultivated countrysides around the lakes. The gneiss and granite of the Baltic Shield is cut into an infinity of forested hills, and powerful rivers cross this directionless landscape on their way to Lake Mälaren or the Baltic Sea. Mining, smelting, forging, and forestry overshadow the rôle of the farmer in the regional economy. Although this territory, known as Bergslagen, contains so much of Norrland in its physique — even the climate is tinged with the harshness of the far north — history has joined this region to the central lowlands. Farmers and miners from the south settled this tract in the later Middle Ages. For eight centuries the Swedish economy has rested heavily on its copper and iron mines, its smelt mills and forges [Plate 19]. Again, this mining region played its part in some of the most vital events in Sweden's history. In the sixteenth century, the free miners from these forested hills marched with the farmers of the shores of Lake Siljan in support of Gustavus Vasa's struggle against the crown of Denmark. Further, the strength of Protestant Sweden in the seventeenth century depended upon the support of these peasant communities.

The third large part of Midland Sweden was acquired late in

time. The strip of territory in the west between Lake Vänern and the Skagerrak's coastline became Swedish by conquest in the period of explosive territorial expansion at the beginning of the seventeenth century. The Göta älv, a short but immensely powerful river draining Lake Vänern, provides the key to this region. Swedish troops captured this corridor to the ice-free Skagerrak between 1604 and 1617 in the reigns of Charles IX and his famous successor, Gustavus Adolphus. Göteborg, Sweden's window on the west and now her greatest port, was founded by Gustavus Adolphus in 1618 at the mouth of the Göta älv. Two decades later, in 1645, Sweden extended her base in the west of the peninsula with the acquisition of the provinces of Bohuslän and Halland [Fig. 15]. The first, a coastal region of rocky, red granite hillocks and miniature fjords, once belonged to Norway. Halland, a narrow coastal plain of post-glacial marine clays, was captured from Denmark.

Midland Sweden forms a regional unit today largely because of its associations with the evolving Swedish state. So much of Sweden's history has been enacted in this 'heartland' region that has formed the economic core of this Scandinavian community for almost two thousand years. We shall now sketch the geography of the three parts of Midland Sweden.

I. EAST CENTRAL SWEDEN

The most ancient provinces of Sweden, Svealand and Götland, lie between the wide expanse of Lake Vänern and the confused coastline of the Stockholm archipelago. Here is the greatest tract of lowland in the country, giving way northwards to the higher forested waste of the Bergslagen and bounded on the south by the dull, level skylines of Småland. This plain, at less than five hundred feet above the sea, is a region of great geological and structural complexity. Its ancient granites and gneiss belong to the Baltic Shield, and they still preserve fragments of erosion surfaces first formed by nature's primitive forces at the beginning of geological time. Earth movements in the Tertiary period disturbed these old rocks. Today the whole region forms a depressed zone, crossed by numerous faults trending from east to west and dividing the country into a number of large compartments. These faults often protrude in the landscape as long, sharply defined

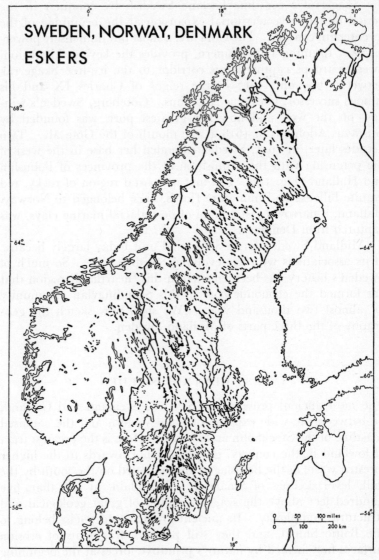

FIG. 13

Narrow sand and gravel ridges, eskers, stretch for miles across the Swedish countryside. Often they are oriented in a NW-SE direction and provide an important topographical element in the siting of farms and the location of towns.

scarps where a forested upland block overlooks a depressed and cultivated plain. Such is the Kolmärden, the cliff-like feature composing the northern shore of the fjord leading into the Baltic Sea from Norrköping. A similar fault scarp accounts for much of the bold southern shore line of Lake Mälaren.

In the lowest parts of this broken peneplain lie the great lakes, remnants of the temporary gulfs and large sheets of water that covered this area in post-glacial times. From their shores stretch level plains, floored by the clays and sands that were deposited in those temporary seas. Consequently each lake, its shore line and adjacent plain of high fertility form regional units whose names, topography, and customs are ingrained in the life and history of the Swedish nation. Miniature regions such as Uppland, the scarcely wrinkled plain that comes down to the shore of Lake Mälaren, or Närke, the prosperous clay lowland between Lake Vänern and Lake Hjälmaren, form distinct and individual areas in eastern Sweden.

One other feature distinguishes the physical geography of Sweden's eastern midlands. Here are some of the finest eskers in the country [Fig. 13]. These ridges of sand and gravel mark the courses of vigorous rivers that flowed beneath the ice at the time when the Quaternary glaciation was rapidly waning in Scandinavia. They run for great distances across the countryside, usually pointing to the north-west and the south-east. Eskers have had great importance in the historical development of this region, often marking out the directions of roads and the sites of farms and villages. Several eskers are named after well-known towns on their course. For instance, Uppsala lies astride such a ridge that runs for three hundred miles northwards into the wilderness of Dalecarlia, and this ancient city and capital of pagan Viking Sweden has given its name to the whole feature.

(a) *Uppland*

Uppland ranks first among the long-settled regions of eastern Sweden. Only a few thousand years ago this plain emerged from a rapidly receding Baltic Sea. Occasionally the sinuous course of an esker or an ice-smoothed mass of granite breaks its unruffled surface. Uppland is a wealthy and comparatively densely populated agricultural province. Towns are rare and unimportant, apart from its regional centre and an early capital of Sweden, Uppsala [Plate 18].

In many senses Uppsala may be compared with Trondheim as a spiritual centre, a shrine of the national life. Under the roof of its twin-spired, Gothic cathedral, the greatest in Sweden, stands the tomb of Gustavus Vasa, the founder king of the modern Swedish nation. Here, too, is one of northern Europe's most famous universities. But Uppsala's history penetrates beyond the medieval centuries deep into Sweden's primitive dark age. Three miles north of the city at Gamla Uppsala (Old Uppsala) stand three huge mounds, constructed from the sands of the Uppsala esker about A.D. 500 as the burial places of the Svea kings [Plate 17]. This pagan Uppsala formed the primitive capital of the Svea whose conquest of the Goths, the people of the lakes region, led to the foundation of the Swedish nation. Today, Uppsala is more than a memorial to Sweden's past and her greatest centre of learning. To the old town, with its narrow streets and gabled houses, has been added an industrial quarter. There, the engineering plants and tall rectangular blocks of flats are characteristic of twentieth-century Sweden.

(b) *Västmanland*

The other rich regions of lowland eastern Sweden each possess their distinguishing marks. Västmanland, lying to the west of the Uppland plains, is strongly overshadowed by the forested, mineral-bearing region of Bergslagen. The largest town of this lowland *pays*, Västerås, stands on the shore of Lake Mälaren. It has grown into an important electrical-engineering centre, partly as a result of its contacts with the iron- and steel-making and metal-working Bergslagen. Another rich part of Västmanland stretches between Lake Hjälmaren and Lake Vänern where a plain is dotted with prosperous red farms. The shores of Lake Hjälmaren are very different from those of the deeply indented Lake Mälaren with its countless bays, wooded peninsulas, and thirteen hundred islands. Here a smooth and regular shore line results from the lowering of the lake level towards the close of the nineteenth century to win a wide strip of fresh clays for agriculture. Like Uppland this countryside devotes its life mainly to farming. There is only one important town, Örebro, a place with about eighty thousand people. Its site resembles many town-sites of central

Sweden because it lies where a river cuts across an esker. At the turn of the century Örebro grew rapidly with Sweden's expanding industrial economy when the state railway system fixed its engineering and repair shops there. It also manufactures most of the boots and shoes sold in the Swedish home market.

(c) Götland

The narrow trench of Lake Vättern splits into two the historic province of Götland. Westward of this fault-bounded and lake-filled trough — a rift valley piercing the heart of the Småland upland — lies Vestergötland. The eastern half of the province, Östergötland, stretches between Lake Vättern and the Baltic.

The two big lakes of eastern Sweden perform vastly different rôles in the regional geography of the country. Lake Mälaren has always focused the life of the plains around it. Stockholm stands astride the esker that constricts the exit of Lake Mälaren [Fig. 14] into the Baltic Sea and its shores are flanked with historic towns, some of which now rank among the chief industrial centres of Sweden. On the other hand, the long and narrow Lake Vättern failed to become a centre for the regions around it. Vestergötland turns away from it, looking northward to Lake Vänern. For miles the cliff-like shores of the lake lack important settlements, and there are few harbours to give shelter against the violent storms that break over this narrow rift valley.

The Motala river drains Lake Vättern, threading its way to the Baltic through a chain of small lakes. This valley forms the axis of Östergötland. Its good soils depend on the underlying sediments of Cambrian and Silurian age, preserved in the deeply depressed area close to Lake Vättern, and on a thick succession of post-glacial lake and marine deposits. The traditional crops of this agricultural province are rye and barley, but the region grows considerable amounts of wheat and sugar-beet, exacting plants in these northern latitudes. The chief industrial centres are Norrköping, the main textile town of Sweden, and Motala with its engineering plants at the exit to the Göta canal.

Vestergötland owes its prosperity to the thick cover of post-glacial marine clays flanking the southern shore of Lake Vänern. Here and there, lonely hill masses rise from this lowland to heights of almost a thousand feet. Unlike the features of the countryside around Lake Mälaren, these hills are not upfaulted fragments of the gneiss floor, but younger remnants of Silurian limestones and sandstones preserved by a capping of volcanic rock. Today, they stand up above the sub-Cambrian peneplain whose level surface truncates the pink and grey gneiss that forms the foundation rocks of this region.

The plain of Vestergötland owes some of its individuality to its westward outlook. Vestergötland is oriented towards Lake Vänern and its outlet to the sea lies through the Göta valley and the port of Göteborg. The climate of the region, too, has a maritime tinge, coloured by this outlook towards the west. Summers are cloudier, rainfall slightly higher, and the winters are more often broken by invasions of mild Atlantic weather when temperatures rise a few degrees above freezing point. These facts find a reflection in the traditional farming system of Vestergötland. Oats and root-crops play an important part, the fields of the province yielding about a quarter of Sweden's harvest of oats. It has the highest density of cattle in the country and is famous for its cheese and butter.

(d) *Södermanland*

The core of eastern Sweden lies in these small fertile plains, but this area also contains tracts of poor country, each bearing many distinctive traits. For instance, Södermanland, a poor province, lies immediately south of Lake Mälaren [Plate 20]. Here the gneiss plateau — its level surface probably dating from Pre-Cambrian times — slopes gently to the Baltic. In places this low plateau is disturbed by faults of Tertiary age, so much so that the drainage pattern first sketched in early Tertiary times has suffered some dislocation. Today, with the additional interference of stony morainic deposits, this is a region of hundreds of small lakes, a natural landscape not unlike parts of the interior of Finland. But Södermanland, lying on the threshold of Stockholm, felt the economic stimulus of this large and rapidly growing city. Within the past century much of its impoverished landscape of forests and peat-bogs has been reclaimed for farming. The region also owes its recent economic evolution to the main railway lines from Göteborg and Malmö that converge across it on their way to the capital.

Södermanland is a province of big estates and large country houses, revealing themselves at the ends of long avenues of oaks or lime trees. These big estates played their part in a movement that has reclaimed nearly forty thousand acres of peat-bog in the region during the past three-quarters of a century. Large country mansions and castles, reminding one of the disturbed history of this Baltic region, contribute a distinctive feature to the personality of Södermanland — a feature not common in northern Europe which is largely the domain of the free peasant and unknown to feudalism.

Södermanland is only one of the many examples of regional poverty amid the bountiful plains of recent marine and lake clays in eastern Sweden. Uppland, for instance, fades northward into a region of forests and peat-bogs where the timber-cutter and the miner take the place of the farmer. There, too, the density of population declines notably. Again, eastward of Stockholm lies the rocky archipelago where scattered slips and patches of good clay still nourish archaic farming communities. Like Söderman-land, the archipelago has been deeply affected by the rapid growth of the capital city. Since 1900 this region of tiny rib-like islands has been heavily depopulated, and summer cottages, the retreats of Stockholm's business men and their families, steadily replace the farmhouses.

(e) *Stockholm*

The minor regions of Midland Sweden contribute much to the life of the nation, but today the overwhelming importance of the central lowlands arises from the presence of the capital city. Stockholm runs Copenhagen close as the biggest city in northern Europe. Both have populations of nearly 800,000 in their built-up cores. If we include the outlying industrial and residential suburbs, connected to the capital by a network of suburban rail-ways, Stockholm already contains over a million people.

Stockholm forms a region in itself, as worthy of study as the plains of Uppland or the rocky archipelago that takes the same name [Fig. 14]. Today, Stockholm is the administrative and commercial centre of the nation. Among the rectangular streets of Norrmalm, the quarter on the north bank of the narrows through which Lake Mälaren pours its waters into the Baltic, stand the banks and business houses that represent all the indus-tries of Sweden. This city occupies a magnificent site where rocky islands and forested peninsulas are interlaced with the waters of the Baltic and inland Lake Mälaren. Deep-water berths for the biggest ships abound, only hampered by the long winter freeze that makes Stockholm dependent on the sinuous thread of a channel cut by ice-breakers through the grey whiteness of the frozen sea.

Stockholm's history reflects so clearly the fortunes of the Swedish nation. After her foundation in the twelfth century, the first phase of growth came in the later Middle Ages as a member of the Hanseatic League. Like Bergen, Stockholm acted as a centre for the exploitation of a vast tract of country. In the sixteenth century, Stockholm became the favourite of Sweden's new line of kings, the House of Vasa. She obtained trading concessions

1	Gamla staden		
2	Norrmalm	5	Södermalm
3	Östermalm	6	Skeppsholmen
4	Kungsholmen	7	Djurgården

FIG. 14

Stockholm occupies a number of islands at the exit of Lake Mälaren into the Baltic Sea. The core of the city, the *gamla staden* (the old town), was founded in the middle of the thirteenth century. The rapid expansion of the city in the seventeenth century is represented by the northward growth of Norrmalm with grid-iron street plans on either side of the Stockholm esker's narrow ridge.

at the expense of other towns on the shores of Lake Mälaren, an economic trend that culminated in the seventeenth century when she gained a monopoly of the trade of Norrland. Again, one notices a parallel with the history of Bergen at an earlier date when that city dominated the commerce of Arctic Norway. Both cities have stood for something more than the average provincial town in the lives of their countries because they had a direct part in the economic development of the northern territories, 'colonial' regions which in those times were scarcely explored.

The topography of Stockholm reveals the main periods in the growth of the city, periods that were vital in the evolution of Sweden as a whole. The medieval city-core stands on two islands amid the narrow strait where the waters of Lake Mälaren race swiftly towards the Baltic. On the northern shore lies Norrmalm, a suburb that began to grow about the middle of the sixteenth century on land that Gustavus Vasa confiscated from the church after Sweden accepted the Lutheran branch of the Protestant Reformation [Fig. 14]. Early in the seventeenth century, while Sweden soared to a peak of political power among the Baltic states, the capital city expanded rapidly. At the accession in 1611 of her great king, Gustavus Adolphus, Stockholm's population numbered about eight thousand. In half a century, by 1663, it had risen to forty thousand. The first half of the twentieth century has witnessed an even more startling growth of Stockholm. With a population of only 300,000 at the turn of the century, Greater Stockholm has now achieved the status of one of the world's 'million' cities. In this latest phase of development, her town-planning and architecture have influenced building all over the world. The urban area of Greater Stockholm now stretches for thirty miles from east to west and about twenty miles from north to south. Former villages are now transformed into city satellites, their glistening factories of glass and concrete and slab-like blocks of flats and tiny rectangular villas set in the immemorial Swedish landscape of pines and silver-grey birchwoods. Geography has strongly determined the direction of this late expansion. New industrial settlements lie to the north-west of the city, while north-eastwards, pleasant garden-city suburbs spread along the many creeks and straits of the archipelago. Across the strait to the south, the expansion of Stockholm for long has been inhibited by a precipitous fault-scarp that forms one of the chief topographical features of the city.

II. BERGSLAGEN — THE INDUSTRIAL HEART OF THE SWEDISH MIDLANDS

This second major element in the regional geography of Midland Sweden lies to the north of the great lakes and their cultivated plains. The central part of this region, between the lower course of the Klar river and the great elbow bend where the Dal river turns towards the sea, is especially rich in metallic ores. Today this region supplies most of the iron ore for Sweden's steel and engineering industries. It is extracted from vast open quarries at Grängesberg and again in the district of Kopparberg. Iron is not the only mineral found in this region of shapeless hills and forests. The long history of Bergslagen — eight centuries of continuous mining and a dimly-charted past that reaches back into the depths of prehistory — is associated, too, with rich lodes of copper, silver, lead, zinc, and gold.

(a) *Gestrikland*

Bergslagen, the mining region proper, is flanked by two provinces of different qualities. Towards the Baltic Sea, where one of the many faults of the Swedish coastline diverts the Dal river north-eastwards into Gävle Bay, lies the region of Gestrikland. This is one of the most northerly outliers of central Sweden where nature and man have conspired to push back the curtain of dark forests. Here, early autumn frosts are rare. Crops of wheat can be ripened and deciduous trees such as oak, ash, and lime add a touch of colour and variety in a landscape dominated by the regiments of conifers. Gävle, a town of more than fifty thousand with its small suburbs, has been described as the last outpost of central Sweden. Ever since the fourteenth century it has acted as the chief outlet for the mining centres of the Bergslagen, especially the great copper mines of Falun that were so productive in the later Middle Ages and are now abandoned. Today Gävle has a small cotton industry and vast pulp mills.

Economic developments in Gestrikland over the past half-century confirm its likeness to northern Sweden, despite traces in the countryside of more pleasant regions to the south. The last fifty miles of the Dal river have emerged as one of Sweden's greatest sources of hydro-electric power, a rival to Trollhättan at the exit to Lake Vänern or Porjus in the far north [Fig. 64]. Here the Dal river widens into a series of long lakes, separated from each other by shallow gorges filled with boiling rapids. A succession of hydro-electric plants supplies the industries of Gävle and sends power southwards to Stockholm and the towns of Lake Mälaren. Along this same reach of the River Dal, industries arose in the past half century. All concern themselves with metallurgy and engineering, devouring the crudely refined ores that come out of the iron-rich hinterland of Bergslagen. Krylbo, placed where the Dal pierces an esker at its elbow bend, is a famous steel-making town. Gysinge produces steel in electric furnaces and Söderfors has forges and foundries engaged in heavy engineering, while Sandviken is the most famous metallurgical centre in Gestrikland. It was founded in the 1860's amid a wilderness of forest to make steel by the Bessemer process. Today Sandviken has a population of more than twenty thousand and is known the world over for its high-quality steels, its boiler tubes, axles, saws, and metal tyres.

(b) *Värmland*

Värmland, a province that reaches to the northern shore of Lake Vänern, has experienced a very different economic history from Gestrikland. Its wide tracts of pine forest are broken by long rivers draining from eastern Norway. Forests drape more than three-quarters of this gently sloping gneiss plateau. Today, most of Värmland's slender mineral resources lie abandoned and unworked. On the topographical map only the place-name element, *hyttan*, may help one now to locate the site of a ruined and deserted forge, lost amid the forests that could still supply a lavish harvest of charcoal. Apart from an isolated iron and steel plant or some large engineering concern, Värmland lives on its timber resources [Fig. 103]. Sawmills, pulp and paper factories occur at intervals along the Klar river and the other lesser streams flowing into Lake Vänern.

Other traits distinguish Värmland as a region beside its timber industries, unbroken forests, and harsh climate. Here the history of settlement runs completely different from that of the central lowlands and even the mining district of the Bergslagen. Värmland is an area of natural poverty apart from its limitless wealth of timber, a commodity that has only found its place on the world's markets in the past century. The place-names of the region bear witness to a slow and piecemeal settlement at a late date. The elements *skog*, meaning forest, and *rud*, a clearing, abound in Värmland. They tell of the first phase of clearance in this region

61

when men created a frontier of primary settlement out of the primitive wilderness. Many of Värmland's names, too, have a Finnish character. They date back to the early seventeenth century when groups of Finns established farms in these empty forests, and in some of the lonelier parts of northern Värmland Finnish survives to this day as a living language.

For many Swedes Värmland's individuality resides in the fact that this is the native region of two of her great writers — Gustav Fröding, one of her finest lyric poets, and Selma Lagerlöf, whose stories have dealt with many of Sweden's national themes. On the canvas of the imagination these writers have recreated a Värmland that bears the salient features of their native province. In turn they have quickened every Swede's appreciation of this region, just as the English Lake District becomes a more distinctive area because we can observe it through Wordsworth's poetic imagination.

III. THE WESTERN CORE OF CENTRAL SWEDEN

A confused military struggle with the waning power of Denmark in the seventeenth century led to the acquisition of the third geographical element in Midland Sweden. This area, possessed through the political ambition of Swedish kings, stretches from Lake Vänern's western shore to the coast of the Skagerrak with its hundreds of humpy, granite islands. The valley of the Göta river, plunging to the sea across a rough, gneiss countryside, forms the physical core of the region [Plate 22]. Soils are meagre and sombre, coniferous forests set the tone of the landscape; in some districts they cover as much as three-quarters of the total area.

(a) *Bohuslän*

North-westward and seaward of the Göta river lies one of Sweden's most distinctive *pays*, to use the term that French geographers attach to areas with a strong physical unity and a common experience in history. The originality of Bohuslän lies partly in its physical geography and also in the fact that it was Norwegian until the early years of the seventeenth century. The dominant rock, a fine-grained red granite, outcrops along an intricate coastline of winding bays, sheltered sounds, and bare, wind-swept skerries. Inland, the countryside gives way to a desolate region of extensive heaths and complex rounded hills, none of which rise more than about three hundred feet above sea level. The seventy fishing villages strung along the coast of Bohuslän are the chief centre of Sweden's fishing industry [Plate 23]. Their fleets return with more than half of the total Swedish catch. Her trawlers scour the fishing-grounds off Arctic Norway and reach out into the Atlantic as far as the Shetlands. Bohuslän's former links with Norway are clearly written into the topography of the region. For instance, south of Göteborg stands Marstrand. In the late Middle Ages this was a prosperous, privileged town within the Dano-Norwegian state. Its economic power vanished with the foundation and rise of Göteborg — the Swedish key to the control of the west coastline. Today Marstrand has joined that long list of once-fortunate medieval towns that now embellish the tourist literature of Europe.

(b) *Halland*

A few miles south of Göteborg an immense change comes over the geography of western Sweden. The rocky poverty of Bohuslän gives way to the fertile and nearly level plain of Halland. This narrow lowland of clays, deposited in the seas that spilled over Sweden at the close of the Ice Age, rivals Skåne in the wealth of its agriculture. Farm types and farming systems are identical with those of that wealthy southernmost province. The crops include wheat, oats, sugar beet, and a variety of roots grown in the elaborate rotations that revolutionized Swedish agriculture during the nineteenth century. Sweden's wars of conquest in the seventeenth century won Halland from the Danes, but the affinities of this province with Denmark remain indelible. The type of farming and the dominant rôle of agriculture in the region's economy make one think of the Danish islands. Also, the long coastline of this province, fringed with dunes and almost without indentations, resembles western Jutland. The lack of harbours, too, reminds one of Jutland. If Bohuslän reflects many of the features of Norway, Halland is an image of Denmark.

Although much of the scenery of Halland seems alien to Sweden, one is also reminded of some of the most vital features of this country. Not many miles inland this young clay plain ends abruptly against the plateau of Småland. The orderly arable fields and occasional beech copses disappear to be replaced by the tracts of coniferous forest, peat-bogs, and heaths of Småland's gneiss and granite peneplain. The junction of the two regions is one of the clearest in Sweden's geography. Småland looks down on to Halland from a steep scarp, often defined by faults. The rivers flowing from its lake-strewn plateau — the Viskan, Ätran, Nissan, and Lagan — pass to the featureless Halland plain by low waterfalls and rapids. Since the beginning of this century, hydraulic and electrical engineers have tapped the energy of this fall-line. Kassefors on the Lagan river, a waterfall only forty feet high, rivals Trollhättan as the biggest source of electricity in south Sweden. Kinna on the Viskan river has grown into a small textile town with silk, woollen, and cotton industries.

(c) *Göteborg*

Geography and history conspire together to make the Göta valley between Lake Vänern and the sea the most important part of western Sweden. The Göta river opens up a hinterland far more extensive than that of any other river draining to the west coast. Through Lake Vänern this narrow corridor is joined to the whole of Midland Sweden. Westward, the coast line faces the Skagerrak and the open Atlantic. In such a region a great port and city seemed destined to arise, but, as the history of Göteborg shows, its creation required the fulfilment of other important conditions. The first need was the political interest of Sweden — a Baltic power — in this western coast line. This only appeared with the Swedish thrust to the west in the seventeenth century. In 1618 Gustavus Adolphus founded Göteborg on the left bank of the Göta river. Then it was a frontier post of Swedish military power, occupying a narrow corridor of Swedish territory between Norwegian Bohuslän and Danish Halland. Even after the conquest of these coastal provinces Göteborg suffered from Danish raids for another century [Fig. 15].

This city grew and became prosperous with the development of communications that have tied it closer to its immense hinterland. First, at the close of the eighteenth century, the Trollhättan canal was cut to give direct access to Lake Vänern. In our own times it has been deepened, so that sea-going ships can now reach Karlstad and Kristinehamn, the timber and pulp ports on the northern shore of the lake. In the second half of the nineteenth century, railway-building added even more to the importance of Göteborg. Today, it is the focal point of the Swedish railway system, even casting a shadow over the capital itself. One of the chief lines in Göteborg's economic development is the trunk railway to Gävle on the Baltic coast. This opened up Sweden's richest mineral and metal-working region, Bergslagen, to the west coast port. As so often happens, the passive gifts of nature, in this instance the Göta river and the lowlands and lakes within its

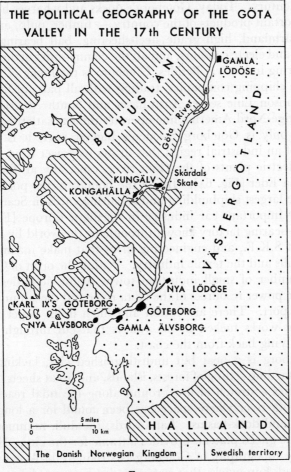

THE POLITICAL GEOGRAPHY OF THE GÖTA
VALLEY IN THE 17th CENTURY

GAMLA
LÖDÖSE

BOHUSLÄN

Göta River

VÄSTERGOTLAND

KUNGÄLV
KONGAHÄLLA
Skärdals
Skate

NYA LÖDÖSE
KARL IX'S GÖTEBORG
GÖTEBORG
NYA ÄLVSBORG
GAMLA ÄLVSBORG

HALLAND

0   5 miles
0   10 km

The Danish Norwegian Kingdom   Swedish territory

FIG. 15

Early in the seventeenth century the Göta valley provided Sweden with a route for expansion towards the shore of the Kattegat from her heartland on the great lakes. Gustavus Adolphus founded Göteborg in 1618, at that time only one among several strong-points in the lower Göta valley. This wedge of Swedish Västergotland isolated Danish Halland from its Norwegian interests in Bohuslän.

hinterland, have been transformed through the building of a system of communications into active geographical factors in the growth of a great city.

Göteborg is now the second city of Sweden, with a population of 404,349 (1960). Gustavus Adolphus regarded his infant foundation on the Göta river as Sweden's window on the west, but the city really took over this rôle only after the middle of the nineteenth century. Today, Göteborg's docks and wharves handle all the important products of the country — timber, pulp, and paper from Värmland, high grade steel-sheeting, ball bearings, transformers and electric motors, and all the commodities of the Swedish engineering industry. Besides, Göteborg is the home of the great Swedish shipping companies, trading with all parts of the world. The Johnson Line serves Australasia and South America, while the Sverige-Nord Amerika line operates the transatlantic services.

Not only is Göteborg Sweden's biggest port, it is also the centre of an industrial region that draws its power from the huge hydro-electric plants of the Göta river, especially at Trollhättan and Lilla Edet [Fig. 64]. Inside the bounds of the port-city one finds the largest shipbuilding and repairing yards in Scandinavia, the only important car industry in northern Europe [Fig. 107], the ball-bearing factory known throughout the world by its initial letters of S.K.F., and engineering firms that make machinery for sugar mills and the textile industry. Within the orbit of Göteborg lie a number of small industrial towns whose activities depend upon the power resources of the Göta river and the stimulus of the near-by port. There are cotton and linen mills, paper factories and glass-works tucked in the valleys that cut through the low plateau lying back from the coast.

Göteborg is a neat but undistinguished city, lacking Stockholm's startling setting of forests, islands, and great sheets of water. It occupies a stretch of low ground along the tidal reach of the lower Göta river where space has been found for a long line of wharves and dock-basins. Landwards, the dull, hummocky skyline of the gneiss plateau provides a frame for the city. Here and there the topography of Göteborg is strikingly broken by rocky, ice-shaped hummocks that are sometimes crowned by churches [Plate 24]. The individuality of Göteborg also rests on its people. Just as Liverpool can point to a rich Irish stratum in her population, so Göteborg finds the roots of many of her most famous business families among foreign migrants of the seventeenth and eighteenth centuries. In the seventeenth century, when this was a frontier town facing hostile neighbours, the development of the city was mainly in the hands of Dutch settlers. It was also a favourite place for emigrants from Scotland until the closing decades of the eighteenth century saw their interests turned towards Upper Canada. One still meets Scots names among the people of Göteborg. There are Carnegies, Dicksons, Sinclairs, Watsons, and Campbells. A man named Keiller started a foundry that became the biggest shipbuilding firm in Sweden. And the proverbial Scots love of education is perhaps reflected in the fact that the Polytechnic in Göteborg was founded by a Chalmers. Time has transformed the families of these Scotsmen into perfect Scandinavians and even their names have taken on a Swedish appearance. For example, Macpherson has been transmuted to von Fersen.

SOUTHERN SWEDEN'S COASTAL PLAINS

(a) *Skåne*

Sweden's most southerly province, Skåne, plays as vital a rôle in the life of the nation as any part of the midlands, not excepting the historic province of Uppland. Skåne is the most densely populated part of the country, containing a million people, a seventh of Sweden's total population.

The individuality of Skåne derives from its southern position and its relations, both physical and historical, with Denmark and northern Germany. This most southern part of the Scandinavian peninsula shares its main climatic features with eastern Denmark. For instance, the mean temperatures of the midwinter months hover about freezing point, unlike those of most of the rest of Scandinavia [Fig. 37]. The mean temperatures for July, on the other hand, reach into the low sixties on the Fahrenheit scale. At Lund, a few miles inland from the Sound, the average temperature of the warmest month is 17 degrees centigrade (62°F.).

The geology and topography of Skåne contain several elements that are foreign to the conventional picture of Sweden. The soft and pleasant landscapes flanking the Sound have a foundation of Cretaceous rocks [Fig. 16]. Here are the limestones and calcareous sandstones that underlie so much of Denmark. Inland, these recent sedimentary rocks give way to much older calcareous sandstones of Cambrian and Silurian date. The latter occupy a

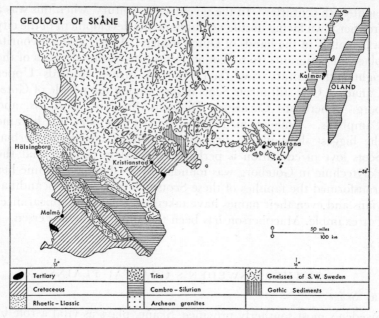

FIG. 16

The geology of Sweden's most southerly province is closely related to that of Denmark Young sedimentary rocks, largely Cretaceous limestones, occupy the south-western tip of Skåne, though even here the covering sediments are interrupted by narrow faulted ridges that throw up the Archean granites and sediments of the Baltic Shield. Inland these ancient gneisses and granites dominate the landscape.

long corridor that cuts diagonally across the peninsula, reminding one of similar rocks that have survived in the lakes region of Midland Sweden. In turn these rocks are supplanted by a rising, hummocky surface of gneiss that signals the natural frontier of Skåne, a frontier with the poor interior province of Småland.

Despite the foundation of Cretaceous limestones that relates Skåne to Denmark and northern Germany, these rocks play little active part in the scenery of the region. They lie buried beneath a varied cover of glacial material and smooth sheets of stoneless clay, laid down in the transitory seas of post-glacial times. But even boulder clays add something to the individuality of this region. The countryside around Malmö was overrun by the great ice-stream that occupied the floor of the Baltic Sea. It left behind a clay rich in finely ground chalk, stuffed with flints and lumps of the parent rock from the floor of the Baltic Sea. The soils of this glacial debris rank among some of the richest in Sweden. Away from the coast, towards the boundary of Småland, the boulder clay changes its character. Here are the deposits left by ice that ploughed southwards across the gneiss plateau of Småland. They are cold and stony. Tracts of outwash sand and gravel abound, and for centuries farmers have found them repulsive.

The individuality of southern Sweden rests on its position as the main point of entry into northern Europe from the trunk of the continent. The Danish islands, blocking the mouth of the Baltic Sea, form a land-bridge that is almost complete. The first Neolithic farmers probably followed this route into Scandinavia and today the ports of Hälsingborg, Malmö, and Trelleborg handle much of the passenger traffic into northern Europe.

In the wars of the seventeenth century, Sweden snatched the province of Skåne from Denmark, but even now its landscape bears many marks of several generations of Danish rule. It is interesting, too, that farming in Skåne followed closely the Danish pattern of development since the beginning of the nineteenth century. Three-quarters of the fertile plain around Malmö is cultivated and forest occupies scarcely ten per cent of the region. The chief arable crop is wheat, and about a quarter of the national harvest comes from the fields of this tiny strip of territory that looks south-westward across the Sound. Skåne has earned the nickname of the 'granary of Sweden', but like most catch-phrases that serve to simplify our thoughts it also distorts the whole truth. The lime-rich boulder clay plains may produce heavy crops of wheat, rye, barley, and oats, but the region is also famous for its great output of sugar beet and forage root-crops. Like Denmark, this province also holds a high place in stock-rearing and dairying; and it produces nearly a half of Sweden's butter.

The landscape of Skåne — a subtle amalgam of physique, economy, and history — looks like the richest parts of Denmark. Her farms lie scattered about a countryside of wide, carefully tilled fields and distant, tidy plantations [Plate 32]. Here centuries of occupation have pushed the forest into the background and tamed the wilderness to man's purposes. The farms themselves often display a plan that is familiar in Denmark, with a central paved courtyard surrounded by low, single-storeyed buildings, thatched and white-washed. Like parts of Denmark, too, Skåne is a region of big estates where manor houses stand reflected amid the lilies on the placid waters of their enclosing moats.

Skåne also contains the third most important town of Sweden, Malmö, with a population of 228,878 (1960). Just as Stockholm and Göteborg play their parts in concentrating and expressing the life of Midland Sweden, so Malmö has emerged as the regional capital of the south. This has been the rôle of the city since the late Middle Ages when Malmö displaced Lund as the chief centre of southern Sweden. Today, Lund is a quiet little university town at the foot of the Romele Åsen — a narrow, rocky granite horst that rises to 500 feet from the plain of Skåne, a fleeting reminder of the Archaean rocks that form the real Sweden. Lund arose as the political and administrative centre of the eastern wing of Denmark's Scandinavian empire in the eleventh century. Later it was eclipsed by Malmö, just as Copenhagen took the place of Denmark's early inland capital at Roskilde [Plate 47]. The attractions of the Sound and its shores have persisted ever since in the urban geography of Scandinavia. Since the beginning of the nineteenth century, Malmö and its satellites, Hälsingborg, Arlöv, Kockum, and Trelleborg have grown rapidly on the traffic of their docks and busy ferry services. New industries, too, have appeared. Today there are sugar mills, breweries, shipbuilding and repairing yards, soap and margarine factories in the ports of the Sound. Together with Copenhagen and its satellites on the Danish side of the Sound, it is claimed that the towns flanking this narrow strait form the only true conurbation in northern Europe [Fig. 23].[1] Malmö shares in the alarming urban expansion that has characterized Sweden in the twentieth century, doubling her population since the early 1930's.

If one sets the riches of Skåne beside the immensity of Sweden, they are scarcely more than 'skin-deep'. Already a few miles inland from the shores of the Sound narrow hummocks of gneiss and granite poke through the cover of Cretaceous sediments, harsh reminders that the hard rocks of the Baltic Shield lie at no great depth. Their level summit-ridges, forested with dark conifers and splashed with peat-bogs, form tiny islands of the primitive landscape that means so much in the life of Sweden.

(b) *Blekinge*

North-eastward from Skåne a coastal plain of varying width stretches into Östergötland. Blekinge, a province captured from the Danes in 1658, looks like an extension towards the Baltic of

the poor interior plateau of Småland. Everywhere the clay lowland seems punctured by rocky Archaean inliers, islands of irredu-
cible poverty.

Northward again from the province of Blekinge, the narrow
plain of Kalmar lies parallel to the coast. Physically it contains
some features that have been described in the previous pages on
Skåne and Midland Sweden. The plain of Kalmar rests on
calcareous sediments of Cambrian and Silurian age. The good
soils that have developed on this foundation are varied by surface
deposits of very recent date — boulder clays, sinuous, sandy eskers,
and the thin skins of clays left by post-glacial seas.

(c) *Öland and Gotland*

Two large islands lying out in the Baltic may be associated with
this region of southern Sweden. Öland, nearly a hundred miles
long, faces across Kalmar Sound to the plain of the mainland. A
cleanly cut escarpment, never more than a hundred and fifty feet
high, runs for the length of the island, close to the west coast. At its
foot lies a narrow plain with beach deposits of the Ancylus Lake
and Littorina Sea, more extensive forerunners of the Baltic Sea in
post-glacial times [Fig. 33]. These deposits provide the only really
fertile soils in the island, and the main settlements of Öland are
concentrated along this strip. Comfortable farms, backed by
woods of oak, elm, ash, and hornbeam, thrive at the foot of the
little, sharply etched escarpment. For the rest, Öland is a bare,
exposed plateau of Silurian limestone tilted imperceptibly eastward towards the Baltic. With its thin red soils and low-growing
vegetation of rock roses, harebells, wild strawberries, juniper, and
saxifrages, this heathland gives a weird impression of some remote
Mediterranean scene in the clear brilliance of a Baltic summer.
Sheep graze the open spaces of Öland's heaths and the island is
famous for horse-rearing.

Gotland, placed midway in the sea between mainland Sweden
and the coast line of the U.S.S.R., possesses a different physical and
economic character. Prosperous dairy farms occupy a large tract of
warm, rich, calcareous marls; market gardens and nurseries supply
butter, vegetables, fruits, and flowers to the Stockholm markets.

In the history of the Baltic area both Gotland and Öland hold
positions not unlike Crete and Sicily in the Mediterranean. They
seem to have been touched and penetrated by all the movements

of peoples around the Baltic Sea. They have participated in every phase of the economic life of this inland sea. For instance, the first Neolithic settlers reached these islands as early as their occupation of the plains of Skåne and Uppland. In Roman times and at the beginning of the Dark Ages, they acted as intermediaries in the trade that flowed between Central Europe and the mysterious lands of the northern Baltic. Hundreds of Roman coins have been dug up in the two islands, as well as things of gold, silver, bronze, glass, and pottery that came from lands further south. Between the twelfth and fourteenth centuries Gotland rose to a pinnacle of economic power in the exploitation of its site as a member of the Hanseatic League. It served also as an entrepôt for north-western Europe in trade with the shores of the Black Sea and the Arab world beyond.

Today, Gotland, Öland, and the plain of Kalmar have much in common, a regional unity imposed by the process of historic change. Their old central position in the world of the medieval Baltic has crumbled. Changing geographical values have left them isolated. Today the centres of highest economic interest lie in the channels at the mouth of this sea, around the shores of Lake Mälaren, and in the bustling commerce of Göteborg. Today Kalmar [Plate 30] is mainly a tourist town, noted for the rather austere baroque architecture of its cathedral standing solitary on the central square. Visby, whose maritime code once held sway over all the Baltic, now profits as a tourist centre living within its medieval walls and containing six ruined gothic churches [Plate 31]. Population, too, has declined in these economically stagnant areas. Öland lost a quarter of its farmers and fishermen in the last decades of the nineteenth century by migration to North America. But the past half-century has introduced a new phase in the economic history of Gotland. Its limestones have long been famous as a source of building material in the Baltic Sea. Since the foundation of the cement industry in 1874, they have contributed a valuable item to the trade of the island and in recent years to Sweden's international commerce. Lime-burning and the cement trade introduced capital into Gotland that in turn stimulated agricultural development. Marshland reclamation went on in the southern part of the island and the number of cattle doubled between the 1870's and the 1930's. Above all Gotland was able to find an expanding market for her agricultural products in Stockholm.

SWEDEN'S REGIONS OF LATE COLONIZATON

(a) *Norrland*

Norrland, a vast area of thinly populated territory, occupies the whole of northern Sweden [Plate 25]. It is a region of pine and spruce forests, containing one of the world's most valuable reserves of iron ore. Like Arctic Norway, Norrland's mineral resources are still not fully charted and only partially developed. Here is a region that even today calls for the qualities of the pioneer and the frontiersman.

The interior of Norrland shares many features with the bare uplands of eastern Norway. Topographically, it belongs to the backbone of Scandinavia, the Swedish-Norwegian frontier often coinciding with the water-parting that throws off rivers to the Atlantic and the Gulf of Bothnia. Structurally, the interior of Norrland belongs to the Caledonian system [Fig. 17]. It contains remnants of large rock masses that were moved eastward along thrust planes in that remote period of Palaeozoic mountain-building. Today these fragments survive, largely due to the resistant quality of their rocks, as heavily weathered and dissected mountain groups. For instance, the smooth outline of Areskutan faces east across the Silurian lowland of Jämtland. The long slopes of this *fjäll*, leading from a summit level at nearly five thousand feet, provide a favourite Easter skiing ground for the tourists from Stockholm. The mountain itself is a granite remnant of one of the overthrust rock masses of Caledonian age [Plate 29]. Further north and again close to the Norwegian frontier, Sweden contains some of the highest mountains in Scandinavia outside the Jotunheimen. They belong to the Sarek massif that remained remote and unexplored until the close of the nineteenth century. These mountains, with their many small glaciers, are carved out of the highest of the gigantic, overthrust rock slices of the Caledonian structures, and they are largely made of a tough, resistant gabbro.

Desolate tundras occupy the *fjäll* zone of most of inner Norrland. Late into the summer the rounded, shapeless mountains are flecked with snow patches. At lower levels an open scrubland of silvery-grey birches covers the countryside. A corridor of Silurian sediments bounds the eastern flank of the *fjäll* country, forming the second great natural division of Norrland. Eastward again, this partially cleared and settled corridor ends abruptly against

73

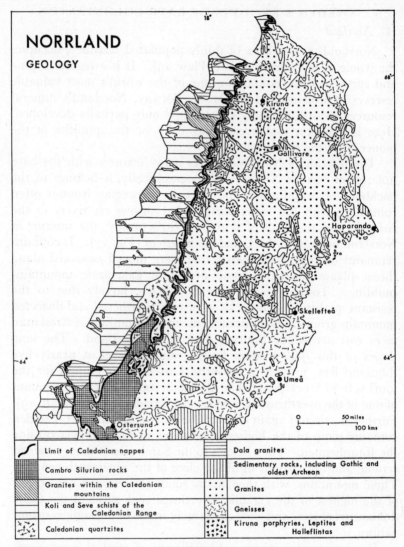

NORRLAND

GEOLOGY

Kiruna

Gällivare

Haparanda

Skellefteå

Umeå

Östersund

Limit of Caledonian nappes		Dala granites	
Cambro Silurian rocks		Sedimentary rocks, including Gothic and oldest Archean	
Granites within the Caledonian mountains		Granites	
Koli and Seve schists of the Caledonian Range		Gneisses	
Caledonian quartzites		Kiruna porphyries, Leptites and Halleflintas	

FIG. 17

The geology of Swedish Norrland divides into two major zones along the eastern boundary of the overthrust rock-masses of the Caledonian system. In the west, along the Norwegian border, are the Caledonian structures; for the rest Archaean granites and gneisses of the Baltic Shield make up most of Norrland. The corridor of Cambro-Silurian rocks is an important feature in the settlement and communications of inner Norrland.

the Archaean plateau — the primordial gneiss and granite — a forbidding region of silent forests and peat-bogs that forms the core of Norrland and its third major natural region.

The open valleys of a series of rivers cross the three main physical regions of Norrland from the Swedish-Norwegian frontier to the coast of the Gulf of Bothnia. From the Väster Dal in the south to the Torne river on the boundary with Finland, these valleys help to integrate the economic life of Norrland. Their upper courses make deep slots in the wilderness of the *fjäll*. Long lakes fill the valley-floors and the bare slopes are laced with the white ribbons of waterfalls. These lakes of inner Norrland contain Sweden's greatest untapped source of water power. Terminal moraines block the eastern ends of many of the lakes where they abut on the corridor of Silurian sediments. The valleys broaden across this strip of smiling territory before they plunge into the Archaean plateau. The conjunction of east-west valleys and the northward-pointing Silurian corridor produces the only zone of permanent settlement in the interior of Norrland. Little towns serving vast areas of nearly empty territory have arisen at the eastern ends of the lakes, linked by the railway that runs northwards from Östersund into the iron-mining country beyond the Arctic Circle.

The Archaean plateau, Sweden's chief source of softwood timber, ends abruptly against the coastal plain of the Gulf of Bothnia. The rapid uplift of northern Scandinavia since the Ice Age raised this clay lowland from the floor of the Gulf of Bothnia. Today, rough bosses of granite rise like islands from the level stretches of young post-glacial sediments [Fig. 43]. Although much land still awaits reclamation, groups of farmers have actively colonized this coastal region since the end of the eighteenth century. Most of Norrland lies at the margins of cultivation in northern Europe and there is no great incentive to farm these potentially valuable soils. The risks of frost in late August limit the agricultural economy to hay-crops and potatoes [Fig. 55]. Today, the expansion of agriculture in the coastal plain of Norrland is hampered even more by the diversion of interest towards the other resources of the region — the forests and iron ores that have become such a vast source of profit in the past half-century. The settlements strung along the coastline of the Gulf of Bothnia are chiefly concerned with industry. In the north, amid a group of smaller coastal towns, stand the mineral-processing ports of

Luleå and Skellefteå. Further south, where the Ångerman and Ljungan rivers converge, stand Härnösand and Sundsvall with their sawmills and plants producing pulp, hardboard, and cellulose — economic capitals of the great timber empire of Norrland [Figs. 88 and 91].

The great natural divisions of Norrland, as we have noticed, lie parallel to the trend of the Bothnian coastline. Each valley forms a corridor to the sea, taking in the bleak and treeless *fjäll*, a strip of the Silurian depression, the forests of the Archaean plateau, and the more productive coastal plain. Each valley acts as a natural unit, performing its most important task as a floatway by which the timber of the interior reaches the ports and processing plants along the coastline [Plates 26 and 27]. Other regional differences, subtler in quality, can be detected as one moves northwards through Norrland. These differences owe much to climate and latitude, but they are also explicable by the history of Sweden's occupation and exploitation of this region.

There is an old proverb in Sweden which says that oaks, cray-fish, and noblemen come to an end at the Dal river, the conventional frontier of Norrland. It is certainly true that deciduous trees and the comfortable manor houses of aristocratic families who have adjusted themselves to Europe's most complete welfare state form part of the milieu of Midland Sweden, while Norrland is a raw region of pioneers, mining and timber-cutting communities, and small, independent farmers.

The provinces of central Norrland — Jämtland, Härjedalen, and Ångermanland — already held an interest for Sweden at the close of the Middle Ages. At that time the northern regions were still mysterious and largely unexplored territories, the home of the Lapps, and of no political or economic value to Sweden. Then, the remote interior of Jämtland, centred on the shores of the Stor lake, naturally turned towards Norway and the port of Trondheim. It was only in Sweden's great period of expansion in the seventeenth century that these lands were officially annexed to the Swedish crown. Today, middle Norrland stands pre-eminent as a region of forests and the forest industries.

Northward of the Ångerman river begin the two vast territories of Västerbotten and Norrbotten. Forests slowly give way in importance to the open tundra and within the forest-belt stunted birchwoods play an increasingly dominant rôle. The climate of these most northerly provinces is markedly continental.

The long dark winters are accompanied by long spells of clear weather, broken only by the rare disturbances that pass across the upland barrier from the Atlantic bringing severe blizzards. Mean January temperatures in Swedish Lapland are as low as − 16° centigrade (3°F.). The mean temperature of July is barely 16° centigrade (60°F.), though the thermometer not uncommonly reaches 24° centigrade (75°F.) in the long summer days of the north. Precipitation, too, has a continental characteristic, never reaching more than twenty inches for the year in Lapland [Fig. 36]. The summers of the far north, though lasting no longer than three months, enjoy long hours of limpid Arctic sunlight. After the winter snows have been reduced to melting streaks in the last week of May, clouds of mosquitoes rise from among the bog myrtle and the carpets of white anemones to plague the traveller in Lapland.

As one travels north towards the Finnish frontier the administrative provinces grow bigger in area and emptier of people until Norrbotten, with the population of a small English town, reaches the size of Portugal.

(b) *Småland*

At first glance, Småland — the extensive, monotonous upland that occupies the heart of southern Sweden — looks like a repetition of Norrland. Numerous lakes, whose waters mirror the serrated blue-green silhouette of coniferous woods, fill the southern part of the region. Pine and spruce forest alternates with peat-bogs and heathlands where the pale, ash-grey podsol soils are exposed to the sky.

The geology and morphology of Småland display many features of Sweden's northern territories. The Archaean gneisses and granites of the Baltic Shield appear once more. The sub-Cambrian peneplain, a feature that can be observed over miles of country in northern Norrland, helps to explain the monotony of Småland's major landforms. But the analogy with Norrland must not be pressed too far. Even in the realm of physical geography there are many distinctive local features, while the settlement history of this area and the contacts of the region down the centuries with other parts of the Baltic have been totally different from Norrland's.

Two major features distinguish the physiography of Småland.

It has been deeply affected by the earth movements, often along ancient fault-lines, that shaped the Skagerrak and Midland Sweden in Tertiary times. Today, the highest part of this ancient, but now strongly disturbed, peneplain forms the broken, rounded upland at the southern end of Lake Vättern. Here the Taberg, overlooking the match factories of Jönköping, reaches a little over eleven hundred feet. The Pre-Cambrian surface dips gently eastwards so that the boundary between Småland and the plain of Kalmar becomes very hard to plot. On its western flank Småland ends abruptly in a scarp overlooking the plain of Halland — a feature that forms a real 'fall-line' in Sweden's economic geography.

A second feature that distinguishes the landscape of Småland results from the rapid retreat of the ice-sheet in late glacial times [Fig. 32]. The ice-front, ever-shifting and melting away northwards, held up transitory lakes. Coarse, sandy deposits accumulated on these lake-floors. In the southern and eastern parts of Småland narrow eskers lie like ribs across the landscape and add to the confusion of surface deposits, creating a complex region of lakes and ill-defined drainage that can be matched only in Finland.

Småland's climate, too, makes this region distinct from Norrland, and also from the surrounding lowlands. It is the wettest part of Sweden, receiving forty inches of rain along the high western edge that faces the Skagerrak. Småland's exposure to the North Sea is clearly imprinted on its winter climate, a time when fogs blanket the plateau or endless sheets of stratus cloud roll in from the sea. At this time, Norrland usually stands in the grip of the Arctic anticyclone with clear skies and some of the lowest temperatures in northern Europe [Fig. 37]. Småland's winter is distinctly harsher than that of the neighbouring plains. For instance, snow lies at least a month longer than in the coastal districts of Halland. Frosts, too, come in late spring to shorten the growing season on this plateau.

Småland's individuality does not rest solely on these unique features of morphology and climate. Its claim to be treated as a separate region depends equally upon its rôle in the history of northern Europe. Until the beginning of the seventeenth century Småland acted as a frontier zone, a no-man's-land, between Denmark, the state focused on the Sound, and Sweden with its centre to the north in the lakes depression. In the later nineteenth century, this historic rôle as a separating region was completely reversed. Småland then lay between two well-populated lowlands — the coastal plain of Skåne and the lakes depression. As a result of this position between Sweden's two chief cores of population, Småland became criss-crossed with a network of trunk railways.

Småland also has a distinctive settlement history. In the late Middle Ages, farmers filtered into the region, following valleys that led into the interior plateau from the surrounding plains. They settled by lake shores and especially in the shallow depressions floored with the sands of ephemeral glacial lakes. But even today, extensive tracts of northern Småland are empty of settlement. Amid the forests and heaths farmers have only managed to reduce about 3 per cent of the total area to cultivation.

The last two centuries witnessed the rise of industries in Småland. In the latter half of the eighteenth century the glass works of this lonely heath country created an international name for Swedish glass. During the past hundred years, small industrial settlements arose in the higher and more forested parts of northern Småland close to the railway routes. They make furniture, toys, and, more recently, paper-pulp.

It is worthwhile to examine the position of the regional capital of this thinly populated district at the heart of southern Sweden. Jönköping lies at the southern end of the long trench occupied by Lake Vättern, overshadowed by the hills of Småland, but scarcely within the region. Today Jönköping possesses the biggest match factory in Sweden, and its neighbour, Huskvarna, a garden city tucked in the dark green hills, produces armaments, cutlery, sewing machines, and bicycles. Power for these industries comes from the waterfalls of an unimportant river that runs into Lake Vättern from the Småland hills. In reality these twin towns stand as outliers of the group of industrial towns in Midland Sweden, and the negative character of Småland is underlined by the fact that it must turn outside itself to find a regional capital.

CHAPTER 4
Denmark

DENMARK is the smallest among the Scandinavian states. Her 16,576 square miles amount to an eighth of the area of Norway, and one could fit most of Denmark into the midland lowland of Sweden. But Denmark's total population of just over four and a half million places her second only to Sweden among the states of Scandinavia.

Although limited in area Denmark possesses many natural advantages over her northern neighbours. She is the most southerly of the Scandinavian states, a fact that counts for much in the climates and economic geography of these high latitudes. The dark winter, an oppressive background to the lives of fishing communities in Arctic Norway, plays no part in the traditions and literature of Denmark, no part of the country lying further north than the British Isles. Winter for the Danes means the invasion of piercingly cold continental air from the north-east when temperatures may fall to twenty-five degrees below zero on the Centigrade thermometer. Not every Danish winter brings intense cold. As a North Sea country, Denmark's normal winter is composed of a succession of mild, rainy spells with interjections of cold, clear weather as Jutland and the archipelago become enveloped in continental air. Often there is no snow at Christmas; but once or twice in a century Denmark experiences the winter of extreme cold when the channels between the islands are transformed into solid ice, and the Baltic freezes as far out as Bornholm.

The summer climate of Denmark again reveals its relations with the lands around the North Sea. Summer, especially in Jutland, may be wet and short of sunshine, but it has the compensating advantage for agriculture that Denmark enjoys the warmest autumns of any Scandinavian country. The average October in Denmark is three degrees warmer than April and there is no great risk that crops will be destroyed by premature frosts early in September. The advantages of Denmark's site stand out clearly in a brief comparison with Finland. The latter, locked in the

Denmark

interior of the Baltic Sea, feels all the harshness of a continental climate in high latitudes. There, summer bursts suddenly in the middle of June, but by late August frost is a common danger in the interior of the country. Denmark, on the other hand, forming a bridge of islands in the mouth of the Baltic Sea, enjoys many of the advantages of an Atlantic climate, without the extreme cloudiness and depressed summer temperatures of western Norway.

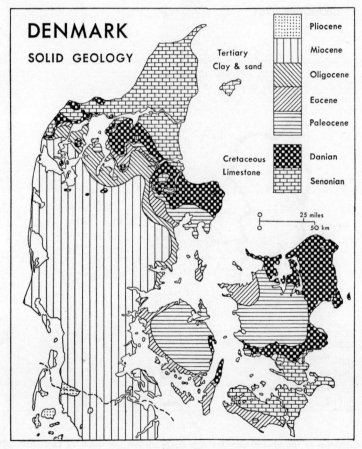

FIG. 18

Denmark's oldest rocks outcrop as limestones of Cretaceous age in the eastern part of the archipelago and across the northern end of the Jutland peninsula. Towards the west and south successively younger rocks of Tertiary age form the solid geology that is largely buried beneath the debris of the Quaternary ice-sheets.

Latitude and climate both place Denmark on the southern fringe of Scandinavian Europe. The scenery of Denmark establishes an even closer link with Central Europe. Only one fragment of Denmark, the island of Bornholm, reveals the old rocks of the Baltic Shield at the surface. A granitic intrusion forms two-thirds of this island, giving it a bare, wild, northern coastline [Fig. 24].

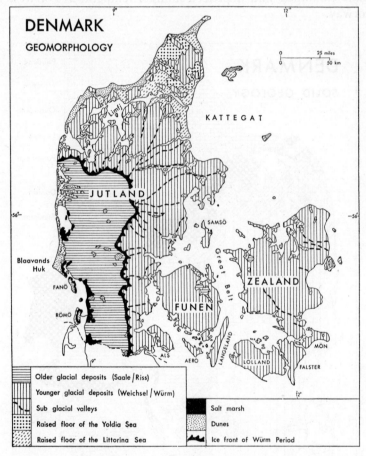

FIG. 19

The deposits of the Quaternary Ice Age cover almost the whole of Denmark. The country is divided into two main regions by the line of terminal moraines deposited along the ice-front of the last ice period (the *Würm* of the Alpine chronology and the *Weichsel* of the ice succession in central Germany). The archipelago and eastern Jutland belong to the varied and richer boulder clays of the newest glacial deposits. Central and western Jutland are covered with the poor outwash sands of this glaciation that lie strewn across the weathered clays of the earlier *Riss/Saale* glaciation.

For the rest, Denmark resembles much of the north German plain in its geology and scenery.

The foundations of Denmark are a series of sedimentary rocks from the late Mesozoic and Tertiary periods [Fig. 18]. The lowest member, a thick layer of Cretaceous chalk, is followed by hard coral limestones and softer calcareous marls. Higher still, a succession of Tertiary rocks — mainly clays, marls, and sands — reaches up to the Pliocene period. Although these rocks contribute much to the Danish economy as sources of underground water and in the provision of raw materials for cement- and brick-making, they play a minor rôle in the scenery of the country. The debris of the Scandinavian ice-sheet covers most of the islands and the peninsula of Jutland [Fig. 19]. The Danish landscape was carved in the last few thousand years from the boulder clays, sands, and gravels deposited in the last phase of the Quaternary glaciation. In Sweden, Norway, and Finland the moving ice ground its way across features such as the sub-Cambrian peneplain that have been in existence from the beginning of recorded geological time, while the miniature hills and little plains of Denmark have been formed entirely from the soft deposits of this last, brief phase of northern Europe's physical history.

On the small scale of an atlas map Denmark looks monotonously uniform. The lumpy terminal moraines of east Jutland reach only 500 feet in their highest points, the Ejer and the Himmelberg. For the rest, the country would seem to be a dull and undiversified plain. In truth, Denmark displays an astonishing variety of features within the narrow limits imposed by a geology that is largely Quaternary in date. There is a world of difference between the closely cultivated landscape of southern Zealand on the outskirts of Copenhagen and the barren storm-battered dunes along the coastline of northern Jutland. As the later pages of this book will attempt to show, the subtleties of the Danish scene have been deeply exploited by her inhabitants over the past four thousand years.

The distribution of population in Denmark reflects the natural variations in the geography of the country [Fig. 20]. The most densely peopled regions are the islands of Zealand and Funen, together with the sheltered, eastern coast of Jutland. Western and northern Jutland, traditionally a region of open heaths and peat-bogs, is still comparatively thinly populated, despite the extensive reclamation of land in the past three-quarters of a century. In a sense, Jutland may be compared with Swedish Norrland, Arctic Norway, or the dark, still forests of the Karelian border country as a region of recent colonization. In the case of Jutland, it was the drainage of peat-bogs and the reclamation of poor tracts of heath that attracted settlers into the wilderness [Fig. 40].

Denmark, too, belongs to the Scandinavian world in another way. Her economy and the quality of the national life depends upon keeping a high level of trade, especially with the industrialized and densely populated states bordering the North Sea. But her internal resources are slender. She has no coalfields, and lacks the compensating reserves of hydro-electric power that belong to her Scandinavian neighbours. Nor can her economy fall back on the minerals and forest products that enrich the other north European nations. Denmark's prosperity depends above all on the initiative and resourcefulness of her people, who have created in the past century one of the world's two most efficient agricultural economies [Fig. 52]. It is interesting to remember that the other European nation which has driven the output of its farms to such high levels is the Netherlands — another small state whose natural resources are mainly limited to the soil.

Denmark's pattern of trade, too, is different from those of the other Scandinavian countries. Sweden's markets, for instance, are far more extensive. Her engineering products reach all parts of the world and the sharp rise in the consumption of paper in the past decade has opened up a big market, though one that experiences severe competition from the softwood forests of Canada and Newfoundland. Norway's fish products sell widely in both western and southern Europe and her tramp steamers pick up trade from almost every port in the world. Denmark, on the other hand, is confined largely to two heavily industrialized states of the North Sea basin — the United Kingdom and Western Germany — for the sale of her dairy products. The continuance of these markets depends upon hotly-argued trade agreements and the maintenance, on the part of Denmark, of standards that other agricultural producers have done their best to imitate.

Denmark lacks the primitive strength that rests in the economies of the other north European states. She faces many of the problems of the small west European states whose resources lie entirely in the soil — nations such as the Netherlands and Eire. Of these three, Denmark and the Netherlands have very much in common. Both have achieved an agricultural revolution that the rest of the world has not noticed sufficiently. And in the past quarter of a century both states have gone a long way towards industrial maturity. So far, Eire has failed to find any of these courses and her poverty, social discontent, and massive emigration

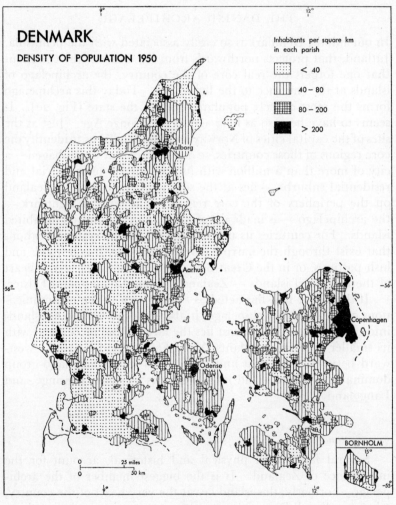

DENMARK
DENSITY OF POPULATION 1950

Inhabitants per square km in each parish

☐ < 40
▥ 40 – 80
▦ 80 – 200
■ > 200

Aalborg

Aarhus

Copenhagen

Odense

0   25 miles
0   50 km

BORNHOLM

FIG. 20

The harsh contrasts of population distribution noticed on the maps of Norway and Sweden are absent from the geography of Denmark. The population densities are highest in the islands and eastern Jutland — the regions of the newest glacial deposits. The most thinly peopled districts coincide with the outwash sands and gravels of western Jutland.

show what can happen to a small, ill-endowed European state in an epoch of industrial growth. In some ways it is astonishing that Denmark has achieved so much.

THE DANISH ARCHIPELAGO

In our minds, Denmark is so easily associated with the peninsula, Jutland, that projects northwards from the trunk of the continent that one forgets the real core of the country, the archipelago of islands at the entrance to the Baltic Sea. Today this archipelago forms the most densely populated part of the state [Fig. 20]. It seems to have been so as long ago as the Bronze Age. Just as the sites of the capital cities of Norway and Sweden led us to identify the core regions of those countries, so one notices that Copenhagen— a city of more than a million with its tenuous arc of industrial and residential suburbs — lies at the south-eastern corner of Zealand on the periphery of the core region. The core of Denmark — the archipelago — is made up of more than a hundred inhabited islands. For centuries its unity rested on the sea communications that exist through the narrow sounds fringed by beech woods and lush pastures, or in the Great Belt, a little inland sea at the heart of the four chief islands — Zealand, Funen, Lolland, and Falster.

If the Great Belt has acted as a focal area in the communications of the Danish archipelago, it also serves to divide the islands into two groups. To the east lies the large island of Zealand with its smaller southern pendants, Møn, Falster, and Lolland; westward between the Great and Little Belts stands an island-group dominated by Funen and its dependants — Aerø, Taasinge, and Langeland.

(a) *Zealand*

Several facts, both physical and historical, account for the importance of Zealand. It is the biggest member of the archipelago. Formerly, this island lay at the very heart of the country, when medieval Denmark was the greatest power in northern Europe and her territory stretched across southern Sweden into the wilderness of Småland. For at least a thousand years Zealand has contained the capital of the Danish state, first at Roskilde [Plate 47] and, since the middle of the fifteenth century, in Copenhagen.

The foundation rocks of Zealand belong to the Cretaceous and Tertiary periods; but they scarcely appear at the surface, lying buried beneath a cover of glacial clays and sands [Fig. 19]. The low chalk cliffs at Stevns Klint, south from Copenhagen across the wide bay of Køge, form a rare exception. For the rest, the island consists of gentle plains of ground moraine and wrinkled boulder clay hills along the arcs of terminal moraines. Her morainic hills lie mainly in the central and north-western parts of the island, with another group overlooking the Sound on the fringes of Copenhagen. In places these hills, clothed with beech woods, rise to over four hundred feet above the sea. The soft and varied scenery is broken here and there with tiny lakes, many of them lying in hollows that once contained masses of ice clotted amidst the confused dump of clay and sand.

The agricultural prosperity of Zealand rests on the nearly level clay plains that rarely reach more than a hundred feet above sea level. Such a one is the Hede, the coastal lowland south-westwards of Copenhagen. It is likely that this region has been in continuous cultivation since the early Bronze Age [Fig. 39]. Today, as it stands on the doorstep of the capital, the Hede is deeply affected by the big market among the city population. Everywhere the concentrated methods of the market-gardener, producing fruits and vegetables, are important on the small farms close to Copenhagen. The coastal plain of the Great Belt forms Zealand's other fertile lowland. Here is a countryside of medium-sized farms, between fifty and a hundred and fifty acres, set among large, hedgeless fields. They yield good harvests of wheat, barley, sugar beet, and fodder root-crops, but like most Danish farms their chief economic interest lies in dairy cattle [Fig. 54]. Among the farms of western Zealand some great estates have survived. Today, these country mansions — castles is perhaps a better term, because so many have a military motif in their architecture and the grey-green ring of a moat around them — form one of the chief tourist attractions of the island.

Copenhagen — now a city of a million — overshadows all the other towns of Zealand. Of the rest, few have more than ten thousand people. Most of them are pleasant, but not very active, market centres with populations of about five thousand. Those that display any active economic life are ports and railway centres. For instance, Helsingør, at the narrowest part of the Sound and immortalized for the guide-books as the place where Shakespeare set the tragedy of Hamlet, maintains an economic life of its own, free of the tentacles of the capital city [Plate 45]. It is an important ferry-port for Hälsingborg, one of the main ways into Sweden. It is famous, too, for its shipbuilding yards. Holbaek, at the head of Isefjord, that placid stretch of sea biting deeply into the pastoral landscapes of northern Zealand, has its flour mills and engineering works specializing in agricultural machinery. Næstved, too, on the railway that leads southwards to Gedser and the ferry to Germany, has a famous porcelain factory. Most of Zealand's inland towns are historic centres that have declined relatively in importance with the expansion of Copenhagen and the focusing of urban life on the coastline. Roskilde, Copenhagen's forerunner as the capital of Denmark, holds a position in the national life not unlike that of Trondheim or Uppsala in Norway and Sweden. Denmark's kings find their traditional burial place in Roskilde's fine Gothic cathedral [Plate 47]. Sorø gathers around a Benedictine monastery founded in the twelfth century, while Ringsted seems to have been the centre of a pagan Denmark before the first church was established at Roskilde early in the ninth century.

(b) *Copenhagen*

The shrines of Denmark's past — medieval churches and Bronze Age tombs — lie among the wheatfields and woodlands of Zealand's interior, but today her economic life is centred upon the coastline. Copenhagen's history epitomizes the changing political relationships and economic geography of the Baltic, the sea to which it provides the key. Because this city forms the link between the Baltic and the North Sea and the bridge between central Europe and Scandinavia, trade and commerce have always played an important rôle in its life. Until the beginning of the nineteenth century Copenhagen was also deeply involved in the struggles for political power in northern Europe, a fact arising from its crucial position at the mouth of the Sound. The castle built by Archbishop Absalon on the island of Slotsholm provided the first nucleus of Copenhagen. Today the great palace of Christiansborg stands on this site [Plate 48]. Under the shadow of the first fortress of the twelfth century, medieval merchants gathered to transact business. There were fishermen with dried and salted herring, caught along the coastline of Skåne, and businessmen from the towns of north Germany and the

Netherlands. But Copenhagen's medieval history is dominated by a long struggle with the Hanseatic League — that economic empire that created Visby and meant so much to the prosperity of Bergen. Later in Copenhagen's history, the early seventeenth century was a time of desperate conflict with Sweden. And even later, in the Napoleonic Wars, the city was bombarded and burnt, and the Danish navy destroyed. Only the last half of the

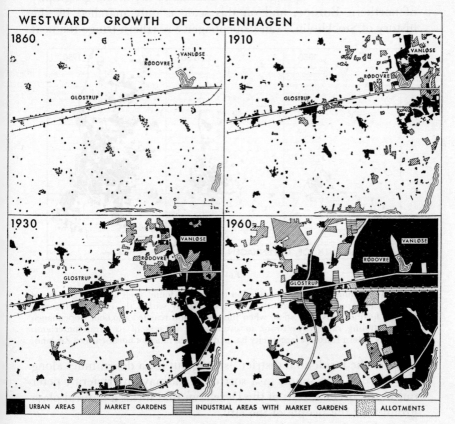

WESTWARD GROWTH OF COPENHAGEN

| URBAN AREAS | MARKET GARDENS | INDUSTRIAL AREAS WITH MARKET GARDENS | ALLOTMENTS |

FIG. 21

Copenhagen presents the problems of the expanding city and its rural hinterland that are familiar in many parts of western and central Europe, but scarcely known elsewhere in Scandinavia. In 1860 villages to the west of Copenhagen were still undisturbed by the city's growth. By 1910 the expansion of the capital is especially clear along the line of road and railway. The spread of market gardening points to the rise of an urban market. The maps for 1930 and 1960 show the quickening of the process. Rødovre is swallowed up in the continuously built-up land of the capital.

nineteenth century saw the dismantling of Copenhagen's defences and the abandonment of the right to collect dues from all ships passing through the Sound. With these changes and the rejection of her military rôle, one can date the last stage in the development of the city as an industrial and commercial centre.

Since 1900 Copenhagen has expanded rapidly northwards, absorbing several once independent villages [Figs. 21 and 22]. Such a process of rapid growth is unusual in the urban geography of northern Europe, and on this scale is only matched by the history of Stockholm. On Copenhagen's northern fringe the neat

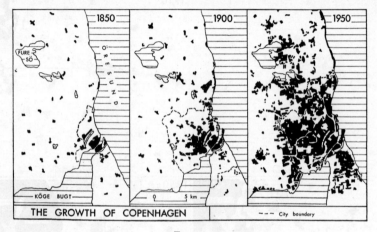

FIG. 22

In 1850 Copenhagen, with a population of 130,000, found itself at the beginning of a period of rapid growth. Most of the city still lay within the early seventeenth-century fortifications. By 1900, when the population reached 450,000, Copenhagen was expanding rapidly westward to swallow the villages of its rural hinterland. Today, northern Europe's largest city has laid claim to much of north-eastern Zealand.

villas of the residential districts, strung out for a dozen miles along the shore of the Sound in a sort of Scandinavian 'riviera', peter out in the beech forests of the Dyrehavn that forms a natural playground for the people of the city.

As in Oslo, one of the chief functions of Copenhagen's wharves is the import of fuel and the raw materials of industry. Timber, metals, grain, fertilizers, coal, fuel-oil, and tropical oil-seeds rank among the chief commodities that pass through the port. Copenhagen's hinterland for the redistribution of these imported goods covers most of the archipelago. On the other hand, the populated parts of eastern Jutland turn towards Denmark's second city,

Aarhus, while the west centres on Esbjerg. Since the end of the nineteenth century Copenhagen has emerged as the busiest port in northern Europe. In turn, the activities of the waterfront have stimulated industries so that today she displays all the economic variety that one associates with capital cities and great ports.

Copenhagen stands head and shoulders above all the other manufacturing centres of Denmark. She is the main centre of the clothing and textile industries and produces a wide range of engin-eering goods from marine engines to electrical apparatus. Flour mills, oil-seed-crushing plants, and a margarine factory form

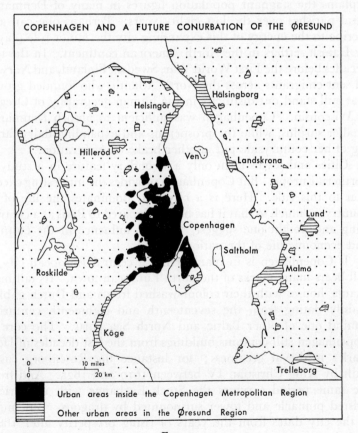

COPENHAGEN AND A FUTURE CONURBATION OF THE ØRESUND

Hälsingborg
Helsingör
Hilleröd
Ven
Landskrona
Lund
Copenhagen
Saltholm
Malmö
Roskilde
Köge
Trelleborg

0   10 miles
0   20 km

■ Urban areas inside the Copenhagen Metropolitan Region
▤ Other urban areas in the Øresund Region

FIG. 23

The narrow arm of the Öresund that connects the Baltic with the Kattegat has attracted towns and industries to its shores. Copenhagen, the capital of Denmark's former Scandinavian empire and northern Europe's largest city, promises to become the centre of the first conurbation in Scandinavia.

industries typical of the port. There are the great Carlsberg breweries, whose profits have contributed much to the cultural life of the nation. Copenhagen also has a china factory that makes porelain of world-wide fame.

No other Scandinavian country shows such a concentration of industry in one city. Since the 1880's Copenhagen has exercised a magnetic attraction upon the people of Denmark's countryside and of her small towns. They streamed steadily into the suburbs of the growing capital, especially from Zealand and the group of islands eastward of the Great Belt. The rise of Copenhagen partly explains the stagnant population figures in many of Denmark's rural parishes over the last eighty years. Perhaps one can also ascribe to the energy of this expanding city the minor rôle played by Danish settlers in the North American continent. In the two decades before the First World War, Sweden, Finland, and Norway all sent emigrants across the North Atlantic who founded groups that still stand out distinctly in the human geography of Oregon or Wisconsin. Copenhagen was sufficient to absorb Denmark's smaller surplus, while the prosperous and expanding dairy farming of her countryside put another brake on emigration.

Cities and towns form only a secondary feature in a study of northern Europe. But Copenhagen provides the interesting exception to this rule. Here is a city that dominates the life of its country, so much so that it has been compared to Paris as a centralizing and, might one suggest, 'stifling' influence in the cultural and economic life of the nation.

If Copenhagen is in many senses a central European city, it still bears many marks of the north European town. Its tall merchants' houses with their colour-washed fronts and Dutch gables, mainly dating from the seventeenth and eighteenth centuries, remind one of other Baltic and North Sea ports. The core of Copenhagen still contains buildings from the last decades of Denmark's medieval greatness; for instance the Rosenborg castle built by King Christian IV between 1610 and 1625. And from the same period survives the Stock Exchange with its curious twisted pinnacle and tower surmounted by dragons. But much of the city dates from the years of rising prosperity after 1880. Certain features of Copenhagen bear a distinctly Scandinavian label. There is the open-air museum in the great forest-park at Lyngby on the northern fringes of the city which contains full-size specimens of every type of traditional architecture found in

Denmark, from small town houses to fishermen's huts and peasant cottages. Similar cultural museums enrich the surroundings of both Oslo and Stockholm. Perhaps, too, the forests that press to the city's northern edge and the shady parks that have taken the place of the fortifications that once hedged Copenhagen reflect another feature of the Scandinavian capitals — the desire to keep in touch with the countryside.

(c) *The Smaller Islands of the Eastern Archipelago*

Three islands, Lolland, Falster, and Møn, lie off the south coast of Zealand, almost closing the passage from the Baltic Sea into the Great Belt. They are flat, low-lying islands. The highest part of Lolland reaches only eighty feet above the sea. Everywhere a sheet of heavy clays with slight variations of relief produces a rather monotonous landscape. The eastern end of Møn alone offers some striking variation of scenery, where a narrow belt of Cretaceous chalk falls precipitously to the sea in harsh, grey-white cliffs from heights of four hundred feet. Open downs form part of this little tract of country, but much of the rest is covered by beech woods that grow to the cliff-tops and fill the deep ravines reaching down to the sea [Plate 44]. For the rest, these islands contain some of the best soils in Denmark. Climate, too, presents its bounty to the farmer in the form of an earlier spring than that of the northern coast of Zealand, and the heat of the summer is often prolonged deep into the autumn. The heavy clays and the reliable summers make Lolland and Falster the chief areas for the growing of sugar beet in Denmark [Fig. 53].

The regional distinctiveness of these southern islands expresses itself in other minor and subtle ways. Oaks, poplars, and willows are common on the heavy clays, whereas the beech is more usual on the lighter, sandier soils of Zealand. Colourful hedges of dog-rose, hazel, and wild plum often enclose the fields of the shallow, damp depressions. Farms with white-painted shingles and low thatched roofs set amidst orchards suggest a warmth and richness that is absent from the northern parts of Zealand or the exposed coast of northern Jutland.

Bornholm may be classed with the eastern islands of the archipelago, even though it stands alone in the Baltic a hundred miles to the east of Zealand. Politically, it is the only surviving remnant of Denmark's medieval Baltic empire that crumbled in the seventeenth century with the southward expansion of Sweden. Physically, Bornholm forms a fragment of the Scandinavian mainland. Two-thirds of its area consists of an outcrop of grey granite and gneiss, part of the Pre-Cambrian Baltic Shield [Fig. 24]. The ice-sheets of the Quaternary period obliterated the island, so that

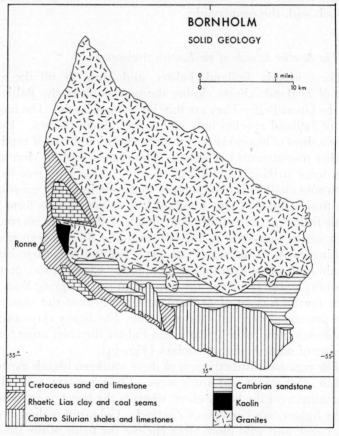

FIG. 24

The regional geology of Bornholm is sharply divided into a low granite plateau that fills the whole of the northern part of the island and a belt of younger limestones, sandstones and clays that underlie the farmlands in the south.

today polished, rounded hummocks of granite rise from a broken skin of boulder clays.

The individuality of Bornholm is clearly written into its economic and human geography. For instance, it is the only abundant source of hard rock for building in Denmark and the cutting of granite blocks is one of its chief industries. Bornholm's site in the middle of the southern sleeve of the Baltic Sea enjoys a peculiarly mild climate, so that one can see mulberries growing in the south of the island and grapes ripen out of doors in the same district behind the soft, dune-fringed coast line. Bornholm, too, has a distinctive settlement pattern. Apart from the fishing villages on the coast and its little regional capital, Rønne, there are no compact, nucleated villages in the island. In the interior one finds scattered, isolated farms of no great size.

Again, the history of Bornholm sets this island apart from the rest of Denmark. Like Swedish Gotland, it has enjoyed the advantages and penalties of an island situation in the Baltic Sea. Bornholm became Danish in the middle of the thirteenth century, but was often an object of envy to her neighbours and enemies. For instance, for a period in the early sixteenth century it passed into the hands of the merchants of Lübeck, and again in the next century was occupied for some months by Swedish garrisons. Bornholm's isolated and important position in the Baltic Sea was felt again after the Second World War when a Russian garrison occupied the island for nearly a year. Once again, Bornholm's rocky granite coast and the little sand beaches have returned to their more normal function as one of the chief tourist attractions in Denmark.

(d) *Funen and the Islands of the Western Archipelago*

The largest island among the western members of the archipelago is Funen. As a geographical region, it possesses several features that make it distinct from its eastern neighbour, Zealand. Tertiary clays and sands underlie the cover of glacial materials in this island, and these soft rocks outcrop along the coast in low, crumbling cliffs. A smooth plain of ground moraine occupies the north of Funen and forms the most fertile tract in the island. South of this plain of Odense runs an arc of tumbled sand and clay hills that rise in places to more than four hundred feet. Extensive deciduous woods still clothe these hills and there on the poorest soils tracts of open heath occur.

The quiet scenery of Funen, shaped over many centuries by the hand of man, has acquired such epithets in the guide-books as 'the garden of Denmark' or 'the pearl of Denmark'. These trite phrases, although lacking precision as descriptive metaphors, do contain a germ of truth about this island. Despite the northern outlook of the Odense plain, it possesses many of the qualities of Copenhagen's Hede or the smiling inner islands of Falster and Lolland. The shelter provided by the near-by coast and hills of Jutland softens the climate in the same scarcely-perceptible way as in those islands with a southern aspect which we have already noticed. It is certain that farmers have cultivated the plain of Odense since the early Bronze Age. Today it houses the densest rural population in Denmark, with almost three hundred people to the square mile. This, too, is a region of small and medium-sized farms, many of them less than twenty acres. Its crops include those that only flourish on the best soils and in the most favourable local climates of central Europe — hops, tobacco, sugar beet, plums, and cherries [Figs. 52 and 54].

The life of Funen has not suffered the upheaval that came to Zealand in the last century with the rapid growth of Copenhagen. Odense, the regional capital, has a population of 105,915 (1955). It is Denmark's fourth port, and its trade is largely handled by the small ships that nose their way up the ship canal from Odense fjord bringing fertilizers, fuel, and manufactured goods to this mainly rural island. Today, the economic activity of Funen focuses on the main railway that crosses the island between the Great and Little Belts. Nyborg, the port where the train-ferry embarks for the twenty-mile journey across the Great Belt, revived with the railway age. Its great fortress, founded towards the end of the twelfth century, stands symbolic of the geographical value of this site amid the inland sea of the Great Belt. This castle, tradition says, was built to protect the core of the medieval Danish kingdom from the raids of Baltic pirates. Whatever the reasons for its foundation Nyborg certainly played a critical rôle in the history of the state as the meeting place for medieval Danish parliaments, composed of bishops and noblemen. Parts of Nyborg castle were badly destroyed in the Swedish wars of the seventeenth century, and again there was a battle outside its walls in the Napoleonic conflict. Today, Nyborg plays an equally important part in the geography of Denmark as a busy ferry port for cars and trains in the chief line of communication between Copenhagen and Jutland.

The south coast of Funen and its three pendent islands — Langeland, Taasinge, and Aerø — stand remote from the chief economic changes of the twentieth century. For instance, some of their little country towns are especially rich in houses of the seventeenth and eighteenth centuries. Their ports, Svendborg and Faaborg, have been outstripped by Odense and Nyborg. The history of the little ports of Funen in the past century and a half

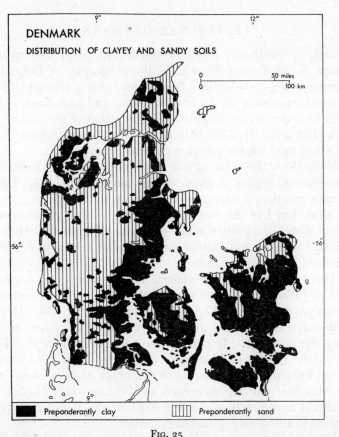

FIG. 25

Danish soils are derived from the products of glaciation in the Quaternary period. In the archipelago and eastern Jutland clay soils with a high content of lime preponderate and provide the foundation for Denmark's oldest and best farming. Central and western Jutland possess large tracts of poor sandy soils developed on the outwash materials from the Weichsel/Würm ice-front. Much of this area was converted from heath to farmland in the great reclamation movement of the nineteenth century.

resembles the story of the string of ports in south Norway around Kristiansand. Like Arendal and Lillesand in Norway, Denmark's Marstal and Svendborg were famous in the last century as centres of the nation's fleet of sailing ships. They have never caught up with the age of steam, and the focus of economic interest has turned to the north of the island and the main-line railway that crosses the plain of Odense.

PENINSULAR DENMARK

Jutland, a peninsula pointing northward from the trunk of Europe, is the largest element in the geography of Denmark, a province as big as Belgium. Even today, after a century of active colonization among the reclaimed heaths and peat-bogs, it has a population density noticeably lower than that of the rest of Denmark [Fig. 20]. It is the only part of the country where there is still waste land for the creation of new farms.

Viewed on the scale of our atlas maps, Jutland looks like a homogeneous region, a physical unit northwards of the Danish-German frontier, a natural dike between the North Sea and the Kattegat, but like the rest of Denmark, it displays considerable variety within the limited range of its glacial deposits. Above all, Jutland's western and eastern outlooks have helped to define two regions of historic importance.

There are distinct differences, too, between the north and south of Jutland. The basement rocks of the northern and north-eastern parts belong to the Cretaceous period [Fig. 18]. Here the chalk outcrops in places and forms low cliffs at sparse intervals along the coastline. It reaches the surface again near Aalborg and at the mouth of Mariager fjord to give rise to a valuable cement industry. West and south, the chalk and limestones of the late Mesozoic age are succeeded by Tertiary clays — rocks that lie almost completely concealed beneath the boulder clays and outwash sands of the Quaternary period.

In the few thousand years since the retreat of the ice-sheets from the Scandinavian north, Jutland has experienced a marked uplift in relation to sea level. About eight thousand years ago, before the Baltic took on its present shape, its basin was filled with the warmer, saltier, more extensive Littorina Sea. At that time, north Jutland was an archipelago interpenetrated by wide arms of salt water [Fig. 33]. Today, Limfjorden, cutting across the peninsula for more than a hundred miles, a placid, inland water-way set amid emerald meadows, stands as a remnant of this vanished post-glacial sea. The coastline of north Jutland is typical of an emerged shore. For many miles it runs straight or gently curving, with no major indentations to provide sheltered harbours. Off shore, the wide sandy beaches slide imperceptibly under the North Sea, forming a coast notoriously treacherous for its submerged and shifting sandbanks and the fierce winter storms that come from the exposed north-west.

South Jutland, on the other hand, has not been shaped by the forces of a post-glacial uplift. Southward from Esbjerg the coast line bears all the features of a recent submergence. Behind a line of low islands, capped with sand-dunes, stretch extensive lagoons and salt-marshes. In their shelter the thriving port of Esbjerg was founded less than a century ago, and, earlier still, in the late Middle Ages, the busy port of Ribe flourished. The east coast, flanking the Little Belt, shows similar submerged coastal forms. Here from the German frontier northwards a succession of narrow, salt-water estuaries penetrates inland for many miles through meadows and woods. They are the drowned parts of valleys, first formed by rivers beneath the retreating Baltic ice-sheet at the close of the final glaciation.

Other differences exist, far harder to define, between north and south Jutland. A journey southward through the peninsula takes one imperceptibly from the world of Scandinavia to that of northern Germany. Near the German frontier, Denmark faces her only minority problem in the largely German-speaking towns of Tønder, Højer, Løgumkloster, and Tinglev. Historically, Slesvig or south Jutland is a Danish province with a mainly Danish-speaking countryside, but the towns of this region have attracted German immigrants since the end of the Middle Ages. As a marchland it has long been a zone of conflict, particularly since the middle of the last century, when an expanding Germany resorted to the settlement of her claims in this region.

Denmark lost south Jutland in a brief war with her powerful neighbour in 1864. Until the close of the First World War, this fertile province became the object of a strong political campaign to make it German. Denmark recovered most of Slesvig by a plebiscite in 1920 after Germany's defeat in the First World War, though the natural capital of the region, Flensburg, remained just across the German border. Even though the wrongs of 1864 were righted, she gained a minority that became infected with the virus of political propaganda from across the border in the 1930's — a fact that persuaded Denmark to reject any further claim on

99

territory in Schleswig-Holstein at the end of the Second World War. South Jutland provides the only example in northern Europe of a minority problem of the central European type, where a linguistic minority group looked towards a government and political organizations centred outside the nation. In this case, many Germans in south Denmark saw their spiritual capital in Berlin rather than Copenhagen.

Other affinities, less harmful, may be noticed between south Jutland and northern Germany. The scenery and economy of the north German marshlands projects into Denmark as far north as Esbjerg. One also remembers that eight centuries ago Frisian settlers came to this tract of bleak salt-marshes to apply the methods they had learnt in the flat country around the Zuider Zee for the conquest of such wastelands. South Jutland towns, too, possess something of the atmosphere of the German town, and even the stone for the building of the gothic cathedral at Ribe came from the Rhineland.

(a) *East Jutland*

The sharpest differences in the geography of Jutland lie between east and west. In every sense, east Jutland represents an extension of the Danish archipelago. The numerous small ports and towns along its coast line have always shared in the life of the 'inland sea'. Here, too, the raw climate of the North Sea coast is already softened in the lea of the hummocky clay hills that form the spine of Jutland.

East Jutland begins at Mariager Fjord and stretches south to the German frontier. Its physical unity lies in the series of estuaries, *fjorden*, and the confused clay hills of the Baltic terminal moraine that contains the highest parts of Denmark. On these heavy soils with a certain valuable lime-content the typical pattern of Danish farming has established itself [Fig. 25]. They grow wheat, barley, oats, and forage root-crops; but dairy cattle and pigs form the financial core of the farm economy, feeding the co-operative dairies and bacon factories scattered through the countryside. The agriculture of east Jutland represents the norm for Denmark. It lacks the tinge of the exotic belonging to the market gardening and orchards of parts of Zealand and Funen, but at the same time it is obviously richer than the farming of settlements recently won from the heath and the peat-bog in the west of the peninsula.

East Jutland also has its old towns and cities, while in the western heathlands urban settlements often developed only with the building of railways and the coming of road transport. The 'station-town' is a phrase from the Danish vocabulary that applies especially to the raw areas of later settlement in west Jutland.

Aarhus is the chief town of the Jutland peninsula. Next to Copenhagen it is the second port and town in Denmark — a statement that can be misleading until one recalls the great disproportion between the capital and the other Danish towns. Aarhus has a population of 118,943 (1955) and depends upon the life of its docks and the industries that have grown there mainly within the past half century.

The traffic of Aarhus reflects the nature of its immediate hinterland — the most densely populated part of Jutland and a region devoted mainly to agriculture. It imports fertilizers, and coal is one of the largest items handled across the wharves. In relation to Jutland's agriculture, Aarhus stands complementary to Esbjerg. The latter, because of its direct links with the British Isles, has taken on the rôle of exporting the bulk of Jutland's dairy products. Aarhus, on the other hand, mainly supplies the consumer needs of the countryside, and it is interesting that a good deal of her traffic is with the capital city and great primary distributing port, Copenhagen.

Along with the expanding trade of her docks, Aarhus developed as the chief industrial centre of the Jutland peninsula. Ships are built and repaired in her dockyard. There is a small textile industry, and since the end of the last century Aarhus emerged, along with Copenhagen and Esbjerg, as one of the chief centres of the margarine industry in Denmark.

History and geography have combined to make Aarhus the regional capital of Jutland. The port-city stands on the wide arc of a bay surrounded by broken, wooded hills, part of the belt of terminal moraines that stretches the length of eastern Jutland. The exact site of the city is fixed by the little plain deposited where a former sub-glacial river once entered Aarhus bay. The little, misfit stream that follows this valley and trickles into the harbour has been covered by the growth of the city; and the harbour, much of it constructed since 1900, is almost entirely an artificial creation. Its nine miles of quays shelter behind breakwaters built out into the bay.

The buildings and topography of Aarhus reflect its place as

the regional capital of Jutland. Its cathedral, with red brick walls and a green copper roof, dates from the twelfth century, suggestive of Aarhus's importance in medieval Denmark. Nor has this city escaped the Scandinavian mania for open-air museums. In the Vestebro Park, close to the centre of the city, nearly fifty examples of town houses have been gathered from all over the peninsula. Aarhus museum, too, reconstructs some of the prehistory of Jutland in the many objects gathered from the peat-bogs of the region.

(b) *North Jutland*

Jutland, like so many other regions of Europe, is one of those areas where the mind can exercise itself in defining the subtler nuances of the landscape. For instance, east Jutland with its varied boulder clay hills, prosperous farms, and thriving market towns gives way in the northern part of the peninsula to an area of very different qualities. Above all, the flat lands of north Jutland feel the effect of exposure to the sea. It is battered by heavy north-westerly gales, and sandstorms are experienced close to the desolate, dune-fringed coast of the Jammer Bugt. The climate, too, has features that belong to other low-lying, level regions close to the sea — features that may be matched around the Zuider Zee or in the Lincolnshire Fens. For instance, in spring and early summer the skies of Jutland display an intense clarity or else the grey-green pastures become lost in the mists that drift inland from the cold North Sea. The distinctiveness of North Jutland from the rest of the peninsula may be ascribed to several other features. There are fewer trees and woods; close to the coast they stand bent and stunted in the wind. The landscapes of north Jutland are less tamed than those of the rest of Denmark. For instance, in the east lies the biggest unreclaimed peat-bog in the country, the Lille Vildmose. The whole northern coastline stands bleak and exposed with scores of miles of high sand-dunes, a few small forlorn summer resorts and only two unimportant fishing harbours in a distance of a hundred and fifty miles. The individuality of the region runs deeply into its human geography. For instance, the people of the small *pays* or minor regions that can be distinguished in North Jutland — Himmerland, Vendsyssel, Han — speak their own dialects rich in archaic words. Lastly, the separateness of north Jutland as a region is secured by its topography and physical history. The continuous line of morainic hills that occupies east Jutland breaks up into smaller, lower, and isolated groups. The central feature of the region is formed by Limfjorden, an inland waterway of broad lagoons, islands, and narrow channels that stretches for a hundred miles from the east to the west coasts, isolating the whole of the northern part of the Jutland peninsula. Finally, the recent emergence of this region — a confused archipelago at the time of the Littorina Sea — serves to brand north Jutland as a separate area.

The life of north Jutland focuses on the intricate winding shore of Limfjorden, turning its back on the barren ranges of dunes that face the North Sea. At its widest, Limfjorden is a miniature inland sea, fringed by small towns that act as market centres for the pastoral districts around, exploiting, too, the eel fisheries and oyster beds of these waters. Aalborg is the biggest town on Limfjorden and the regional capital of North Jutland. It stands where the maze of inland waterways narrows into the constricted channel of the Langerak. There has probably been a settlement at this important point on the sheltered water-route across the peninsula since the early Bronze Age. Aalborg also acts as the bridge into the remoter parts of north Jutland beyond the Limfjorden, a feature of the town's geography that has been greatly emphasized in the last century with the coming of the railway and road transport.

Aalborg like its rival in east Jutland, Aarhus, contains an old city core to which an industrial quarter has been added in the past few decades. Its twelfth-century cathedral is dedicated to Saint Botolph, a name that occurs again among the patron saints of churches in eastern England. Here is a memory from a thousand years ago, when the North Sea formed the core of a kingdom stretching from the English Midlands to the Baltic.

Aalborg's industrial growth followed a different pattern from its neighbour farther south. There, in Aarhus, the industrial revolution started with the founding of the first margarine factory in 1883, while Aalborg was stimulated by the opening of the first cement works in 1893. Today, the half-dozen cement factories that surround the town exploit the Cretaceous limestone that outcrops in a miniature downland along the shore of the Langerak. Her industries also include breweries, distilleries, a fertilizer plant that makes super-phosphate, and ship-repairing yards. The rise of these industries, like those of Aarhus, has rested very much on the import of British coal.

Towns are not important in north Jutland, except for the fishing ports of Skagen and Frederikshavn. Skagen arose behind the dune-crowned shingle spit that terminates Denmark's bleakest stretch of coast line. It is now the chief fishing port of Denmark with a trawler fleet that ranges the North Atlantic between Arctic Norway and east Greenland. Until the middle of the nineteenth century Aarhus, with a valuable herring fleet, was an important fishing port. It is interesting to note how improved communications led to the transfer of the main fishing centres to the farthest tip of Jutland.

Viborg, an inland city with a granite cathedral, stands where the clay hills of central Jutland fall to the level, exposed plains and peat-bogs of the northern half of the province. Viborg claims to have been in existence since the beginning of Denmark's history as a nation. Her first bishop was enthroned almost nine centuries ago, and markets have been held there for more than a thousand years. Today, her economic life is eclipsed by the two ports and industrial centres, Aalborg and Aarhus. As in the history of Roskilde and Copenhagen, once again we notice the relative decline of an old inland town at the expense of growing coastal centres.

(c) *West Jutland*

Western Jutland forms another distinct region in the geography of the peninsula. The broken, wooded landscapes of the morainic hills change sharply to monotonous sand and gravel plains, deposited in the closing centuries of the Ice Age by melt-waters streaming away from the stagnant ice front that lay through the middle of Jutland. Here and there, low hills of heavily weathered boulder clay interrupt the immense spreads of glacial outwash sand. These older glacial clays bear witness to an earlier stage of the Ice Age when the whole of Jutland was buried beneath the glaciers of the Riss period [Figs 19 and 20].

Only a century ago, extensive tracts of heathland covered the poor, ash-grey soils of west Jutland. Before the middle of the nineteenth century, Jutland's rare and isolated villages depended upon flocks of sheep that grazed the open heaths. The natural poverty of the region encouraged domestic industries on the farms which were important for their spinning and weaving of wool and linen. This marriage of simple manufactures and farming was a common feature of Europe's poorer regions until the middle of the nineteenth century. For instance, one of the roots of the industrial revolution in east Lancashire can be traced to the textile manufactures of small farmers in the poor moorland districts.

Farming in western Jutland has undergone severe changes since the 1860's. Thousands of acres of heath and peat-bog have been won over for agriculture [Fig. 40]. For Denmark this thinly peopled and poorly developed district held some of the qualities of a colonial area without the spectacular attractions of Swedish Norrland or the remote provinces of Norway beyond the Arctic Circle. Today, western Jutland presents to the traveller a chequer-board of improved land, with fields of oats, potatoes, and rye interspersed with patches of heath and planted coniferous woodland where splashes of pale, colourless soil light up the shade beneath the trees.

It is curious that the events which led to the colonization of Jutland's wastes also brought into existence a fresh port on her western coast. As we have noticed, when Denmark lost the fertile province of Slesvig in the Danish-Prussian War of 1864 her interest turned to the development of Jutland. This same military defeat deprived her of the west-coast port of Tønning, and immediately a survey of the Jutland coastline was started to find a site for the establishment of a new port. As a result, Esbjerg was founded in 1869. It lies at a point where subtle changes appear in the character of west Jutland's coastline. To the south there are lagoons, salt-marshes, muddy creeks, and windy, dune-capped islands. North of Esbjerg, the crumbling boulder clay cliffs of the Blaavands Huk begin the 'iron coast' of north-west Jutland — two hundred and fifty miles long and one of the most inhospitable shores in northern Europe.

The position of Esbjerg was determined by the Graadyb, a channel providing at least twenty feet of water and a unique feature on this coastline of shallow, silting estuaries and wave-battered sandhills. Esbjerg grew rapidly after the opening of the railway across Jutland in 1874, a line that has now become the chief artery of Denmark. This town, named after the clay hill that overlooks the harbour, is now the biggest settlement in western Jutland with a population of 50,921 (1955) [Plate 46]. Like most late nineteenth-century towns it is a dull brick-built place, but with its short history and monotonous architectural unity it is symbolic of one phase of Danish economic history — the rapid growth in the export of dairy products towards the end of the last century. Esbjerg stands as the chief link between the Danish countryside and its market in the British Isles. In serving this function it is not surprising that Esbjerg has failed to achieve any regional importance. In fact, its hinterland spreads to the whole nation, but only the slenderest ties have developed between Esbjerg and its immediate region in Jutland.

Esbjerg is only the latest of a series of ports that have flourished on the coast of west Jutland. Tønning was withdrawn from the Danish sphere by a political catastrophe. Earlier still, from the thirteenth to the eighteenth century, the trade of this region centred on Ribe and Ringkøping. Both have been overtaken by physical, political, and technological changes in the past three hundred years. Ribe, a magnificent medieval town that shared with the members of the Hanseatic League those golden decades of the Baltic and North Sea trade, decayed with the waning of Denmark's political power in the seventeenth century. The great growth in the size of ships in the nineteenth century excluded her from the expanding trade that turned to the new port of Esbjerg. Ringkøping, likewise, has ceased to be a port of any consequence. Its wide fjord, almost closed on the seaward side by two long, opposing, dune-crowned shingle spits, finds little traffic now but pleasure yachts.

CHAPTER 5

Finland

FINLAND's tiny population of just over four and a quarter million occupies a state eight times as big as Denmark. She is larger than Italy and about as big as the combined areas of the republics of eastern and western Germany. Like her neighbours, Sweden and Norway, she is abnormal among the nations of Europe in possessing a good deal of empty territory [Fig. 27]. Finland offers the same attractions and dangers of a 'northland' with the possibilities of colonization. Here the 'pioneer fringe' is still an active idea in the life of the nation.

The individuality of Finland does not rest only on the frontier character of her peasant culture — a culture adapted to the environment of her vast interior forests and intricate lakes. Finland's interior position in the world of the Baltic Sea has also imprinted itself on the history, economy, and society of her people. Again, the life of the nation is coloured by a severe climate, hardly distinguishable from the 'snow-forest' climate of northern Russia. The whole peninsula, a term that seems hardly applicable to this blunt projection so firmly embedded in the mass of the continent, lies in the grip of winter from the beginning of December until the end of March [Fig. 37]. At this season the temperatures of the short daylight hours usually remain below freezing point, even on the milder south-western coastline [Plate 35]. In the remote north, on the bare Lapland tundras, the thermometer dips below freezing point in the first week of October and the whole region is held in winter's grasp until the beginning of May. Winter leaves its imprint in other ways, reminding this people of their 'marchland' position on the fringe of Atlantic Europe. For instance, until the middle of the last century bears would invade the forests on the fringes of Helsinki during the winter months. Fifty years earlier, English travellers could write of the menace to farms on the coastal plain from hungry wolf packs out of the interior forests. Even today, it is said that a third of Finland suffers from the incursion of bears across the Karelian frontier in winter.

Finland's northerly and continental position among the Scandinavian states is apparent from an analysis of the air masses that make the country's weather from day to day. Most of the air above Finland originates in cold northern sources over Siberia, the Arctic Ocean, or northern Greenland. It is the presence, almost unbroken from October to April, of continental Siberian and Arctic air that explains the harshness of the Finnish winter. Even in high summer, air from the frozen ocean to the north can force temperatures to between six and five degrees centigrade — a level at which vegetable growth ceases. Killing frosts may occur in early June or late August. Invasions of warm air are far less common in Finland. When warm air reaches the Baltic from the distant anticyclone over the Azores, Finland experiences moist, rainy weather with layers of low stratus cloud and blankets of autumn fog along her south-western coast line. On rare occasions in summer, Finland becomes covered with warm air from an anticyclone over central Europe. Then she experiences uncommonly high temperatures when the thermometer may rise above thirty degrees centigrade in the interior of the country.

Finland's continental position is again evident in the pattern of her rainfall [Fig. 36]. Like all the lowlands of northern Europe, apart from those directly exposed to the Atlantic, the average annual rainfall of the country ranges between twenty and twenty-four inches, but of all the Scandinavian states Finland suffers most from the effects of drought in the early summer. If the spring anti-cyclone over Scandinavia keeps its strength well into the summer, Finland goes without rain at the most critical period for crops.

Finnish history clearly reveals the country's position as a 'marchland' state. Finland is the most northerly member of a chain of 'marcher' states that stretches through east-central Europe. On the east they are flanked by the power of the continental giant, Russia. To the west lie Sweden, Germany, and Austria, none of which has remained disinterested in the belt of territory that extends from the Finnish lakes to the Balkan peninsula. Among the marchland states today, Finland stands farthest from the shadow of the Soviet Union. Even so, she has not escaped completely the twilight that envelops Poland, Czechoslovakia, and the other marchland nations of eastern Europe. Russia fought through Finland's forests and over her frozen lakes to a double victory in the Second World War. In the years since

1944, Finland's foreign relations have been governed by the proximity of the Soviet Union, the fresh memory of lost lands in Karelia, and the knowledge of naval bases leased to Russia along her southern coast line.

Finland's borderland position between the heart of the continent and the ocean, between eastern and western Europe, is clearly written into the economic geography of the country. This stands out sharply in an examination of her trade relations. Finland's trade with the North Sea countries has rested on the products of her forests. In the years before the Second World War, sawn timber, pulp, and paper made up 80 per cent of her exports. For the industrial countries of western Europe Finland represented part of the primitive northern fringe of the continent, rich with the timber that had disappeared by the seventeenth century from the older states of the North Sea basin. Since 1945, an important part of Finland's trade has been with the Soviet Union, at first in the form of reparations payments. The Soviet Union took the products of her engineering industry — electric cables, the equipment for hydro-electricity plants, railway waggons, and diesel ships and barges. For the Russian, Finland belongs to the nations of the Atlantic margin — a country with a highly specialized engineering industry.

In the regional studies of the other Scandinavian states we noticed that each displays a number of historic core regions — areas of early settlement, of prosperous farms, and the setting for the evolution of towns and industries. In Finland, the same pattern is apparent, but here the primitive hinterland with all its problems and potentialities presses hard upon the settled, southern coastal fringe, the historic core of the state.

FINLAND'S SOUTHERN COASTAL FRINGE

The whole of Finland belongs to the Baltic Shield, the primitive structural unit around which the European continent has been built in the course of geological time. This, too, is the least disturbed part of that ancient shield. Over large tracts of Finland's interior the Pre-Cambrian peneplain remains to this day, and forms the dominant feature in the landscape.

A huge gap occupies the geological record from the earliest times until the Quaternary Ice Age. There is nothing between her oldest rocks, memorials of Earth at the beginning of geological time, and the spreads of boulder clay, sinuous esker ridges, and the high ramparts of terminal moraines left by the glaciation a few thousand years ago. For the past ten thousand years, Finland, like the rest of Scandinavia, has been recovering from the immense weight of the Quaternary ice-sheets. As a result much fresh land, floored with level marine clays, emerged from the Baltic Sea. These recent clay plains form the historic core of the Finnish nation [Fig. 26]. There, forests have slowly given way to agriculture over the past thousand years and towns have been founded. Finland's coastal regions are the most densely populated part of the country, performing the same functions as the Danish archipelago, Midland Sweden, or the shores of Oslo fjord in the society and economy of their own nations.

Finland's coastal fringe looks out to sea in three directions. Her south coast stretches from the port of Hanko to the Russian frontier. A second strip of the Finnish coast looks south-westward into the Baltic Sea. Here, behind its complex archipelago, Turku stands as a regional capital. Her longest coast forms the eastern shore of the Gulf of Bothnia, extending northwards into increasingly severe climates and with a history of settlement and economic development closely joined to Swedish Norrland until the beginning of the nineteenth century.

The double and triple ridges of the Salpausselkä terminal moraine form an inner boundary to the coastal plain of the Gulf of Finland. Faults of Tertiary age have badly disturbed the sub-Cambrian peneplain in this region. Although this ancient erosion surface dominates the landforms of the mainland and its thousands of islands, it has been broken into numerous, almost imperceptibly depressed or uplifted blocks. Faults often determine the direction of channels, straits, and the sinuous corridors of fertile lowland so recently elevated from the sea. Again, fractures coincide with the low, straight cliffs forming the coastlines of some of the flat, shapeless islands.

Another factor in the regional unity of Finland's southern strip arises from the rapid retreat of post-glacial seas. Inland, the winding plains, sometimes broad and again suddenly narrow, separate steep-sided massifs of granite. These intermixed lowlands and miniature uplands represent land that only a few thousand years ago was an archipelago in an icy sea. Today, the clays of the old sea-floor are cultivated, while dark stands of conifers and

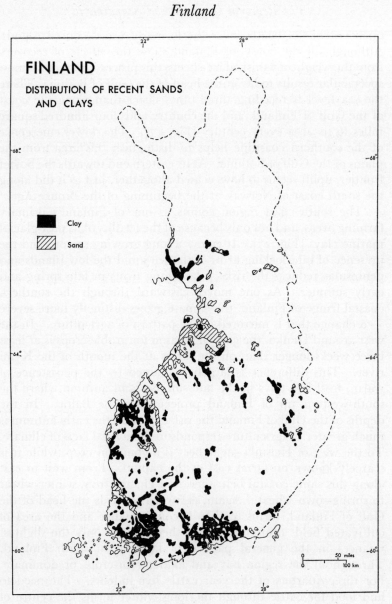

FIG. 26

Some of the most valuable land in Finland belongs to the deposits of post-glacial date
that emerged from the temporary seas that covered much of the western and southern
parts of the country. The extensive clays of the Turku-Loimaa plain in the south-
west are especially notable, and this was the core region of early settlement.

open patches of heath cover the formerly wave-scoured islands. Although all the coasts of Finland show the effects of recovery from the weight of vanished ice-sheets, this process produces its most spectacular results today at the head of the Gulf of Bothnia. There the sea level is receding three times faster than along the coast of the Gulf of Finland, and the country adds four hundred square miles to its area every century [Fig. 47]. The slower emergence of the southern coastline helps to distinguish this area from the plains of the Gulf of Bothnia. At its eastern end towards the Soviet frontier, uplift seems to have ceased altogether, just as it did along the south coast of Norway at the beginning of the Bronze Age.

The south coast region counts as one of Finland's primary farming areas, and not only because of the fertility of its post-glacial marine clays [Fig. 27]. It enjoys a long growing season, and the presence of interlocking arms of the sea amid the low islands and peninsulas reduces the risk of damaging frosts in late spring and early summer. As one moves eastward through the southern coastal fringe of Finland, the climate grows distinctly more severe — a change that is mirrored in the pattern of agriculture. In the west around Hanko, the growing season for arable crops is at least three weeks longer than on the farms at the mouth of the Kymi river. This difference is largely explained by the persistence of warm, frost-free days in the late summer and autumn where the south-western tip of Finland projects into the Baltic. In the depths of the Gulf of Finland the risk of frost in the early autumn is much greater. Agriculture responds to these hard facts of climate. To the west of Helsinki sugar beet is a common crop, while it is scarcely known on farms east of the capital. From west to east along this same coastal belt, there is a change from winter wheat to spring-sown wheat. Again, eastward towards the head of the Gulf of Finland, farms tend to become smaller and the area of cultivated fields diminishes. But these are all only the slightest nuances in the general pattern of farming in south Finland. Throughout the region hay and fodder root-crops predominate. For three-quarters of the year cattle live indoors. The need to find food for cattle through the long winter forms the centre of interest on nearly every farm. This fact is clearly stated in the rural landscape, where every scene seems to contain the long hay-racks to quicken the drying of the crop in the moist days of late summer and the crude log huts, whose walls slope inward from the eaves, where hay is stored through the long hard winter.

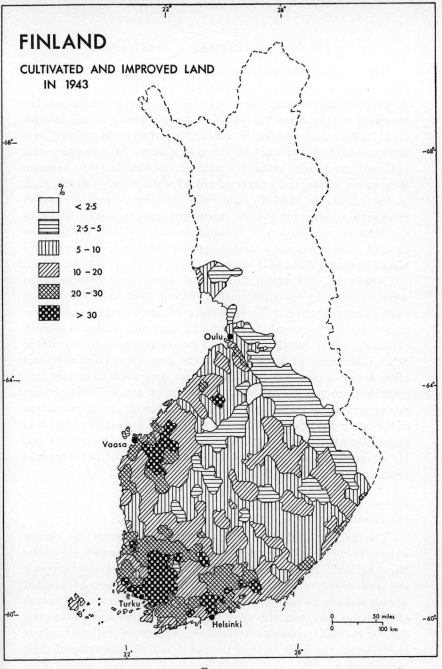

FINLAND

CULTIVATED AND IMPROVED LAND
IN 1943

%

	< 2·5
	2·5 – 5
	5 – 10
	10 – 20
	20 – 30
	> 30

Oulu

Vaasa

Turku

Helsinki

0   50 miles
0   100 km

FIG. 27

The core regions of settlement and occupation stand out on this map, belonging to
the tracts where more than a third of the land has been improved for farming. Outstanding is the plain of fertile post-glacial marine clays that stretches inland from
Turku. Subsidiary tracts belong to the hinterlands of Helsinki and Vaasa. The
frontier of agricultural settlement, beyond which less than 2·5 per cent of the land
is cultivated, cuts diagonally across central Finland from the Karelian border to the
mouth of the Oulu River and the head of the Gulf of Bothnia.

I

The coastal lowland contains most of Finland's towns and cities. The towns of the interior are small, few, and far apart. Among the forests and lakes that lie north of the Salpausselkä moraine, the small towns, each with only a few thousand inhabitants, reflect two periods in Finland's history. Many are new settlements, founded only in the past quarter of a century and gathered, as a rule, around a pulp or chemical factory at some focal point in Finland's maze of inland waterways. Others, such as Savonlinna or Mikkeli, date from the long period of Swedish colonization, beginning in the thirteenth century and ending with the Russian annexation of Finland in 1809. These towns grew around grim medieval fortresses, strong-points on a fiercely contested frontier [Plate 38].

Nearly all of Finland's towns lie close to the coastline and were founded by Swedish settlers during their five centuries as rulers and colonizers. Twenty-three of the coastal towns came into existence by royal decree in the sixteenth and seventeenth centuries, when Sweden's political power flowered in the Baltic Sea. Like many planned towns of the past, these coastal centres often reveal a poor appreciation of the geographical factors that contribute to the growth and prosperity of a town. Sometimes one geographical feature has been seized without any appreciation of the other qualities or defects of the site. For instance, Helsinki came into existence in 1550 by a royal decree of Gustavus Vasa. He aimed to create a rival port to Tallin, a great medieval trading centre on the opposite shore of the Gulf of Finland.

(a) *Helsinki*

The ideas that filled the minds of Helsinki's founders are clearly written in the geography of the port today. It possesses one of the finest harbours in northern Europe. The city has grown across a low and deeply serrated peninsula. An archipelago of wooded islands screens its two wide bays and the numerous small creeks of the peninsula from the open sea. Today, the huge bay to the east of Helsinki provides a sheltered anchorage for the biggest liners, while the little bays of the peninsula have developed their specialized functions as coaling wharves, an oil dock, or quays for general cargo and passenger traffic.

From the beginning Helsinki's greatest asset has been her harbour; her greatest defect the lack of a natural geographical hinterland. The city stands at the mouth of the Vantaa river, an insignificant and unnavigable river draining a few score miles of country from the Salpausselkä moraine to the sea. She had no natural water communications with the great lake systems that penetrate the depths of Finland.

Helsinki might well have remained unimportant but for the radical change in the political relationships of Finland at the start of the nineteenth century. In 1812, three years after Finland became a Grand Duchy of the Russian Empire, Tsar Alexander chose Helsinki as the new capital of the country. By moving the administration of the state from Turku, he aimed to establish a capital less exposed to Swedish political influence. Capital cities tend to create their own hinterlands, extending their influence through government agencies and officials to the furthest frontiers of the state. Likewise through their museums, universities, technical institutes, banks, and business houses they become the core of the whole nation in so many activities. Helsinki proved no exception to these rules. Her isolation from the interior broke down in the closing decades of the nineteenth century with the growth of the railway network. For instance, the first railway in Finland — sixty-six miles of line — ran from Helsinki to Hämeenlinna at the foot of the most westerly chain of lakes. The chief aim of this line was to tap the timber resources of the lakes region. It tried to make good the obvious defects of Helsinki's river.

Railways and roads helped Helsinki to overcome her natural difficulties, but one must not exaggerate the directing influence of the state in the creation of the capital city — at least before Finland obtained complete political freedom in 1917. Russia saw Finland only as her chief outpost on the Baltic. Consequently, the growth of the railway network in the late nineteenth century was governed largely by strategic motives, the lines fanning out from the Leningrad isthmus to the coast of the Gulf of Bothnia. By 1870 the trunk line from St Petersburg to Lahti and Hanko was complete. For much of its course it followed the bevelled ridge of the Salpausselkä moraine. Soon after 1900 another railway was laid with an obvious strategic intention, cutting by Savonlinna across the forested and thinly populated lakes plateau to Vaasa on the coast of the Gulf of Bothnia. Helsinki failed to occupy an overruling position at the core of the nation's transport system while the country was a Russian province. Only in the twentieth century and with the creation of the Finnish state has the capital emerged fully into its own rights. The network of main roads, a product largely of the past thirty years, shows the masterful position of Helsinki. In the same way the internal air routes of Finland are focused upon the capital.

Helsinki has grown enormously in the past half century. Her population was scarcely a hundred thousand in 1900. By the outbreak of the Second World War Helsinki counted more than three hundred thousand people. Today she has a population of 452,800 (1960). This rapid growth of the capital city in the twentieth century can be matched in the other countries of northern Europe, and, in fact, in most parts of the world today, but in Finland other towns have not expanded as rapidly. Unlike Denmark and Sweden, Finland is still mainly a country of peasants and less than a third of her people live in towns.

Helsinki's industries are characteristic of several capital cities. They display a great variety; factories are often small and concentrate upon satisfying Finland's internal market. Usually it is hard to find any clear explanation for the siting of a particular industry in Helsinki, apart from the stimulus given by the pool of labour, the local market provided by the city and its surroundings, and the facilities offered by the port for the supply of raw materials from abroad.

Helsinki is the biggest centre of the engineering industry in Finland. Its foundries and factories produce a wide range of articles, including machine tools, farm implements, dynamos, and electric motors. There are yards, too, for ship-repairing and ship-building. Again, Helsinki is the chief centre of the textile and clothing industry. The port of Helsinki made the capital the site of the largest rubber industry in Finland, but a regrouping of the industry later transformed the Tampere district into the main centre. Today, Helsinki also possesses food-processing plants, chemical works, printing presses, and a glass and china industry. The capital and its immediate neighbourhood form the largest industrial region of Finland, possessing about half of the manufacturing plants of the whole country. It is a tribute to the magnetism of a capital city and its port that it should evolve to this level of industry without the help of local supplies of power and in the absence of immediate resources in raw materials.

The topography of Helsinki today reveals something of the capital's history and hints at Finland's peculiarities as a nation. For instance, this city contains two cores. The oldest part is focused on the chain of little islands that blocks the entrance to the wide, sheltered bay. One of these islands, Suomenlinna, contains a huge fortress built by the Swedes in the eighteenth century. Today, its parks and gardens provide one of the city's tourist attractions, and the island possesses some of the oldest houses in Helsinki. The second core lies at the south-eastern end of the peninsula, the heart of the modern city with its parliament building and the offices of government and commerce. This part of Helsinki reflects the century of Russian rule in Finland in its urban topography. It started with an event that has ushered in the replanning of more than one European city — a devastating fire in 1808 that destroyed most of the earlier wooden town. As a result, the centre of the city was replanned in the early years of the nineteenth century by a young German architect, Ludvig Engel, and given the shape that befits a capital city. Its core is the Great Square — a vital element of the city in the minds of eighteenth-century town-planners as a space for great public gatherings and military parades. This square is flanked by buildings in a pure classical style, the University and the State Council building, and the pale beauty of the Great Church under its vast dome [Plate 33].

Alongside the classical style of the centre of Helsinki stands a very different mode of building that belongs to Finland's period of independence since 1917. It is the work of her own architects, creating a national style that has much in common with contemporary building in the other Scandinavian countries. There is the Parliament House as rock-like as the bare, ice-moulded hummocks on which it stands, the tall tower of the Olympic stadium, and the harsh, clean lines of blocks of flats in the newer suburbs, spreading rapidly in the past thirty years.

As a city, Helsinki points to other disparate elements in Finland's history. For instance, she has a Swedish theatre as well as a stage devoting itself to plays in Finnish — the National theatre. They remind us of the two groups of people who shaped the Finnish nation — the Swedish-speaking merchants, town-dwellers, and farmers along the coastal fringe, and the Finnish-speaking peasants of the forested interior [Fig. 49]. A century ago Helsinki was a Swedish city. Today, just over sixty thousand speak Swedish in Helsinki, and their relations to the rest of the population of the capital reveal the drastic changes that have taken place in Finland over the past quarter of a century. It is said that 96 per cent of the Swedes — or preferably Swedo-Finns — now living in Helsinki are also able to speak Finnish. They still play an important rôle in the nation's economic life as owners and managers of factories and industrial corporations. They contribute much to the civil service and higher education. But the fact that nearly all the Swedes in Helsinki are now bilingual is symptomatic of the new nationalism that has emerged in this young state to absorb the two constituent groups.

Porvoo, situated to the east of Helsinki amid the granite archipelago, has an early history similar to that of the capital. It was one of the chief towns in medieval Finland, growing around the nucleus of its castle and cathedral. Like Helsinki, Porvoo lacked effective natural links with the interior — its valueless river, the Porvoonjoki, draining from the hilly barrier of the Salpausselkä moraine. It is not an exaggeration to say that Porvoo shows us what Helsinki might have remained if historical events had not transformed it into the nation's capital at the beginning of the nineteenth century. Today, Porvoo contains little more than eleven thousand people. Its wharves export some timber and what was once its chief industry, the building of wooden sailing ships, has now vanished. Today, it is a pleasant little tourist town, a standing memorial to Sweden's colonization of the northern shore of the Gulf of Finland.

(b) *Hanko and Kotka — ports of the Gulf of Finland*

Apart from Helsinki, the chief ports of southern Finland are Hanko, placed at the western extremity of the Salpausselkä moraine, and Kotka, commanding the timber-rich hinterland of the central lakes system from the mouth of the Kymi river.

Although there is evidence of a trading settlement on the Hanko peninsula as long ago as the thirteenth century, Hanko itself dates only from the railway age. The port was founded in 1847 with the building of the railway from Hyvinkää to Hanko. The harbour usually remains open throughout the winter, a most notable advantage in ice-bound Finland. In a mild winter this exposed, south-westerly coast remains free of ice. In other years, when fishermen at the head of the Gulf of Finland ply their trade from little wooden shelters close by holes cut in the surface of the frozen sea, Hanko can still be kept free for ships with the help of ice-breakers. Ice is only likely to be an obstacle to the use of Hanko after the end of January. At that time, Kotka, the nation's second port, lying in the depths of the Gulf of Finland, is closed to traffic.

Hanko, even more than Helsinki, lacks a natural river-way to the heart of the country. Its growth depended on the expansion of the railway network. Strategic motives played an important part during the last century in the development of this nearly ice-free coast line. Perhaps it is significant that the wharves and port facilities of Hanko belong entirely to the state. Russia, too, as she has glanced aside from the continental heart of Eurasia towards the Atlantic, has taken an interest in this port exposed to the west. At the Treaty of Moscow in 1944 she obtained a lease to use Hanko as a naval base for the next half century. A similar demand from Russia in 1939 helped to precipitate the cruel Winter War with the Soviet Union.

Hanko is still a small town with a population of only eight thousand. The old regional centre of the south-western archi-pelago, Turku, overshadows Hanko as a port. Hanko's wharves deal mainly with imports, especially in the depths of winter, and dairy products are the chief export. Refrigerator trains roll down to her quays in summer with loads of butter from Finland's co-operative dairies. In this concentration upon dairy products, destined for the British Isles and Germany, Hanko may be com-pared with Denmark's leading export harbour, Esbjerg.

Kotka is a new town, founded only at the end of the nineteenth century on two islands at the mouth of the Kymi river. Already Kotka has a population of thirty thousand and its chief asset is the Kymi river, giving direct access to the lakes plateau. Here lie some of the main timber-cutting regions of Finland [Fig. 29]. In addi-tion, the rapids of the Kymi between the rim of the lakes plateau and the sea provide an outstanding source of hydro-electric power. After the loss to Russia of the lower course of the Vuoksi river, draining from Lake Saimaa into Lake Ladoga, Finland concen-trated upon the development of her reserves of power along the Kymi. Here is the site of a chain of large-scale, modern industries — sawmills, wood-working factories, pulp and paper mills — forming one of the chief cores of manufacturing in Finland. In many ways the lower part of the Kymi river may be compared with the last few miles of the Glomma in Norway.

Kotka, too, forms a rapidly growing centre with pulp-mills, paper works, a sugar refinery, and a large state-owned, super-phosphate plant. Here industry is composed of big modern units.

Tall factory chimneys rise amid the flat, forested islands and the interlocking arms of the sea. Unlike the small and varied factories of Helsinki and Turku, they work for a voracious and expanding external market. Kotka possesses a safe, deep harbour where large ocean-going ships can load directly at the wharves. Although ice closes the port from the end of December until the middle of April, the trade of Kotka suffers less damage than might appear at first, because midwinter is the time when the pulp and sawmills are isolated from their raw material coming out of the hinterland of forests.

The coastal fringe of southern Finland stands out as a major region because of its experience in history, first as a main area of Swedish settlement, as the site of the second capital in the century of Russian rule, and lastly as the core since 1917 of the new independent state of Finland. The southern coastal fringe, too, is one of Finland's most highly cultivated regions in a country that is still largely the domain of lake, forest, bog, and tundra [Fig. 27]. But beneath these symbols of regional unity, the near view of the traveller and the local geographer, working in the field, discovers an amazing diversity. This is a coastline of highly complex and individual archipelagos whose channels become an endless maze to all but the experienced navigator. Inland, the numerous minor regional variations coincide with changes in the basement rocks of the Archaean shield and in the distribution of deposits of postglacial marine clays.

The areas that lie inland from Helsinki and Kotka both form regions important for agriculture. Clay plains are extensive, though everywhere interrupted by the hard, ungrateful 'islands' of gneiss and granite. The lowland along the lower Kymi river is one of the most fertile fragments of southern Finland, and here, for once, the clays are so extensive that the title of 'plain' may be applied with honesty. Suddenly to the east of this river another distinctive *pays* appears. It is a district of steep-sided granite hills and narrow, winding depressions filled with recent clays. Good farmland is scarce, and extensive forests and bogs cover this thinly peopled countryside. North of the coast road that runs from the former Finnish port and city, Viipuri, to Hamina, there is not a single east-west road in this confused region of granite hills. Today, the new frontier between the Soviet Union and Finland crosses this no-man's-land. To the east, this empty countryside gives way to the lost lowland around Viipuri, the furthest outpost of Sweden's late medieval colonization of the shore of the Gulf of Finland.

FINLAND'S SOUTH-WESTERN COAST

A second distinctive region of Finland's coastal fringe looks out to the open Baltic Sea between the mouths of its two branching gulfs. Its individuality lies in the extensive archipelago that stretches westward towards the coast of Sweden, the fertile clay plains forming the mainland between Turku and Loimaa, and the powerful influence that Sweden and Swedish settlers have exercised over this area in times past.

(a) *The Archipelago*

In the south-west the sea is peppered with islands, large and small, forested or grimly barren, for more than a hundred miles from the Finnish mainland [Fig. 28, Plate 42]. This archipelago almost closes the entrance to the Gulf of Bothnia and for centuries it was a piece of high strategic value in the power politics of northern Europe.

Thousands of islands make up the Åland archipelago, mingling under the clear skies of early summer with the blue waters of a complex pattern of sounds and channels. Here the red Rapakivi granite and the hard gneisses of the ancient peneplain of south-western Finland are partly submerged, but amid the confusing details of the islands' coastlines and their separating channels there may be discerned, however faintly, some structural unity. The major features — the general trend of a coast over many miles or the axis of a major strait — are frequently determined by faults.

The archipelago is unique in many other ways. For instance, communications depend almost entirely upon the sea and the smaller islands often have no roads. The sea, too, penetrates deeply the economy of the region. Among the tiny central islands of the archipelago and in the bigger outer isles fishing is still the chief occupation. On some of the rocky and least fertile islands less than 2 per cent of the land is cultivated, and yet their coasts are clustered with tiny villages whose inhabitants fish the calm summer waters for Baltic herring, cod, and flounder. In the depth of Finland's dark, harsh winter they have not forgotten the

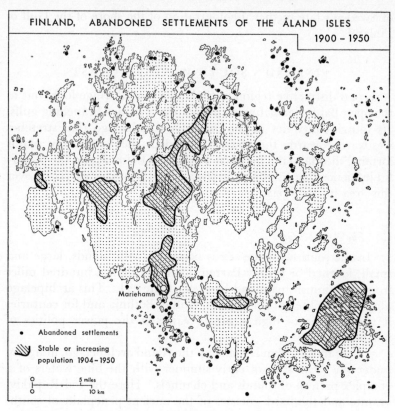

FIG. 28

On many small islands and lonely promontories farms and the homes of fishermen have been abandoned. On the larger and more accessible islands population has remained stable or increased. This trend in the population geography of an archipelago is illustrated even more vividly in the demography of the island clusters at the approach to Stockholm.

age-old occupation of fishing through holes cut in the icy lid of the frozen sea — a technique handed down over ten thousand years from the first primitive hunters who entered this region after the Ice Age.

Mariehamn, the chief port of the Åland islands, lies more than half way to the Swedish mainland. In the last century it was the chief centre of Finland's great sailing fleet. Her ships made themselves famous in the exciting grain races from the ports of the southern hemisphere to western Europe. Today,

Mariehamn belongs to the decaying ports of the Baltic Sea. Like Norwegian Arendal and Danish Svendborg, she failed to keep up with the technical changes that transformed the shipping industry in the past hundred years. Her population only numbers four thousand, and in 1953 five sailing ships alone were left of the great fleet that used to range the high seas.

The sea colours the geography of the south-western coastal strip of Finland in several other ways. For instance, it is the only part of the country where deciduous trees are a common sight. One of the showpieces of Finland, at least for Finns brought up on the cool dark-greens of the coniferous forests, is the park at Turku that boasts the biggest oak wood in the country. Here, too, in the south-west, Finland enjoys its most oceanic climate. The growing season in the archipelago stretches out to a hundred and seventy days. The patchwork of fields on the cultivated islands gives the highest crop-yields in Finland, and most of the country's apple, plum, and pear orchards are in this region.

The geography of the archipelago shows considerable variety and each island and group of islands is worthy of individual study. The largest group of islands, Ahvenanmaa or Åland, lies far out to sea. Here agriculture is more important than elsewhere in the archipelago and occupies about 10 per cent of the central island and its near neighbours. The well-tilled fields, the most productive farmland in Finland, coincide with rich clay soils, deposits of the changing seas that followed the Ice Age. But the northern part of the Åland isles reveals one of those contrasts that occur again and again in northern Europe. The young post-glacial clays give way to the shaggy, unproductive scenery of the Rapakivi granite, and along the northern coast the archipelago reaches its greatest heights in a line of wild, red granite cliffs more than four hundred feet above the sea.

Many of the islands that dot the sea between Åland and the mainland are tiny, treeless, windswept rocks. They lack the good clays of the outer members of the archipelago, and as a result fishing becomes the chief occupation. On some islands there is scarcely any cultivated land.

With the inner islands, new features enter the geography of the south-western archipelago. Many form partially submerged portions of the mainland's forested peninsulas. Here the straight coastlines of bays and sounds often show the influence of faults in the scenery of the region. Recent clays mask the bedrock of granites and schists over wide areas, and consequently agriculture plays the chief part in the economy. In some parishes farmland occupies as much as a fifth of the total area. Unlike the remote outer islands, the inner parts of the archipelago are not entirely dependent upon water communications. Several are joined to the mainland by bridges, and buses and other vehicles use the ferries across the narrow sounds. Industry, too, has penetrated the inner islands of the archipelago, largely as a result of the proximity of Finland's third port and second city, Turku. Kemiö has engineering industries and on another island, Parainen, the outcrop of a band of dolomitic limestone has given rise to a lime and cement industry. Lately, the nearness of Turku has affected the inner islands in another way. Now they serve as a summer resort for this industrial and commercial city, their shores dotted here and there with summer cottages. Nowadays, the summer cottage by the sea is an essential element in the lives of Scandinavia's middle classes, a fact that has also deeply influenced the geography of the Stockholm archipelago and the shores of Oslo fjord in the past half century.

(b) *The Turku-Loimaa Plain*

The mainland of south-western Finland possesses the country's most prosperous farming region in the plain that lies inland from Turku. The most up-to-date types of commercial farming have developed in this region. More agricultural machinery is used here than in any other part of the country, and in some parishes of this plain, with its level stone-free soils, as much as half of the land is under cultivation — an abnormally high proportion for Finland. It is a region of comparatively large farms, with many of a hundred acres and some reaching up to three hundred acres in area. In the past thirty years, big estates have been reduced by various acts of land reform and, above all, the need to resettle refugees from the lost lands of the east since the Second World War. Today, this is the main dairying region of Finland. Small orchards screen its large, prosperous-looking farms and the fields grow sugar beet and winter wheat as well as the more usual hay-crops and potatoes of the Finnish agricultural scene. In many senses, this tiny plain is comparable to other regions in the south-western corners of Scandinavia's peninsulas — Skåne, the granary of Sweden, or Jæren, the little boulder-clay-covered lowland to the south of Stavanger that forms one of the more fertile areas of Norway.

Turku and Pori are the main towns and ports of south-western Finland. Pori, with a population of 54,024 (1960), serves the valley of the Kokemäenjoki — a centuries-old highroad to the dark forests of inner Finland followed by fur-traders and settlers in times past. Pori is the latest in a succession of ports that arose along the lower reach of this river, each left stranded over the years by the steadily rising coastline of the Gulf of Bothnia. It is only a summer port, exporting the timber products of its hinterland. In the depth of winter, all the activities of this coastline concentrate on Turku when icebreakers move southwards from Vaasa and Pori, to keep a clear channel to the open sea through the straits of the archipelago.

Next to Helsinki, Turku is the main city of Finland. Until 1812 this was the capital of the country and, above everything, Turku symbolizes Finland's link with Sweden [Fig. 49]. The site dates from Sweden's earliest contacts with Finland in the darkness of the twelfth century. At the time of the first crusade (A.D. 1154–1155) when Sweden's armies widened her empire and brought Christianity to the north coast of the Gulf of Finland, Turku was an outpost of fur-traders. Today, Turku's castle and cathedral, forming the core of the city, recall Finland's valuable connections with medieval Sweden. It is perhaps not too much to say that this was the stimulus from outside that started the evolution of the Finnish nation. Many items in Turku's history reflect in miniature Finland's national story. Turku's university became a centre of culture in Finland in the late Middle Ages. Many of her scholars went to the universities of Germany, and one of them, Michael Agricola, became a powerful force in the national life of Finland during the sixteenth century. He brought the Lutheran Reformation into this part of northern Europe. He translated the New Testament and much of the Old Testament into Finnish and drew up a Prayer Book and Catechism in the language of his country. Today, Michael Agricola is remembered as the father of Finnish as a written language, not only for his translations of the scriptures but because he composed the first Finnish grammar.

As a result of its historic associations and extreme south-westerly position, Turku symbolizes the external influences in Finnish nationalism, but this city, founded by Swedes, does not live only in the past. With a population of 124,243 (1960) it is a busy industrial centre, where sugar-refining and tobacco manufactures are two of the chief occupations. Turku ranks third among the engineering centres of Finland, and her shipyards almost monopolize the nation's shipbuilding industry. Apart from the good fortune of her history, the greatness of Turku rests upon her site. Four deep-water channels lead to the open sea through the complexities of the south-western archipelago, kept free for shipping throughout the winter by a fleet of icebreakers gathered from Finland's other icebound ports. Inland from Turku lies the fertile, level plain of Loimaa, one of the oldest areas of settlement in the country.

THE COASTAL PLAIN OF ÖSTTERBOTTEN

Northward from the mouth of the Kokemäenjoki, the nature of Finland's coastal region slowly changes. This coastal lowland of the Gulf of Bothnia, a rather featureless plain composed of glacial sands and clays, merits attention as a separate region. Over considerable tracts the Pre-Cambrian rocks, the gneiss and granite that is the most essential element in the Finnish scene, lie hidden beneath young sediments. Lakes, too, another component in the idealized picture of Finland, are almost absent. This region is remote from the lakes plateau, turning its back on the forested interior to look across the Gulf of Bothnia towards Sweden. As a result Östterbotten, as the Swedish-speaking Finns know this region, was heavily colonized from the west. Today it remains one of the most strongly Swedish parts of the country [Fig. 49]. Her coastal towns, like most of Finland's towns, began their existence as Swedish trading posts under the protecting shadow of a Swedish castle. Oulu, the only large town at the head of the Gulf of Bothnia, began as a fur-trading centre with the northward thrust of Sweden's economic interests at the close of the Middle Ages. In 1950 they built a castle at the mouth of the Oulu river, and, like several other places on the other side of the Bothnian gulf, in Swedish Norrland, Oulu received a town charter in the early years of the seventeenth century.

The individuality of the plain that flanks the Gulf of Bothnia lies not only in the predominance of recent sands and clays [Fig. 26] and the lasting impression of the Swedish colonization that was completed before the end of the eighteenth century. Here, too, is a region where land has emerged rapidly from the sea in the few thousand years since the close of the Ice Age. Even today the coast rises at the rate of a yard a century — three times faster than along the shorelines of south-western Finland [Fig. 47]. Again it is a region of harsher climates than those of the favoured archipelago of Ahvenanmaa, a fact reflected in the shorter growing season and restrictions in the types and varieties of crops.

Östterbotten is a region of dairy farms and most of the fields are given over to hay and fodder crops. Two-thirds of the improved land is used for hay. On the farms of the milder southern fringe of Östterbotten, winter wheat can be grown, but as one moves northward it gives way to barley, that hardy crop which ripens in the cool light of northern Finland's long, summer days.

A northward journey through this region reveals a gradual impoverishment of farming and the pattern of settlement also changes from the southern to the northern parts of Östterbotten. In the south, from Kaskinen to Vaasa and far beyond, farms occupy the clay-floored plains of short, parallel rivers draining to the Gulf of Bothnia. Here are continuous belts of cultivated fields, land that was slowly cleared over the past four centuries. Beyond Kokkola and away to the head of the Gulf of Bothnia, the pattern of settlement changes. Small hills break up the landscape. There are extensive stretches of ungrateful sands. The favoured clays become rarer and the continuous areas of tamed and cultivated land disappear. It is as if the struggle between the farmer and the wilderness has not yet been resolved, for even in the wide and level plain of the Oulu river the forest still holds its own.

The differences between the northern and southern parts of Östterbotten penetrate other sectors of the economy. Timber industries are not important in the south, lacking, as it does, water communications with the rich forests of Finland's interior. At Vaasa the chief industries are cotton-spinning and weaving, flour-milling, and sugar-refining. North of the Oulu river the forest industries — timber-cutting, woodworking, pulp and paper making — reassert themselves as the main occupations. This is partly a result of the fact that the great rivers of the north — the Kemi, Ii, Simo and Oulu — all rise far in the interior of the country, giving access to vast and newly exploited forests.

Oulu, with a population of 58,315 (1960), has emerged as the chief town and port of the north. Like Kotka at the other extremity of the country, Oulu owes its industries and its trade to the riches of the vast hinterland provided by a river. The sawmills, paper mills, and hardboard factories of this port are certain of further expansion now that sources of abundant electricity have been gained in the recently constructed power stations of the Oulu river.

Östterbotten forms the most northerly part of Finland's coastal belt of population. But this belt of cleared and long-settled land is nowhere continuous for great distances. The discontinuity of coastal settlement is most clearly illustrated in Östterbotten, because the whole region stands isolated from the rest of settled Finland to the south by a wide zone of forests and peat-bogs that stretches to the very coastline. This natural barrier and the close historic links of the area with the further coastline of Sweden have contributed to its regional distinctiveness.

THE LAKES PLATEAU

Inland from the crinkly coastline and island-splashed sea of the Gulf of Finland lies the Finnish lakes plateau — perhaps the biggest and most homogeneous region in the country. The individuality of the lakes plateau arises not only from its isolation from the sea and a curious landscape of countless lakes that cover almost a quarter of the area [Plate 35] ; the region is also one of the chief centres of the peasant culture that has given its folklore and language to the modern nation-state of Finland.

This large region contains nearly sixty thousand lakes. The grand total is not yet known with any certainty, largely because of the lack of adequate maps for the remoter parts of the interior. Another source of difficulty arises from the very complexity of the lakes. They possess some of the most intricate shorelines on the face of the earth, with deeply penetrating inlets and hundreds of forest-clad peninsulas. Sections of the same lake, sometimes linked by narrow, winding straits, often bear entirely different names, providing difficulties for the compilers of maps. These lakes, too, are studded with countless islands and bridged by the winding, sandy causeways of eskers [Plate 36]. Nevertheless, despite the complexity of its minor landforms, the scenery of the interior plateau may be resolved into three great lake-systems. The largest group lies in the east where Lake Saimaa and its several thousand relatives find an outlet to Lake Ladoga by the

Vuoksi River. Lake Päijänne [Plate 39] forms the core of the central system of lakes and its waters spill southwards to the Gulf of Finland down the Kymi river's valuable staircase of rapids. The most westerly group of lakes, with Pyhäjärvi as its largest member, drains to the Gulf of Bothnia through the Kokemäenjoki.

Each lake-system provides a complex of water communications unique in the geography of Europe. In summer, steamers ply between the little settlements, reaching into the very depths of Finland, though this leisurely system of transport has suffered heavily in the past few years with the growth of road travel. Huge timber rafts float through the lakes and their connecting straits and canals to the sawmills and pulp factories. In winter, too, the great lakes play an important rôle in the communications of Finland's interior when their frozen surfaces provide the traditional winter roads of the peasantry.

In the past century, the demands of the forest industries led to the improvement of this natural network of communications. For instance, thirty-six canals have been cut to extend the hinterland of Lake Saimaa northwards and eastwards. Natural channels have been dredged and widened to ease the passage of timber rafts. The Vääksy canal makes a most important link in the central lake-system because it joins the small southern lake of Vesijärvi to the great northward-pointing axial sheet of water, Lake Päijänne. By this means, Lahti, one of the youngest cities of Finland and a centre of sawmills, plywood, and furniture factories, has access to the whole forest-rich hinterland of the central part of the lakes plateau.

Despite the intricate shores of Finland's lakes and the absence of any dominant landforms in the area, it is still possible to discern some guiding lines in the physical geography of this region. The low platform of grey granites that underlies most of the lakes plateau was disturbed in late Tertiary times by movements within a complex of faults. On the southern rim of the low plateau, segments of the old peneplain have been uplifted into a series of blocks. These slightly raised blocks play a most important rôle in the landscape of today, because they are largely responsible for damming back the great lakes of the region. Many of the lake-basins seem to have a structural origin as well, and the general line of some of the most complex and intricate shores is often determined by a fault.

At a still later date, the Quaternary glaciation endowed the area with many distinctive features. The low, shapeless hills between the lakes often carry thick deposits of glacial drift on their summits. Today, some of the best farms in the lakes plateau stand on these soils. Winding eskers and morainic features, such as the great flat-topped barrier of the Salpausselkä, add to the confusion of this landscape, holding up lakes by interrupting the natural drainage lines and, at the same time, providing causeways across this wilderness of forest and water for roads and railways.

The recovery of Finland from the vanished Quaternary ice-sheets left its imprint on the scenery of the lakes plateau. The drainage system of the interior has experienced some remarkable changes in the few thousand years since the disappearance of the ice. The northern and western parts of the old peneplain have risen more rapidly than the south-eastern fringes of the country. But in detail the movements seem to be more complicated than a simple south-eastward tilting of the Baltic Shield. There is evidence that blocks of this faulted peneplain reacted to the post-Quaternary movements with a certain independence. Some segments of country were uplifted at a greater rate than others, and there is clear proof, especially from the south-eastern edge of the lakes region, of subsidence taking place. As a result of these earth movements, the great sheets of inland water have been tilted towards the southern edge of the country. Until the beginning of the Bronze Age the double ridge of the Salpausselkä formed the main watershed of Finland. The extensive lake-systems of Saimaa and Päijänne emptied north-westward by rivers flowing towards now vanished arms of an enlarged Gulf of Bothnia. The general tilting of the land mass towards the south and east brought about a reversal of the drainage with a break-through of rivers across the Salpausselkä barrier. For instance, the River Kymi developed as the main outlet of Lake Päijänne about 400 B.C. The tilting of the lakes towards the south has had an important effect on the landscape and economic value of their shorelines. At the northern ends of the great lakes a considerable amount of land has emerged in the past centuries, providing stretches of good clays for farming and settlement [Fig. 26, Plate 35]. In the south, on the other hand, the lake shores plunge steeply and their value for agriculture is negligible.

The farming of the Finnish lakes region is as distinctive as its physique. Less than 10 per cent of the area is cultivated. For the rest it consists of forests, bogs, and the unruffled surfaces of endless, island-spattered lakes. Agriculture depends upon the coarse, stony boulder clays that partly hide the granites and gneisses of the ancient peneplain. Only rarely, at the head of some quiet bay, a deposit of rich, lacustrine clay provides the foundation for more prosperous farming. The farms of this region still display many archaic features. Rye and potatoes — so often the mark of marginal, near-subsistence farming in Europe — are the chief crops of Finland's lake region. Hemp, a crop that has almost disappeared from the other Scandinavian countries, grows widely on the hill farms. Machinery, as potent a factor in the agricultural revolution as in the realm of industry, penetrates but slowly the life of these inland farms. Field drains, too, a simple device that has helped agriculture enormously in northern Europe over the past century and a half, still remain unknown to many lonely hill farms above the lakes. Cattle graze on the natural meadows and the rich grasses that spring up in summer in forest clearings made by the traditional methods of burning. Hay is not widely grown and large amounts are imported for the winter from the productive coastal farms of Östterbotten. Small and scattered farms characterize the lakes region. They stand isolated from each other on lake shores or amid the stony, forested hills of the country between the lakes. Their fields are usually tiny and carefully cleared of a sterile burden of glacial erratics.

The survival of primitive and archaic features in the farming of Finland's lakes plateau has much in common with other remote interior regions of Scandinavia. The long valleys of central Norway preserved a peasant culture that has contributed an important element to the modern Norwegian nation through its language and folk-tales. Likewise, Sweden finds the relics of a peasant agriculture still alive in the techniques, farm implements, and costumes of the isolated inland lakes region of Dalarna. The lakes plateau of Finland played the same rôle in the life of the Finnish nation. Here, amid the quiet forests, a peasant culture survived into the twentieth century, practising methods of farming and forest burning that were much more widespread in Europe a millennium ago. For centuries this region has stood for the other half of the nation, a part different from the coastal plain with its Swedish-speaking towns and its outlook across the surrounding seas. The peasant culture of the lakes plateau helped to preserve Finnish as a living language, and deeper still, its folk-tales, gathered together in the great legend of the Kalevala, represent the prehistoric roots of the modern Finnish nation.

Besides forming the home of a peasant culture practising a primitive way of farming, the lakes plateau is the chief centre of Finland's timber industry. This hummocky, gently-broken countryside possesses some of her finest stands of softwood forest [Fig. 29]. Pine and spruce grow more rapidly than in the stunted, open forests of far northern Finland [Figs. 85 and 86]. Above all, the

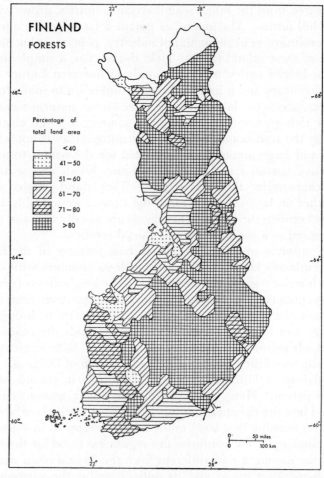

FIG. 29

The predominance of forests on the lakes plateau, in the eastern frontier region of Karelia, and in a wide belt across northern Finland is clearly apparent. Less than half of the land is covered with forest only in the long-settled districts close to the coastline and in the furthest north where the birch woodlands give way to the tundra.

rise of the forest industries was aided by the network of natural waterways, themselves linked together and improved by the construction of floatways. The small, scattered farms supply labour for the timber-cutting camps, the pulp factories, and the sawmilling plants. Further north, the nearly empty forest lands still suffer great handicaps in their development from poor communications and difficulties of finding labour. Timber-cutting and wood-working, too, have always played an important part in the life of the peasant farmer on the lakes plateau. Here it was easy to convert a primitive domestic industry into a modern forest industry with a wide market for its products in western Europe and even across the Atlantic.

Town and Industrial Sites in the Lakes Plateau

The processing plants of the forest industries are scattered across the lakes plateau, normally in relation to two powerful geographical factors — hydro-electric plants, and communications provided by railways and waterways. First, many sites of sawmills and paper-pulp and cellulose factories belong to those of hydro-electric power stations [Figs. 92 and 94]. For instance, Valkeakoski, in the western system of lakes, is an industrial centre of thirteen thousand people situated on a fall between lakes Mullavesi and Vanajavesi. It produces paper, cellulose, and artificial fibres. Again, the junction of railways and water routes in this confused region of lakes and forests stimulated the growth of industrial centres. A long string of timber-working towns adorns the southern coastline of the great lakes where they abut against the Salpausselkä ridge with its main-line railway. For example, Lahti, a town of more than sixty thousand people, acts as a regional centre at the southern end of Lake Päijänne. Its sawmills, plywood, and furniture factories can easily pass their products on by rail to the ports of the Gulf of Finland.

Further east, an important industrial district occupies the long southern shore of Lake Saimaa. Here a series of manufacturing towns draw their timber from the deep forests to the north and east towards the Karelian frontier [Plate 37]. Lappeenranta, which has long acted as a market and distributing centre for Lake Saimaa, has sawmills and manufactures plywood, paper-pulp, and sulphuric acid. Lauritsala possesses similar industries, but the real core of this industrial belt lies in Imatra, a town of more than thirty thousand people, situated where the Vuoksi river breaks across the Salpausselkä barrier on its way to Lake Ladoga. The power stations of Imatra feed the industries of the southern lake shore. This industrial zone of Lake Saimaa suffered severe dislocation by the frontier changes that closed Finland's war with the Soviet Union in 1944. Fortunately, the power plants of the Vuoksi river remained in Finnish hands, but the whole area lost its natural outlet through the Saimaa canal to the port of Viipuri.

Savonlinna, a town not many miles from the Karelian frontier, clearly illustrates the value of intersecting land and water routes in the growth of industrial sites in the lakes plateau [Plate 38]. It lies amid the labyrinth of lakes that form the Saimaa system, standing astride the narrows of Kyrönsalmi strait. The thick-set, triple-towered fortress of Olavinlinna rises from a tiny island in the middle of the strait, a symbol of Sweden's deep thrust into the heart of eastern Finland in the fifteenth century. Not many yards from the castle, a girder bridge spans the narrow ribbon of water, carrying the railway that threads its way north-westward across the lakes region to Jyväskylä and the port of Vaasa on the Bothnian coastline. Once again this railway illustrates the strategic motive that has prevailed so often in Finland's history. It was built early in the twentieth century to provide a direct route for military supplies across the wilderness of central Finland, from St Petersburg to the Gulf of Bothnia. Today, Savonlinna, at this crossing place of land and water routes, has its sawmills and plywood factories, but with its little bathing beaches, hedged with pine forests, and the sombre castle of Olavinlinna, it also attracts some tourists in the summer months.

Another main line cuts through the lakes plateau from south to north. Along this route Kuopio has grown rapidly with sawmills and factories for the manufacture of spools, plywood, and matches. The town stands where the north-south railway crosses Lake Kallavesi, a northerly member of the Saimaa system. Still further north along this railway lies Iisalmi, a raw young timber town at the head of Lake Saimaa's chain of waterways.

The chief city and manufacturing centre of interior Finland is Tampere [Plate 34]. The textile industry took root there a century and a half ago and Tampere's population numbered 126,573 people by the 1960 census. Tampere occupies a site whose morphology is repeated many times in the geography of towns in northern Europe. It stands where an esker, the Pyynikki, holds up the waters of the most westerly of the great lakes, Näsijärvi. Here at Tammerkoski rapids, water power provided the first incentive to the establishment of industry.

Tampere's site has long been favoured in Finnish history. Even in medieval Finland the forerunner of this modern textile and engineering city, then called Pirkkala, exercised a control over the interior of the country that stretched into the far north of Lapland. For more than three hundred years, until the close of the sixteenth century, this little settlement monopolized the trade and gathered the taxes from a vast part of the interior of the country. Curiously enough, the medieval advantages of this town were repeated in another form at the beginning of the nineteenth century, when a decree of Tsar Alexander I allowed the import of all kinds of factory machinery and raw materials into Tampere free of duty. This economic privilege prevailed for nearly a century, from 1819 until its abolition in 1905. It had much to do with the founding of factories at an early date and also the rise of a cotton industry, depending entirely upon imported raw materials, in this remote inland site.

Today, Tampere ranks among the leading textile centres of northern Europe. A Scotsman, James Finlayson, opened the first cotton mill in 1828. By the 1850's the linen industry settled in the town, and today Tampere contains members of almost all branches of the textile industry. It has large cotton-spinning and weaving mills. Most of the factory-produced knitted goods of Finland are made there, and not far away at Valkeakoski stands a plant that manufactures synthetic textiles for the mills of Tampere. At an early date in the last century Tampere became a centre of the tanning industry; now it makes half the boots and shoes of Finland. It is also the main centre of Finland's rubber industry and has flour mills and engineering shops. It is probably true to say that historical events, rather than any resources of the geographical environment, established this city as the leading industrial centre of Finland's forested interior. Until 1917, the year when Finland gained her political freedom, the market for Tampere's industrialists extended deep into the Russian Empire. Today the city holds a predominant position, alongside Helsinki, in Finland's domestic market; and the wide range of her industries owes not a little to her favoured economic position in the nineteenth century.

NORTHERN FINLAND

Northwards from the lakes plateau, and inland from the coastal plain at the head of the Gulf of Bothnia, lies the least populated part of Finland. Like Arctic Norway or Swedish Norrland it stands as a tract of empty 'colonial' territory in relation to the long-settled areas of the coastal fringe. But northern Finland is perhaps more repulsive than its counterparts in Sweden and Norway. It has nothing to match the system of communications provided by the deeply penetrating, ice-free fjords of northern Norway, and it lacks the abundant mineral wealth that led to the development of Norrland.

No outstanding features of landscape plot the frontiers of northern Finland, yet this most distinctive region may be discerned in several ways. Settlement becomes extremely sparse. Nowhere has more than one per cent of the land been improved and cleared for farming [Fig. 27]. Most of Lapland's farms and hamlets lie strung out tenuously along the river valleys [Fig. 62]. Vast tracts of country are completely empty. The character of the forest changes, too, on the higher ground and under the harsher climate of northern Finland. Pine is the predominating forest tree, but northwards, with the shorter summers and severely low temperatures of Lapland, it gives way to the birch. The northern forests are much more open than the dense stands of timber that characterize the lakes plateau and trees grow more slowly and possess a sharply conical form. The undergrowth that accompanies the tall pines and spruces changes as one passes northwards through Finland. The forest floor of the northlands is chiefly composed of bilberries, lichens, and liverworts. In the furthest north of Lapland, along the Norwegian frontier and on the high, hummocky hills that border Karelia, the stunted birch forests give way to open pastures with low-growing plants [Plate 41]. Here, in these areas of tundra, the reindeer moss tinges the landscape with a greyish-white colour, except in early summer when the hillsides become splashed with the colours of arctic-alpine flowers.

Bogs cover much of northern Finland. In the Kainu lowland, an almost uninhabited region of rivers and small lakes close to the Soviet frontier, half the area is taken up by bogs. As a rule, the bogland consists of a deep layer of peat crowned with thick hummocks of sphagnum moss and, here and there, clusters of stunted pine trees.

Finland

Finland is not notable for the grandeur or variety of its land-forms. Everywhere her soft skylines betray the presence of the ancient peneplain that truncates the granites and gneisses of the Baltic Shield. For the rest, the intricacies of her landscape can be ascribed usually to faulting in Tertiary times, or else they are a legacy of the intense glaciation of the region in the Quaternary period. But the far north presents some subtle variations on these dominant themes. Large tracts of Lapland are without lakes, and in the Karelian border country rounded hills reach to more than a thousand feet above sea level. These bare-topped hills, breaking through the garment of dark-green and silver-grey forest, lie oriented from north-west to south-east, following the structural line of a forgotten mountain-building movement that convulsed the rocks of the Baltic Shield deep in Archaean times. Today, this belt of higher, more rugged country survives either through the resistance of its rocks or else as a result of movements in the old peneplain in late Tertiary times.

Northern Finland has a harsher climate than the rest of the country. For half the year mean temperatures stand below freezing point. Among the bare hills, where Finland meets Norway, the sun remains above the horizon for two months, but here the endless summer sunshine gives little help to agriculture. There are few settlements in this desolate country. Farmers have only small plots of potatoes and hay, and their living largely depends upon the herds of reindeer that roam the open tundra.

The Cores of Settlement in Northern Finland

The economic life of northern Finland concentrates upon three areas, again illustrating the rôle of communications in these remote territories. The first is the chain of lakes and tributary waterways along the middle and upper parts of the Oulu river. This region is rich in forests and followed by one of the two long-distance railways of northern Finland. Logs are assembled on Lake Oulu, the natural focus of this inland region, for the sawmills and factories of Kajaani or else for despatch down the Oulu river to the pulp and paper mills on the coastline. Kajaani, with a population of 14,000, has emerged as one of the few industrial and administrative centres in this wilderness of northern Finland. Like so many towns in Finland's interior, it lies on a waterway joining two lakes. A fortress stands at the core of the settlement and today it is the gathering-point for roads, railways, and water routes that run out towards the Karelian frontier.

A second centre of economic interest lies much farther north, around the shores of Lake Inari, pinched between the Soviet and Norwegian frontiers. Here, in a down-warped and faulted segment of the old peneplain, lies an image of Lake Saimaa. With its complex shore lines, its many bays and peninsulas, Lake Inari looks like a northern fragment of the lakes plateau. In the wilds of northern Finland it is almost a paradise, and, despite its harsh climate, the shores of Lake Inari and the surrounding hills — often faulted structures — carry good stands of pine forest. Before the Second World War, forestry was developing in this region and woodworking industries had appeared at Inari, but the adjustment of frontiers since the war and the loss of Petsamo, Finland's warm-water port on the Arctic Ocean, have turned this area into a cul-de-sac and blunted its economic development. The Arctic highway, the road that once formed the backbone of Lapland from Rovaniemi [Plate 40] to Petsamo, now ends blindly against the Soviet frontier. The Finns also lost an important power station at Jänniskoski with the frontier changes in this region. The economic development of the Lake Inari area was something that had to be carefully nurtured, even when the outlet through Petsamo lay close-by. The severing of its northward communications seems to rule out development in the near future.

The most prosperous district of northern Finland occupies the lowland that stretches along the Kemi and the Torne rivers. Here, forests stretch unbroken for miles, and settlements are limited to the valleys of the chief rivers. There is no richer timber region in the whole of northern Finland, even though the trees put on only half the annual growth of forests in the south. The Kemi river forms the chief floatway and close to its mouth stands Kemi, a port and the largest centre of population in northern Finland with 28,000 inhabitants [Figs. 90 and 93]. It has some of the largest sawmills and pulp factories, and the biggest export trade among the ports of the Gulf of Bothnia.

This region, too, possesses another feature in common with Swedish Norrland and the coastline of Finnish Östterrbotten. It is fringed by a narrow plain of post-glacial marine clays that provide soils, for farming, unequalled elsewhere in Lapland. Despite its inherent fertility, the coastal belt is not closely cultivated and farming only takes up about 2 per cent of the land. However, considerable development has taken place in the past decade with the settlement of refugees from the lost lands in the east. With the harnessing of the whole river basins of the Kemi and Oulu, the north also faces the pleasing prospect of becoming the country's chief source of hydro-electric power [Figs. 66 and 67].

The economic activities of the valleys of the lower Kemi and Torne illustrate some of the principles that are fundamental to the understanding of the geography of Finland. Access to the Baltic shoreline and the rôle of Sweden in Finnish history define one important element in the national life — an element that joins together the regions facing the sea. Inland, amid her forests and lakes, lies the other Finland — a remote and isolated region that has nurtured the traditions of a peasantry and that possesses in abundance the raw materials, the timber of the coniferous forests, by which Finland secures her economic survival in the modern world.

PART II

SOME FACETS
OF SCANDINAVIAN GEOGRAPHY

CHAPTER 6

Scandinavian Landscapes and Climates

MUCH of the individuality of northern Europe derives from a geological history that extends back into the remote depths of time. The vital epochs in the story of the evolution of its scenery lie at the very beginning and end of the geological time-scale. The Baltic Shield, occupying 90 per cent of the area of Finland and three-quarters of the surface of Sweden, forms a core of ancient rocks, created and shaped in that long geological dawn — the Archaean age. A second major geological province covers the greater part of Norway. It consists of the sediments laid down in lower Palaeozoic times and folded in a world-wide mountain-building movement, the Caledonian, at the close of the Silurian period. Fenno-Scandia seems to have existed as a fairly stable land mass during the vast span of time between the lower Palaeozoic and the Tertiary epochs. Parts were affected by faulting in Permian and Tertiary times, and in the latter period Scandinavia suffered vertical oscillations of great amplitude. The Quaternary Ice Age, a brief and recent phase in the great vista of geological time, saw northern Europe buried beneath a succession of thick ice-sheets. The Ice Age left a profound impression on the scenery of Scandinavia. Glaciers ground the valleys of western Norway into steep-walled troughs whose floors sometimes lie several hundreds of feet below the present sea level. The scraped surfaces of Finland and lowland Sweden were littered with spreads of boulder clay, hummocky terminal moraines, sand and gravel sheets, and the sharp, sinuous forms of eskers. The human geography of northern Europe could almost be written in the terms of a hard struggle against the disastrous effects of the Ice Age, a struggle that has taken place since the first Neolithic colonists reached this region about four thousand years ago.

Scandinavia owes much of its strong personality to the fact that its scenery was first shaped in the Archaean period. The Baltic Shield is exposed at the surface in Finland, over most of Sweden except in the southern province of Skåne, and in the

143

monotonous, forest-covered plateau of south-eastern Norway. On its south-eastern margin, along the shores of Lake Ladoga and Lake Onega, the primeval Archaean platform disappears beneath the clear-cut escarpment forming the edge of the scarcely disturbed Palaeozoic sediments that cover much of northern Russia. On the border of Sweden and Norway, this ancient Archaean platform is masked by the broken front of rock masses that were pushed eastward on to its rigid foreland in the folding of the Caledonian mountains [Fig. 30]. The name 'glint' is given to the scarp-like, eastward-facing feature of these overthrust masses, and the long front of the Caledonian *nappes* in western Sweden is known as the 'glint-line'. The Baltic Shield consists of vast tracts of grey and red gneiss, a great variety of granite intrusions, a series of fine-grained, ripple-marked, reddish sandstones that have been scarcely folded, and narrow zones of porphyries and leptites that stand out in the economic geography of Scandinavia because they are the main sources of metallic ores.

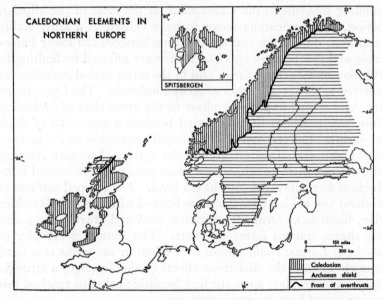

FIG. 30

Two major structural units underlie the geography of Scandinavia. The Archean shield forms the foundation of Finland, most of Sweden, and the southernmost part of Norway. The greater portion of Norway belongs to the province of the Caledonian folds along with north-western Britain and Spitsbergen.

1. THE TOWN HALL, OSLO. The severely functional architecture of the town hall in Norway's capital represents one aspect of the urban scene in Scandinavia

2. KRISTIANSAND. The chief town on the coast of Sørlandet, southern Norway. The core of the old town with a grid-iron plan is seen in the middle distance, and beyond is the tall chimney-stack of the nickel and copper refinery. In the foreground is a spacious suburb built since the Second World War

3. LAKE MJØSA, in south-eastern Norway, is one of the limited tracts of agricultural wealth and ancient settlement in the interior of the country. The Cambro-Silurian schists and limestones contribute to the fertility of the ground moraine. Note the extensive clearances for farms, the result of a settlement process that started more than a thousand years ago. The long, dark rectangles in the fields are wire fences with drying hay, a characteristic feature of the Norwegian landscape

4. GUDBRANDSDAL. This long valley, deeply entrenched in a dull plateau, is characteristic of the scenery of eastern Norway. Shapeless mountains rise from this upland plain that is the scene of summer grazing grounds. In the middle distance (*left centre*) a high bench provides the site for a *seter*, a cluster of summer farms. Otta is the settlement in the valley floor, cut by the single-line track of the main railway from Oslo to Trondheim

5. RØROS, a mining town founded in the wilderness of eastern Norway in the seventeenth century. In the foreground (*right*) the main street of this linear settlement climbs to the baroque miners' church and the steep edge of the esker on which this town lies. The still active copper workings are seen in the middle distance and beyond is the ragged edge of the improved land with its scattered hay barns

6. BERGEN, the regional capital of Norway's western fjords, has grown across the strandflat and is overshadowed by barren mountains made of the Ulriken gneiss. This former outpost of the Hanseatic League now owes much of its prosperity to the small ships that serve the intricate fjord coastline of Vestlandet and the daily coastal express that connects it with Trondheim and the northernmost parts of Norway

7. THE BREMANGER METAL REFINERY, SVELGEN. The site of this factory producing high-quality iron alloys is typical of the electro-metallurgical industries in the fjords of Vestlandet. It lies on a sheltered bay on a large island at the mouth of Nord fjord, utterly devoid of communications by land. Company houses form a distinctive settlement type neatly ranged in the open forest above the fjord shoreline

8. THE SKERRY-GUARD. Countless islands compose the partly submerged portions of the strandflat in western Norway

9. FJORD SETTLEMENT IN VESTLANDET. Vik on one of the arms of Sogne fjord is an example of many communities in the Vestlandet fjords that are sited on tiny deltaic plains overshadowed by precipitous glaciated slopes rising for hundreds of feet from the sea. The cultivated land of the few farms occupies the flat surface of the delta. The left foreground shows the steep slope of a terrace that is symptomatic of recent changes in sea-level. Vik acts as a service centre, having communications by bus and boat, and is a tourist resort. On the skyline in the far distance (*left*) may be seen the ice plateau of the Jostedal

10. JOTUNHEIMEN. A spring view across the Jotunheimen provides an impression of the wastes that lie between the western fjords and Norway's eastern valleys. Glaciated landforms with pyramidal peaks and sharp arêtes rise above the dull landscapes of rolling plateaus

11. TRONDHEIM, Norway's third city after Oslo and Bergen. The urban core gathers around the cathedral (*middle distance, right*) in a meander loop of the river Nid. In the distance Trondheim fjord is screened from the open Atlantic by a hummocky ridge of gneiss. In the foreground the Technical High School stands on a terrace of post-glacial marine deposits that form tracts of fertile, cultivated land at places around the shores of Trondheim fjord.

12. MOSJØEN, two hundred miles north of Trondheim, is a township characteristic of northern Norway. Here the Vefsna river enters the fjord of the same name. Its valley forms one of the several inland longitudinal corridors used by the road and railway in northern Norway. Note the Arctic highway and single-track railway to Bodø in the foreground. Mosjøen is the site of an aluminium smelter

13. TRÆNA, in the skerry guard of Arctic Norway, shows the two chief types of island found along the Atlantic coast. In the foreground, the low flat island consists entirely of the strandflat. In the background, Træna displays glaciated mountains that rise sheer from the gently sloping rim of the strandflat. Here in the north, corrie glaciation was active down to the present sea level and below. The settlement in the foreground combines fishing and farming

14. SOLSØM ON THE ISLAND OF LEKA, NORTH NORWAY. Here settlement is confined entirely to the strandflat. The abrupt break of slope and former cliff line on the inner edge of the strandflat gives way to barren mountains. Former wave-scoured islands stand out as rocky hummocks from the gentler surface of the strandflat

15. VÆRØY, LOFOTEN ISLANDS. A wall of gabbro and granite islands screens the sheltered fishing ground of Vestfjord (*right*) from the open ocean. Settlement is limited entirely to the strandflat. In the middle distance the lower slope of a sharply serrated ridge is completely shrouded in block scree that is still accumulating

16. SVARTISEN, a small icefield just north of the Arctic circle in Norway. This is the only glacier that still reaches the sea in Norway. The distant view of rock, snowfield, and tundra is characteristic of so many hundreds of square miles of Norway

17. OLD UPPSALA. At the core of the dark age kingdom of the Svea, the historic nucleus of Sweden. In the left foreground are the burial mounds of the Svea kings, raised from the sands of the Uppsala esker. The church (*centre*) stands on the site of a pagan temple. In the background the fertile, cleared landscape of the Uppland plain, enriched by post-glacial deposits. The fields beyond the belt of trees in the foreground were formerly cultivated in strips. Here at Gamla Uppsala the farms have retained their sites in the village

18. UPPSALA, an early capital of Sweden with one of the finest cathedrals in northern Europe. Today it is Sweden's greatest centre of learning and a growing industrial town. In the distance the level sub-Cambrian peneplain, enriched here in Uppland by post-glacial deposits

19. LATORPSBRUK IRON MINE, BERGSLAGEN. The landscape of an extractive industry — open quarries, mineral railways, flooded former workings, and spoil dumps — may be seen in Scandinavia's richest and oldest mineral region

20. LANDSCAPE IN SÖDERMANLAND. The province of Södermanland to the south of lake Mälaren illustrates the extent of forest in the poorer tracts of the Swedish midlands. This is a region of hundreds of small lakes held up by stony morainic deposits. The gneiss plateau is planed by the sub-Cambrian peneplain whose monotonous profile forms the far horizon. In the foreground is Stänhammar castle, one of the many estates of this province

21. THE GOTA CANAL. The Göta canal winds across the landscape of the Swedish Midlands between lake Vänern and lake Vättern. Opened in 1832, the canal was designed as a major traffic artery between the North Sea and the Baltic. Today it is used mainly for tourist traffic. The village (*right, middle distance*) shows the effect of the land redistributions and the break-up of the open field system that culminated in the laws of 1827 (*lagaskifte*). The farms are now scattered about the site of the former open fields away from the core of the village at the church. Note the cleared land of another parish in the distance isolated by a woodland tract

22. THE GÖTA RIVER NEAR TROLLHÄTTAN. The Göta river spills out of lake Vänern across the Archaean gneiss plateau of the Baltic Shield. On the horizon is the level skyline of the sub-Cambrian peneplain. The steep northern bank of the river is rocky and largely forested. The southern bank is gentler, composed of recent fluvial deposits in a broad terrace that is cleared of forest and cultivated. Note the heavily dissected strips of land along tributary streams

23. SMÖGEN, A FISHING VILLAGE IN BOHUSLÄN. Formerly the chief centre of the west Swedish fisheries, Smögen has declined at the expense of Hönö Klova. The settlement has grown across the bare hummocks of red granite that make up the coastline of Bohuslän. Note the tiny flat islands in the distance devoted entirely to fish drying and curing gear

24. GÖTEBORG, now the second city of Sweden, was founded on the estuary of the Göta river in 1618 by Gustavus Adolphus. The city has grown in a topography of rocky ice-shaped hummocks. Often these hummocks are crowned by churches and, in this example, by a seventeenth-century fort

The Archaean rocks represent an immense span of time, perhaps equal to the whole of geological history since that distant epoch. They provide a record, however faint and complex, of three major mountain-building movements before the Caledonian, and in northern Norway are preserved the fossil remains of terminal moraines deposited in a glaciation at this utterly remote time.[1] The oldest rocks of the Baltic Shield seem to be the ore-bearing leptites. They probably began as a series of sedimentary and volcanic rocks that underwent great changes in the earth movements occurring in later Archaean times. The large masses of plutonic rocks — granites, gabbros, and syenites — that occupy so much of the Baltic Shield, were put into place at different stages, probably separated from each other by great gaps of time. The connection between the granites and the leptites is beautifully demonstrated in Bergslagen — an area of confused hills and forests in central Sweden whose ores of silver, lead, copper, zinc, and iron have been famous for eight centuries. Here the metal-rich leptite series was invaded by granites of three different ages so that today the leptites form narrow, steeply dipping belts between the stock-like granite masses.

A succession of fine-grained sandstones — the Jotnian sandstone of Finland and the Dala sandstone of Sweden — lies almost undisturbed upon the granites and gneisses. They were probably laid down towards the close of Archaean times, and perhaps represent the Scandinavian equivalent of the Torridonian sandstone of north-west Scotland, a rock that now forms a lonely series of mountains rising from the hummocky surface of the Lewissian gneiss in Ross and Sutherland. The horizontal position of the Jotnian and Dala sandstones and their unchanged character show that they were laid down after the earth movements of Archaean times had subsided. Since that remote age, before any form of life appeared on the surface of the earth, the Baltic Shield has remained comparatively stable, suffering only vertical movements and the effects of faulting in a few special areas such as the central lakes depression of Sweden and within the drowned trough of Oslo fjord. The agents of denudation reduced the tough rocks and complicated structures of the Baltic Shield to a plain by the close of the Archaean epoch. This feature — the sub-Cambrian peneplain — still forms one of the most dominant objects in the landscape of northern Europe [Plate 18]. It appears as the monotonous ground-plan of the *Bergkulland* — the gently inclined plateau of northern Sweden that stretches from the mountains on the Norwegian frontier to the recent coastal plain at the head of the Gulf of Bothnia.[2] In Finland, it borders the shore of the Gulf of Finland, and remnants are found preserved in Norway's high bleak plateau of the Hardangervidda. Again, the sub-Cambrian peneplain underlies the fertile plains of Uppland northwards of Lake Mälaren, from where it dips gently eastward to be drowned amid the countless channels of Stockholm's skerry-guard.

The second important physical unit within Scandinavia consists of the complex remnants of the Caledonian mountain chains [Fig. 30]. These structures occupy almost the whole of Norway. South-westwards they are related to similar elements in the British Isles, and the same structural features and rock-types are found again in Spitsbergen to the north. In the first three periods of the lower Palaeozoic — the Cambrian, Ordovician, and Silurian — sediments accumulated to great thickness in a zone lying along the western and northern flanks of the rigid Baltic Shield. At the close of Silurian times, movements in the earth's crust folded, crushed, and metamorphosed these sediments. Masses of rock moved bodily eastwards on to the resistant Baltic Shield and today these structures define the tabular outlines of the mountains of western Sweden [Plate 29]. Within the zone of severe folding, slices of the old Archaean floor sometimes rode up over the younger sediments. Today, the very roots of this ancient range of mountains form the basis of the scenery of Norway.

Two rock types predominate in the landscapes of northern Norway. On the one hand, the lightly metamorphosed sediments of Cambrian and Silurian age occur as dolomitic limestones or mica schists, often forming long narrow bands of lower ground running parallel to the coastline and followed for great distances by the main valleys [Fig. 8]. The granites and gneisses, on the other hand, belong to masses of plutonic rocks injected during the process of mountain-building. They often stand up as bare, dome-like mountains. For instance, the sombre, serrated peaks that look down on Lyngenfjord have been chiselled out of a mass of gabbro. To the north of Ofoten fjord resistant granites form a group of large islands, while the winding, sheltered channel between them and the mainland coincides with an outcrop of Cambro-Silurian schists.

In a few places the Silurian sediments of Scandinavia escaped the changes brought about by great heat and compression during the making of the Caledonian mountains. If these unaltered rocks happen to be limestones, rich warm soils form upon them. But fertile tracts are rare in the vast, sterile wilderness that makes up so much of northern Europe. Such a region fringes the shores of Lake Mjøsa in southern Norway. This was one of the few parts of the interior where Bronze-Age farmers established themselves. Hamar, the main town in the Mjøsa lowland today, became one of the first bishoprics of Norway. And even now the smiling fields and the air of rural prosperity in this tiny region, enclosed by the forest-covered plateau, bear witness to the presence of Silurian sediments that escaped metamorphism when the Caledonian mountains were uplifted [Plate 3]. Shreds of soft Silurian rocks survive on parts of the Archaean plateau in Sweden, usually preserved as a result of later faulting. Jämtland, one of these areas and a remote part of inner Sweden, was first sought out by farmer settlers in the dark ages. They found far richer soils on the moraine-covered Silurian limestones and shales than on the cold, sterile, boulder-clogged clays that mask the hard, Archaean rocks. Today, Jämtland is the centre of flourishing agricultural communities, set amid the wilderness of a Swedish Norrland that can only support far-scattered mining settlements and lonely groups of timber-cutters.

After the Caledonian earth-storm, Scandinavia was excluded from any of the later mountain-building movements that shaped the geological structures of the rest of Europe. But this does not mean that the landscape had achieved its present shape before the end of Palaeozoic times, remaining without change ever since. In the Permian period, southern Scandinavia was shattered by a series of faults that have left their marks on the present scenery. The chief features that owe their origin to these late Palaeozoic earth movements are the Norwegian Channel, the central lakes depression of Sweden, and the faulted northern coastline of the Gulf of Finland. The Norwegian Channel is a sunken strip of the earth's crust bordering the land mass of south Norway. It forms a deep tectonic trough in the continental shelf, reaching a depth of almost 2500 feet in its eastern part. In the Oslo district, the Permian crustal fractures are associated with igneous activity and produce a zone of distinctive landforms. Masses of syenite and granite cut through the older rocks, and lavas flowed out northwards as far as Lake Mjøsa over the peneplain that was already in existence in Permian times [Fig. 31]. Today, the granite masses

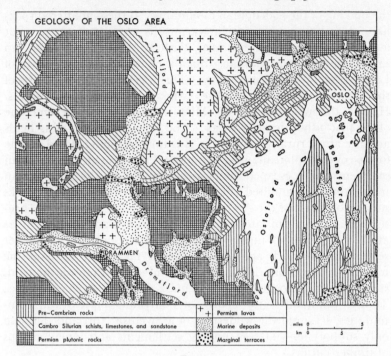

GEOLOGY OF THE OSLO AREA

Pre-Cambrian rocks

Cambro Silurian schists, limestones, and sandstone

Permian plutonic rocks

Permian lavas

Marine deposits

Marginal terraces

FIG. 31

To the north and west, Oslo is encircled by the barren hills of the Permian granites and lavas. East of Oslo fjord are the rocks of the Archaean shield. The Cambro-Silurian limestones and the shreds of superimposed marine deposits of post-glacial date provide the most favourable setting for settlement and farming around Oslo. Another corridor of early occupation follows the band of marine deposits from Drammen to the southern arm of Tyrifjord.

and the related lava sheets stand out as a zone of thinly populated country to the west of Oslo — the infertile acid soils and grey-green forests, broken by lakes and peat-bogs, providing an effective barrier to settlement.

Younger rocks of Mesozoic and Tertiary age scarcely appear in the geology of Norway, Sweden, and Finland. Almost everywhere the ancient, long-since peneplained Archaean rocks are covered directly by clays, sands, and gravels of the Quaternary Ice Age — a time so recent that in its closing phases Palaeolithic men lived along the ice-free margin of Norway's Atlantic coast. During the long gap of Mesozoic and Tertiary time, for which there is but little record in the rocks of the Scandinavian peninsula, the geological history of Denmark and the lands that fringe the southern shore of the Baltic Sea was vastly different. In central Jutland, the rocks of the Pre-Cambrian basement are believed to lie buried beneath younger sediments at depths greater than 15,000 feet.[3] A succession of seas invaded the site of Denmark in Jurassic, Cretaceous, and early Tertiary times, and a thick series of sands, clays, marls, and limestones was deposited [Fig. 18]. Although these sediments form the geological foundation of Denmark, they rarely have any direct effect on the landscape of the country. Nearly everywhere glacial deposits lie at the surface, and only in rare places, such as the famous three-hundred-feet-high cliffs of Senonian limestone in the island of Møn, are the Mesozoic rocks exposed to the light of day [Plate 44]. Nevertheless, the sedimentary rocks beneath the glacial boulder clays and sands make a powerful impression upon the economic life of Denmark. The chalk outcrops at Aalborg are quarried to supply cement works; at Faxe coral limestones provide a source of fertilizers. Tertiary clays are widely dug for the making of bricks, and the deep layers of limestone provide Denmark with a precious reserve of fresh water, as for instance in the highly fissured Danian limestone that underlies Copenhagen.

The Tertiary period added many fresh features to the landscape of northern Europe. Ahlmann, the great Swedish geographer, has suggested a pattern of physical evolution that involved the Scandinavian peninsula and its Atlantic margin in Tertiary times.[4] At the close of the Cretaceous period the Scandinavian peninsula and Finland probably consisted of a vast plain. Rivers flowed south-eastward to a sea that lay over the site of Denmark and the north European plain. Scattered, isolated massifs of rounded hills, such as the Dovre and the Jotunheimen [Plate 10], stood out from this mature lowland, forming its only relief. Powerful vertical movements in the earth's crust during the Tertiary period uplifted this peneplain, the strongest zone of uplift coinciding with the ancient axis of the Caledonian folds in Norway. Ahlmann believes that there were two main phases of earth movement. The first — in early Tertiary times — started a new cycle of erosion on the old peneplain and the general pattern of the present drainage system was sketched out. This erosion-cycle was already well-advanced when a second uplift came in the Pliocene period, towards the close of Tertiary times.[5] It is thought that in this fresh period of uplift Scandinavia rose by as much as a thousand feet. A new cycle of river erosion started in valleys that already had a mature appearance, but this fresh phase in the physical history of northern Europe was severely interrupted by the onset of the Ice Age and its changing climates. A landscape with strong features engraved on the extensive remnants of a monotonous, uplifted peneplain was thus subject to the powerful modelling influences of a succession of ice-sheets after the close of the Tertiary epoch.

Since the Second World War, fresh work on the landforms of Scandinavia has produced evidence suggesting that Ahlmann's scheme of events in the Tertiary period is over-simplified. For instance, Rudberg, in a detailed study of the landscapes of a section of northern Norrland, recognizes the traces of thirteen different cycles of erosion. He believes that these features, sometimes looking like extensive steps in the landscape, are explained by a complex cycle of uplift in western Norway during the Tertiary epoch.

THE QUATERNARY PERIOD AND SCANDINAVIAN LANDSCAPES

If the anatomy of northern Europe took shape in Tertiary times, it was more or less clothed with a flesh of glacial deposits in the Ice Age. Although the half-million years of the Quaternary glaciation represent only a tiny fraction of geological time, the Ice Age contributed some of the most characteristic features of the north European scene. Only two onsets of ice have been clearly recognized in Scandinavia, but as the Quaternary Ice Age shows a general pattern of four major ice periods over widely scattered parts of the northern hemisphere, one may assume that the Baltic lands suffered a glaciation more complex than that revealed in the record of the deposits.

The first known ice period in northern Europe was probably the most extensive. An ice-sheet buried the highest parts of Norway and stretched out into the Atlantic as a formidable ice-barrier. The second glaciation, probably coinciding with the Würm period of Alpine glaciology, was more restricted. The massifs of the Dovre and the Jotunheimen rose above the surface of the ice and their hard rocks were subject to the frost-shattering that created a spectacular landscape of peak, arête, and precipice in these famous tourist districts [Plate 10]. A comparatively thin ice-sheet lay over northern Norway towards the close of the Ice Age.

The great mountain-masses stood out from glacier-filled valleys, suffering severe weathering in the harsh temperature changes of the glacial summers. One of the most striking features of Norwegian scenery — the contrast between the monotonous upland surfaces of the south and the frost-shattered landscapes of the north — is largely explained by the disposition and thickness of the Scandinavian ice-sheet in the closing phase of the Quaternary glaciation. The contrast is enjoyed at its extreme if one travels from the high plateau of the Hardanger massif, with its smooth skylines, to the knife-like arêtes and precipitous cirque walls cut in the naked gabbro of the Lofoten islands [Plate 15]. In the last ice period, glaciers flowed out from the mainland of northern Norway, reaching sea level along the eastern coast of the Lofoten islands where they failed completely in overriding this long mountain wall projecting into the Atlantic. Instead, this mountainous string of islands endured a local glaciation. Glaciers filled the short, steep valleys and at their heads they carved an immense number of cirques, creating the fantastic outlines of the present landscape.

In recent years, views about the nature and processes of glaciation in northern Europe have been modified as a result of much intensive local research. The last great ice period, coincident with the Würm in central Europe or the Wisconsin in North America, is now thought by Scandinavian glaciologists to have been more extensive than it seemed to earlier workers. The growth of glacier ice over Scandinavia is thought to have passed through two main stages. First, glaciers grew in the main mountain-masses and filled the deep valleys draining to the coast. This was the stage of 'alpine' glaciation, when hundreds of cirques were formed in Scandinavia's mountains. As ice accumulated, the 'alpine' glaciation gave way to an extensive continental ice-sheet. Scandinavia became a bleak ice plateau whose summit ridge, imperceptible as a topographical feature, migrated eastward towards an axis over the Gulf of Bothnia. Westward, the margin of the continental ice stretched out to the sea off the Norwegian coast. Doubt is cast upon the view that the peaks of northern Norway stood out above the ice-surface at the time of maximum glaciation. It is thought, too, that the 'alpine' landforms are preserved in the present landscape from the time when they were chiselled out at the onset of the last major ice period. Academic thoughts on the Quaternary period will, no doubt, pass through

FIG. 32

A number of stages may be recognized in the retreat of the Scandinavian ice from its line of maximum advance in the fourth ice-period (Weichsel/Würm). At the Fini-glacial stage, about 8000 B.C., the ice-front stood still for eight centuries, laying down contemporaneous morainic features in the *Ra* ridges of southern Norway, the end-moraines of central Sweden, and the Salpausselkä ridges of Finland.

countless reassessments, but there is no question about the over-whelming part played by ice in the making of the Scandinavian landscape.

Countless features of both the lowland and highland scenery of northern Europe can be attributed to the Quaternary Ice Age. Parts of the Danish coastline were shaped by lobes of ice in the last ice period. For instance, at one stage of the final retreat of ice from central Europe, large glaciers occupied the Great and Little Belts — primary features in the geography of the Danish archipelago. These great ice lobes laid down lateral moraines that today form low clay peninsulas, flat islands, and the pleasant, crumpled miniature hills that are now known as 'the Alps of Funen'. In other parts of the Danish islands the ice left behind unbroken clay plains. They stand out across the centuries as the most fertile parts of the country. Such areas are the northern lowland of the island of Funen and the smooth plain close to Copenhagen, called the 'Hede'. They received the first Neolithic farmers four thousand years ago [Fig. 39]. By the twelfth century, these plains were thoroughly cleared and thick with villages, and since the first tax records of the seventeenth century, they have stood out in the financial statistics of the Danish state as the areas capable of yielding the heaviest fruit of taxes.

Along the eastern side of the Jutland peninsula the ice left its mark in another way. This was the furthest limit of the advance of the ice-front in the last glaciation of Europe where a confused line of morainic hills was deposited [Fig. 32]. Here in the Himmelberg massif, at over five hundred feet above sea level, the Dane points proudly to the finest scenery in his country — a land-scape of beech forests, tiny lakes, and green fields. Within Jut-land's belt of terminal moraines, there is another curious and valuable feature in the form of valleys cut by powerful rivers that flowed beneath the ice. Often, these east-west depressions are today silent and empty of water, or else they are occupied by unimportant misfit streams. But, near the east coast a slight depression of the land since the Ice Age caused the sea to invade these valleys. Here in South Jutland and Slesvig is Denmark's most deeply indented coastline, and on the quiet waters of each 'fjord' there stands a port.

The Quaternary ice-sheets were the main factor in shaping the scenery of Denmark. Likewise, some of the chief elements in the topography of Sweden and Finland were created in the closing stages of the Ice Age. As the ice-front retreated rapidly north-wards across central Sweden, sub-glacial rivers deposited sinuous bands of sand and gravel along their channels beneath the ice [Fig. 13]. Today, these sandy deposits form the clear, upstanding ridges of eskers. The first roads, established in the early Bronze Age, followed these dry causeways across the forest-thick plains of Midland Sweden. Springs, bursting out at the base of the eskers, have attracted the founders of farms and villages for the past four millennia. Many market and industrial towns grew from settle-ments first established where a river or lake cuts the line of an esker.

The effects of the Ice Age were equally vivid in Finland. Eskers rise like low causeways from the labyrinth of lakes in the interior, providing features of great advantage to the settlement and communications of this difficult region. The Salpausselkä terminal moraine is another outstanding piece of the topography of Finland that owes its origin to the Ice Age. It is a double ridge of boulder clays reinforced with deltaic sands and gravels laid down by streams flowing from the stationary ice-front. Its bevelled top also suggests that this complex feature was later planed off by the waves of transient late-glacial seas. The effect of this terminal moraine on the planning of communications in Finland is espe-cially clear. When Russia built the first trunk railway through Finland from St Petersburg to Hanko, it followed for nearly the whole of its length the sinuous natural embankment of the Salpausselkä.

The few thousand years of post-glacial time were as vital as the Ice Age in the shaping of the modern geography of northern Europe. De Geer, the Swedish geologist, used the summer deposits of silt in vanished lakes to calculate that less than ten thousand years fill the gap between our own day and the time when the Quaternary ice-sheets finally disappeared.[6] This period is characterized by rapid fluctuations of sea level, largely a result of the recovery of the Fenno-Scandian land mass from the weight of the Quaternary ice.

The greatest uplift of land in post-glacial times took place in the region of the Gulf of Bothnia. Here the horizontal bands of shingle and sand, relics of the abandoned coastline of the earliest and greatest submergence, stand today at almost nine hundred feet above sea level. The first submergence was very extensive because Scandinavia had scarcely started to recoil from the weight

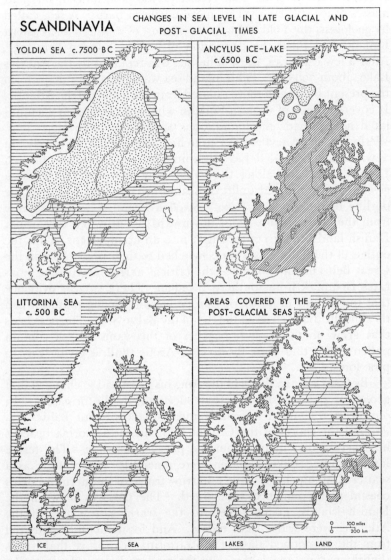

FIG. 33

The retreat of the ice-sheets at the close of the Quaternary period was accompanied by an ever-changing succession of seas whose deposits of silts and clays today form the most fertile tracts of Scandinavia. The Yoldia and Littorina stages show the southward migration of the Baltic's main outlet from the depressed belt of Midland Sweden to the straits of Denmark's archipelago.

of the ice-sheets in the final glacial period, and indeed, stagnant masses of ice still lay over its more northern parts. A sea, called by geologists the Yoldia Sea, covered most of southern and eastern Finland and filled the depression of central Sweden [Fig. 33]. After a few centuries, the Yoldia Sea was replaced by the Ancylus Lake, about 7000 B.C. This inland sea was different in shape from the present Baltic and more isolated from the waters of the Atlantic. It covered much of western Finland where the clays that accumulated now provide the foundations of prosperous farming areas. Westward, the Ancylus Lake stretched across Midland Sweden in a wide island-studded bay, draining to the Skagerrak through Lake Vänern and along the valley now occupied by the Göta river. The continued uplift of Scandinavia rapidly distorted the outline of the Ancylus Lake. Sweden's central depression rose from the waves and a slight downward tilt drowned the former Danish land-bridge, converting it into an archipelago. Thus the outlets of the Baltic basin were switched to their present site in the Great Belt and the Sound — the critical narrow strait that separates Denmark from southern Sweden. There is clear evidence that the climate of northern Europe was improving rapidly when the Ancylus Lake covered the site of the Baltic Sea. The peat beds that grew on the highest beaches of this vanished sea contain pollen grains that show the treeless Arctic tundras giving way to pine forests.

By 6000 B.C. the shape of the Ancylus Lake had so changed that geologists give a fresh name to its successor, the Littorina Sea. In outline it resembled an enlargement of the present Baltic Sea. Around the shores of the Gulf of Bothnia, the Littorina beaches lie several miles inland from the present coastline. The fertile lands fringing Lake Mälaren were emerging at that time as a scattered archipelago, while a narrow fringe of southern Sweden's coastal plain remained submerged. The passages between the Danish islands, giving access to the warm salt waters of the Atlantic, were wider than today. And fossil shellfish, gathered from the abandoned clays of the Littorina Sea, prove that it was slightly warmer and saltier than the modern Baltic. In Littorina times, Scandinavia seems to have enjoyed the most favourable climate of the whole post-glacial period. Pollen gathered from the peat-bogs of central Sweden shows that the oak tree spread far into Scandinavia at this time. In fact, its natural limits in the Bronze Age — about three thousand years ago — stood further north than they do today. At an earlier epoch of prehistory, between 4000 and 2000 B.C., the tree line probably lay a thousand feet higher up the mountains than at the present time, and some believe that in this brief climatic optimum glacier-ice disappeared from the high plateaus of south-western Norway.

Littorina times ended about 500 B.C., when the continued uplift of Scandinavia slowly brought the Baltic Sea into its familiar shape. The Belts, that vital contact with the great ocean, narrowed and became shallower; the Baltic's link with the warm salt waters of the Atlantic was more tenuous than that of the Littorina Sea. At the same time, there is evidence that the climate changed for the worse. The spells of settled, sunny weather that were perhaps frequent in the Bronze Age gave way to more disturbed conditions. There was more rain and snow; and if scientific weather records had been collected in the barbaric Iron Age they might have revealed average annual temperatures with means two or three degrees below those of the foregoing epoch. The tree line shrank down the mountain slopes; the kingdom of the Arctic tundras spread southwards; glacier-ice once again accumulated along the backbone of Scandinavia.

The strandflat of western Norway ranks among the most discussed of the young morphological features of Scandinavia. It forms a discontinuous, hummocky bench along Norway's Atlantic coastline. In its outer parts this platform is submerged beneath present sea level; elsewhere, as in the archipelago of Sunnmøre, the strandflat appears as the chief item in the morphology of innumerable low islands [Plate 8]. In many other places it assumes the form of a narrow, coastal plain abruptly terminated on the landward side by a former sea cliff [Plates 13 and 14].

This feature, that largely determines the sites of farms and fishing settlements in northern Norway, has been produced by a complex succession of events since late Tertiary times. Glaciation, the work of rivers, and intricate changes of sea level have shaped the strandflat.[7] It is believed that stream peneplanation helped to define this feature in the first phase of its formation as early as Miocene times — a view that is inconsistent with Ahlmann's hypothesis of an extensive uplift of Scandinavia towards the close of the Tertiary period. Submergence in the Pliocene period led to extensive wave action, and the cutting of an abrasion platform across the older surface levelled by the work of streams. Glaciers and the enveloping ice-sheets of Quaternary times ground their way across the strandflat; and the returning sea in the inter-glacial periods helped to obliterate the imprint of ice action. The last ice period, the glaciation of Würm times in Alpine Europe, probably endowed many stretches of the strandflat with the hummocky features that it bears today. In its outer parts, marine abrasion has been active once again in smoothing the surface of the strandflat during the few thousand years that have elapsed since the waning of the ice. Despite this complex history, it is likely that marine action has played the lion's part in the creation of this most important feature of Scandinavian geography. The exposed, western coastline of the Lofoten islands bears out this contention. There the strandflat is extensively developed above present sea level [Plate 15], and off Moskensøy it occurs as a submarine abrasion platform more than five miles in width that cuts to the very heart of the granite and gabbro mountains, so that their highest summits now fall to the sea in dizzying cliffs.

More than half a century of research and argument has failed to find a completely satisfying answer to the problem of the origin of the strandflat. Recently, evidence has been produced for a new kind of glacial mechanism in the creation of this coastal bench. Wolf Tietze,[8] a German geomorphologist, believes that the strandflat results from planation by shelf-ice on a tidal coastline. The ice accomplishes an abrasive action as it falls and rises with the tides. The final exposure of the ice-planed platform derives from the post-glacial changes in sea level and the general recovery of the land masses that have borne the weight of the ice-sheets. Tietze believes that strandflats are actively forming at the present time beneath the vast aprons of shelf-ice around the Antarctic continent.

The changing seas and fluctuating climates of the last ten thousand years left a deep impression upon the modern geography of northern Europe. Glacial clays and sands were attacked by waves and redeposited on the floors of these shallow seas. Today, they form the plains of recent clays in Sweden, Finland, and south-eastern Norway [Fig. 34]. These belong to the richest and most populated regions, and almost four thousand years ago they attracted the first Neolithic farmers. The historic provinces of Midland Sweden each contain a nucleus of post-glacial sediments. Uppland, with its ancient capital of Uppsala and the giant earth-works of Viking princes, is focused on the rich clays to the north of

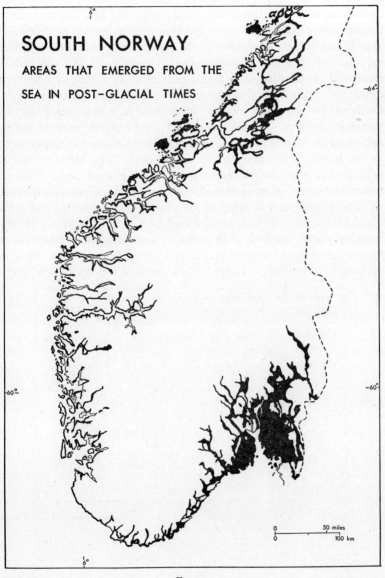

SOUTH NORWAY

AREAS THAT EMERGED FROM THE

SEA IN POST-GLACIAL TIMES

FIG. 34

The chief key to the settlement geography of Norway lies in the tracts of country that emerged from the post-glacial seas enriched with a skin of fertile marine deposits. The shores of Oslo fjord are outstanding as the greatest tract of land to emerge from the sea. A similar valuable zone of post-glacial deposits belongs to the south-eastern shore of Trondheim fjord.

Lake Mälaren. The greatest area of stoneless post-glacial clays in Sweden stretches southwards from the edge of Lake Vänern. Here lies the core of Götland, one of the first regions settled by Neolithic and Bronze Age cultivators in the second millennium B.C. The evidence of their thorough occupation remains to this day in the hundreds of standing stones and passage-graves that lie scattered amid the smiling farmlands of this province. Centuries later, Götland became the centre from which Christianity spread through Sweden. At the same time, the earliest Swedish towns appeared on these plains and among them Skara rose to importance as the home of the first bishop in Sweden. The latest events of geological history — the deposition of post-glacial clays — determined the scenes of some of the main landmarks of Swedish history.

The abandoned beaches of the vanished post-glacial seas form a crucial frontier in the human geography of Scandinavia. Heavy boulder clays, choked with erratics, compose the countrysides above the strips of shingle and degraded cliffs that mark the sites of ancient coastlines. Large tracts are covered with dark, coni-

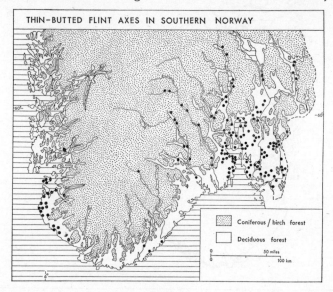

Fig. 35

The distribution of these tools in southern Norway provides a clue to the first occupation of the country by farmers. Their sites are limited to the coastal zone of mixed deciduous forest. Above all they are concentrated on the post-glacial marine deposits around Oslo fjord and the boulder clays of the Jaeren plain in south-west Norway. Based on a map from J. G. D. Clark: *Prehistoric Europe*, Methuen & Co.

ferous forests, and these regions remain thinly populated. Below the old beaches stretch the rolling plains whose rich, stone-free soils result from the sorting action of waves in the post-glacial seas. The extent of cultivated land on these recent plains is unmatched in northern latitudes. The value of such young marine and lake clays stands clearly displayed in the geography of south-eastern Norway. Post-glacial marine deposits reach several miles inland along the eastern shore of Oslo fjord [Fig. 31]. They can be found as high as five hundred feet above sea level, forming a thin, fertile skin above the hard granites and gneisses of the Archaean platform. Here, 20 per cent of the land is cultivated, an exceptionally high proportion in a country whose arable farming takes up less than 3 per cent of the total area [Fig. 58]. Fields of wheat and occasional orchards add an exotic colour to this corner of south-eastern Norway, and the population density rises to 250 per square mile. Beyond the edge of the post-glacial marine clays lies a cold, broken landscape of forest, peat-bog, and lake. Here, settlement proceeded slowly through the dark ages and into late medieval times. Farms are scattered and mainly pastoral, villages are rare, and the population density falls to a level of less than fifty persons to the square mile.

CLIMATE AND SCANDINAVIAN GEOGRAPHY

The relations between climate and the lives of men often defy simple analysis. The city-dweller finds the march of the seasons little more than a disturbing or titillating influence in the background of his life, but in northern Europe it is hard to isolate oneself from a climate that swings between the extremes of a summer filled with light and a winter that brings long hours of darkness, frozen seas, and icy winds out of the Arctic.

The annual pattern of climate and its various aberrations leave a clear impression on the economic life of the Scandinavian countries. The farming year of Arctic Norway and Swedish Norrland is crammed into a summer that lasts for barely three months [Fig. 55]. Barley is the only grain that ripens satisfactorily in the long hours of polar sunshine between the melting of the snows at the end of May and the onset of hard frosts in the September nights. Potatoes are the only other successful crop in these far northern latitudes. The long coastal strip of Arctic Norway, stretching from Trondheim fjord to the North Cape, lies at the very margin of cultivation in Europe. Here, the success of farming in the summer season depends largely upon the direction from which the wind blows. If air from the Arctic predominates during the summer months, the daily temperatures usually lie between 2° centigrade (35° F.) and 10° centigrade (50° F.) — too low to encourage the growth of plants. When the winds over Arctic Norway swing to the south, the air originates in a warm source over the heated land mass of central Europe. Summer temperatures rise to between 15° centigrade (60° F.) and 24° centigrade (75° F.) and the crops ripen in the tiny fields along the strandflat. At Tromsø, they say that when the wind veers from the south-east to the west or north the grass stops growing. The slightest digression from mean temperatures in the summer months is fatal in the marginal region of north Norway. The records of a plant-breeding station close to Tromsø clearly illustrate this hard fact. Over the period between 1930 and 1950 they show that grain crops failed to ripen in three of the summers — summers of predominant Arctic air and low temperatures.

The sites of farms in the long valleys of south-eastern Norway display with great clarity the influence of climate. Here, as in the high Alps, settlement is often limited to sunny, southward-facing slopes. Other facts of micro-climatology have determined the positions of farm buildings. They are frequently situated on high shoulders and benches above the valley floor, to escape the severe inversion frosts that form on still spring nights when the continental anticyclone blankets the massif of southern Norway. These farms take advantage of still another peculiarity of the local climate. On summer days, the soil temperatures of southward-tilted slopes often reach astonishingly high figures. Crops ripen more quickly than on the opposite side of the valley that looks to the north away from the sun. Often the northward-facing slope is empty of all permanent settlement, being occupied only by forest and, at higher levels, the *seters* — the grazing grounds of the summer months.

Of all the seasons winter makes the deepest impression upon the human geography of northern Europe. In a normal year, ice begins to block the ports along the Baltic shoreline from the beginning of December. At the head of the Gulf of Bothnia the iron-exporting harbours are not free again for shipping until the middle of May. Among the fishing and farming communities that inhabit the hundreds of little islands close to the coasts of

Sweden and Finland, the seasons of summer and winter symbolize two totally different patterns of life. In the Replot archipelago, a group of tiny granite and gneiss islands off western Finland, the in-shore channels are frozen solid for twenty-six weeks in an average year. In winter they cease to be islands, and bus services run across the frozen sea to the mainland. This is the season when open boats are dragged on sledges for miles to the ice-free harbours in the outer archipelago, where they can embark on long and dangerous expeditions in the Gulf of Bothnia in search of the grey seal.

Long, dark nights and a snow cover that lasts for weeks form the usual background to life in the Scandinavian winter, but sometimes winter strikes more deeply at the economic roots of these northern countries [Fig. 38]. Harsh frosts, when the ground is bare of snow, are an especial danger for the autumn-sown grains of South Sweden and Denmark. For instance, the south of Sweden was swept by a heavy Arctic gale with air temperatures as low as - 29° centigrade (- 20° F.) on January 25th, 1942. No snow lay on the ground, and, as a result, the autumn-sown wheat was destroyed over a large part of the rich province of Skåne. Likewise, a bitter winter with little snow and severe frosts causes a freezing of the soil to greater depths. In Swedish Norrland and Arctic Norway, this may delay the start of the growing season in the following spring by as much as a fortnight. The farmers of northern Norway commonly try to preserve the snow-cover by placing wooden snow-breaks in the fields so that they shall not be swept completely clean by the winds.

Towards the northern limits of Scandinavia, man is hardly tolerated by a hostile climate. No wonder that in these countries the unfashionable views of the geographical determinist seem valid and full of truth. Norwegians believe that the physical environment is an ever-present force in the shaping of character. In quiet arguments across the café tables of Oslo the stock example is the man from Arctic Norway who is usually described as 'hard-working, but irresponsible and given to fits of deep melancholy'— traits that are ascribed to the long winter night. At least the Swedes appreciate the depressing effects of winter in the remote wilderness of Norrland. There, the state pays its civil servants on a salary scale adjusted to the lengthening hours of the winter night.

Apart from the overwhelming influence of latitude in the

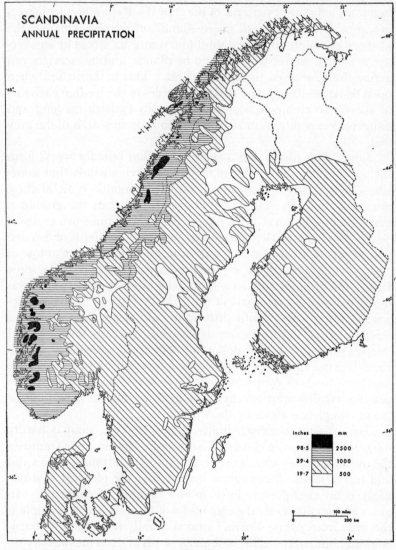

inches	mm
98·5	2500
39·4	1000
19·7	500

100 miles
200 km

Fig. 36

The wettest parts of Scandinavia are found where Norway's mountains and plateaus face the Atlantic depressions in Vestlandet and the north. Here rainfall may soar to 200 inches per year. Large areas of northern Europe in Swedish Lapland and northern Finland and the dry valleys of eastern Norway receive less than 20 inches of rainfall a year.

pattern of northern Europe's climate, one must take into account the contrasted elements of the Atlantic Ocean and the vast land mass of Eurasia that lies to the east. Warm air masses from the Atlantic frequently envelop the coastline of western Norway, so that the mean temperatures of the winter months in these latitudes are abnormally high [Fig. 37]. The mean temperatures of January along the whole of this narrow coastal fringe lie close to 0° centigrade (32° F.). Bergen, for instance, records a mean temperature of 1.6° centigrade (35° F.) in January. This zone of winter warmth is confined to a narrow fringe of the most exposed parts of the coastline; at the heads of the long, branching fjords, deeply recessed in the snow-covered plateau, the winter months are on the average six degrees colder and from time to time the still waters freeze over.

The Atlantic and its warm air masses are not only the main cause of western Norway's warm winters, but the source of the bulk of the rain that falls on Scandinavia [Fig. 36]. Depressions, moving from the west, follow the guiding lines of Norway's blunt, highland massif. Many turn northwards along the coast to fill up and lose their energy over the Arctic Ocean or the tundra barren-lands of Lapland. Others move south-eastwards, steered by the warm waters of the Skagerrak and the Kattegat, into the basin of the Baltic Sea. The depressions of the late winter and early spring often follow this latter route and 'secondaries' sometimes form along the south Norwegian coastline — a result of the contact of cold air lying over the snow-blanketed plateau of the interior, and the warmer, moist air over the sea. It is the rarely broken succession of depressions moving along the west Norwegian coast combined with the presence of high mountains that produces some of Europe's heaviest rainfall figures. An annual average of 120 inches of rain falls on the seaward ends of western Norway's fjords. On the slopes of her high plateaus, exposed to the west, rainfall may rise to more than 200 inches in the year — a result of the close contact of a warm sea, high mountains, and the presence of ice fields and glaciers that force the temperatures of the humid maritime air still lower.

In winter, the great high-pressure system centred over Eurasia spreads its influence westward. This snow-covered continent stretches northwards to the shores of the Arctic Ocean to form a vast source of cold, dry, polar-continental air. The winter in Scandinavia enacts a struggle between the air masses from two

Some Facets of Scandinavian Geography

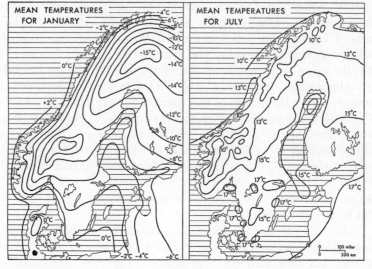

FIG. 37

The isotherms for January show the great contrasts of temperature between the Atlantic coastline of Norway and the interior of the Scandinavian peninsula. The northward bend in the winter isotherms over the Gulf of Bothnia reveals a minor local influence of this sea on temperatures. In summer the islands of greatest warmth appear with the 17° centigrade isotherm over the mouth of Oslo fjord, along the eastern shoreline of the Kattegat, and in Midland Sweden.

strikingly different sources — the warm, moist Atlantic and the harshly cold centres over Siberia and the Arctic Ocean. Regions that lie far from the influence of the Atlantic experience long spells of clear, cold, continental air in their winter weather. In north-eastern Lapland, for instance, the mean temperatures of January range between −16° centigrade (3° F.) and −14° centigrade (6° F.). Further south, in central Sweden and throughout Denmark, the winter struggle between the two air masses is not so clearly resolved. In two out of three winters the weather fluctuates fitfully between spells of cloudless Arctic air and cold thaws, when the temperatures hover about freezing point and sheets of grey stratus cloud roll in from the south-west. In Denmark only one winter in three may be truthfully labelled as 'continental'. Then snow lies on the ground for several weeks and in brief, intensely cold snaps the temperature of Jutland's interior might falls as low as −25° centigrade (−13° F.). For about five winters in a century, the Arctic holds its grip on northern Europe for several months. Ice-floes gather in the warm mouth of the Baltic, and it was in such a winter in 1658 that Charles Gustavus X marched his army across the frozen Sound from Sweden to lay siege to the walls of Copenhagen.

A succession of severe continental winters came to northern Europe in the early 1940's. Such a time was the winter of 1939–40. The beginning of this winter remained remarkably mild in the south of Sweden, but by the middle of January a massive invasion of polar-continental air came to dominate the weather scene until the second week of May. On January 15th, the day of the first onslaught of this cold air-mass from the north-east, temperatures around Lake Vättern fell as much as thirty-five degrees in a few hours. The lake froze rapidly, and by January 22nd the ice was so thick that steamship communications closed down. On February 7th the first cars were able to drive across the lake, and it was not until almost three months later that the ice became too thin to allow the passage of motor traffic. By February 20th of that year, when Scandinavia was in the full grip of the continental anticyclone, temperatures of − 34° centigrade (− 30° F.) were recorded around Lake Vättern. The ice finally broke up in late May under the influence of light, cool winds from the north-east. In normal years Lake Vättern is frozen intermittently for brief periods through the winter, the ice breaking rapidly with each incursion of warm winds from the south-west.

SCANDINAVIA'S REGIONAL CLIMATES

The climates of Scandinavia range between two extremes — extremes that are described by the terms continental and maritime. Along the coastal fringe of Norway the Atlantic reveals its influence in every facet of the climate. The high rainfall, reaching as much as two hundred inches, is spread through the year with a maximum in the months of late autumn. By contrast, there is a distinct minimum in the rainfall curve for late spring, when the sea is at its coldest and the Scandinavian anticyclone usually succeeds in enveloping the coastal regions. A raw, moist winter with blizzards of snow and days of drizzling rain gives way to an unsettled summer that lasts for three or four months. It is not unusual to see the first fresh mantle of winter snow on the high peaks of Sunnmøre in the first week of September. Even in summer the temperatures

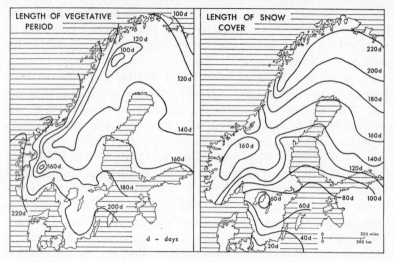

Fig. 38

The length of the growing season is a critical element in the geography of Scandinavia. The most favoured tracts are the south-western coasts of Norway, Sweden, and Finland. The length of snow cover increases steadily with latitude. In the highlands of south-western Norway snow lies for more than 160 days and altitude helps to cancel any benefits that may be gained from exposure to mild Atlantic air.

on the fahrenheit thermometer rarely rise into the high sixties in this most maritime of northern Europe's climates.

The continental type of climate develops in areas screened from the Atlantic, over the plateau of central Finland and in Swedish Norrland where the backbone of mountains to the west erects a barrier to weather from the ocean. Here the winters of severe Arctic cold give way to summers of uncommon warmth. Over the empty tundras in Swedish Lapland, temperatures may reach the upper seventies fahrenheit, breeding clouds of mosquitoes amid this wilderness of peat-bogs. But even at the height of summer there is always the risk of invasion by Arctic air, bringing the dreaded late summer frosts that can ruin Norrland's potato crops. Rainfall scarcely exceeds 25 inches in these parts of Scandinavia and late spring and early summer droughts harm the germination of crops, curtailing a growing season that is already rigidly limited by the incidence of spring and autumn frost.

Between these extremes, various regional climates blend the characteristics of Atlantic and continental Europe. For instance,

Jutland, with its grey skies and trees bent by the North Sea gales, has a climate with marked Atlantic features, but it lacks the excessive rainfall of the Norwegian fjords. On the other hand, the eastern islands of the Danish archipelago — Zealand, Falster, and Møn — enjoy a climate with a distinctly continental tinge. Snow lies longer there than in Jutland, and in the settled, sunny summers the farmer can grow a more varied range of crops than is economically possible in western Denmark. Even in the recesses of the Baltic similar nuances of climate can be observed. The weather patterns of the Atlantic faintly appear in the climate of the islands off south-western Finland, where a trace of summer may linger in early October under the influence of warm air from the west and the heat-retaining capacity of the mass of water in the Baltic Sea. It also seems that the rôle of Scandinavia's high, seaward-facing mountains and plateaus in the production of orographic rainfall is weakly reflected in south-western Finland, where the ridge of the Salpausselkä moraine coincides with the wettest part of the country (about 30 inches per year) and is responsible for the creation of a certain amount of relief rain. Amid the forests of Karelia, on the Russian border, Finland experiences a true continental climate, and the onset of winter is sharply announced at the start of September with the occurrence of regular frosts.

ENVIRONMENT AND MAN IN SCANDINAVIA

Scandinavians live close to the harsh facts of their physical environment. Climate and landscape provide an austere setting for the histories of the Scandinavian nations, a setting that has undergone some radical changes during the few thousand years that have elapsed since the first human occupation of this area. As we have already noticed, the melting of the Quaternary ice-sheets from northern Europe produced an important series of adjustments in sea level during post-glacial and historic times. These topographic changes deeply influenced the settlement history of the lands bordering the Baltic Sea. The fertile plains around Lake Mälaren have risen continuously since their first settlement by Neolithic farmers about four thousand years ago. Village sites that lay close to sea level when they were first established in the Bronze Age now stand in a zone between thirty and a hundred feet above the sea. This belt of country, composed of rich marine clays, first emerged from the receding Littorina Sea three thousand years ago. Today Lake Mälaren is a shrunken relic of that sea. It became isolated from the Baltic 800 years ago as a result of the continued uplift of the land. The narrow entrance to Lake Mälaren assumed a crucial importance in the thirteenth century, because of the need to exclude the Baltic pirates from the new towns and trading centres that were founded by the church and Hanseatic merchants around the shores of this placid inland sea. The island of Staden blocks the narrow channel leading to Lake Mälaren and it was there in 1252 that Birger Jarl built the castle which became the nucleus of the city of Stockholm [Fig. 14].

The Baltic's changing sea levels have favoured or damaged the economic health of villages and towns. Around the coast of the Gulf of Bothnia, the shoreline still retreats at an astonishing rate. For instance, the Replot islands off western Finland are emerging from the surrounding sea at the rate of a yard a century. Within each generation the farmers share out new land freshly risen from the sea, and the shallowing channels between these low, hummocky islands of gneiss and granite are regularly dredged to make way for boats and spawning fish. When, under the influence of Nature's relentless process, they become too shallow, the estuaries and winding sea straits are transformed into meadows.

Just as the Baltic shorelines are subject to continuous change through the uplift of the Scandinavian land mass, so the agriculture of these northern countries is sensitive to climatic fluctuations. During the historic period, minor fluctuations have followed the great climatic oscillations of Quaternary times. Already we have noticed the post-glacial warm period between 4000 and 2000 B.C. when it is likely that many of the Scandinavian glaciers vanished from the landscape. Doubtless this climatically benign epoch favoured the Neolithic colonization of northern Europe. Scandinavian climatologists claim that their statistics point to a notable improvement in the climates of the northern countries since the beginning of this century. It is thought that since 1920 the far north has enjoyed milder conditions than at any time in the previous eight centuries. Between 1850 and 1940 the mean January temperatures of Stockholm rose by 2° centigrade (3.6° F.) and at Helsinki by as much as 2.7° centigrade (5° F.). Further north, the rise in the mean temperatures of the midwinter months is even more striking. In Spitsbergen, the mean January temperature of Longyearbyen rose by as much as 10° centigrade (18° F.) between 1910 and 1940. Climatic statistics for Scandinavia also reveal a rise in the mean temperatures of the summer months, though the evidence lacks the clarity of the winter figures. It seems that there was a trend towards cooler summers until 1915, and this was replaced by a succession of warmer, more 'continental' summers until the early forties. Some workers believe that the climatic amelioration of the twentieth century has been halted since 1940.[9] There are signs that the glaciers have ceased to retreat in the uplands, and there is an ominous hint of a lowering of the 'firn-line' once more.

Life in Scandinavia, above all among the mountains and in the northern provinces, is set against this background of a slowly changing climate. It is not too cynical to suggest that the agricultural triumphs of the first half of the twentieth century have been achieved in the most notable spell of higher temperatures since the days when Stockholm was founded and Bergen began to enter the European trade in dried and salted fish. The next half-century, if it comes to match the Iron Age as a period of climatic deterioration, is likely to present the agricultural scientist with much harder problems. The peoples of Scandinavia live close to a harsh landscape and in the shadow of a hard climate. Here, perhaps more than anywhere else in our continent, man seems to display a direct and intelligible relationship to his physical environment.

CHAPTER 7

The Historical Development of Scandinavia

THE geography of Scandinavia today is the result of two distinct processes. This region received its physical shape in the course of a long evolution extending through the vast span of geological time — a theme discussed in the previous chapter. In addition, Scandinavia has undergone some equally striking changes at the hand of man in the past four thousand years. The process of historical development, starting with the first farmers and destroyers of the natural forests, lasted for a full four thousand years in areas of early settlement such as the loamy plains of the Danish islands. Elsewhere, in some of the remotest parts of northern Europe the story of settlement is still at its very beginning. Today the axe and the bulldozer are clearing stretches of virgin forest in the heart of Finland to make way for fresh farms. This juxtaposition of areas where men have lived for several thousand years and forests and peat-bogs that have given way to young farms in the past few decades provides one of the keys to the understanding of the geography of Scandinavia. Perhaps more vividly than anywhere else in Europe, historical geography can be written in the terms of clearance of forest and the creation of new farms. The great internal colonization of Scandinavia in the Viking age, an undocumented history of a thousand years ago, has been handed down to us in the names of hundreds of farms in the long valleys of eastern Norway. Again, the painful clearing of the boulder-choked glacial clays of Småland at the close of the Middle Ages is evident today in the endless stone walls that form the field boundaries in that poor region of southern Sweden. And amid the dark forests of Finnish Karelia the 'frontiersman' is still with us, hacking fresh acres of farmland out of the woods of Europe's only surviving 'pioneer fringe' [Figs. 61 and 62].

Northern Europe's first areas of permanent settlement appeared in late Neolithic and Bronze Age times, when the earliest farmers cleared land for their crops of wheat and barley and established the first villages. This was preceded by an age of shifting settlement when forest burning created temporary spaces for the migrant farmer and his crops. The relics of prehistory reveal in their distribution the focal areas of permanent settlement. Chambered tombs, stone circles, Bronze-age burial grounds, hoards of Roman coins, and the huge mounds that conceal the 'ship-burials' of Viking kings — all show a pattern of occupation confined to the fertile lake plains and the coastal lowlands, a design that must have prevailed until after A.D. 1000.

GEOGRAPHY AND DANISH HISTORY

The historic centres of settlement in Denmark lie in the islands and among the morainic hills of eastern Jutland. Within the archipelago the large eastern island of Zealand has stood supreme. Two geographical facts gave Zealand its important place in Danish history. The fertile, loamy soils of its plains provided favourable ground for early settlement [Fig. 25], and its eastern coastline, flanking the crucial passage of the Sound between Denmark and southern Sweden, has long been of high political value in the mastery of the entrance to the Baltic Sea.

Two districts in Zealand — the Hede to the south of Copenhagen and the wide lowlands in the south-west of the island — contain some of the finest soils in Denmark. Here the Quaternary ice-sheets, scraping their way across the Mesozoic limestones that now form the floor of the Baltic Sea, deposited a clay with a high lime content. The long history of settlement upon these two fertile plains of Zealand is attested by the Neolithic burial places [Fig. 39], the upright stones, and the smooth curves of Bronze-age barrows that stand amid the ripening barley and the straight-furrowed fields of sugar beet and turnips.[1] Place-names, too, bear witness to the antiquity of villages in these rich regions where the abundance of the primitive 'inge' element suggests that many settlements were in existence in the Iron Age about the beginning of the Christian era. Although the modern village names date only from this late time in prehistory, there is every reason to believe that on several of these sites settlement has been continuous since middle Neolithic times, when the first farmers gave up their shifting agriculture on burnt-over forest clearings for permanent fields of wheat and barley, cultivating seeds that had been handed on from their native habitats in the eastern Mediterranean by

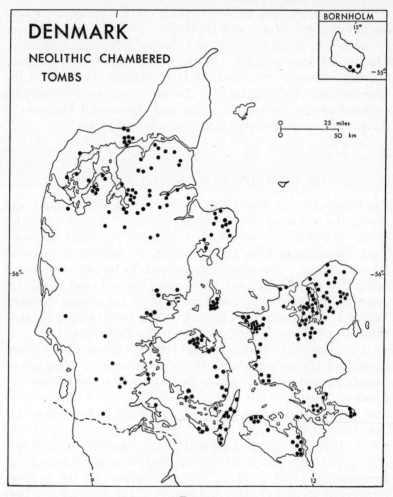

FIG. 39

The distribution of the burial places of the first agricultural settlers of Denmark shows the attraction of the Danish archipelago and north-eastern Jutland with their tracts of good soils based on the varied deposits of the final ice period. The sterile sands and gravels of central and western Jutland were almost completely neglected.

generations of migrating farmers. At a later date, in the seventeenth century, the pre-eminence of these same fertile plains stands clearly revealed in the statistics of a taxation assessment based on the productivity of the soil. In the figures of this *hartkorn* valuation of 1664, the Hede and the lime-rich clays of south-west Zealand rank among its highest values.

Zealand's supreme position among the Danish islands springs not only from its fertile soils but also the strategic value of the Sound, the chief entry to the Baltic Sea. After the eleventh century, trade began to expand in Central Europe and scores of new towns appeared on the map. With the growth of European trade, Denmark found herself in a vital position between the North Sea lands and the Baltic — a permanent and passive relationship of the physical environment was made active by the events of history. She controlled the seaway to the Baltic ports with their fish and furs, copper ores and timber products. In addition her island stepping-stones provided a land-bridge to the wilderness of Scandinavia. It was in that period of high prosperity, between A.D. 1100 and the close of the fourteenth century, that Zealand established its pre-eminence in the political geography of the Baltic area. Copenhagen — Koepmanna Havn, the merchants' port — is first mentioned in a saga of A.D. 1043; but Copenhagen's future as the main city of Denmark does not become apparent until a century later. For the first time, in the twelfth century, trade between the North Sea ports and the Baltic focused on the narrow passage of the Sound [Fig. 23]. The old portages across the neck of the Jutland peninsula, routes that had been known since the Bronze Age, fell into disuse. German and Dutch merchants set up business in Copenhagen and the city grew rich from the herring fisheries along the neighbouring coastline of south Sweden. Copenhagen had to wait another three centuries before it became the political and administrative capital of Denmark. It was only in 1445 that the kings of Denmark shifted their royal residence from Roskilde [Plate 47], an inland town at the head of a long, quiet estuary, to the busy commercial city and fortress on the Sound.

The growth of Copenhagen stands as a symbol of medieval Denmark's position astride the mouths of the Baltic Sea. This city was the focal point of a state that stretched far beyond the political bounds of modern Denmark. Her frontiers then lay in the forests of Schleswig-Holstein to the south, across the thinly peopled upland of Småland, and in the cold wastes of Arctic Norway, but the wealth of this huge medieval state was largely won in the islands of the Danish archipelago and along the coasts of south Sweden.

By the middle of the seventeenth century political relationships had changed severely in northern Europe. Sweden advanced her power to the west and south, at the expense of Denmark, between

1600 and 1650 [Fig. 12]. By 1660 the Danes had lost all their rich provinces on the other side of the Sound. Copenhagen, the medieval town that had prospered as the centre of Denmark's Scandinavian Empire, was changed into a frontier city staring across the sea to a Swedish shoreline. The political attrition of Danish territories continued with the loss of Norway in the Napoleonic Wars, and Denmark reached her present shape in 1864 when the loss of Schleswig-Holstein at the base of the Jutland peninsula enriched Germany with a third of Danish territory and some of her best farmlands.

At the close of the nineteenth century, Denmark found herself with an economic core astride the Baltic gateway in the islands of Zealand, Funen, Lolland, Falster, and Møn. Western and northern Jutland remained a poor and thinly populated region, ill-endowed by nature. Behind Jutland's hungry coastline lay the

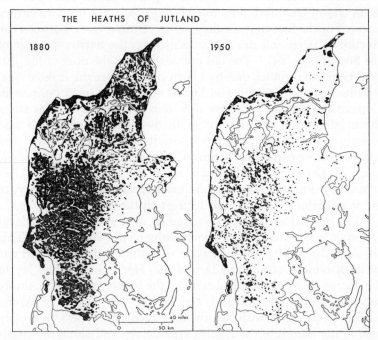

FIG. 40

The heathlands of Jutland were extensive in the region of glacial outwash sands and gravels that lay to the west of the ice-front of the fourth ice period. The disappearance of the Danish heathlands since the last quarter of the nineteenth century represents one of the most spectacular changes in the landscape of northern Europe.

176

huge peat-bogs and barren heathlands resting on the glacial out-wash sands and gravels of the last ice period. The military defeat of 1864 and the loss of her smiling province in Schleswig-Holstein turned Denmark to the conquest of the desolate spaces of west Jutland [Fig. 40]. In 1866 groups of patriotic Danes formed the 'Danish Heathland Society' to reclaim Jutland's wastelands. The barren stretches of glacial sand were improved with clay dug out of the sub-soil. The reclamation of the peat-bogs began with the cutting of drainage ditches. Within a generation, a new town — one of several — Herning, had arisen as a railway and market centre in the midst of one of Jutland's most desolate heaths. The countryside was covered with new farms, standing screened from the damp North Sea gales by neat rectangular plantations of conifers. In western Jutland Denmark discovered a region for settlement and colonization and since 1866 she has reclaimed an area scarcely less than that of Belgium.

THE HISTORIC PATTERN OF SWEDEN

Sweden first appeared as a political entity nearly fifteen hundred years ago, in that dark age when the kings of the Svea expanded southward from their homeland on the fertile plains of the northern shore of Lake Mälaren. There they are remembered today by the great burial mounds close to Uppsala at the very centre of their kingdom [Plate 17]. The Svea, in their movement southward, conquered the Goths and absorbed the twin foci of their terri-tories — Vestergötland, composed of the extensive plains along the southern shore of Lake Vänern, and Östergötland, whose centre lay in the gentle landscape of post-glacial sediments north-eastwards of Lake Vättern. The core of modern Sweden consists of the united territories of the Svea and the Goths, a medley of harsh, forested blocks of upland and fertile plains that have been farmed ever since the first Neolithic settlers penetrated this region.

Today, this same area cradles many of Sweden's towns and industries. Stockholm stands at the crucial exit to the little inland sea of Mälaren, and several manufacturing towns cluster along its shores. For instance, Eskilstuna lies a few miles south of Lake Mälaren where the Hyndevads river plunges across a fault-scarp by a waterfall and rapids. Here, at this power-site, one of Sweden's largest engineering centres has grown up. Southward of the industrial region around Lake Mälaren one reaches the ancient province of Östergötland, where Norrköping, the regional capital, has a site not unlike that of Stockholm. The town stands astride an esker that is breached by the Motala river at the head of the quiet *fjärd* of Braviken. The abundance of archaeological finds in the neighbourhood of Norrköping hints that this was an important trade centre for Östergötland as long ago as the Bronze Age. Again, the large number of primitive and early elements in the place-names of the Norrköping district points to the full settlement of this area at a remote period of Swedish history almost two thousand years ago. Today, Norrköping is famous as the chief textile town of Sweden. Its modern industrial history dates from 1625 when Gustavus Adolphus encouraged a famous immigrant and industrialist from the Low Countries, Louis de Geer, to set up the manufacture of textiles. Motala, another industrial centre within the ancient region of Östergötland, came into existence only in 1832 at the junction of the Göta canal and Lake Vättern. The Göta canal, connecting the lakes of central Sweden and joining the Baltic to the Skagerrak, was the most important factor in the early growth of Motala. Today the canal has little value, except as a picturesque tourist attraction [Plate 21], and Motala has evolved into a town specializing in heavy engineering. Away to the west on the plains of Vestergötland lies a third important area with scattered towns and industries. Here are some of the oldest towns of Sweden. Among them, Lidköping is well known for its machine tools and above all for the saws that go to the mills and lonely timber camps of Sweden's northern forests; while Tidaholm manufactures cars and has one of the biggest match factories in the country.

The historic core of Sweden stretches from the Baltic coast to the shores of Lake Vänern. Today it forms a centre of relatively dense population and is famous above all for its engineering industries, but in no sense is it a 'Black Country' or a 'Ruhr'. The industrial towns are small — some have a population of thirty or forty thousand, many contain no more than ten thousand people. The dominant impression of east-central Sweden is a region of agricultural richness, a landscape that has been tamed by man over the past four thousand years [Plate 21]. But here the taming of the wilderness is not quite complete and never will be, because, above the clay plains with their hundreds of scattered farmsteads, rise, here and there, isolated fault-bounded blocks of the basement Archaean rock. Their ponderous shapes, dressed in dark forests of pine and fir, are ever-present reminders that here men live at the very northern limits of the systems of farming known to Central Europe.

Medieval Expansion from Sweden's Core Region

Ever since the Svea kings created a crude political unity in central Sweden almost fifteen hundred years ago, this region — focused on the three lakes — has been the centre from which colonizing movements attacked the bordering, ill-populated wildernesses of Småland and Norrland [Fig. 12]. The first great epoch of forest clearance in northern Europe started with the Vikings about the beginning of the ninth century. Hundreds of farms and hamlets appeared within the forests on the fringe of the old settled areas. Settlers followed the valleys of rivers leading northwards from the shores of Lake Mälaren and the plain of Uppland, the Kolbäcksån, Dalälven, and Gävleån. The place-names of these Viking clearances tell their own story of those still, summer days long ago, when the fallen giants of the forest were dragged together and burnt in a great pyre to clear another few acres for the farmer. The place-name elements, *ryd*, *bo*, and *seter*, that pepper the modern topographical maps of Sweden all conceal the same history of the attack on the forests by axe and fire a thousand years ago.

A similar expansion of settlement in Viking times took place among the forested valleys of south-eastern Norway. Farms with names ending in *rud*, meaning a clearing, first appeared in the tenth and eleventh centuries. It is often forgotten that this expansion of settlement and agriculture in Scandinavia during the Viking times accompanied the raids of the Norsemen around the whole North Atlantic basin. Some have even suggested that many of the clearances in the Norse homeland were the work of 'thralls' — slaves brought from distant places across the sea by Viking chiefs.[2] Perhaps it is more reasonable to explain the energy of this pagan, illiterate society in the terms of a general increase in the population of northern Europe during the ninth and tenth centuries. However, one fact is certain: this first great period of expanding settlement came to an end in the fourteenth century. Brøgger, the Norwegian prehistorian, attributes the end of this vigorous, expansive phase to the ravages of the Black Death in Scandinavia about 1350. Many of the highest farms on the slopes of the long valleys of eastern Norway were abandoned for ever in the fourteenth century. Several questions can be asked about this enigma of medieval history. For instance, were the decimations of the Black Death alone responsible for the retreat of settlement in Norway ? [3] Perhaps the Viking farmers had already transgressed the economic margin of successful cultivation when they created their highest and loneliest settlements. The retreat of farming in the fourteenth century would then seem to be the acceptance of failure after several decades of blind experiment and impoverishment. Again, the geographer might read a slight worsening of climate into this abandonment of upland sites — a weather fluctuation that transformed a successful farm into a failure.[4]

In Sweden, the northward expansion of settlers from the good lands along the shores of Lake Mälaren continued with growing energy during the fifteenth and sixteenth centuries under the impetus of the search for minerals. The tract of country that stretches to the lower Dal river was rich in copper, gold, iron, and silver-lead ores, and from the thirteenth century onwards a steady stream of prospectors, miners, and smiths trickled into this hummocky, forested landscape on the Archaean rocks. For at least six centuries this region has been called the Bergslagen, a name that commemorates these scattered mining communities of the late Middle Ages, who lived under a special set of laws with direct privileges from the Crown.

The Bergslagen played a part in the economic evolution of Sweden as vital as that of the plains around the shores of the great lakes. Until the close of the nineteenth century when the vast iron reserves of the Arctic north were developed, the Bergslagen supplied almost the whole of Sweden's output of iron and precious industrial metals. It was through these commodities, and above all her high quality bar-iron, that Sweden gained a pre-eminent position in the markets of Europe.

This region of late medieval colonization, the Bergslagen, was complementary to the rich, lake-shore farmlands in the evolution of Sweden. Her mines, metal-working and, later, engineering industries helped to make Sweden the strongest of the Scandinavian states. It is interesting that this region of confused hills and forests, where scarcely 5 per cent of the land has been cleared for farming, has long stood out as a strong centre of Swedish nationalism. Sweden's national leader of the fifteenth century, Engelbrekt Engelbrektsson, found strong support for his struggle against the Danes among the isolated and independent mining groups of the Bergslagen. Later, in the years after 1520, the Bergslagen miners believed that they gave success to Gustavus Vasa by their support of his campaign to establish a strong and independent Sweden.

The fertile plains around Sweden's great lakes were not only the source of a silent, outward expansion of farmers and miners into the surrounding forests; they also formed the geographical focus of more grandiose movements of settlement and political expansion into the neighbouring Baltic lands. For more than three hundred years, from the middle of the eleventh century to the close of the fourteenth century, Swedish farmers colonized the fertile coastal plain of Finland — a plain formed of post-glacial marine clays deposited on the floor of the transitory Littorina Sea [Figs. 49 and 51]. This movement of medieval settlers was at its height towards the close of the twelfth century — a period of great economic activity wherever we turn in Europe. It was a time when scores of new towns were created on the plains of Germany, a time when fresh land was broken for farmsteads on the slopes of Dartmoor well beyond the thousand-foot contour. It was in 1157 that the Swedish crusade against the pagan Finns began under the banner of Eric the Holy. By 1293 Sweden's campaigns of conquest, conversion, and colonization reached their eastern limit towards the head of the Gulf of Finland with the founding of the fortress town of Viipuri.

Sweden expanded in all directions from her historic core at the eastern end of the central lakes depression [Fig. 12]. Her medieval colonization of Finland left an indelible mark on the life of that country. In a phase of aggressive political expansion in the seventeenth century, she snatched her rich, southern plain of Skåne and the rocky fishing coast of Bohuslän from Denmark. By the close of the eighteenth century, the tide of political expansion had completely turned and Sweden was deprived of all her conquests on the eastern shores of the Baltic. In the next generation she turned once more to the active settlement and development of her own wilderness that stretches from the Dal river northwards beyond the Arctic Circle [Fig. 41]. Today, Swedish Norrland is the most important 'colonial area' within the state boundaries of any power in Europe. Only three hundred years ago Norrland, with its endless dark forests [Plate 25] and boiling rivers, was treated in the capital city like some remote colonial appendage. From time to time her governors sent reports to Stockholm of the rumoured wealth of this uncharted region. For instance, in 1636 the Governor of Norrland wrote of 'the finding of mountains with Swedish diamonds, some as big as a man's head, and some thrice as large'.[5] Occasionally there were pronouncements about 'the small value of the woods in Norrland' — a curiously inexact appraisal of this region's greatest natural resource. The exploration of the empty northlands long remained incomplete. For instance, the Sarek massif, a major geographical feature containing some of the highest mountains in Scandinavia and feeding more than a hundred small glaciers, remained undiscovered until the 1880's.

The Settlement and Economic Development of Norrland

Men have lived in Swedish Norrland since prehistoric times. Nearly four thousand years ago, small groups of hunters built their timber huts on the shores of the Gulf of Bothnia. Since those times the continuous recession of the Baltic shoreline has left these hut sites of the Arctic Stone Age stranded high above the present sea level of the Baltic. Today, the refuse of meals consumed four thousand years ago — the bones of seal, wild boar, elk, and bear — form the 'kitchen middens' that lie along the abandoned shore-lines between 90 and 120 feet above the present sea level. But despite the early occupation of Norrland by peoples whose way of life scarcely differed from that of Palaeolithic hunters and food-gatherers in Europe ten thousand years earlier, large tracts of this territory of northern Sweden were neglected and unsettled until our own day. Norrland long remained a 'colony', and in this wilderness of forest and barren Arctic tundra the historic frontiers of pioneer settlement can be distinguished. The 'frontiers' of the fur trader, miner, forester, and farmer are elements as essential to the understanding of the history of Norrland as to the comprehension of the settlement history of North America in the nineteenth century.

Farmers from the richer lands of central Sweden slowly penetrated the valleys of southern Norrland in the later Middle Ages. The shores of Lake Stor in the district of Jämtland were a particular centre of attraction. Their fertile soils, derived from shales and limestones of Silurian age, stand out from this poverty-scarred wilderness of Archaean rocks, and even today central Jämtland remains the most densely populated part of northern Sweden. It contains a cluster of nearly fifty thousand people — not as much as a fair-sized industrial town in England. The society of its pleasant, wooden villages still has an archaic, medieval flavour. The fields that look down to the lake bear their crops of rye, oats, and barley — hardy grains that manage to survive in this most favoured part of Norrland. Even now cattle are sent in high summer to graze the remote clearings in the forests, to the ragged pasture with its collection of wooden huts known as the *fäbod*, and temporarily inhabited for a few weeks [Plate 28].

The age of the parishes in this vast tract of northern Sweden provides a striking clue to the extent of its medieval settlement. By the fourteenth century, most of the parishes of southern and central Norrland were on the map, but the iron-rich hills and the forested plains of the northern provinces of Västerbotten and Norrbotten were still nearly empty of people. There the creation of parishes was the task of the eighteenth and nineteenth centuries.

The second stage in the colonial history of Norrland belongs to the seventeenth and eighteenth centuries. Sweden had achieved national unity and her kings began the conscious development of the empty northern territories. The silent, unplanned clearance of forest by medieval farmers gave way to the more rigorous policies of state. In the thickly forested south-western fringe of Norrland the Swedish crown encouraged the immigration of Finns. [Fig. 41]. The earlier medieval settlement of this region by the Swedes had limited itself to the long, narrow valley-corridors where villages had been established on the alluvium and sandy soils of river terraces. The Finns entered the dark, uncleared forests on the segments of Archaean plateau between the river valleys. From their isolated farmsteads or tiny hamlets they practised a system of farming that depended on the burning of successive tracts of forest. It was common for a number of farmers to band together to clear a section of woodland often many miles from their homesteads. They would select a stretch of sloping ground, preferably facing southwards, to secure good drainage and the greatest immunity from the inversion frosts that are a risk at any time in Norrland's summer. The trees were felled to form a compact layer of timber and brushwood and then left until the following year for burning. At the beginning of the next summer, a still, clear day was chosen to set alight this pyre of primeval forest

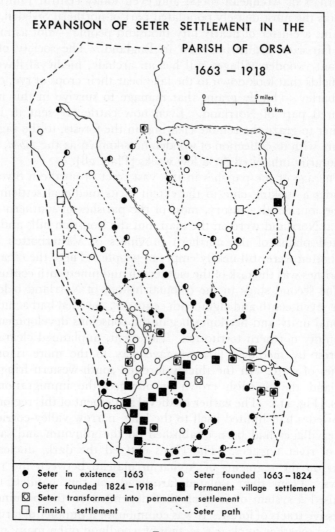

EXPANSION OF SETER SETTLEMENT IN THE
PARISH OF ORSA
1663 – 1918

0   5 miles
0   10 km

Orsa

● Seter in existence 1663   ◐ Seter founded 1663 – 1824
○ Seter founded 1824 – 1918   ■ Permanent village settlement
◉ Seter transformed into permanent settlement
□ Finnish settlement   ⌁ Seter path

FIG. 41

The province of Dalarna, astride the headwaters of the Dal River system in central
Sweden, illustrates many features of settlement history. From permanent villages
close to the lake shores, *seters* — temporary summer farms — were founded among
the forests of the surrounding hills. Many date from the late medieval period;
others were founded during the time of population expansion in the nineteenth
century. Finnish settlements, dating from the late seventeenth century, occupy the
forested plateaus between the valleys.

giants. A few hours later, when the deep layer of wood-ash had scarcely cooled, it was usual to sow a crop of rye.

The forest clearings gave a fantastically rich harvest of grain in their first year. In the remote hinterland of the Dal river's two great headstreams, the Väster and Öster Dal, the whole of the rye harvest of two centuries ago came from such clearances in the forest. Parish tithe accounts reveal that the freshly cleared forest lands could yield as much as ten times the harvest of arable fields along the shores of Lake Mälaren and Lake Vänern — the most fertile parts of Midland Sweden. But after the first abundant harvest of rye from the freshly burnt ash the value of these forest clearings declined sharply.[6] For a second year rye was sown and harvested, and then the land was turned over to grass. At first it would give a few crops of hay; later it reverted to poor pasture and the cattle were driven there in summer. After some years the forest clearing would be abandoned completely. Then Nature's first colonizers of waste land, the birch and the alder, returned to the scene. Later the giant conifers would heal this tiny wound in Norrland's forest cover.

This phase of settlement history left a strong impression on the geography of Norrland. Today, more than twenty thousand Finns live in the forest-lands of Sweden. One can recognize their settlements, both on the ground and on large-scale topographical maps, by their place-names and the pattern of isolated farms and little hamlets. Their farms often stand on terminal moraines, natural features that provided the best soils and the driest land amid the confusion of marsh, bog, and forest that made up the primitive landscape of the Archaean plateau. Today, the great stone walls that enclose every tiny field form a peculiar feature of these forest settlements. They stand as a memorial to the slow and painful taming of the heavy glacial clays, dense with boulders.

Perhaps the most valuable relic of this system of forest-burning and shifting cultivation remains in the fine stands of pine that ultimately recolonized so many acres of the old cleared lands. The peasant communities of northern Europe have used this method of forest-burning, known in Sweden as *svedjebruk*, for at least two thousand years. It died out in Sweden at the beginning of this century, largely as a result of the great revolution in the economic geography of Norrland that started in the eighteen-fifties. The more rational use of timber in the sawmills and pulp factories made it essential to stop this uneconomic exploitation of

Sweden's greatest natural resource. Its extinction was aided by the growth of Norrland's railway system towards the close of the nineteenth century, which allowed the import of foodstuffs to formerly isolated, self-sufficient communities; and the rising outputs of Sweden's main agricultural regions enabled the 'colonial' north to lean upon the more favoured south for its food supplies.

During the eighteenth century, a steady stream of settlers flowed towards Norrland to create new farms [Fig. 41]. In that time the agricultural population of this vast northern territory was trebled, but even then much land awaited cultivation and even wider expanses of tundra and forest were destined to resist the steady pressure of the farmer. This colonization of two centuries ago made its best progress in the coastal plain and lower tracts of the great river valleys, where the sediments of the vanished post-glacial seas provide the finest soils in Norrland. Here, too, a series of towns had been founded in the first quarter of the seventeenth century during the reign of Gustavus Adolphus, a king who carried Sweden to a position of political leadership in northern Europe and who encouraged the creation of towns and the establishment of industries. Sundsvall, Piteå, and Luleå all came into existence on the narrow coastal plain of the Gulf of Bothnia in 1621; Umeå was founded in the following year [Fig. 42]. These towns — market centres for the surrounding countryside — acted as focal points of colonization in the coastal plain. From their harbours ships plied along the Baltic coast to Stockholm and the 'heartland' of Sweden. A second stream of farmer colonists penetrated the long zone of Silurian limestones and shales that lies in the interior of Norrland westward of the desolate, forested Archaean plateau. Here, little groups settled at the eastern end of each of the great lakes that fill the upper valleys of rivers draining from the mountain backbone on the Norwegian border. The 'church villages' at the foot of every lake — for example Stensele, Avaviken, and Jokkmokk — formed the cores of huge empty parishes and provided centres for further settlement in the interior of Norrland. Around the churches of these remote settlements in the interior of Norrland stand the boathouses and log cabins, the property of distant lakeside farmers who used them only on the occasions of fairs and religious festivals, when they would reside at the 'church-village' for several days. In our times, some of these villages have become important points on the railway that follows the furrow of Silurian rocks to the iron fields of Gällivare in the far north.

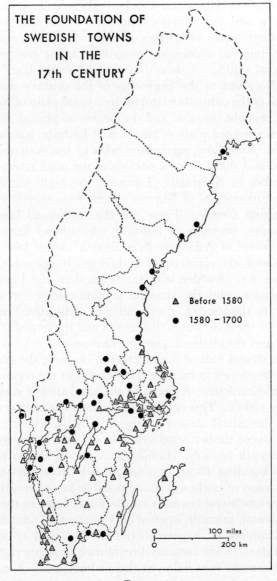

THE FOUNDATION OF
SWEDISH TOWNS
IN THE
17th CENTURY

△ Before 1580
● 1580 – 1700

0   100 miles
0   200 km

Fig. 42

Until the end of the sixteenth century urban life in Sweden was confined to the
midlands and the south. The seventeenth century, particularly in the reign of
Gustavus Adolphus, was a period of economic and political expansion. A chain of
new towns along the coastline of the Gulf of Bothnia carried Swedish influence into
remotest Norrland.

Two zones of sedimentary rocks — the young, stoneless clays of the coast and the Silurian limestones in the interior — have received their waves of settlers over the past three centuries in Norrland, but this colonizing movement never reached its full geographical limits. A survey of 'potential farmland' made in Swedish Norrland at the beginning of the century showed that only a fifth of the cultivable land in the coastal plain of Norrbotten had been brought into use, and the Archaean plateau, lying back from the sea-fringed plain of the Gulf of Bothnia, has ever defied the farmer. Even now, agriculture takes up less than one per cent of its area, and the plateau is notable as the main reserve of coniferous timber in Norrland. Likewise, the high Arctic tundras among the mountains of Norway's border country have resisted the colonizing farmer. These are the traditional lands of the nomad Lapps, breeders of reindeer who spread from the cold northern fringe of Asia into Scandinavia almost two thousand years ago, and who claim rights to their grazing grounds that date back to 500 B.C. Sweden still counts ten thousand Lapps among her population, and the struggle to define their territories has given rise to the idea of 'the frontier of civilization' in Swedish Norrland — the zone where the nomad and the settled farmer, the primitive and the civilized, meet in Europe.

In the second half of the nineteenth century, the economy of Norrland developed in an industrial sense, but the region retained its colonial character. A boom in the sawn-timber trade started during the 1860's. This came from the vast demand for softwoods from the industrial countries around the North Sea basin — countries whose timber resources were already scarce by the end of the sixteenth century. England, in particular, with its late-Victorian building boom, consumed vast quantities of 'deal'. This expansion of trade was made possible by the construction of the first steam-driven sawmills on the Baltic coast in the previous decade. Steam sawmills opened at Vivsta varv, near Sundsvall, and at Kramfors in Ångermanland in 1848 and 1853. These were vital dates in the industrial revolution of northern Sweden.

In the century that followed this technological change, Norrland experienced a succession of economic upheavals. The rich iron ores of the north were first worked on a commercial scale at the end of the nineteenth century. Mining began at Gällivare in the 1880's, and the vast iron mountain at Kirunavaara, containing more than half of the workable iron ores of Sweden, was first tapped in 1903. By the time of the outbreak of the First World War, Swedish Lapland exported six and a half million tons of iron ore annually, helping to feed the blast furnaces and steel mills of the Ruhr and northern England.

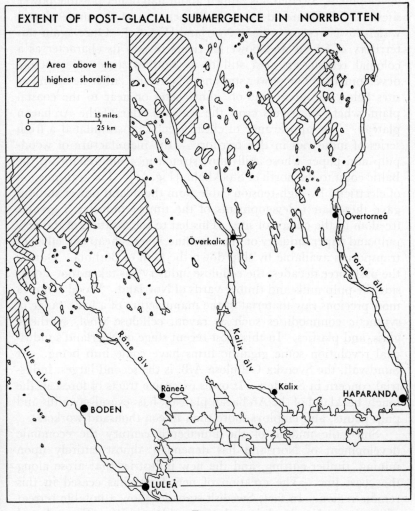

EXTENT OF POST-GLACIAL SUBMERGENCE IN NORRBOTTEN

Area above the highest shoreline

15 miles
25 km

Övertorneå

Överkalix

Torne älv

Kalix älv

Räne älv

Lule älv

Räneå

Kalix

HAPARANDA

BODEN

LULEÅ

FIG. 43

The land of northern Scandinavia has risen at a spectacular rate from the succession of post-glacial seas. In Swedish Norrbotten the rivers reach out to the Gulf of Bothnia across a plain masked with marine clays that form the chief foundation for farming in this northern province. Here and there former islands in a transitory sea stand out as hummocky forested hills above the smooth plain.

The start of the twentieth century brought the third and perhaps the most important stage of the industrial revolution in Norrland, when the power of her rivers was harnessed for the production of electricity. Today, after half a century of rapid development, Sweden has tapped about half of her possible power sites. Of the remainder nearly 80 per cent of the undeveloped water-power resources lie in Norrland [Fig. 64]. Once again this territory of forests and powerful rivers reveals its character as a colonial region, an area still in a youthful stage of economic development. The power stations of Norrland either lie inland at sites below the great line of 'glint' lakes or near to the coastal plain, where the rivers cross the seaward edge of the Archaean plateau. The appearance of cheap electricity stimulated a fresh series of industries in this territory — the manufacture of wood-pulp and paper whose mills now stretch in a long chain up the Baltic coast to the north of Stockholm [Fig. 91]. The transmission of electricity by high-tension cable from the inland power stations gave these latest developments of the timber industry a greater freedom in the choice of site. This led to the location of the new pulp and paper industry on the coastline, where cheap and efficient transport is available by ship down the Gulf of Bothnia. During the past three decades, the cellulose industry has taken root alongside the pulp mills and timber yards of Norrland. Wood is now a most precious raw material in the manufacture of a wide range of synthetic commodities such as rayon, cellulose wool, synthetic glass, and plastics. In this most recent stage of Norrland's industrial revolution some gigantic firms have come into being. At Sundsvall, the Svenska Cellulosa A.B. is the second largest industrial concern in Sweden. It owns extensive tracts of forest in the lonely backland of the Archaean plateau, has several sawmills and pulp plants, and employs more than fifteen thousand workers.

Since the middle of the nineteenth century the economic development of Norrland has depended almost entirely upon mining, timber-cutting, and the new industries that arose along the coast line. The creation of new farms has ceased in this remote region. In fact, Swedish statistics show a notable retreat of farming in Norrland since the Second World War [Fig. 44], and it has become state policy to contract the total area of farmland and to allow the worst of the nation's marginal land to fall back to wilderness. Today the population is clearly concentrated around the big industrial plants in the ports of the Gulf of Bothnia. Few

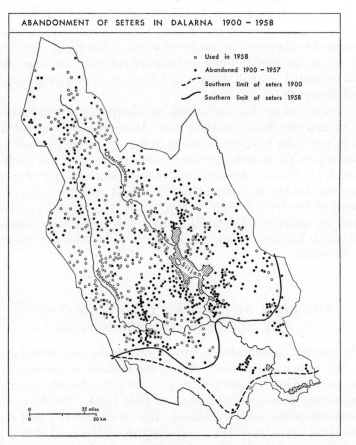

ABANDONMENT OF SETERS IN DALARNA 1900 – 1958

o   Used in 1958

•   Abandoned 1900 – 1957

– – –   Southern limit of seters 1900

———   Southern limit of seters 1958

FIG. 44

The settlements of the shores of Lake Siljan have preserved many of the traditional features of Swedish farming, but even in this conservative area the abandonment of scores of summer pastures has taken place in the past fifty years.

Swedish migrants have willingly settled in Norrland since the beginning of the century. More than other regions it has suffered by the drift of people from the countryside to the towns and cities of the midlands — a movement that has affected Sweden since the First World War. Even the big industries of Norrland, with their offers of high wages and welfare services, fail to attract sufficient workers to this wilderness beneath the low, northern sun. Thus, among the states of Europe Sweden is unique in her desire to absorb foreign immigrants. Since the Second World

War refugees from Latvia, Lithuania, and Estonia — Baltic states that are now part of the Soviet Union — have been readily accepted in the forest industries of Swedish Norrland. In the last few years the remote mills and timber camps of the north have also attracted a small stream of labour from Norway, Finland, and Denmark.

Today, more than two-thirds of Norrland's population lives on the narrow, Baltic coastal plain. It works mainly in sawmills, pulp, paper, or cellulose factories, and in the string of small ports that export the mineral ores and forest products of this northern territory. Within the past half century scarcely any new land has been broken for cultivation. Norrland, now the earner of so much of Sweden's foreign exchange, has transferred its economy from an agricultural to an industrial base and in the twentieth century it has been losing population to Stockholm and the cities of the south.

THE ROLE OF HISTORY AND GEOGRAPHY IN THE DEVELOPMENT OF NORWAY

The historical geography of Norway reveals the same broad design as that of her neighbours. Again, the modern economic core of the state occupies a limited area — the more densely populated south-east, focused on the shores of Oslo fjord. Northward and westward of this settled lowland, with its capital city and small, industrial towns, stretches a vast wilderness of forested valleys and high, barren *fjell*. Northward again, beyond this barrier of thinly peopled upland lies Arctic Norway, a territory that possesses all the colonial characteristics of Sweden's Norrland, if not its economic potentialities.

Norway faces in two directions — east towards the Skagerrak and her Scandinavian neighbours and westward out to the Atlantic. This double outlook has clearly influenced the historical evolution of the state. During the past thousand years, Norway developed with her political power and economic strength focused in two areas. The first lies along the ragged fjord coast southwards of Trondheim. Here is the real home of Norwegian nationalism in the independent communities of each mountain-shrouded fjord, finding its link with the outside world through the trading city of Bergen and an expression of its nationalism in the historic associations of Trondheim. Only in the nineteenth century did Oslo and its hinterland emerge as the core of modern Norway. This state with a dual outlook has grown from these two historic areas, and perhaps this division of interest between the Atlantic and the Baltic worlds can partly explain Norway's late emergence in the first decade of the twentieth century as an independent polity.

Along the mountain-bound fjords of Vestlandet lies a string of settlements, small, lonely, and isolated from each other, that together can outshine the Oslo region as the historic centre and former economic focus of Norway. In the south, Stavanger clings to the northern edge of the Jæren plain, a tiny lowland of less than three hundred square miles and deeply covered with boulder clay. Farmers have tilled this soil since the first Neolithic settlers crossed the Skagerrak [Fig. 35]. Northward from Stavanger lies Vestlandet's chief city, Bergen, a place that has long given a sense of economic unity to the scattered farms and hamlets of Norway's western fjords. Particularly after 1860 Bergen took on many of the functions of a capital city for the long and intricate fjord coastline between Stavanger and Trondheim. The regular steamer services that were established just before 1870 turned her into the regional centre for all the little settlements of the nearer fjords of Sogne and Hardanger. Now, in the middle of the twentieth century, a threat has arisen to Bergen's elaborate network of fjord and coastal shipping lines, as the building of new roads and the extension of bus and lorry services begin to divert the interests of settlements in the lonely inner fjords eastward over the mountains towards the railways that lead to Oslo.

Bergen seems to have no hinterland in the conventional topographical sense [Plate 6]. It lies trapped between the sea and a barren, repulsive range of mountains carved out of the Ulriken gneiss. Yet for nearly ten centuries, most of the south-western coast of Norway has been tributary to this trading city that was founded between A.D. 1070 and 1075 by King Olav Kyrre. The power of Bergen and its hinterland have been defined by the shipping routes that thread their way through the skerries and bind this city to the most distant parts of Atlantic Norway. For almost five hundred years Bergen stood as one of the strongest outposts of the Hanseatic League. In the late Middle Ages, this Hansa city monopolized the fish trade from the whole coastline of western and Arctic Norway. Bergen was the main assembly-point for the export of dried fish southwards to markets in Europe and the

Mediterranean lands. This phase of Bergen's prosperity under the wing of the Hansa was clearly written into the topography of the city. The tall, wooden houses of the German quay, though many have perished by fire and war, recall to mind the wooden towns of northern Germany. The very landscape around Bergen bears the marks of this thriving fish trade of the Middle Ages. The bare, low islands of the strandflat, seaward of the city and scoured by Atlantic gales, are completely treeless apart from some miserable, scattered birch coppice. As late as A.D. 1000 these islands probably bore sturdy pinewoods that have since been destroyed by Bergen's appetite for timber in fish-curing, for fuel, and for the building of ships and houses.

Even though Bergen is not now the largest town in Norway and was overtaken after 1840 by the growth of Oslo, it is still a strong-point in the economy of the state. Although the cold grip of Bergen's monopoly of the fish trade disappeared two centuries ago and countless little ports along Norway's coastline are now engaged in this traffic, this former Hansa port still stands far above its rivals in the export of cod and herring [Fig. 79]. Bergen is also notable as the centre of the greatest technical changes in the fishing industry, an occupation that has remained extremely conservative in its methods and organization in Norway. In many places along the Norwegian coastline, cod are still preserved by methods that must have been familiar to Hansa merchants in fifteenth-century Bergen. The *stokkfisk* are dried on wooden frames; while the *klipfisk* are split, salted, and laid to dry on the surfaces of flat rocks. But Bergen transformed fishing into a factory industry with its canneries and its plant for the manufacture of fertilizers, cattle foods, and cod-liver oil.

Bergen is not only eminent as a regional capital and leader of the fishing industry — an industry that accounts for about a fifth of the value of Norway's export trade. Out of the city's long contact with the countries around the North Sea basin has arisen her importance as a centre of Norway's merchant navy. Bergen's shipowners operate a fleet of about two million tons, a fifth of the whole merchant navy of Norway. About 80 per cent of this fleet plies between foreign ports, and the earnings of her distant merchantmen and tankers help to bring in foreign exchange to buy the raw materials and foods that Norway's barren tundras and cold forests cannot produce. Before the Second World War, the 'invisible' imports of currency earned by Norway's merchant ships covered the cost of about a third of her needs from foreign countries. Since 1945, at a time when the prices of raw materials have never stood higher, the earnings of the merchant navy have paid for only a fifth of the nation's imports, but by 1957 the freight rates from Norwegian shipping once again amounted to one third of the nation's bill for imports.

Bergen and Oslo are the great focal points of the Norwegian economy. Yet they perform vastly different functions in the national life. Oslo joins together the two ancient provinces that flank the eastern and western coast lines of her long fjord — the Østfold and the Vestfold. Here are Norway's most prosperous and progressive farms, sited on lands that were submerged and enriched with the clays of post-glacial seas [Fig. 34]. This same region forms the heart of industrial Norway. Six great valleys converge on Oslo fjord out of the back country of barren *fjell*. Each provides a lavish source of hydro-electric power and each valley contains a nucleus of industries, however tenuous and dispersed in pattern.

In the geography of modern Norway, the lowlands that flank the Oslo fjord are the precise equivalent of the lakes depression of Midland Sweden. Here, a prosperous and progressive agriculture blends with industry in a countryside that has attracted a stream of immigrants over the past half century from the western fjords and the lonely, forested valleys of the east. The population of the capital city has come from every province in Norway. Most of them are such recent city dwellers that their spiritual roots still lie in their native fjords and dales, a fact that becomes obvious in the hundreds of peasant costumes worn in Oslo on days of national celebration. Today, the coast lands of Oslo fjord form the core of Norway [Fig. 4], but this has only been true for little longer than a century. Bergen, on the other hand, stands as a symbol of Norway's contacts with the outside world. It is almost as if the great barren *fjell* that rears up behind Bergen had forced this city to look ever outwards upon the Atlantic.

The peculiar geographical qualities of Trondheim fjord and its region have long made themselves felt in Norwegian history. Here Nature provided an environment where men could develop a richer and more coherent society than in the isolated, mountain-bound fjords of the south-west or the cold, empty territory that stretches northwards far beyond the Arctic Circle. Trondheim fjord is an extensive inland sea, following the Caledonian grain of the country for almost a hundred miles and screened from the Atlantic by a rough, desolate upland barrier of gneiss [Plate 11]. Around the shores of the fjord lies a considerable lowland, a landscape of rounded hills whose heights rarely reach fifteen hundred feet above sea level. They consist of calcareous sandstones of Cambrian and Silurian age and their lime-bearing qualities place them among the most valued areas for farming in northern Norway. Nearer the shores of Trondheim fjord, at heights below six hundred feet, the landscape is composed of a flight of postglacial marine terraces, a feature arising from the recovery of the Scandinavian land mass after the melting of the Quaternary icesheets [Fig. 34]. These stone-free clays and alluvium, deposited within the last 20,000 years, form the basis of the present prosperity of the Trondheim region. Its ploughed fields and pastures, its dairy cattle and harvests of barley remind one of the tamed landscape around the shores of Oslo fjord, a landscape whose clearance and cultivation started soon after the first Neolithic farmers penetrated northern Europe [Fig. 35].

Along with Bergen and Oslo, Trondheim evolved as a third focusing point for a state whose basic weakness was a lack of physical unity. Olav Tryggveson founded Trondheim in A.D. 997, but it only grew into a prosperous town in the twelfth century — a time when Church and Crown were actively sowing the seeds of urban life in Norway. Trondheim, already the capital of an embryonic state in the closing years of the tenth century, held a leading place in Norway's political and economic life until the end of the fourteenth century. Even at this early period much of the trade of northern Scandinavia passed across the quays of Trondheim. Her archbishops collected tithes from hundreds of farms scattered along the strandflat and built their huge, gloomy cathedral out of the profits of a trade in whalebone, fish, and furs that tapped a hinterland encompassing the Lofoten islands and the mysterious forests of northern Sweden.

The sharp decline of Trondheim in the late Middle Ages arose from economic and political changes. As the Hansa city of Bergen closed its monopolistic grip on the fish trade of the whole of Atlantic Norway, so Trondheim sank to an inferior position. An even greater blow came from the extinction of the Norwegian royal line early in the fourteenth century and, later, the passing of the crown to Denmark in 1380. With the control of the state removed to the southern shores of the Skagerrak, Norway became part of the political and economic hinterland of Denmark — a nation more concerned with the trade of the Baltic and the conflicts of central Europe. Trondheim, placed midway along Norway's North Atlantic coastline, never recovered from this medieval change in the balance of power. Henceforward, she remained for centuries on the lonely oceanic fringe of the Scandinavian world. The political decline of Trondheim after 1380 led to the rise of Oslo. This city, the focal point of the south-east, became Denmark's bridgehead into Norway and evolved into the administrative capital of the state. Although Trondheim is now best known for its exports of salted herring, its fish canneries, and timber yards, one strand of its modern life is rooted deep in the town's early history. The bones of Olav, Norway's patron saint and the founder of Trondheim, lie in her cathedral, and they have made the city a spiritual centre of the national life.

Arctic Norway — a Colonial Northland

North of Trondheim fjord begins another Norway [Fig. 7]. This territory forms a mere façade to an interminably long coastline, gashed by scores of major fjords. It looks out to the Atlantic across a continental shelf covered with thousands of islands. Three-quarters of this colonial land of northern Norway lies beyond the Arctic Circle, and in this region of long summer light and oppressive winter darkness European civilization makes its deepest penetration into the polar world. Admittedly, not much more than the population of Leicester or three fair-sized Lancashire cotton-towns is spread over this vast landscape of bare, glacier-scoured rock, snowfield, and tundra.

Arctic Norway lacks the economic potentialities of Swedish Norrland. Even though it contains extensive deposits of low-grade iron ores, so far they have proved hard to mine and difficult to extract [Fig. 98]. Nowhere in her northland has Norway stumbled across the easy wealth of a Kiruna or a Gällivare. Again, Arctic Norway lacks a fertile lowland comparable to the belt of post-glacial marine clays that fringes the Gulf of Bothnia. The most attractive sites for farms and villages occur only on the strand-flat, a discontinuous rocky bench that in favoured parts of the coastline achieves a width of a few miles [Plate 14]. Inland, settlements cling to the raised deltas and terraces that occasionally break the dark, rock-bound walls of the fjords. Only in the eighteenth century did a later wave of settlement reach the more favoured longitudinal valleys of the interior, frowned upon by inhospitable uplands still flecked with snow at the height of the northern summer. In fact, it seems that the repeated use of sites and the long continuity of many settlements in northern Norway may result from the very limited area of attractive land. Modern farms often stand where the Viking had his *vin* on the shore of some lonely fjord, and the fields of the same farm may yield traces of a forgotten hunting community of the Arctic Stone Age. Again, northern Norway lacks the forest wealth of Swedish Norrland [Fig. 83]. Stands of timber are rare in this landscape whose very beauty depends upon the austere bareness of its landforms.

Norsemen first actively colonized the far north at the close of the Viking period when the first Norwegian state was created. By the twelfth century, many parish churches were in existence in Arctic Norway. For instance, Senja, a large island guarding the important navigation channel south of Tromsø, then contained six parishes. The suspected upsurge of population in northern Europe at the close of the Viking age probably sent emigrants beyond the Arctic Circle, who went north to exploit the cold seas rich in cod and whale. In the later Middle Ages northern Norway was a political no-man's-land, where Russian and Norwegian interests met and often clashed. The Russians plundered and burnt their way southwards as far as the Lofoten islands in 1302, 1316, and again in 1323; and as late as 1613 Norwegians collected taxes in the Kola peninsula. But even in this dark age of ill-defined frontiers the present line of the iron curtain was fore-shadowed along Varanger fjord's dull, low shores. There the Norwegians built the fortress of Vardøhus in 1307 to protect the province of Finnmark, and in the same century Russia started to lay claim to the Kola peninsula through the establishment of Greek Orthodox churches in that remote northern tundra.

During the fourteenth century, an age of economic regression in many parts of Europe, Norway lost interest in its most northern territories. For another three hundred years, the history of this region acquires something of the mystery of its icy landscape when the sea mists roll in from the Atlantic. This was a period of waning population, and the history of northern Norway is punctured by the record of great famines when the peasants were driven to make their bread from a flour ground out of birch bark. There are many theories to explain the changes. Some would like to put the blame on a climatic fluctuation that brought more storms into the North Atlantic and increased the number of years with failing harvests.[7] But so often these are circular arguments that start from the known historical facts of dwindling trade and ruined harvests, deducing from them a climatic situation for which no meteorological records exist. Then the argument returns to the records of famine and declining commerce to find an explanation for these in the terms of the newly discovered, but hypothetical, climatic change. Perhaps even more fantastic is the idea that the seamen of the fourteenth century forgot how to navigate the stormy, exposed stretches of coastline that lie between Trondheim fjord and the sheltered channel in the lea of the Lofoten islands.[8] Such a communal atrophy of skill or loss of memory among a people whose livelihood depended upon the sea seems most unlikely.

The economic stagnation of northern Norway arose from the profound political changes at the close of the fourteenth century with the annihilation of the first Norwegian state. The union of the Danish and Norwegian crowns in 1380 deeply changed the administrative relations within the state. In that year Olav V shifted the capital from Trondheim to Oslo. Seven years later, Norway's political centre of gravity migrated farther south when her government was transferred to the Danish capital and, in even a political sense, Norway became no more important than Jutland. These changes transformed the political geography of north Norway; her Atlantic coastline was now the farthest fringe of a state whose heart lay at the mouth of the Baltic Sea. In the same century, the Hansa city of Bergen gained full control of the fish trade of northern Norway. This remote monopoly of the trade in dried fish badly damaged the economy of the north, and the fishermen of these lonely settlements helped themselves out by means of an illegal traffic with the Russians. Last but not least, a slackening of interest in the far north probably arose from the declining population in the last part of the fourteenth century. The Black Death ravaged Scandinavia in 1350 and it has been reckoned that two-thirds of Norway's population perished in this plague. With the release of pressure upon the resources of her land — a pressure that was probably present since the ninth century — the Norwegians contracted their interests to the coast lands of the south-east, the terraces and raised deltas of her vast south-western fjords, and the smiling shoreline of Trondheim's inland sea. As we have noticed earlier, high farms on the upper slopes of her eastern valleys became derelict; similarly Norway forgot about her colonial province beyond the Arctic Circle.

This was not the first time in the history of the north that the Norwegians lost interest in their remotest territories. Prehistory records a similar retreat from the strandflat sites beyond the Arctic Circle between the early Bronze Age and the beginning of the Iron Age about 500 B.C. During the late Neolithic period and at the start of the Bronze Age, farmer-settlers penetrated the western coastline of Norway to the latitude of the Lofoten islands at 68° north. It is likely that the centuries of unusual warmth in the climate of northern Europe, known as the sub-boreal period, explain the succesful settlement of sites in Arctic Norway by the first primitive farmers. The worsening of climate at the beginning of the Iron Age with the onset of sub-Atlantic times seems to lie behind the total abandonment of the north by farmers. At this time, the most northerly agricultural settlements were confined to the south-western fjords at 60° north latitude, to the south of Bergen.

The latest phase in the history of this remote region started towards the end of the eighteenth century, when a steady trickle of settlers began to colonize northern Norway. Farmers from southern Norway migrated to the valleys of the Bardu and Måls rivers — valleys that had remained uninhabited until that time. Of even greater importance was the foundation of a series of new towns. Tromsø came into being in 1794 in a geographical setting not unlike that of Bergen. Along the coast of Atlantic Norway with its rocky headlands and deeply indented fjords political or social unity does not arise out of Nature's bounty. Tromsø stands on a small island in the long, sheltered shipping channel that leads northwards for some four hundred miles behind the barrier of the Lofoten islands and the Vesterälen. Like Bergen, Tromsø occupies a central position on a long stretch of fjord coast. Her shipping lines run out southwards to Bodø and Trondheim; northwards they reach to Hammerfest, a whaling port founded on an island and the most northerly town in the world. Tromsø is the most important town in northern Norway, where the sealing and whaling fleets set out to explore the Arctic Ocean. It is the last port of call for ships going to Spitsbergen, that large Arctic island whose coal mines and strategic position midway between northern Europe and Greenland attract both Russians and Norwegians.

Although settlers carved out fresh farmland two centuries ago and new towns were created, northern Norway still bears many of the marks of a colony. For instance, it contains two clear ethnic groups with distinct economies. The Norwegians live close to the coastline, their small towns and villages usually tied to the promontories and islands of the strandflat [Plates 13 and 15]. Inland, the late colonization of Norwegians is equally restricted by the harsh facts of the environment where in the valleys of the Måls and Bardu, the new farms, hacked out of the forests by migrants from the south, are confined to the marine sands laid down in transitory

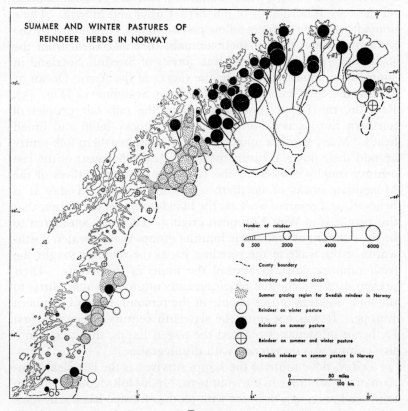

FIG. 45

The economy of the Lapp reindeer herders in northern Scandinavia pays little attention to national boundaries. The migratory herds move from inland winter grazings, particularly on the fringe of Sweden's coniferous forests, to summer pastures on the Arctic coastline and among the mountains of northern Norway. The mountains of the Norwegian-Swedish border also provide summer grazing grounds for herds that belong to Swedish Lapps.

post-glacial seas that flooded the lower parts of these valleys scarcely ten thousand years ago. Norwegian coastal settlements depend upon the prolific fisheries of the continental shelf and farming plays a subsidiary rôle in the economy. Cattle are reared ; crops of potatoes, oats, and barley are grown under the ever-present threat of failure. Arctic Norway lies at the very physical limits of a farming system that evolved in the geographical conditions of temperate Europe.

Inland, on the monotonous plains of Finnmark, the Lapps survive with a culture whose affinities lie outside Atlantic Europe on the bare tundralands of northern Russia and Siberia. These nomadic reindeer-herders follow precise routes, determined by the instinctive wandering of their animals, that take them from the sheltering fringe of the coniferous forests of Swedish Norrland in winter to summer pastures on the shores of the Arctic Ocean or among the high mountains of northern Scandinavia [Fig. 45]. Racially, the Lapps stand apart from the tall, fair peoples of northern Europe because of their short, stocky build and broad heads. Many theories upon the origin of this northern folk centre around their physical distinctiveness. Anthropologists of the last century usually considered the Lapps as westerly outliers of the Mongolian stocks of northern and central Asia. Today it is believed, as a result of work on the blood-groups of the Lapps, that this people is of West European origin.[9] They are considered to be the remnant of prehistoric hunting groups that retreated northwards in the wake of the receding ice as the reindeer sought the fresh summer pastures beyond the limits of the forests. Their present distinctiveness of physique and culture owes not a little to the long isolation of this people in the remotest parts of northern Europe. It was not until the sixteenth century, when the first Lutheran missionaries reached the pagan Lapps, that this primitive culture was threatened with disintegration.

Today, the culture of the Lapps survives as the last clear remnant of the primitive in our continent. In his full vigour, the Lapp reindeer-herder can dispense with all that Europe has learnt since the first Neolithic farmers settled in Crete and the Aegean islands more than six thousand years ago. For centuries the Lapp has concentrated all his abilities on the exploitation of the narrow environment of the tundra. The skills of this culture are those of the illiterate and the primitive, and in northern Europe it survives on the fringe of European civilization.

Today, about twenty thousand Lapps live in Arctic Norway, and among these only about two thousand still pursue the nomadic life of the reindeer-herder. The rest have turned to permanent settlements along the shallow valleys of the interior of Finnmark. They live by fishing, milking a few cows, and snaring ptarmigan through the long winter months. For more than half a century many forces have been at work disintegrating the culture of the Lapp reindeer-herders. The missionary and the teacher did much to break the closed circle of the Lapp mind, changing unconsciously the economic basis of their society. Two Lapp towns have grown in the lonely wilderness of Finnmark around mission stations at Kautokeino and Karasjok. The collapse of the nomadic herding economy was hastened in the closing phases of the Second World War, when the Nazi scorched-earth policy in northern Norway and Finland caused the destruction of many herds of reindeer. Although the Norwegian government bought reindeer for the Lapps as part of the ten-year development plan for north Norway, it failed to prevent the almost total collapse of Europe's last primitive culture.

Since 1900, mining has penetrated Arctic Norway's economy based on marginal farming, fishing, and reindeer-herding. Facing the Russian frontier across the waters of Varanger fjord lies the biggest reserve of iron ore in Norway [Figs. 97 and 98]. It occurs in rocks of Archaean age among outcrops of banded quartz. Although the reserves are immense — they are calculated at a thousand million tons — the iron-content is low, ranging between 33 per cent and 36 per cent. The Varanger ores were first worked in 1916 and the iron was exported in the form of concentrated briquettes with a metal content of 66 per cent. In 1944, the German army destroyed the plant on Varanger fjord, another item in the scorched-earth policy that inflicted such severe damage on northern Norway.

At the end of the Second World War Norway planned the reopening of the Varanger ore field with increased outputs. A new concentrating plant was built on the shore of Varanger fjord and production began in 1951. Further south, she aims to use the iron ores contained in the marble-micaschist series of Nordland province. These are lean ores, ranging between 20 and 33 per cent in iron-content, whose exploitation was prevented until lately by technical difficulties in processing. For instance, the haematite and magnetite ores of the Dunderland valley were worked from time to time between 1906 and 1939, but there were always great technical obstacles. Now there are good prospects that iron mining in Arctic Norway will expand and develop steadily. In 1955 a great steel plant, the first in north Norway, opened at Mo i Rana, almost on the Arctic Circle. A hydro-electric station provides power for the electric arc furnaces and coke is imported by sea. The smelting, steel-making, and rolling mills are all on the same site, and it intends to supply half of Norway's needs in steel.

New power stations and the paraphernalia of heavy industry seem to signal a fresh stage in the development of Arctic Norway [Figs. 68 and 69]. The North Norway Plan, published in 1951, showed that the Norwegian government intended to encourage the economic growth of their 'colonial' north. In the heady language of regional planning, this ten-year scheme proclaimed as its aim 'the full economic development of the region . . . and its full economic and political integration in Norway'.[10] The plan proposed to develop mining, to build power stations and fish-processing plants, and to make Bodø with its airfield the great centre of communications in the north. The North Norway Plan wants to preserve the society and economy of the reindeer-breeding Lapps, but it is hard to believe that this primitive way of life can survive the penetration of heavy industry and the improvement of communications. Finance for the recovery of Arctic Norway from the heavy damage of the Second World War has come from two main sources. Marshall Aid brought the Varanger iron mines back into production. The ambitious ideas of the North Norway Plan are financed internally from such sources as the surpluses of the national unemployment insurance fund and some of the profits of the state-controlled football pools. Arctic Norway is not likely to attract funds from abroad because of the restrictions that Norway places on the investment of foreign capital. Thus the development of this remote fringe of Norway seems to hang upon the continuance of the wave of prosperity that has enveloped the world since the end of the Second World War. A return, unlikely as it may seem, to the restricted international trade and acute unemployment of the 1930's would probably starve Arctic Norway of the capital for its development. In northern Norway today we see an image of that other high period of prosperity in the thirteenth century and, as in that remote period, its future seems to hang on events in the heartland of Norway and in the distant world beyond.

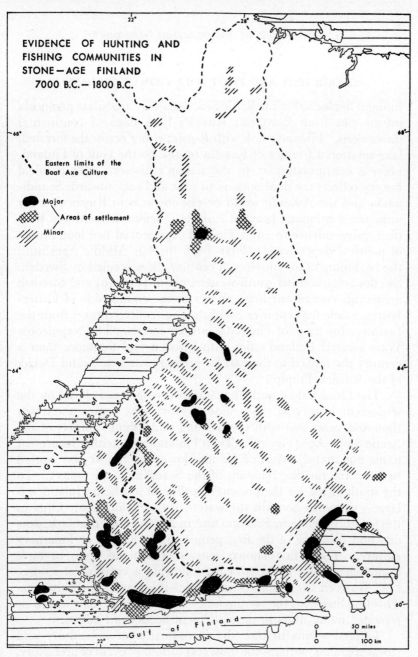

EVIDENCE OF HUNTING AND
FISHING COMMUNITIES IN
STONE — AGE FINLAND
7000 B.C. — 1800 B.C.

Eastern limits of the
Boat Axe Culture

Major

Areas of settlement

Minor

Gulf of Bothnia

Gulf of Bothnia

Lake Ladoga

Gulf of Finland

0   50 miles
0   100 km

FIG. 46

The discovery of innumerable stone axes and objects of bone shows that small groups
of hunters and fishermen occupied most of Finland before the settlement of the first
farmers, the Boat Axe people, between 1800 and 1600 B.C. Even in the pre-agricultural
era the southern coastal regions were the most important part of the country. The
restriction of the Boat Axe Culture to the south-west emphasizes the limits imposed
by climate upon the first farming communities.

Some Facets of Scandinavian Geography

GEOGRAPHY AND THE EVOLUTION OF FINLAND

Finland lies locked in the Baltic Sea, a scarcely articulate peninsula jutting out from European Russia's land mass of continental dimensions. Finland's link with Russia, either across the forested, lake-smattered frontier of Karelia or else by the Gulf of Finland, plays a continuous part in the nation's history. Her political history reflects the dual outlook to west and east, towards Scandinavia and the Atlantic world or else inwards to Russia and the immense continental heart of Eurasia. Before she achieved political independence in 1917, Finland experienced two long phases of political dependence. First, from the late Middle Ages until the beginning of the nineteenth century she was ruled by Sweden. Swedes colonized her south-western plains [Fig. 49] and Swedish aristocrats carved out huge estates in the countryside of Östterbotten, while for centuries Swedish kings collected taxes from the lucrative fur-trade of Finland's interior forests. The Napoleonic Wars severed Finland's ties with Sweden and for more than a century she looked to the east for government as a Grand Duchy of the Russian Empire.

The Finnish dual outlook is stamped with equal clarity on the settlement history of this region, a story that begins about ten thousand years ago with the hunting and fishing cultures of the Arctic Stone Age [Fig. 46]. Then Finland bore neither its present name nor shape. Most of the interior of the country lay buried beneath the melting remnant of the Scandinavian ice-sheet. To the south of the ice the present coastline of southern Finland was largely drowned beneath the waters of the Yoldia Sea. Only in the far north, close to Petsamo and in Norwegian Finnmark, does one find evidence of the first people in the Komsa or Finnmark culture. These first known settlers of Finland seem to have approached from the south-east, following a corridor of ice-free land between the Fenno-Scandian ice-sheet and the White Sea. This first link with the continental land mass to the east was to be repeated many times in the settlement history of Finland.

Finland seems to owe the introduction of agriculture and stock-breeding, perhaps the most revolutionary event of prehistory, to the west. The arts of farming came with a people from across the Baltic Sea in the time between 1800 and 1600 B.C. They reached only the clay plains of the south and south-western parts of the country, where climate and soils alone favoured the crops and techniques of farming that had originated at least three thousand years earlier under the vastly different scenes and climates of the eastern Mediterranean. This prehistoric economy, known as the Boat Axe Culture [Fig. 47] and marked by the finely worked stone axes that are close imitations of similar tools made

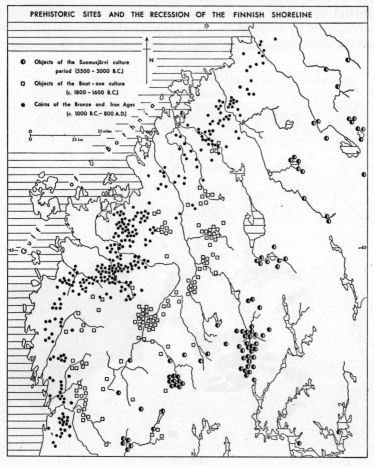

FIG. 47

This strip of the coastline in southern Östterbotten clearly shows the relationship of prehistoric settlement to changing sea level. The primitive axes of the Suomusjärvi culture are found at sites furthest from the present coastline along the former shores of the Ancylus Lake at one hundred and fifty feet above present sea level. The Boat Axe Culture flourished on coastal sites that are now ninety feet above sea level. During the Bronze and Iron Ages plains freshly emerged from the sea were systematically occupied.

of copper in Central Europe, found its immediate links with that part of the continent.

The Finns, ancestors of all but 10 per cent of the present population of the country, reached this region of northern Europe from the south-east [Fig. 48]. Their entry into Finland dates from the early Iron Age, a period that begins about the time of Christ and lasts until A.D. 1300 in this part of Scandinavia.[11] They reached Finland across the narrow sea from the shores of Estonia and Latvia. In its vocabulary and grammar the Finnish language betrays affinities with the tongues of central and south-eastern

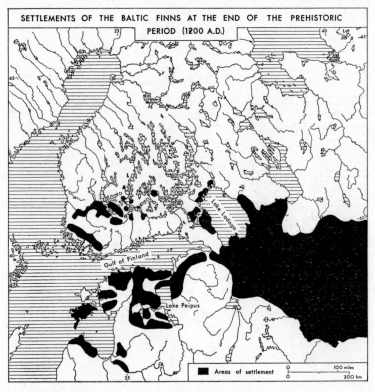

SETTLEMENTS OF THE BALTIC FINNS AT THE END OF THE PREHISTORIC PERIOD (1200 A.D.)

Areas of settlement

FIG. 48

At the beginning of the long Scandinavian Iron Age the Finnish settlement took place from the south across the Gulf of Finland and along the shores of Lake Ladoga. Their main settlement areas were the plain of Turku, the western lake system, and the northern shore of Lake Ladoga. The coastline of Östterbotten and the northern shore of the Gulf of Finland were left unoccupied and open to Swedish settlement in the twelfth century A.D.

Russia. The settlement of Finland probably represents the end of a long folk migration from a remote region of the southern Urals. The journey must have been accomplished over several generations. For instance, it is believed that people of this Finno-Ugrian stock first reached the southern shore of the Gulf of Finland, in Estonia, about the beginning of the Bronze Age, twelve hundred years before they took the next step across the few miles of sea to begin farming the fertile clay plains of south-western Finland.

The seed that was to discover its full flowering in the Finnish nation in the twentieth century was planted nearly two thousand years ago, but some prehistorians believe that the connection of Finland with the east and the Finno-Ugrian stock can be traced back to much earlier times. Archaeology has uncovered a culture that occupies the whole of the third millennium B.C., at a time before the techniques of agriculture had reached this part of northern Europe. It has been labelled the Comb Ceramic Culture, because with these peoples the art of pottery first became known in Finland. Despite their ability in making large clay vessels decorated with deep hollows and grooves, these fishermen and hunters knew nothing of the arts of farming and their only domesticated animal seems to have been the dog. The Comb Ceramic Culture was widespread in northern Europe and its sites have been recognized close to the mouth of the Vistula in Poland, as well as at places far to the east beyond the Urals in western Siberia. Some believe that this economy originated among the Finno-Ugrian stocks and that the sites of the Comb Ceramic Culture, often related to the abandoned beaches of the receding Littorina Sea, are evidence of the first entry of the Finns into their country.[12]

A study of settlement history shows that the roots of modern Finland are turned towards the east. Their language, apart from its many loan-words, is not related to the tongues of western and central Europe. Finland's epic poem, the Kalevala, that was written by Elias Lönnrot in 1835 is based on the folk-poetry and mythology of the Finno-Ugrian peoples. For its chief source of inspiration the Kalevala turns eastward to Karelia with its dark forests and innumerable lakes, where a peasant people survived into the nineteenth century, scarcely affected by the many influences that had entered Finland through her south-western gateway since the first Swedish settlements of the twelfth century.

The main settlement of Finland in the Iron Age reveals the

rôle of geography in the shaping of the country. Finnish topographers and historians constantly note the division of their country into two sharply contrasted parts. J. G. Granö, in his minute study of the regional divisions of Finland [13] uses the term 'settled' or 'agricultural' Finland for the coastal south and west, adopting the label 'unsettled' Finland for the inner and northern parts of the country with its forests and empty tundras. The great nineteenth-century topographer and historian, Topelius, expressed the same idea in much more vivid language when he described the north as 'a kingdom of death' and the south of the country as 'a kingdom of life'.

The frontier between the two areas has shifted widely in the course of history. Today, it is a border zone stretching from the shores of Lake Ladoga, now part of the Soviet Union, through the large lakes of Pielisjärvi and Oulujärvi to the head of the Gulf of Bothnia. Eight hundred years ago, at the close of the prehistoric period, agricultural or settled Finland was scarcely more than a coastal façade, making its greatest depth of penetration in the south-western part of the country where it reached inland to Tampere and the southern margin of the lakes plateau [Fig. 48].

Geography seems to have led the first Finnish-speaking settlers of the Iron Age to the south-western parts of the country. Up to A.D. 400 these scanty groups of farmers, who also sought the riches of the fur-bearing forests, settled the clay plain of Loimaa and other fertile tracts in the area of Finland's mildest climates. Archaeology suggests that in this period the valley of the Kokemäenjoki became the main highway towards the interior, a task that it was destined to fulfil at other periods of Finland's history. This river-way directed the Finnish farmers from the south-west towards their first interior settlements in the western lakes system on the shores of Lake Näsijärvi, around the site of Tampere. The next four hundred years witnessed the slow penetration of the Finns further into the heart of the country, when their farms formed tiny clearings in the forest on the shores of the most westerly of the central lakes, Päijänne. It took nearly a thousand years for this farming frontier to reach the limits achieved by those first prehistoric farmers in Finland, the Neolithic peoples of the Boat Axe Culture in the second millennium B.C. But the Finns reached far beyond the pioneer fringe of permanent settlement, because farming was scarcely the mainstay of their economy. Their hunting and fishing expeditions penetrated the forests of Karelia and seem to have reached northwards into the wastes of Lapland [Fig. 50].

Towards the east, another core of Finnish settlement appeared in the Iron Age on the shores of Lake Ladoga. Already, at the close of the Iron Age, the permanent problem of Finland's history, the dual outlook towards the east and the west, has made its appearance. By the beginning of the twelfth century the Finns were living in three distinct tribal areas. On the fertile plains close to the ragged south-western coastline were the people of Suomi. Some distance inland, the folk of Häme inhabited the country between the Kokemäenjoki and Lake Päijänne on the edge of the central lakes system. Both these peoples looked westward towards the Baltic, trading their products with the Goths, who once found the heart of their territories in the lower Vistula valley. The third core of Finnish settlement, the people of Karjala, lay isolated to the east around the shores of Lake Ladoga. After the middle of the twelfth century, when the first Christian missionaries came to these pagan farmers, fishermen, and fur-traders of the north, the geographical dichotomy of Finland revealed itself. The tribes of the west and centre were converted to the Catholic Church by missionaries from Sweden. In 1155 the first crusade reached south-western Finland led by an Englishman, Bishop Henry of the freshly created Swedish diocese of Uppsala, who was to become the patron saint of the Finns. The Christian missionaries established their centre at Turku, already a base and collecting centre for the fur trade in Finland. Over the centuries Turku has symbolized the Swedish influence in Finland. Not until the middle of the twentieth century do the census returns report the bulk of the Swedish-speaking population of the city as bilingual, speaking Finnish as their second tongue.

The third centre of Finnish settlement, the shoreline of Lake Ladoga and the province of Karelia, has experienced its contacts with the outside world from an easterly direction. While the Swedes were actively converting the western Finns to Catholic Christianity, missionaries of the Greek Orthodox Church turned their Karelian cousins eastwards towards Novgorod. In Finland, as in the eastern basin of the Mediterranean Sea, the later crusades against the pagan and the Infidel also became a struggle between the two great wings of the Christian Church. The Third Crusade, starting in 1293, took the Swedes to the head of the Gulf of Finland. There, on a tiny island, they founded the fortress of Viipuri, the core of a town whose rôle in Finland's national history was to rival that of Turku. The Third Crusade turned into a war that smouldered and flared up for more than a quarter of a century between Greek Orthodox Russians from Novgorod and the western Catholics from Sweden.

Swedish interests in Finland began with the Christian missions in the middle of the twelfth century. Their direct political interest ended after six centuries in 1809 when Finland became a Grand Duchy of the Russian Empire, a state of dependency that was to last for little more than a century. The Swedes left the deepest of impressions upon the geography of Finland. They colonized the almost empty coastal regions that had been neglected by the Finns in the dark-age period of settlement, and even today the Swedish-speaking communities have a distinctly peripheral distribution [Fig. 49]. Inland, one passes to the true areas of Finnish culture. The Swedes founded towns and cities, and during periods of economic and political expansion, such as the middle of the sixteenth century, they encouraged the Finns to push forward the frontier of settlement into the heart of the country.

It is interesting that the course of Swedish settlement, trading activities, and missionary work before the fifteenth century followed a geographical pattern that closely resembles the progress of Finnish occupation during the long centuries of the Iron Age. The First Crusade of the middle of the twelfth century established the Swedes on the rich, clay lowlands in the hinterland of Turku. It will be recalled that the first settlements of the Finns were attracted to this same Loimaa plain. The Second Crusade in 1249 led the Swedes under Birger Jarl, founder of Stockholm, to the western edge of the lakes plateau and the countryside of the people of Häme. Again, the valley of the Kokemäenjoki assumed its rôle as the chief route leading to the interior. The last crusade, at the beginning of the fourteenth century, witnessed the invasion of Savo and Karelia, the parts of the country most remote from Baltic influences that were also settled by the Finns at a late date.

Finnish history is deeply coloured by the western and eastern outlooks of the country, and within Finland the peasant cultures of Karelia and the east show pronounced differences in detail from those of the west. Finland's ethnologists and human geographers recognize a frontier that runs from the mouth of the Kymi river to the coastline of the Gulf of Bothnia near Kokkola. This line divides the dialects of Finland into eastern and western groups.

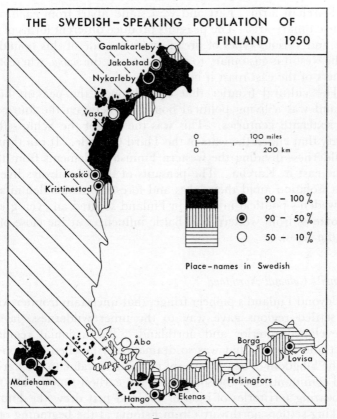

FIG. 49

The Swedish-speaking population of Finland descends from the medieval colonization of the coastlands of the Gulf of Finland and the Gulf of Bothnia. The strongholds of the Swedish language today are in the Åland islands and on the plain of Östterbotten. Note the low proportion of Swedish speakers in Helsinki (Helsingfors) and Turku (Åbo) where the rapid expansion of industry since 1920 has attracted Finnish-speaking migrants from the interior.

Many other traits of peasant life find their frontier in this zone. There exist notable differences in the design and layout of farm buildings. In the west, the threshing place, drying barn, and straw barn are in the same building, while in the east, the drying and threshing barns are usually separate. The compact, orderly village is common in western Finland; in the east, dispersed forms of settlement are the order of the day. On the farms of western Finland one finds the open corner fireplace, a traditional feature of the Scandinavian farm. It is unknown in the architecture of the Karelian farm. East and west stand apart from each other in the culinary arts. The peasants produce different forms of sour milk and various types of bread on either side of this boundary. In the west it is customary to smoke meat in the *sauna*, whereas the farmers of the east roast it in the oven.

The cultural frontier that cuts through the peasant life of Finland was a living political boundary between the fourteenth and sixteenth centuries. This was the line of the Schlusselburg Treaty that ended the wars of the Third Crusade. It ran through a wilderness dividing the western Finnish settlements from those of the east in Karelia. The peasants of the east always lived in great isolation amid their lakes and forests, but this delimitation of Sweden's political interests in Finland secured an even greater remoteness from western and Baltic influences at the close of the Middle Ages.

Finland's Colonial Northland

Beyond Finland's pioneer fringe, that uncertain frontier where the settled regions gave way to the inner wilderness, lay her undeveloped interior and northland. This colonial region of forest and tundra, that was so dramatically labelled by Topelius as 'the kingdom of death', was of permanent value to the agricultural communities of the south from the earliest times. The rich, fur-bearing territories of interior Finland first drew the Finnish-speaking settlers northwards from Estonia at the beginning of the Iron Age. It is highly probable that the same hunting grounds were exploited centuries before, during the Bronze Age. Furs are perishable goods and no evidence of this trade in prehistoric times from the northlands has been handed down to the archaeologist. The only clue to a regular traffic between the northern forest lands and the southern parts of the Baltic Sea rests in exotic objects of metal and Swedish flint that have been found in the remote places of the north. It is believed that these were goods traded from central Europe and southern Sweden in exchange for the furs of the northern forests.

Even if the regular exploitation of Finland's interior cannot be thoroughly established before the Iron Age, there is little doubt of the continuous and increasing importance of this region in the centuries that followed. The Frisians, a people of pirates and traders based on the islands, estuaries, and sheltered lagoons of

Germany's North Sea coastline, began to exploit the fur traffic from Finland in the ninth century A.D. In the interior of the country, close to the site of the modern industrial city of Tampere, they established the trading post of Pirkkala. A similar Frisian fur-collecting station was set up at Birka on an island in Lake Mälaren to develop the same traffic in central Sweden. Pirkkala was in a position to use that immemorial route to the coastline along the valley of the Kokemäenjoki. Northwards, her trappers reached the head of the Gulf of Bothnia and crossed the wasteland of the Lapps to the Arctic Ocean. The grip of the Pirkkala community on 'colonial' Finland lasted for several centuries, and for nearly three hundred years, from the close of the thirteenth century, the merchants of Pirkkala monopolized trade and the collection of taxes in Lapland on behalf of the Swedish crown.

Apart from the long-distance routes of the trapper that reached out into northern Finland, the forested interior of the country was bound closely to the communities of the settled south and west. Each village possessed hunting and fishing grounds in the interior that were reached by tracks along the inward-pointing valleys [Fig. 50]. The hunting and fishing grounds of the tribes of eastern Finland stretched for a great distance beyond the scattered farms and hamlets of Savo and Karelia in the southern part of the lakes plateau. Their hunting trails led to the shores of the Gulf of Bothnia in the district of Oulu across the wilderness of Lake Oulujärvi, following the line that is recognized today as the frontier between 'settled' and 'unsettled' Finland.

The trails that ran through forests and along the ridges of eskers not only served to keep Finland in touch with the riches of her colonial hinterland, they also acted as routes followed by migrants in search of fresh land for farming. The first cultivated clearings were made along these routes to the wilderness. On a larger scale, the first settlement of the lands at the head of the Gulf of Bothnia may be linked with the ancient fur trails to the north. For instance, the route established by the Frisians in the late Middle Ages from Pirkkala to the Lapp territories was also used by settlers on their way to the north. It followed the most westerly of the great lakes, Näsijärvi, on which Tampere stands today. Thence it passed by Alitari and the valley of the Ähtävänjoki to reach the sea near the site of Kokkola. The rest of the way led by sea to the head of the Gulf of Bothnia and the mouth of the important valley leading to the interior of the northland — the

Torniojoki. Through peasant customs and dialect words, the population of the Torne valley may be linked with the lakes region of western Finland, showing that the trappers' trails also served as routes for migrating farmers. Similarly, the settlement of another district at the head of the Gulf of Bothnia can be related to the traditional highways of the hunters and fishermen. The

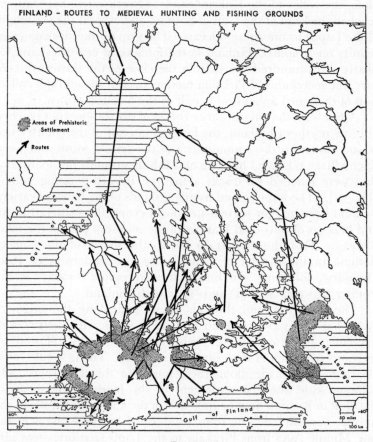

FINLAND – ROUTES TO MEDIEVAL HUNTING AND FISHING GROUNDS

Areas of Prehistoric Settlement

Routes

FIG. 50

Routes followed by hunters and fishermen led into the forested interior of the lakes plateau from the long-settled districts of the shore of Lake Ladoga and the plains of south-western Finland. Note the long-distance trails followed by fur trappers into Lapland, (1) from Pirkkala by the Ähtävänjoki to the shore of the Gulf of Bothnia and thence by sea, (2) from Karelia by lake Oulu and the Oulu valley. In the sixteenth century these routes were used by colonists making permanent settlements in the Finnish interior.

Karelians ranged the forests far to the north and west of their homeland on the shores of Lake Ladoga. One regular route followed by Karelian fur-trappers penetrated to the Oulu valley by way of Pielisjärvi and Oulujärvi. Permanent settlers followed this same route to the north so that the native stock of the Oulu district today displays cultural affinities with eastern Finland. Just as the established Indian trails directed the feet of American pioneers across the Appalachians towards the Blue Grass prairies and the Ohio valley at the close of the eighteenth century, so the

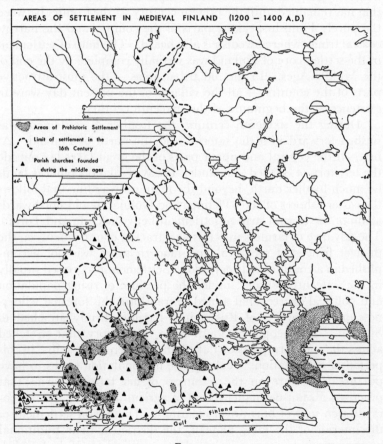

AREAS OF SETTLEMENT IN MEDIEVAL FINLAND (1200 – 1400 A.D.)

Areas of Prehistoric Settlement

Limit of settlement in the 16th Century

Parish churches founded during the middle ages

FIG. 51

Many of the medieval parishes of Finland lie in the fertile plains that attracted pre-historic settlers; the rest belong to the coastal tracts. As late as the sixteenth century the interior of the upper lakes and Lapland remained without permanent settlements.

forest routes of hunters and trappers determined the pattern of the settlement of the Finnish wilderness at the end of the Middle Ages.

The frontier between Finland's colonial wilderness and the settled zone with its farms, fields, and villages remained almost unchanged throughout the Middle Ages [Fig. 51]. The Swedes began the colonization of the nearly empty coastal districts in the middle of the twelfth century. By the fourteenth century, parish churches had been built by Swedes on sheltered bays all along the coast of the Gulf of Bothnia. It was in this period of the late Middle Ages that a frontier was completed within settled Finland that has remained until the present century — the frontier between the purely Finnish-speaking parts of the country and the narrow coastal fringe where Swedish is also heard. The map of settlement in the settled core of Finland was virtually complete by the end of the Middle Ages. In the old tribal areas — the most attractive parts of the country — all the villages of the present day were in existence at the beginning of the sixteenth century.

During the sixteenth century, the frontier of settlement was pushed forward into the interior and the north of Finland. At first, all the central and upper parts of the great lakes lay outside the territory of 'settled' Finland. Today, Finland's pioneer lands lie much further north, beyond the main railway line that follows the eastern shores of lakes Pielinen and Oulujärvi, and northwards again of the coastal strip of settlement between Oulu and Tornio. The advance of farmers into this vast tract of country between the pioneer fringes of medieval and modern times was not accomplished in a continuous progression. Settlement progressed rapidly in the sixteenth century, under the pressure of rising population and political decrees that aimed to transform this forested wilderness on the borders of Russia into territory firmly attached to Sweden. The people of South Savo, a territory that stretched across the southern parts of Lake Saimaa, were very active in this period of colonization. A sharp rise in population seems to have put great pressure on the resources of her farms — farms that practised a semi-permanent kind of agriculture using the temporarily rich soils of burnt-over clearings. The Savon settlement of the interior of the lakes plateau, the district of their traditional hunting grounds, was precipitated by a political act of the Swedish crown. King Gustavus Vasa decreed that the hunting and fishing grounds in the Finnish wilderness would become royal property if they were not permanently settled and brought under the plough.

There followed a vigorous colonization of the upper parts of Lake Saimaa, and by the 1550's the Savons were beginning to settle the shores of Lake Oulujärvi, that remote northern outlier of the lakes plateau. At the end of the sixteenth century they even began to approach the hinterland of the Gulf of Bothnia, reaching central Östterbotten.

Nearly two hundred years of stagnation followed the active colonizing period of the sixteenth century. The manpower that might have given its energy to the expansion of the area of permanent settlement was partly spent in the long wars fought by Sweden during the seventeenth century, and settlers from Savo lost interest in the Finnish wilderness, turning instead to the deep forests of Värmland in central Sweden. The usual checks to population growth — plague and famine — seem to have affected the Finns in the seventeenth century and applied the brake to further colonial expansion.

There have been various attempts to calculate the population of Finland for periods before the first reliable census of 1751,[14] and they point to a stagnant or declining population in the decades about 1700. In the 1690's the population of Finland was about half a million. The year of 1696 brought a summer of severe crop failures and a harsh famine. Hunger took about a third of the country's population and this year is remembered in Finnish history for 'the Great Death'. An eight years' war with Russia, the Great Northern War ending in 1721, scorched the countryside and saw many Finns carried off into Russia as serfs. The Treaty of Uusikaupunki ended this war, and with the loss of the port and fortress town of Viipuri and southern Karelia to the Russians it clearly marked the decline of Sweden's power in Finland. A recent estimate claims that at the end of the Great Northern War Finland's population stood at little more than a quarter of a million.[15]

A long period of expansion in colonial Finland begins with the nineteenth century. It is foreshadowed by a half-century of population growth during which the numbers of the country were doubled. The first census of 1751 revealed a population of 421,500. By the first decade of the nineteenth century, Finland's total population had grown to a little more than 900,000. This expansion was accommodated mainly by changes in the countryside, while the more spectacular leaps of population in the late nineteenth century and our own times have been accompanied by industrial expansion and the growth of towns and cities. In the earlier phase of growth new farming techniques increased outputs in the long-settled plains of the south-west, isolated farms in forest clearings pushed the pioneer fringe further into the heart of the country, and permanent fields slowly took the place of the shifting economy of Karelia. In this pre-industrial period, tar, burnt in the distant pine forests of Pohjanmaa, was Finland's chief export.

The exploitation of the varied resources of her pine, spruce, and birch forests provides the key to the development of colonial Finland in the past century and a half. As in Sweden, the national economy has come to rest on the natural wealth of the least populated part of the state. Swedish Norrland and interior and northern Finland have much in common. Both their landscapes possess ancient foundations in the peneplained Archaean rocks of the Baltic Shield. Thousands of square miles of softwood forest, sawmills, pulp and paper plants, and hardboard factories flaunt their wealth to the outside world.

Deep differences also exist between 'colonial' Finland and similar territories in her neighbour nations, Norway and Sweden. Finland lacks the immense mineral wealth that enriches Swedish Norrland. Unlike her Scandinavian neighbours, the history of Finland's empty territories has been deeply affected by her dual outlook to the east and west. The loss of the Arctic corridor to Petsamo and of strips of territory along her eastern borderland are only the most recent territorial adjustments that have influenced Finland's 'colonial' lands. Again, unlike her neighbours, the empty lands have had to provide living space for some of the thousands of refugee families from the lost lands of the east and south since the Second World War [Fig. 60]. Although industry eats into the forests, and power stations begin to block the lonely rivers of northern Finland, this poorest of the Scandinavian states is remarkable for her pioneering farmers amid the forest wilderness in the middle of the twentieth century.

Northern Europe is unique in the geography of our continent by reason of its large tracts of thinly populated territory, regions that in their economy and historical development merit the adjective 'colonial'. The long-settled heartlands — the centres of agriculture, commercial and industrial towns, and administrative capitals — reflect in their locations the scant favours that physical geography has given to this most northerly part of the continent. It now remains for us to consider the economy and political rôle of Scandinavian lands in the world of today.

CHAPTER 8

The Agricultural Geography of Scandinavia

EUROPE was the cradle of the industrial revolution, and as one surveys the economic geography of the continent it is easy to overlook the importance of agriculture in her life. It is even easier to forget that parts of rural Europe experienced a revolution in the nineteenth century as crucial as the spectacular changes that came over her coalfields, port-cities, and capitals. Scandinavia's industrial revolution only really began with the harnessing of hydroelectric power in the first decade of the twentieth century. In the most favoured regions of Denmark and southern Sweden the agricultural revolution started a century and a half earlier, and these technical and economic changes in farming have left their indelible marks on the landscape. For instance, the destruction of the open fields of Denmark in the eighteenth century created the present landscape of scattered, isolated farms and caused the disintegration of the nucleated village. Between 1758 and 1830 all but one per cent of the commonlands of Denmark were enclosed and given over to individual farmers. The agricultural revolution came later to Sweden where, even at the end of the eighteenth century, half of the cultivated land was always in fallow. With the introduction of elaborate crop-rotations, new plants and fertilizers, the 'black fallow' disappeared from all but the most backward and archaic parts of Sweden. At the same time, the stretches of open, grassy forest land in central and southern Sweden, whose leaves of oak, ash, and lime provided cattle fodder were transformed into much more valuable, high-yielding meadows. At an even later date, similar radical changes influenced farming in Finland. There the agricultural revolution has gone forward since 1917 when the Finns gained their political freedom from Russia. In Finland, the experiments with new varieties of bountiful spring wheats are of the greatest interest [Fig. 59]; they have created a new pattern of crop distributions, so that in 1947 the acreage under wheat in Finland was, for the first time, greater than that of rye — the traditional crop of the cold north.

Despite these remarkable changes in the methods of farming, it must not be thought that the tractor and the plant-breeding station have destroyed all traces of the past in northern Europe. Archaic systems of farming persist in many isolated areas and amid landscapes of harsh physique. Farming techniques and the designs of tools have been handed down from the Middle Ages, and even from a dimmer mistier past in the Iron Age. Along the shores of west Norway's fjords, peasants still use scythes and sickles, whose forms have scarcely changed over the past two thousand years. Among the remote lakes of Jämtland the custom of transhumance still survives in a few places and cattle make the journey to the *fäbod* that may lie as far as seventy miles from the parent village [Plate 28]. Even in Stockholm's rocky archipelago, not many miles from northern Europe's most thriving capital, the design of farming today is not very different from that depicted in the rich parish statistics of three centuries past. The temporary population of refugees from city life to summer houses and the cultivation of strawberries for the Stockholm market have made deep inroads upon the old ways of life in some of the islands, but elsewhere the familiar habits of farming persist. Machinery is almost unknown and most of the tasks about the farm are done by hand. In late summer, the communal boat sails down the rocky, forest-fringed channels to gather crops of hay from the tiny, uninhabited islands. Just as the history of settlement is still unfinished in northern Europe, so the systems of farming and the societies that go with them stand in sharper contrast to each other than elsewhere in our continent north of the Alps.

DANISH AGRICULTURE

Denmark is unique among the states of Scandinavia because its economy turns around farming. As one looks through Denmark's national statistics the same fact of the overwhelming value of agriculture may be discerned with monotonous regularity. We learn that two-thirds of the area of Denmark is occupied by arable land — a figure that is rivalled only by the similarly intensive agricultural economy of the Netherlands [Fig. 52]. Just before the Second World War, livestock and animal products — meaning butter, bacon, eggs, cheese, and condensed milk — formed nearly three-quarters of the total value of Danish exports. Since 1945, farm products have ceased to monopolize the list of commodities in Denmark's annual report of exports. For instance, in 1957 the value of agricultural produce only amounted to 46 per cent of the sum of exported goods. This figure hints at Denmark's rapid evolution in the past decade as an industrial power, but fails to suggest the astonishing growth in the outputs of her countryside, a growth that is summed up in the 300 per cent increase in the nation's agricultural productivity between 1920 and 1960.

The economic health of Denmark depends upon the products of her farms just as in Sweden the iron mines, pulp mills, and forests provide the basis for a high standard of living. Agriculture has kept this key position in Danish life despite the fact that more than a million people, a quarter of Denmark's total population, live in Copenhagen and its suburbs. Over the past half century the farmer has steadily strengthened his position in the state, despite a continuous shrinkage since the beginning of the century in the proportion of the population that earns its living by agriculture. A hundred years ago more than half of the Danish population worked on the land. As late as 1901 agriculture claimed 40 per cent of the population, but by 1960 this proportion had collapsed to a mere 19 per cent. The farmer owes his power over the past century to an agricultural revolution that changed the structure of the economy and left its deep imprint on society and on the very face of the landscape.

'Revolution' is an inaccurate description of the long series of technical, social, and economic changes that gave Denmark one of the most productive and efficient agricultural systems on the face of the earth. The evolution of the modern Danish farm began with the destruction of the system of common tillage on the open fields by a number of state decrees between 1758 and 1792. The big villages, set in their huge, hedgeless fields, were reduced in size within a decade of enclosure. Another and different landscape of scattered farms and enclosed fields took their place. Unlike the English enclosures of the same period, the Danish land reforms did not destroy the small landholders, the men with a few strips in the common fields and grazing rights on the common who formed a vital part of rural society. In England, a continuous stream of impoverished families left the land for the rising industrial towns, and the green acres were left to powerful squires and a yeoman middle class. In contrast, the Danish enclosure movement created a society of free peasants, living on middle-sized farms or on smallholdings. Today, the typical Danish farm has an area of between twenty-five and eighty acres. The last agricultural census showed that there were 81,000 farms in this category and their land occupied 45 per cent of the agricultural area of the country. The smallholdings each occupy less than twenty acres and many have been brought into being as a result of the final subdivision of the large manors since the end of the nineteenth century. They received encouragement from the state through the Smallholding Acts of 1899, 1915, and a final comprehensive Act in 1948. These acts of government created almost 30,000 small farms, some of them arranged stiffly in a line upon the former fields of a great Danish manor.

The land reforms brought a tremendous stimulus to Danish agriculture. Peasants, freed by the abolition of the bondage laws in 1788, worked with their hands to create new farms and clear acres of raw and half-cultivated land. An immense change came over the landscape of Denmark as a result of the work of her enclosing farmers. Swampy fields, bogs, commons, and small pools disappeared from the countryside along with countless copses and spinneys of decaying and ill-tended woodland. The tidy, man-made landscapes of Denmark came into being at the beginning of the nineteenth century as the result of this new attitude to land tenure enforced by the power of the state. New farmsteads were built; old farm-buildings were carried from their ancient sites on the village street to be re-erected in some outlandish corner of the parish. Glacial erratics were piled in heaps and broken up for the building of walls around the fresh fields — walls that have since disappeared from the Danish landscape to supply the need for road metal. Apart from the energy acquired in their newly-won freedom, the Danish peasants worked in what our age would call 'a favourable economic climate'. The Napoleonic Wars brought a long spell of inflation to Europe, and the rising grain prices encouraged Denmark's new middle-class farmers to reduce forests, heaths, and poor pastures to the plough.

Danish agriculture absorbed scores of new techniques in the nineteenth century, including the use of fertilizers, the introduction of field-drains, and all sorts of new machines and gadgets to improve and lighten the daily tasks about the farm. The drainage of land by clay pipes, a method first developed in England in the 1840's, greatly increased the efficiency of Danish farming in the sixties. A system of field-drains helps the soil to dry out quickly after the winter frosts. As a result, tilling and planting can start at an earlier date — an important gain in northern Europe. In the same epoch, lime was first used to improve soils. At first, the heavy clay soils benefited by marling, that is by the addition of clay rich in lime. Round about 1900 cheap transport enabled chalk or ground limestone to be carried to lime-poor soils anywhere in Denmark. But the chief source of soil improvement lay in the thousands of marl pits that were exploited as a result of the propaganda of the Danish Heathland Society after its foundation in 1866. When this movement reached its height about 1900, marl was carried to the fields of one parish after another in the sandy wastes of central Jutland along portable railway tracks that were torn up after the completion of the preliminary task of soil improvement. A century of marling has altered the pattern of crops grown in Denmark. Rye, oats, and potatoes flourish on slightly acid soils. Today they form the main crops in the poorer parts of northern and central Europe — the marginal regions where, for reason of soil quality, climate, or the height of the land, the farms carry an air of poverty. Sugar beet, barley, and wheat, on the other hand, prosper on soils with a slightly alkaline reaction [Figs. 53 and 54]. The addition of lime to Denmark's naturally acid soils doubtless contributed to the expansion of these crops that are a symbol of opulence.

Fertilizers are another important item in Denmark's agricultural revolution. Chemical fertilizers first came into general use in the 1890's, but in the history of Danish farming they have perhaps had less effect on soil fertility than the vast increase in the numbers of cattle and pigs at about the same time. The particular achievement of the twentieth century is the breeding of new plants that are in close harmony with the Danish climate. The most prized of these is an autumn-sown wheat that can resist the killing frosts of the occasional winter when the Arctic anticyclone envelops Denmark.

In the twentieth century, machines introduced even more penetrating changes into Danish agriculture, transforming many of the farmer's immemorial tasks. As early as the 1870's the largest Danish farms began to import machinery from the U.S.A., and by the turn of the century the mechanical binder was a common sight on the middle-sized farms. The drive towards fuller mechanization still goes on. Between 1947 and 1952, Denmark spent much of her Marshall Aid funds on agricultural machinery, especially tractors, from the United States. By 1958, only half the number of horses were at work on Danish farms as ten years before. There were scarcely five thousand tractors in the country at the end of the Second World War; by 1958 the Danes could count 86,000 tractors at work on their farms. Machinery has introduced a minor revolution in farming methods. For instance, everywhere one sees ploughing and harrowing after the gathering of the harvest, a practice that helps to keep down the weeds.

The cream separator, an invention of the 1870's, encouraged the most revolutionary change in Danish agriculture. This machine for the extraction of butter-fat was the fundamental tool in the transformation of Denmark's economy at the end of the nineteenth century, when the export of grain was replaced by dairy products. Before the discovery of the cream separator, high-quality butter for export was produced only on the huge manor farms. With this machine it was possible to mix the milk from different herds of cattle on different farms and to extract the butter-fat. By means of the co-operative dairy the small farmer was able to compete in the rising export trade in butter. The cream separator led to the mass production of butter of a high and uniform quality. Nevertheless, an explanation of the vast agricultural changes in Denmark at the close of the nineteenth century does not rest on the discovery of one machine. The Danes turned to dairy farming in response to the steadily rising prices of butter and bacon in western Europe, when the price of wheat slumped under the influence of heavy grain imports from the New World.

Two institutions of the Danish countryside, the folk high school and the co-operative dairy, played an important rôle in her agricultural changes. The first folk high school was founded in 1844 in Slesvig province, a part of the country that passed to Germany after the defeat of 1864. This school and its many successors arose from the ideas of the clergyman and religious poet, Grundtvig. He carried in his imagination the ideal of a rural society that had received a grounding in philosophy, literature, and national history. Like so many of the elements in Danish society, the folk high schools were created without help from the state, and by the close of the nineteenth century there was scarcely a township in Denmark where some young farmers had not put in a session at the folk high school. The courses in the high schools last for five winter months and are attended by young Danes, from the farms, between the ages of eighteen and twenty-five. They contain no technical or vocational training but, as one Danish writer has expressed it, 'one or two lectures a day are meant to be an intellectual stimulus to give the mind something above common-day life to work and feed upon, to arouse imagination and stimulate reading and thinking'.[1] The folk high schools helped the growth of an educated and alert rural middle class. For instance, nearly all the chairmen of co-operatives have been students in these adult schools. One speculates, perhaps idly, on what might have been the effect of such a movement after the First World War in the backward agricultural states of eastern Europe.

If the folk high school helped to form a middle class in Denmark's countryside, the co-operative movement was the chief means of organizing her agriculture for foreign trade. The co-operatives, like the folk high schools, came into being without help from the state, springing from voluntary movements among the farmers towards the close of the nineteenth century. The first co-operative dairy opened in 1882 at Hjedding in west Jutland, and the contract drawn up between its farmer-members became the legal model for hundreds of creameries all over Denmark. Between 1885 and 1890 more than five hundred co-operative dairies opened in Denmark. By the 1920's there were nearly fifteen hundred. Each dairy serves the farms within a radius of about three miles, using on the average the milk of between 800 and 1200 cows.

The effective trading methods of the co-operative dairy spread to many branches of Danish agriculture. For instance, in 1887 the first co-operative bacon factory opened at Horsens in east Jutland. Today, almost all of Denmark's bacon is produced in co-operative packing plants. Co-operatives, too, deal with a large part of the trade in seeds. In the 1930's, a time of world depression and great trade difficulties, co-operative marketing associations sprang into existence to organize Denmark's trade in butter and bacon on a national scale. But Danish co-operatives are not confined to making butter and bacon and planning export trade; many have been created by groups of farmers to purchase cattle food, fertilizers, cement, and coal.

With the help of co-operative methods, the Danish farmer enriched himself from a difficult and highly competitive export trade. The co-operative dairy led to the extension of scientific ideas to farming all over Denmark. For instance, it produced a high quality of butter that has made the *Lur* brand famous the world over, and there is no doubt that the co-operative movement quickened the life of the Danish countryside. Through their marketing organizations the co-operatives have obtained higher prices for better butter. As a result of widening markets and higher prices more cows were kept on medium-sized and small farms all over the country, and with the rising quantities of skim-milk and butter-milk, which the dairies returned to the farms, large numbers of pigs have been reared. In turn, these have contributed to the expansion of the bacon industry. To complete the cycle, the increasing numbers of animals on the farms have given more manure to the fields to improve the output of crops. It is always hard to find the ultimate cause of a phase of expansion in industry or agriculture, but there is little doubt that co-operatives played an important rôle in the intensified farming of Denmark over the past century.

The pattern of Danish farming changed remarkably after 1880. Grain growing was replaced by a farm economy based on the rearing of cattle and pigs. Even though livestock took the centre of the picture on the Danish farm, there was no widespread conversion of arable land to permanent pasture. In fact, since 1885 the area of land under arable crops has scarcely altered. For decades, just over 85 per cent of all the land used for agriculture has been ploughed for arable crops. Astonishing as it may seem to those acquainted with the history of English farming since the last quarter of the nineteenth century, cattle-rearing in Denmark was accompanied by a rapid rise in the output of barley, oats, wheat, and rye. The volume of the grain crop increased by more than half between 1875 and 1930, although the sown acreage scarcely changed. During the same period, root-crops achieved a position of great importance in the Danish agricultural system. Fodder beets were scarcely noticeable in a general picture of Danish farming in the 1870's; today they equal the grain harvest in their feed value and provide the bulk of the winter food for dairy cattle. Denmark is a remarkably self-reliant state. Despite the great demands of intensive livestock farming, she only imports small amounts of cattle food, mainly the protein-rich cotton seed meal from the U.S.A. Just before the Second World War, imports of cattle feed amounted to less than 15 per cent of the quantity of home-grown cattle foods.

At the close of the nineteenth century Denmark transformed

and intensified its agriculture. For a brief moment, it is instructive to compare her development with that of the British Isles in the same period. There, under the impact of vast imports of cheap wheat from the pioneer regions of the late Victorian world great stretches of cornland fell into pasture. By the 1930's Buckinghamshire was almost a pastoral county, selling its fresh milk in

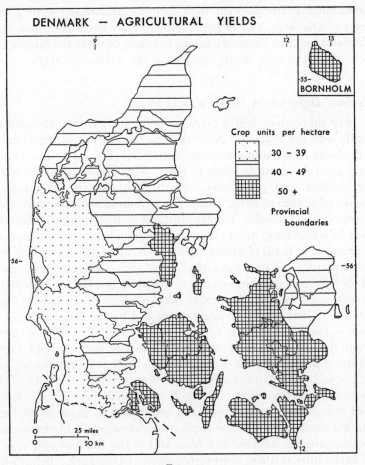

DENMARK — AGRICULTURAL YIELDS

BORNHOLM

Crop units per hectare

30 – 39

40 – 49

50 +

Provincial
boundaries

25 miles

50 km

FIG. 52

The most prosperous agricultural regions of Denmark belong to southern Zealand, Funen, and the islands of the Belts, as well as the fertile shores of Aarhus bay in eastern Jutland. Western Jutland, a region of mediocre glacial outwash deposits, stands out as the least productive area of the country. Northern Zealand in the counties of Frederiksborg and Copenhagen is placed in the medium category of crop-yields because of its large unproductive urban area.

the ever-expanding metropolis. At the same time, hill farms on the Pennines, on Dartmoor, and in the Welsh marches were abandoned. Less than a century earlier, many of these 'marginal' farms had been hacked out of the wilderness during the Napoleonic Wars — a period of growing population, of inflation, and rocketing corn prices. England turned her back on the countryside at the time when the Danes, without the chance of massive industrial development, transformed their farming and raised it to a new level of efficiency and organization. Belatedly, in our own day, England looks to Denmark for an example of what the farmer can achieve in the cool, moist climates of the Atlantic margin.

Regional Differences in Danish Agriculture

For more than half a century Denmark has concentrated on cattle and pig rearing. Nevertheless, the pattern of her farming still shows many subtle regional variations [Fig. 54]. The richest agricultural regions lie close to the eastern and southern coasts of her islands and peninsulas. South Zealand and the smaller, sheltered islands of Møn, Falster, and Lolland are famous for their prosperity. Likewise, eastern Jutland with its shapely boulder clay hills and long, quiet estuaries wriggling between lush pastures is proud of its fields of wheat, barley, oats, and fodder beet that feed as many pigs and cattle as any of the islands. The high prosperity of these favoured regions stands revealed by the area of land under cereals. Normally, corn crops occupy more than half of each parish. Their wealth is again expressed by the large number of pigs — itself a symptom of the quantities of skim-milk received from the dairies. Here one also finds the delicate and exotic plants that do not take well to Denmark's northern climate and heavy soils. Lolland, Falster, and Møn produce the bulk of the Danish sugar beet crop. It was first planted there in the 1870's, and today these regions normally grow enough sugar to fill Denmark's needs and to leave some over for export. Orchards and flower-gardens, tobacco and hops add to the richness and variety of agriculture in these most fertile parts of Denmark. Behind this prosperity loom the large facts of geography; the richness of these regions owes much to the minor nuances of climate and to the fine clay soils with a high lime content. Killing frosts come later in autumn than in the rest of Denmark; summer temperatures are slightly higher and there is a noticeably earlier spring.

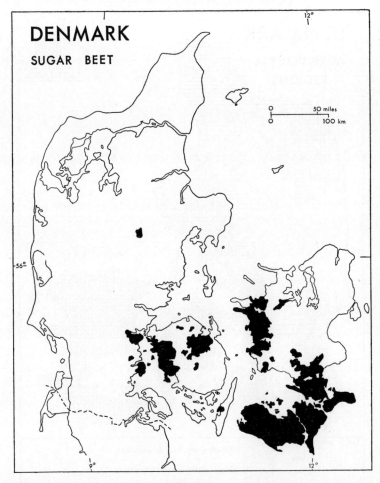

FIG. 53

Almost the whole of the Danish sugar beet crop comes from the most southerly islands of the archipelago — Lolland, Falster, and Møn. These islands enjoy the sunniest summers and possess some of the finest soils in Denmark.

The strongest regional contrasts in Denmark's agriculture exist between Lolland and western Jutland. The shallow valley-floors of Lolland are filled with cultivated meadows and its minia-ture, flattened clay ridges are ploughed for sugar beet, barley, and wheat. By contrast, Jutland's glacial outwash sands and gravels carry the lowest arable acreages in the country. Here more land is in pasture. Cattle still stand at the heart of the farm economy,

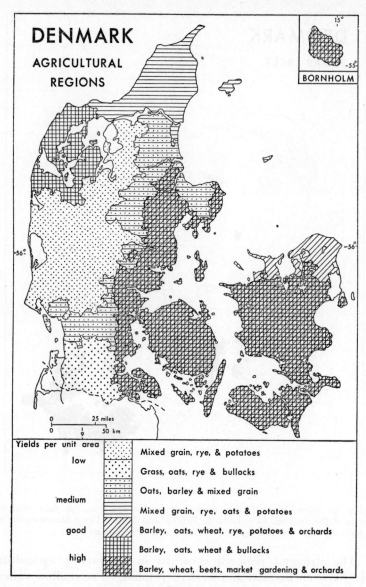

DENMARK

AGRICULTURAL
REGIONS

BORNHOLM

Yields per unit area		
low	⠿	Mixed grain, rye, & potatoes
	⣿	Grass, oats, rye & bullocks
medium	⣿	Oats, barley & mixed grain
	☰	Mixed grain, rye, oats & potatoes
good	⧄	Barley, oats, wheat, rye, potatoes & orchards
high	⊞	Barley, oats. wheat & bullocks
	▦	Barley, wheat, beets, market gardening & orchards

FIG. 54

The opposing poles of Danish agriculture lie in the islands and western Jutland. The islands produce a wider range of crops with the highest outputs. On the poorer soils of Jutland mixed grains, rye, and potatoes predominate with the lowest yields. A frontier between the two types of farming roughly follows the line of morainic hills in east Jutland.

but milk production is lower than in eastern Denmark and beef forms an important and increasingly valuable side-line. Less than a century ago, western and central Jutland was largely an empty heathland awaiting reclamation, and the region's inherent poverty is still revealed in its land values, which are the lowest in the country. Also a family needs a larger farm in west Jutland if it is to enjoy the same living standard as farmers in the more fertile islands.

The two poles of Danish agriculture lie among the heaths and dark fir plantations in west Jutland and amid the hedgeless fields and lush meadows of the southern islands, but between these not very distant extremes the nation exhibits many subtle variations of farming types. For example, the narrow coastal plain of south-western Jutland consists of stoneless, heavy marine clays. It forms the north-eastern limit of the *polderlands* that stretch along the North Sea coast from the Netherlands through northern Germany. From the late Middle Ages Frisian settlers built dikes and reclaimed these marshes. Today, the Danish polders consist of unbroken pastures. The farms do little but fatten cattle. Young stock are bought in spring and sold as fat cattle in the autumn. A well-known jibe in Denmark about south-western Jutland says that farm management in that region consists only of 'opening and closing gates'.

Post-war Trends in Danish Agriculture

Although Denmark's agriculture experienced some remarkable changes in the last century and became dependent upon markets outside her frontiers, it suffered little real harm in the First and Second World Wars. Even the last war and the German occupation, isolating Denmark from her traditional market in the British Isles, inflicted little damage upon her farming. She was deprived of overseas supplies of fertilizer and cattle-food; nevertheless, agricultural outputs were hardly diminished. Such was the independence and stability achieved by her farmers. Crop yields scarcely fell in the dark years of occupation between 1940 and 1945, largely because soil exhaustion was prevented by the abundance of stockyard manure. In their turn, the herds of dairy cattle remained at almost 90 per cent of the numbers in 1939, a result of the planting of linseed to provide protein feed. But milk outputs fell sharply, a change that was reflected towards the end of the war in the halving of the number of pigs in the country.

Since 1945 Denmark has successfully raised her farm outputs

to even higher levels. By 1950, milk yields regained their pre-war level with a total output of 5·3 million tons per year. The fifties have seen a striking rise in the butter yield per cow to 230 kilograms of butter per year, compared with a figure of 130 kilograms per cow during the pre-war decade. These statistics reflect a great improvement in the quality of Denmark's dairy herds that has resulted from the widespread breeding of stock by artificial insemination. But the numbers of pigs provide the best clue to the high level of agricultural production achieved in the years since the Second World War. Denmark reared just over three million pigs each year in the late 1930's; by 1958 there were six million pigs on Danish farms. Throughout her statistics of agriculture runs the same theme of higher outputs and increased efficiency during the post-war years. By 1958 the total production of Danish farms showed a net increase of 35 per cent over the outputs of the years between 1935 and 1939.

Although the pattern of a nation's agriculture changes but slowly when compared with the rate of transformation in the world of industry, some distinctive new trends emerged in Danish farming during the post-war years. A development of the export market has stimulated the manufacture of cheese. In 1939 the exports of Danish cheese were only 8000 tons; in 1959 they reached a figure of 77,000 tons. The fickle influence of public taste plays no small part in the rise to importance of this particular branch of farm exports. Western Germany developed a taste for Danish cheese during the fifties, so that she bought more than half of the total export in 1958 and 1959. To no small degree the pattern of Danish farming is determined by political events and economic actions in foreign countries. The rise in the production of Danish cheese began during the economic crisis of the thirties, when the United Kingdom introduced a quota system for the imports of bacon from Denmark. As a result, the pig herd had to be adjusted to a new and reduced market and, in turn, the surplus of skimmed milk was used in the making of more cheese.

The agricultural statistics of the fifties in Denmark reveal a long-term change in the pattern of arable farming. In almost every parish two-rowed barley covers more ground than any other cereal. Denmark with its moist, cool climates lies in the traditional oat region of north-western Europe and until the late thirties oats were the predominant cereal in the country. Between 1939 and 1958 the area sown with oats has been almost halved, and in the latter year the huge demands for barley as a fodder crop, especially for pigs, produced an output of two and a half million tons — more than half the total national harvest of grain. Less spectacular changes affect the balance of root-crops in Danish agriculture. Turnips that used to predominate on the farms of Jutland are now supplanted by kohlrabi. The mangold, a lover of the clayey soils and summer warmth of the southern parts of Denmark's archipelago, is retreating before the fodder beet — a heavier yielding cross between the sugar beet and mangold. New methods in farming and fresh techniques in the use of agricultural products are changing the farms of Denmark. With the wide-spread use of green fodder the area of permanent pasture has declined sharply. The new markets in deep-frozen poultry and vegetables that appeared in the late fifties are likely to encourage the post-war trend towards market-gardening and the raising of more poultry on smallholdings.

It is remarkable that the high outputs of Danish farming have been achieved with a dwindling labour force and with smaller amounts of imported feeding stuffs. Over the past three decades, workers have drifted from the land to jobs in the towns in all the Scandinavian countries. Poor marginal land has been abandoned in Sweden; in Denmark the attractions of the expanding capital city drew men away from the age-old tasks of the countryside. It is reckoned that Denmark's agricultural labour force equalled 504,000 man-years in 1934 and that by 1958 it had contracted to 315,000 man-years. The greatest reduction in the past quarter of a century affected the hired labour on the Danish farm which shrank to less than half the numbers of the 1930's. Today, the farms of Denmark are, above all, family units, depending upon the farmer, his wife and children, and a host of machines powered by oil, petrol, and the nation-wide electricity grid.

Over the last two decades the flight of active young men from the farms to the factories has induced a rise in agricultural wages. Today in Scandinavia the farm labourer earns almost as much as the unskilled worker in the factory, and as labour on the land becomes scarce and costly, more and more machinery is used for the tasks about the farm. The keynote of Danish agriculture in its upswing in the years after the Second World War has been a greater use of machines and an even higher level of output, and that in a farm economy that has long been reckoned among the most intensive in the world.

Some Facets of Scandinavian Geography

SWEDISH AGRICULTURE

If we look at farming in northern Europe with the eye of the geographer, we are struck by the immense physical differences between Denmark and her Scandinavian neighbours. Two-thirds of the surface of Denmark is cultivated, while only 9 per cent of the area of Sweden and a similar proportion of Finland are taken up by arable and rotation grassland. In Norway the proportion of cultivated land falls to a mere 2·7 per cent of the national territory. The outstanding fact is the vast amount of unprofitable land in Norway, Sweden, and Finland. The high *fjäll*, the endless forests and tundra that stretch across the Arctic Circle are largely beyond the limits of cultivation. In Finland the continuous tracts of farmland belong to the rim of post-glacial marine clays that fringes her coastline. Prosperous farming in Sweden begins with the central lakes depression and fills the plains that surround the ungrateful core of Småland. Norwegian farms cling precariously to the strandflat along the Atlantic coast or concentrate upon the valleys that drain to the broken plains around Oslo fjord. If we forsake the vantage point of the geographer, who views northern Europe's farmlands as tiny pockets of cultivation set against the region's harsh physique, and take up the outlook of the economic historian, we notice that the development of agriculture over the past two centuries faced similar problems and followed similar lines in all the countries of Scandinavia.

Sweden, like Denmark, finally destroyed her medieval systems of farming by governmental decree early in the nineteenth century [Fig. 56]. Before that time, the chief unit in Swedish agriculture was the nucleated village set in its common fields. The three-field system was commonest in Skåne, the island of Gotland, and on the plains around Lake Vänern. The fertile countrysides of Lake Mälaren mainly operated a two-field system and many of the poorer tracts of southern and central Sweden, in Småland and Bergslagen, limited themselves to a single field in a forest clearing. The great Redistribution Act of 1827 brought to completion an enclosure movement that started in the middle of the eighteenth century with the publication of Jacob Faggot's radical pamphlet on *The Obstruction to Sweden's Agriculture and its Remedy*. This agrarian revolution began in Sweden with the laws of 1749 and 1757 that reduced the number of strips in the common fields, leaving undisturbed the organization of the village and its layout

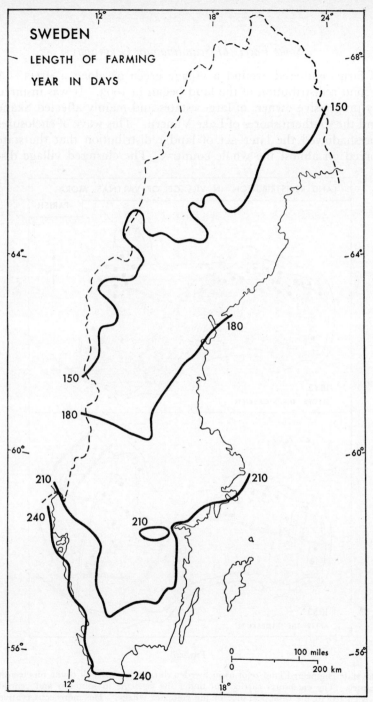

FIG. 55

Sweden extends through 13 degrees of latitude and, from the point of view of agriculture, displays some of the greatest contrasts in Scandinavia. In Norrland the farming year is shorter by more than three months than along the coastal plain of Skåne. The climatic contrasts of northern and southernmost Sweden are exaggerated further in the farming of the two areas by differences of geology and soils.

of farms gathered around a village green or along a street. A second redistribution of the land began in 1803. It was inspired by progressive owners of large estates and mainly affected Skåne and the southern shores of Lake Vänern. This wave of enclosures foreshadowed the later act of land redistribution that the state forced on almost the whole country. The clustered village dis-

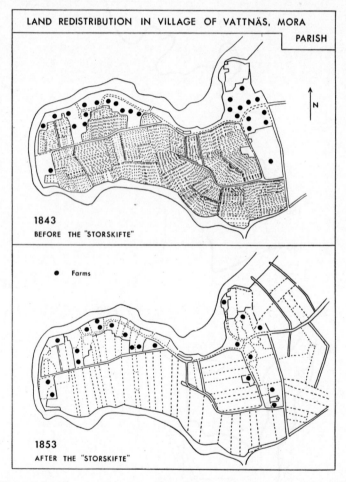

LAND REDISTRIBUTION IN VILLAGE OF VATTNÄS, MORA PARISH

1843
BEFORE THE "STORSKIFTE"

● Farms

1853
AFTER THE "STORSKIFTE"

Fig. 56

The state engineered land reforms in Sweden during the first half of the nineteenth century. The enclosures carried out under the *lagaskifte* in southern and central Sweden led to the disappearance of the compact village. The more conservative reforms of the *storskifte* kept the farmhouses together in the village, achieving a more rational use of the land by blocking together the scores of tiny scattered strips.

integrated and new farms were erected on the compact holdings provided by the fresh division of the agricultural land. The enclosure movement of 1827 swept through the whole country where open-field agriculture had developed, and the Swedish landscape experienced the same transformations as the boulder clay hills and plains of Denmark. The nucleated village disintegrated; open fields with their countless scattered strips gave way to neat, fenced enclosures. Fresh farms, scattered and isolated from each other, arose in the midst of these new compact holdings [Plate 32]. Sometimes a small village was erased completely from the landscape. Flackarp in Skåne was a tight little settlement of eleven homesteads and a church in 1700; today only a single farm bears that name and the church has disappeared.

Less obvious, but more important, were the changes in land use and the rise in productivity that followed the enclosures. With the introduction of crop rotations the fallow steadily declined, so that by the close of the nineteenth century less than 5 per cent of the cultivated land was resting and unproductive. Less than a century earlier almost half of the land was always in fallow, and it is only surprising that around Lake Mälaren traces of this medieval practice still linger so that about 8 per cent of the farm land in that region is in fallow at the present time. Apart from the land that was brought into profitable cultivation each year as a result of the reduction of the temporary wastes of the fallow, it is calculated that the area of arable increased by as much as 300 per cent from the reclamation of peat-bogs and the improvement of former grazing lands in the woods of southern Sweden. Forage root-crops, clover, sugar beet, potatoes and rotation grasses were brought into the agricultural design and largely explain the increased outputs of her countryside.

The most striking feature of Swedish farming in the twentieth century is the breeding of plants to stand the severities of her northern climate [Fig. 55]. Until about 1900 the main grains of Sweden — rye, oats, barley, and wheat — were old native varieties. They could endure the rigours of her northern climate, but their great defects lay in weak straws and low yields. About the end of the nineteenth century high-yielding winter wheats were introduced from western Europe into Sweden, but even in Skåne it was risky to plant these foreign strains because the whole crop could perish in one of those winters when severely cold Arctic air envelops the Baltic lands. However, Swedish plant-breeding institutes overcame this difficulty. The delicate foreign wheats were crossbred with the domestic types to produce a hardy variety with a stiff straw and a high yield. The very severe winters during the Second World War and their dangerous crop failures focused research towards the discovery of even hardier plants. Of recent years, the most notable feature is the development of new, quick-ripening types of spring wheat. They began to penetrate the farm economies of central Sweden in the late 1930's. Today, 45 per cent of the total Swedish wheat harvest is gathered from these new varieties of spring wheat.

The most astonishing change in Swedish arable farming over the past century is the eclipse of rye as the chief grain crop. In 1870 there were five times as many acres of rye as wheat. Rye, the age-old grain of northern Europe, continued to rise in importance until 1900 when a peak of more than a million acres was reached. During this period the area sown to wheat scarcely increased. Then, after 1910, field after field in central and southern Sweden fell out of rye. Between 1931 and 1935 slightly more wheat was sown than rye. In the years after the Second World War rye has occupied less than 400,000 acres; nearly 800,000 acres have yielded crops of wheat. These bare statistics of Swedish grain crops through the decades since 1860 conceal an exciting chapter in the story of the revolution in farming. This particular part of the story was written in the research institutes that have extended the range and the quality of crops against what for so long seemed to be the iron limits imposed by climate. And perhaps this phase of world history will rank in importance with the achievements of those first Neolithic farmers who carried the seed grains of the Mediterranean's semi-desert fringe, the primitive wheat and bar-ley, to the cool, moist climates of north-western Europe.

We have noticed similarities in the agricultural development of Denmark and Sweden since 1800, but it is worth remembering that there are some notable differences — some rooted in the facts of climate and soil, others the result of state policy. For instance, Sweden boasts of no spectacular reclamation such as that of the arid heaths of Jutland, itself arising from national pride bruised by military defeat. Nevertheless, the quiet draining and coloniza-tion of her extensive peat-bogs has created much valuable arable land since 1900. Their organic soils have a high lime and nitrogen content, but are poor in other plant foods. With draining and the use of artificial fertilizers they make first-rate arable land. In 1950, it was estimated that one seventh of Sweden's cultivated land had been recovered from peat-bogs in the past half-century. It is interesting that some of the reclaimed boglands of Småland that were first cultivated about 1900 have lately fallen out of use, as a result of the wasting of the peat soils through the processes of oxidation and their removal by high winds in the period of drought that normally descends on Scandinavia during the late spring.

There is a striking difference in the average size of farms between Denmark and Sweden. Denmark is a country of medium-sized farms; Sweden's farms are small. The average Swedish farm covers twenty-two acres, but a quarter of her holdings are extremely tiny, containing less than five acres. Another quarter of her farms do not exceed twelve acres. To many minds the small farm is the ideal instrument of a peasant democracy where each man tills his own slip of the nation's earth, but it is far from being the best means of economic progress. Small farms hinder the use of machinery, not only because they cannot provide capital for the purchase of expensive tools, but also because their tiny, fenced enclosures are hostile to modern tractors, harvesters, and seed drills that are designed to work across wide spaces. Again, the small farmer in Sweden has been reluctant to adopt more elementary improvements such as field drains, a vital item in the English agrarian revolution more than a century ago. Proper sub-soil drainage by burnt-clay pipes or channels lined with stone or wood lengthens the growing season — an improvement of great value in the marginal climates of northern Europe. In the late spring, when the thaw comes, a field with drains is ready for seeding as much as a fortnight before an undrained neighbour. Yet a government report, published in 1944, shows that of the acreage in very small farms only 5·9 per cent of the land had sub-soil drainage.

In discussing the problem of the small farm in Sweden it must be remembered that agriculture is not the sole means of livelihood to its occupants. The small farm belongs predominantly to the northern forested parts of the country, and their owners are usually more interested in timber-cutting than farming. The farms of the sunny hillsides of Jämtland, sited amid their tiny plots of hay, potatoes, and hardy six-rowed barley, owe their main source of income to the strips of forest that belong to the properties [Fig. 88]. Although the individual forest plots are many times larger than the single farm's acreage of arable and rotation grassland, the exploitation of their timber is hampered by the minute subdivision of the units of ownership. The forest plots frequently have difficult shapes. In the Ragunda district, they consist of long, narrow strips, sometimes running across country for six or seven miles and confined to a width of scarcely more than a hundred feet. In the province of Jämtland, nearly a half of the area of productive forest is attached to the small hill farms.

The steadily rising standard of life in twentieth-century Sweden has clearly underlined the defects of the small farm. It cannot offer a life materially equal to that of the town-dweller or the rich large farmer on the plains of Skåne. The Swedish parliament passed a law in 1947 to try and deal with the problem of the small farm. Over a long period it aims to create bigger farms with a minimum size of twenty-five acres, the area found necessary to support a farmer and his family in full-time agricultural employment. As small farms fall empty and enter the market for sale, the state now has the first option of purchase. With this power over the choice of the next holder, it is government policy to add the land to that of a neighbouring farm and so slowly to achieve the creation of larger farming units. The effectiveness of this policy is measured by the fact that 14,000 small farms disappeared between 1951 and 1956.

Along with this policy of turning smallholdings into moderate-sized farms, the state encourages the building of new industries in the countryside to provide work and an additional income for the 'sub-marginal' farmer. The poor, small farmer, unable to make a living out of his land if it is one of the many 'crofts' without rights in the forest, has long sought additional work in the countryside at timber-cutting, on road-making, in rural crafts, or at the huge pulp and paper mills that have grown up in Norrland. It has been said that the smallholder on the 'incomplete farm' is the biggest problem in rural Sweden. The small farm that is unable to support its owner presents a serious problem in many parts of western Europe. For instance, it has been estimated that in the Netherlands over 75 per cent of all farm holdings are too small for rational and economic management.[2] Sweden has the distinction along with the Netherlands of being the only country where the state has actively intervened to deal with the problem.

There are clear differences between the agricultural policies of the Danish and Swedish governments. They mainly arise from the fact that Danish farms serve a large export trade and form the very roots of the national life, while the Swedish economy largely depends upon the sale of iron ores, timber, paper and paper-pulp, and the products of the engineering, shipbuilding, electrical, and optical industries. For a long time Denmark favoured free trade and disliked the interference of government in the affairs of the farmer. For instance, she is proud of the spontaneous movements that gave birth to the folk high schools and the co-operatives, and only the deep economic crisis of the early 1930's drove the state to interfere in the affairs of the countryside. In Sweden, on the other hand, the state has played a much greater part in rural life. Ever since the economic depression, the government has aimed to shield the nation's agriculture from the effects of fluctuations in world trade and prices. The power of the state over Swedish farming grew even stronger in the Second World War, when the government established rigid price and wage controls that effectively isolated the rural economy from the world movements of prices in the 1940's. Again, the co-operative movement was slow to take root in Sweden. Although the first co-operatives appeared about 1880, imitating the Danish movement that was then in full flood, they only developed into an important instrument for the organization of agriculture in the 1930's.

Lately the Swedish government has done much to direct the development of farming through price-fixing, wage policies, and the enforcement of an eight-hour day for the agricultural labourer. Since 1947 state policies have aimed to give to the farm worker the same standard of life as that earned by his brother in industry. It is claimed that equality was reached about 1950, but at the cost of a system of tariffs, quotas, and subsidies that isolated Sweden from the world prices of agricultural commodities and that encouraged the inflation of the nation's economy. Since 1956 Sweden has changed her methods of controlling the import of agricultural commodities. A fixed tariff has been replaced by an import levy that changes with the prices of goods in the international market and the costs of the same commodities in Sweden. The aim is that domestic prices shall follow international prices, but at the higher level that is needed to secure a uniformly high standard of living within the country. But despite all the paper legislation in Stockholm, the overshadowing control in the economy of the countryside rests on the hard facts of geography. The regional patterns of farming are fixed by the shape of this country that stretches from the mouth of the Baltic Sea to the bare tundras of remote Norrbotten.

Regionalism in Swedish Agriculture

On Sweden's southernmost fringe the farming of Skåne is a model among the intensive agricultural systems of central Europe. In south-western Skåne, where the glacial clays are deposited on Cretaceous limestones, lies the most intensively developed farming area in the country. Here, most crops give their highest yields and 80 per cent of the land's surface is used for arable farming. The plains of Skåne are the main area of winter wheat in Sweden. Likewise, this is the only important part of the country for the growing of sugar beet, a fact largely determined by the concentration of the large refineries in the ports of Skåne's coastline [Fig. 57]. In this region too, oilseeds such as rape and linseed form valuable items in the crop rotations and add an important element to the national economy. More pigs are kept in Skåne than elsewhere in Sweden, another fact that links Sweden's southernmost province with the agricultural economy of the Danish islands. Farming in Skåne is not only favoured by climate and soils, it has benefited, too, from the presence of large and growing towns where the string of urban centres along the shores of the Sound promises to evolve into Scandinavia's only real conurbation. Towns stimulate vegetable and fruit-growing and the highly productive techniques of market-gardening on their fringes. In Skåne, this type of farming has advanced since the end of the Second World War, encouraged by the foundation of canning factories and, in the mid-fifties, deep-freezing plants for fruit and vegetables.

Northwards from Skåne, the natural poverty and harshness of northern Europe are woven into the pattern of farming. Oats take the place of wheat as the main grain crop; the hardier six-rowed barley begins to replace the two-rowed variety that insists upon the milder climates and richer soils of southern Sweden. In fact, grass and oats occupy half the cultivated land in central Sweden. But even here nature has created islands of wealth such as the plain of Vestergötland, a rich, stone-free, clay lowland stretching from the southern shore of Lake Vänern, where spring wheat and the oil crops that have expanded in the post-war years — winter rape, spring rape, white mustard, and linseed — play an important rôle in the economy. Uppland, lying north of the quiet inland sea of Mälaren, forms another fertile province where lime-rich soils are famous for their huge crops of barley.

A third agricultural region begins on the northern edge of the central lakes depression and reaches beyond the Arctic Circle. Grass leys take up half of the cultivated land, and in the far north

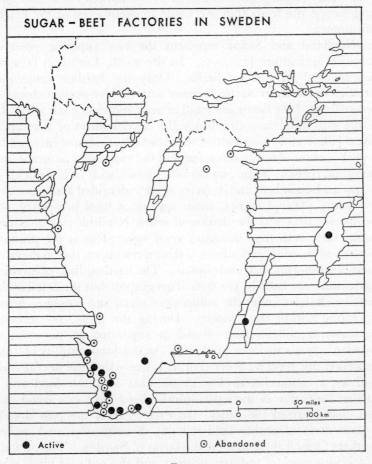

FIG. 57

The lime-rich boulder clays of Skåne province combine with the highest summer temperatures and the longest growing period to provide the best conditions for sugar beet. Closed refineries in the midlands show the retreat of this plant from central Sweden and its concentration on the south and the islands of Öland and Gotland. The abandoned refineries of the south also suggest a rationalization of the industry.

this figure rises to 80 per cent of the farmed area. The long, harsh winter, extending from the beginning of October until the middle of May, excludes the autumn-sown grains, and the main crop is the resistant six-rowed barley that grows quickly and matures early. Potatoes are the only other important crop, and in remote, northern Sweden they are limited to sunny, south-facing slopes where they can enjoy soils warmed by the maximum of insolation and escape the frosts that are liable to occur even at the height of summer.

Norrland and Skåne represent the two opposing poles of Swedish agriculture [Fig. 55]. In the north, European farming has reached its furthest limits. Only the hardiest crops can prosper in the short Arctic summer with its ever-present threat of severe frost. The farms are small in area and strung out along the fertile soils of terraces that fringe the lower courses of Norrland's rivers [Plate 26]. Everywhere these tiny clearings are enclosed by a dark curtain of forest, a reminder of the rawness of nature in this marginal region. Skåne, on the other hand, with its huge fields of wheat and sugar beet and its farms at once identified and concealed by neatly planted copses, wears an air of high prosperity — a prosperity that was foreshadowed when Neolithic colonists first broke these soils four thousand years ago. This is the primary pattern of Swedish agriculture, a design resting on the unalterable facts of landforms, soil, and climate. The hard outlines of Swedish agriculture are fixed by the facts of geography, but the detail of the pattern changes under the influence of social and economic forces operating within the country. During the fifties, the nation's agricultural policies have aimed at supplying 90 per cent of Sweden's needs in farm products. As the total outputs of 1958 exceeded this level by 7 per cent, it is likely that the next decade will see a continuing decline in the area of arable land and a further reduction of the agricultural labour force — a trend that has characterized the fifties. In each year of the past decade 25,000 acres of arable land fell out of cultivation and 20,000 workers forsook their jobs on the farms of Sweden. The nation's quickening pace of industrialization and the reduced birth rates of the twenties and thirties make labour one of the scarcest commodities in the country. In their turn the Swedish farms are among the most mechanized of Scandinavia.

FARMING IN NORWAY AND FINLAND

In many ways the agrarian history of Norway and Finland is profoundly different from that of Sweden and Denmark. Change came slowly to these countries and at a later date; the effects of the agricultural revolution were less widespread and are beginning to reach some remote areas only at the present time. Within the recesses of Finland's forests and along the shores of Norway's western fjords, methods of farming have survived from distant centuries scarcely affected by new ideas. Tractors are hardly known among the rock-bound fjords of south-western Norway. There the pattern of the farm or *gård* has remained the same through many generations. Often the farm stands alone on some fragment of a terrace. Sometimes it is a member of a tiny cluster of farms sited on a gently sloping fan of coarse alluvium, or else a more extensive flat at the fjord head [Plate 9]. Each farm in this part of Norway consists of a tight knot of wooden barns. Close by lies the 'infield' or *inmark*, a stretch of fertile and fairly level land that has been lovingly cultivated for centuries. It yields several hay-crops in the summer and also a small harvest of oats and barley. On these farms most of the work is done by hand, using methods that have changed but little since the Iron Age. The hay harvest is taken by scythe and the cereals are gathered with sickles whose pattern has remained the same for more than the past thousand years. Beyond the small extent of infield stretches the *utmark* or 'outfield', a great expanse of rocky slope and fell, much of which forms summer pasture at three thousand feet or more above the grey, faintly wrinkled surface of the fjords. This is the *seter* where the small farms graze their cows in summer. In western Norway, cattle rearing is about as remote as one can imagine from the methods of the Danish dairying industry. Each farm rarely has more than half a dozen cattle; and their milk, cheese, and butter hardly enter into trade beyond the fjord. Norway's fjords shelter a peasant society that is still largely self-sufficient and rich in archaic elements.

Nevertheless, even among Vestlandet's lonely fjords revolutionary changes are beginning to affect the life of the farm. Improvements in communications and the penetration of this austerely beautiful region by heavy industries founded on the wealth of water power are deeply influencing the traditional rural communities. One of the most striking changes of the past generation

247

is the abandonment of many upland summer farms and the transformation of the economy in those that survive. The old habits of making cheese and butter at lonely groups of huts on summer hillsides are dying out. Many of the *seters* that lie high and hard to reach have been abandoned. Cattle are now kept in the valley all the year round and fed on the rich harvests of heavily fertilized rotation grass. Where the summer pastures are still used, the daily milk lorry now climbs a zigzag mountain road to gather fresh milk for the co-operative dairy.

In many fjord communities the system of land-holding has undergone a minor revolution since the end of the nineteenth century. The oldest farms of Vestlandet are often clustered together on some favourable site exposed to the maximum of the fjord's fitful sunshine and safe from the avalanches of winter and early spring. The property of each farm is a scattered complex of tiny arable strips, meadowland, and slips of woodland. Of late, farms have been redistributed and property re-allocated. For instance, at Aga, lying at the foot of the precipitous western wall of Sørfjord, a cluster of farms, eight in all, stood close to the sea, sheltered from the avalanches that hurtle down from the overshadowing rim of the Folgefonni plateau. Only in 1940 were the lands of Aga redistributed in the interests of more rational farming and the inhabitants moved out to new sites, leaving Aga to be preserved as a monument of a rural Norway that is passing away.

The economy of the fjord farm is changing rapidly in areas favoured with good communications or under the disruptive influence of heavy industries. The inner parts of Sogne, Hardanger, and Nord fjords specialize more and more in fruit growing. With cherries, pears, plums, and apples, the western fjords form the world's most northerly fruit growing region. The success of this fruit farming that almost becomes a monoculture in Hardanger fjord may be attributed to the gifts of the local climates, where interlocking mountains and sea create many meteorological abnormalities. The long growing season of the mild Atlantic coastal fringe is magnified by the daily warming of mountain slopes, particularly in the long sunny days of late spring and early summer. Shelter from strong winds is equally important and this fact determines the location of the orchards in the inner parts of the great fjords. Finally, the sheet of salt water that glistens below the site of nearly every orchard is an insurance against harmful frosts.

Another lucrative variation that has appeared recently in the farming of the western fjords is the rearing of silver fox and mink. Caged in tiny wooden pens, they are fed on fish offal and on still, moist summer days spread a stench over their fjord settlement as obnoxious as the waste gases of the giant industries that pollute the atmosphere of a few places in western Norway. Around Bergen, the growth of industrial communities, effective communications, and this port-city with an urban population of more than a hundred thousand have reacted upon the farming in near-by fjords, encouraging a growing specialization in the production of fresh milk.

From a national point of view Norwegian agriculture is much poorer than those of Denmark and Sweden. The Danish economy rests upon the products of her farms; Sweden is self-sufficient in grains, animal feeds, and dairy products; but in most years Norway imports about a third of her foodstuffs among which the large items are flour, sugar, and cattle foods. Almost 90 per cent of her requirements of wheat have to be imported. The background to the dull statistics of food imports lies in the large tracts of unprofitable land that compose the Norwegian homeland — the ice-scarred north with its hundreds of waning glaciers [Plate 16] and the high plateaus of the south and east where the summer is far too short for good farming.

The problem of how to improve Norwegian agriculture can only be solved within the narrow, rigid limits imposed by environment. So far machinery has helped the Norwegian farmer less than his neighbours in Denmark and Sweden. Above the level of the clay plains that were flooded by the temporary seas of post-glacial times [Fig. 34], there is scarcely an acre of level land, and the farms of inland and upland Norway consist of tiny, scattered patches of arable land and hay meadows. Slopes are often too steep for ploughs, and here the tractor is a useless machine. Apart from the impediments that nature puts in the way of the use of machinery, Norway is, even more than Sweden, a land of small farms. In fact, it has been said that there are not more than forty farms in the whole country of more than 250 acres — the size of an average farm in the English Midlands. Thus, the conservatism and poverty of a nation of small peasant proprietors adds to the impositions of the terrain in preventing any revolutionary and costly changes in the methods of farming.

Nevertheless, in certain favoured parts of Norway new techniques transformed agriculture in the past few decades. Along the fertile coastal plain that flanks the Skagerrak and in the quiet countryside that comes down to the shores of Lake Mjøsa [Plate 3], farming is as prosperous and efficient as in the isles of Denmark or the midlands of Sweden. An agricultural improvement during the first half of the twentieth century stands clearly revealed in Nor-

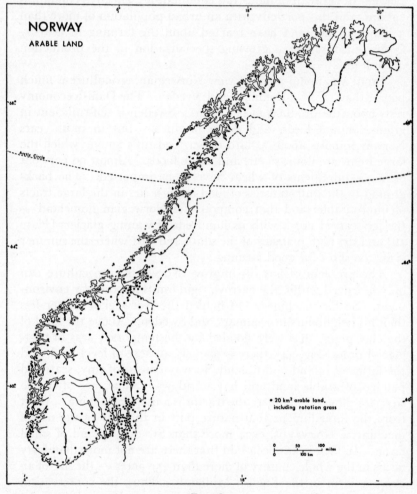

FIG. 58

The harsh and unalterable facts of the physical environment strictly limit Norwegian agriculture. The distribution of arable land points to the early centres of settlement and economic evolution close to Oslo fjord, in the long valleys of the south-east, and on the southern shore of Trondheim fjord. In the west and north arable land depends largely on the strandflat at favoured raised-delta sites within the fjords.

way's national statistics. For instance, the wheat output increased five times in the two decades between the First and Second World Wars, largely at the expense of the traditional food grain of northern Europe, rye. This was achieved by the use of new strains and the financial encouragement of a state subsidy. Another revealing figure shows that in the past half century the area of arable land in Norway has increased by a fifth. But beside this statistic of expanding cultivation we should remember that even now only 3 per cent of the whole country is used for arable crops. As the eminent Norwegian geographer, Axel Sømme, has said, 'we worry less about the quality of the soil than about its quantity' [Fig. 58].[3]

Lately the chief aim of Norwegian agriculture has been self-sufficiency in food for its livestock. She has nearly reached this goal. In the 1930's about a fifth of Norway's animal feed came from abroad. Today she imports only 8 per cent. This notable improvement is the result of the building of silos to store green fodder and the manuring of pastures, a technique that allows them to be grazed for two weeks longer in the spring and autumn. But it can be pointed out, perhaps with some cynicism, that Norway owes some of her improved outputs and extended grazing to the grace of nature in the form of the marked amelioration of northern Europe's climate in the past three decades.

In Finland, the patterns and problems of agriculture assume a different shape again from those of her Scandinavian neighbours. She stands between the Atlantic fringe and the continental heart of Europe, in almost every sense a transition region. Locked in the north-east corner of the Baltic Sea, her landscapes and climate have many elements that belong to the monotonous thinly populated spaces of northern Russia. Politically, Finland was released from more than a century of Russian rule only in 1917, and her agricultural development was deeply affected by the policies of the new nation-state that came into being with the end of the confused months of the civil war in 1918.

The main traits of Finnish agriculture are a product of environment and history. Ever since her political independence Finland has struggled to reach self-sufficiency in the basic grain and fodder crops, a chimera put forward as an economic aim by the fierce nationalism of a small state. The task of achieving economic self-sufficiency at this level is comparable to that of Norway's. Both countries belong to northern Europe's zone of marginal farming.

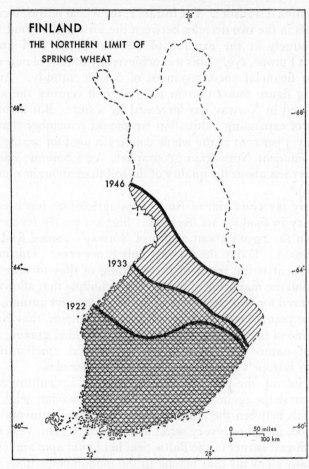

FINLAND
THE NORTHERN LIMIT OF
SPRING WHEAT

1946

1933

1922

0   50 miles
0   100 km

Fig. 59

The constant aim of the Finnish economy is to achieve self-sufficiency in the bread grains. In two decades the work of agricultural research stations, blessed by the northern hemisphere's climatic amelioration, has pushed the frontier of spring-sown wheat to the threshold of northern Finland.

Along her Atlantic coastline Norway has been granted the gift of the world's mildest climates in such polar latitudes, but this bounty is largely nullified by the abundance of high mountains, bleak plateaus, and the scarcity of cultivable soils. Finland, even more than Norway, is confined to the higher latitudes among the Scandinavian states. Her vast, ancient peneplain is covered with boulder clays, coarse sands, and marine silts from the Quaternary period and the post-glacial centuries of temporary submergence [Fig. 26]. Finland possesses soils of considerable fertility, a fertility whose value is severely limited by the harshness of her climate with its short growing season and the perpetual menace of killing summer frost. During the thirties in a series of benevolent summers, Finland grew about three-quarters of her needs in rye and wheat — the essential bread grains. Since the war she has been less successful in satisfying her requirements in these crops. In 1952, she harvested only a half of her wants, though the good year of 1950 had raised Finland's home production so high that only 13 per cent of her bread grains were imported.

Finnish farming is constantly menaced by summer invasions of Arctic air whose killing frosts may ruin maturing crops and destroy the coming harvest in July and August. Within his lifetime every Finnish farmer can expect to see a summer with hard killing frosts and crop failures on a national scale. The destruction of crops in frost-prone regions such as northern Finland, the broken morainic country of the Suomenselkä inland from the Gulf of Bothnia, or among the easterly lakes of Karelia, may be expected two or three times in every decade.

In addition to the natural hardships of her geographical situation, many of Finland's difficulties in the fifties arose from her experience in the Second World War — an experience that her Scandinavian neighbours largely escaped. Finland fought two severe wars with Russia between 1939 and 1944. Her forests and frozen lakes formed a battlefield in the 'first winter war', and at the end of the second war with Russia her northern territory was systematically scorched by the retreating German troops. To the desolation of war was added the loss of territory by the armistice agreement signed at Moscow in 1944. The fresh post-war frontiers deprived Finland of 12 per cent of her cultivated land. Most of it lay between Lake Ladoga and the head of the Gulf of Finland ; the rest was in the Porkkala peninsula, a small segment of territory to the west of Helsinki that was restored by the Russians in 1955. War inflicted severe temporary damage on Finnish farming. Her poor podsol soils were starved of necessary chemical fertilizers and her livestock were decimated. Four years after the end of the fighting Finland still required nearly half a million cattle to equal the national total of 1939. Apart from the losses of land and livestock, war hit severely at her labour force. Seventy thousand Finns were killed. As a result, active young labour has been scarce on the farms in the late forties, and young workers were needed more than ever in this period, when hundreds of new farms had to be carved out of former large estates or else created in the silent forests to house the refugees from the lost territories of Karelia [Figs. 60 and 61]. The shortage of agricultural workers was intensified by the drift of men to new and expanding industries — a movement that partly resulted from the Russian peace treaty with its demand for reparations from Finland in the form of electrical equipment, cables, machine-tools, and ships. Consequently, since 1945 the engineering industries in Finland grew far beyond the needs of the home market and to the detriment of the rapid recovery of her agriculture. Before the war, Finnish rolling mills, engineering shops, foundries, and shipbuilding yards found work for less than fifty thousand people. By 1948 the same industries had doubled in size. Although the late forties were a period of impoverishment in the Finnish countryside and the demands of reparations turned Finland's labour force towards industry, the final effect of these hard times might be considered as beneficial. Before the war, Finland suffered from an excess of rural population. As in the peasant communities of eastern Europe, her farms concealed a good deal of partial unemployment. Again, the decline of the farm labour force has speeded up the mechanization of agriculture.

Finland's farming, eternally set in a harsh environment, has been severely tested in the storms of her recent history. These facts and factors of geography and history underlie the colourless statistics published by the United Nations in a succession of economic surveys of Europe.[4] There, the output of Finland's farms between the years 1934 and 1938 is represented by an index of 100. By comparison, her agricultural output in 1947 is measured by an index of 70, and not until 1951 did she equal the figures for the pre-war period. On the other hand, the indices for industrial production rocket in the years after the war. With an index of 100 to represent the products of her factories in 1938, we find that by 1947 this had climbed to 120. In 1951 it soared to an index of 177. Finland's Scandinavian neighbours all reveal somewhat different economic trends. All show farm outputs well above the 1930's in the post-war years, and by 1951 the efficient Danish farms were producing half as much again as before the war.

The most striking feature of Finland's agriculture since the war has been the resettlement of 420,000 refugees from Karelia,

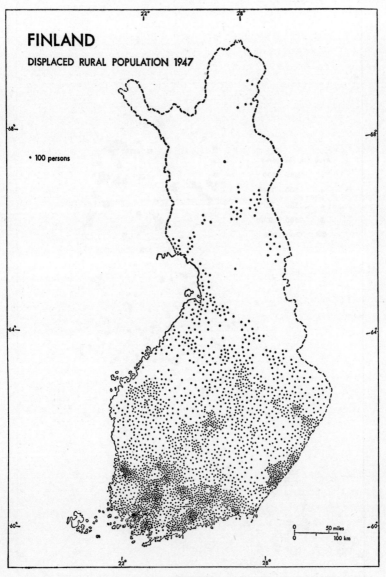

FIG. 60

At the end of the war with Russia in 1944, 420,000 Finns, 11 per cent of the country's population, had to be resettled. By the end of 1947, 85 per cent of this refugee population had been established on fresh farms. This map shows clearly a concentration of resettled farmers in the south-west corner of the country where land was reclaimed from forest and peat-bog at the foot of the Salpausselkä moraine.

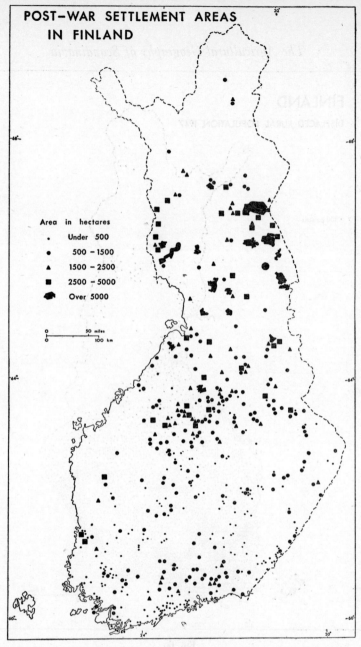

POST–WAR SETTLEMENT AREAS IN FINLAND

Area in hectares

· Under 500
● 500 – 1500
▲ 1500 – 2500
■ 2500 – 5000
⬟ Over 5000

50 miles
100 km

FIG. 61

Three zones of agricultural colonization result from the post-war settlement of dis-placed persons in Finland. The largest tracts of freshly-cleared land lie in southern Lapland where the Asmuntijoki settlement area covers 18,606 hectares (46,500 acres). A second belt of recent clearing for agriculture stretches across the northern part of the lakes plateau, and a third zone in the south coincides with the new farm-lands on the fringe of the Salpausselkä ridges. Two extensive areas have been little affected by this post-war colonization. Northern Lapland lies beyond the physical limits of farming, and the coastal plain of Östterbotten was excluded from the resettling of Karelian farmers because of its predominantly Swedish character.

Porkkala, and the lost Arctic corridor [Fig. 60]. Between 1945 and 1950 thirty-five thousand new farms were created. Some were carved out of existing settlements where farm-holdings were big enough to permit dismemberment, but by far the greater number were hewn out of forest and bogland [Fig. 61]. Land that has so far been neglected because of its extreme poverty is now coming into cultivation. For instance, sterile tracts of the Salpausselkä moraine that long resisted close settlement have been tackled by hundreds of refugee farmers since the war. Behind the double wall of the Salpausselkä, amid the maze of lakes and sinuous eskers, tracts of forest owned by the state or the great timber companies are giving way in patches to the small farms of peasants from the east. The greatest region of post-war reclamations belongs to the northern parts of the country beyond latitude 64 degrees. Here the post-war period has witnessed the creation of a new pioneer fringe in northern Europe [Fig. 62]. Three-quarters of the freshly reclaimed land belongs to Finland's four northern provinces. In some of Lapland's parishes the arable acreage has doubled within a decade. This fresh surge in the taming of Finland's wilderness is sometimes exclusively associated with the work of refugee families from Karelia, but much has been accomplished by farmers extending their own holdings at the expense of the forest and young married soldiers back from the misery of the Russian war who took advantage of the various colonization laws with their offers of land.

The first years of the 'cold farm', raw land freshly won from the wilderness, are inevitably profitless. The families on the new farms live on state subsidies until a decade of hard work shall make them self-sufficient and a profit to the national community. But all this pioneering, unique in modern Europe, that goes on to the sound of the tractor and the crosscut saw powered by the chugging petrol engine might appear to be turning Finland away from the traditional source of her prosperity — the timber of her once endless forests.

At the very best, Finland is a country of marginal farming, and agriculture can never assume the rôle in the national economy that it occupies in Denmark. Dairy cattle form the centre of interest on the average Finnish farm, and the smallness of those farms is revealed when one recalls that three-quarters of the country's cattle belong to herds of less than ten cows. Grain growing is severely restricted by climate and tends to belong to

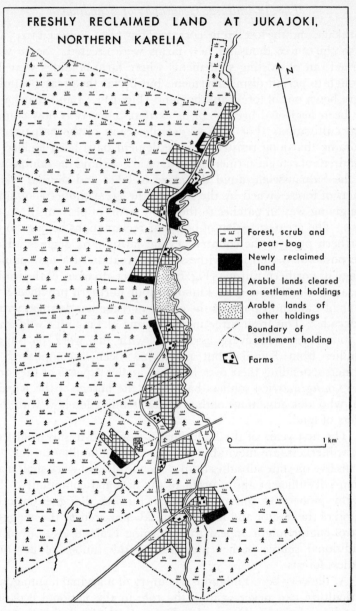

FIG. 62

Jukajoki came into existence in 1947. Ten 'cold' farms and one small-holding were established here along this tiny valley, forming a line of clearings in this wilderness of forest and peat-bog. The need to resettle a displaced population from the lost lands of the Soviet border has pushed forward the frontier of farmland in this way in many parts of Finland.

258

the larger farms in the south-western parts of the country. Before the Second World War wheat, blessed by the good summers of the thirties, promised to become the chief bread grain. Since 1950, a number of crop failures and the needs of the dairying industry for fodder have stimulated an expansion of the area of barley and oats. Wheat, as we have noticed, was dominant in 1950, but in 1958 barley covered twice the area occupied by winter and spring wheat together. As in central Sweden, oats is the chief cereal of Finland's arable farms, and in some parts of the south-west this fodder-crop occupies more than a quarter of the arable acreage.

Dairy farming's pre-eminent position in the Finnish economy today represents more than a close adjustment to the physical facts of Finland's environment. It has received encouragement, too, from the state, through financial subsidies and export premiums to enable the Finnish farmer to compete in foreign markets with producers of cheese and butter whose costs stand at only two-thirds of the Finnish figure. Finland's agriculture only finds an export market for its products with generous help from the state — a sure sign of the marginal qualities of farming in this northern country. Some have doubted whether the state should pursue policies of this kind, and this school of thought conducts a campaign for a more balanced pattern of agriculture.[5] A smaller output of milk, butter and cheese, which would be accompanied by a retreat from foreign markets in these products, would find compensation in a declining import of costly fertilizers and cattle foods.

It is more than likely that Finland will experience a sharp decline of her farm population in the next generation. Mechanization is beginning to make a more efficient use of her labour force and the farm, with fewer hands, can do better than in the past. As in Sweden, the state may resolve to adjust the output from its farmlands to fit the nation's needs, releasing, at the same time, more of her people for the exploitation of the country's greatest and most lucrative resource — the natural wealth of the softwood forests.

CHAPTER 9

The Growth of Scandinavian Industries

A STUDY of settlement and agriculture in Scandinavia reveals the many individual traits of this area — traits that help to distinguish this major region from the rest of the continent. Likewise, the development of Scandinavian industry stands apart from the trends of industrial growth in central and western Europe. The chief difference lies in the late arrival of the industrial revolution in the Scandinavian countries. Although Sweden was the world's largest producer and exporter of high-quality bar-iron in the eighteenth century, she only felt the impact of industrialism in the two decades before 1900. Factory industries began to take root in Norway only at the beginning of the twentieth century, with the notable exception of small water-driven textile mills founded at Oslo and Bergen in the 1840's. Modern industries came even later to Finland. She had to achieve political independence in 1917 before the vigorous cultivation of industry could take place, though one must note the precocious mills at Tampere established more than half a century earlier. Denmark, too, has evolved into a deeply industrialized country during the past half century.

The period since the end of the Second World War has been of crucial importance in Scandinavia's industrial development. The national statistics of the 1950's reveal the achievement of higher levels of industrial activity in all the Scandinavian states. For instance, the power consumed by Finland's industries was more than doubled over the years between 1945 and 1957. Another sign of the new and dominant rôle played by industry in the economies of the north European countries is seen in Norway's employment statistics. Just before the Second World War the primary occupations that bind men to the natural elements of the sea, forest, and field were still uppermost. In 1938 farming, forestry, and fishing claimed 38 per cent of Norwegians, while only 25 per cent of the population was employed in mining and industry. The figures for 1957 show a drastic reversal of the labour force in these two occupation groups, two opposed ways of

260

life. Agriculture, forestry, and fishing now engage only a quarter of Norway's working population. Mining and industry have risen to absorb 32 per cent of her active manpower.

Figures of production and output from all kinds of Scandinavian industry tell the same story of a prosperous period in the late forties and early fifties. Sweden, always the most forward of the Scandinavian states in industrial development, reveals a time of intense activity in the output of so many commodities. Her production of ferro-alloys increased by 150 per cent between 1948 and 1957. Over the same period the Swedish output of sponge iron — an important recent discovery that reduces the consumption of coke — multiplied six times from 26,430 tons to 135,976 tons. Likewise, between 1953 and 1956 Sweden almost doubled her manufacture of cars. The same story of steeply rising industrial outputs applies to Swedish shipbuilding. In 1957 the Swedish shipyards launched eighty-one vessels, the highest annual construction in the history of the industry. So one could accumulate statistics that tell the same story of industrial growth during the past fifteen years among the small states of north-western Europe. In sum, they point to the achievement of a level of industrial maturity well beyond that reached before the Second World War.

Today, each of the Scandinavian countries displays a far wider range of industries. Finland's electrical industry produces V.H.F. transmitters and receivers, refrigerators, washing machines, and many types of electric motor. In Norway, too, the range of industries has been widened, especially in the field of consumer goods. Adding machines and cash registers, radios, tape-recorders, radio-telephone apparatus and echo-sounders are all produced in Norwegian factories. The Norwegian chemical industry has made notable advances in the use of the waste products of pulp mills, and with the introduction of factories in the remote north for the freezing of fish fillets she is working a minor revolution in a centuries-old export industry. Norwegian engineers designed and built the country's first atomic reactor at Halden in 1959, and it is a measure of her new industrial maturity that much of the equipment for this heavy-water reactor was made in the country.

The Swedes have always led their neighbours in the development of industry, and it is not surprising that the country displays many of the features of industrially mature communities. For instance, there is a strong drift of people to the towns and industrial occupations. Between 1950 and 1960 the agricultural labour force declined by a quarter. The engineering industry, already well-developed at the beginning of the century, broadened enormously in the past ten years. Perhaps the most striking example is the growth of the car industry. In 1950 Sweden counted thirty-six cars for every thousand of her inhabitants. By 1958 the same number of people owned 131 cars between them. No wonder that the Swedish car factories were able to double their output within the space of three years in the mid-fifties! Sweden, too, has made the greatest progress among the north European states in exploring the uses of atomic energy. The first research reactor began to work in 1954, and Sweden's Atomic Energy Corporation in which the state owns more than half the shares has built a research centre at Studsvik on the Baltic coast about sixty miles to the south of Stockholm. Now the Swedes, with their flair for large-scale planning, are building an atomic power station as part of Farsta, a new satellite town in the Stockholm conurbation. Farsta will have a population of 30,000 and a district heating scheme fed from an atomic reactor will warm its twelve thousand flats. The same power plant will feed 10,000 kwh. of electricity into the Stockholm network.

A certain sign of industrial maturity in any nation is the export overseas of machines and technical experts. For a long time, Swedish engineering has enjoyed a world-wide reputation, but since the war the Danes and Norwegians have begun to throw out a challenge. Danish engineers have won contracts for work on Turkish railways and their firms are developing subsidiaries in South American states. Lately, Norway has entered the international field in the engineering industry, selling abroad her equipment and technical 'know-how' in the construction of hydro-electric stations. A Norwegian firm secured the contract for the building of the first stage in Australia's huge Snowy Mountains hydro-electric scheme. Recently, too, Norwegians have built and supplied equipment for power stations in Brazil. It is a far cry from the 1840's when machinery was imported from England for the first small water-driven textile mills in Oslo.

Since the late 1930's industrial outputs in the Scandinavian countries have more than doubled, bringing subtle changes in the balance of each nation's economy that have been reflected in commercial relationships with the world outside northern Europe. For instance, the rapid rise of industries has underlined Scandinavia's weakness in fuel minerals and raw materials. The export of power plants to Brazil and ice-breakers to the U.S.S.R. has been purchased at the cost of higher imports of coke and steel-plate from western Europe.

Sweden, the most industrialized among the Scandinavian nations, reveals this trend most clearly. Although she mines almost twenty million tons of high-grade iron ore a year, selling most of it abroad [Fig. 100], Sweden imports steadily increasing amounts of sheet-iron for her engineering industries. Imports of sheet-iron and steel, largely in the form of plate for the ship-building industry, were more than doubled between 1948 and 1957 (1948 — 208,871 tons; 1957 — 490,665 tons).[1] Finland's appetite for sheet-iron and constructional steel has increased rapidly since the war. Her engineering and shipbuilding industries, inflated at first by the demands of post-war reparations to Russia, import a third of their raw and semi-manufactured materials. Although the debt to the Soviet Union is now paid, these industries still find an extensive market in the communist world, and the Finnish trade statistics of 1957 show that the import of sheet-iron and steel is about eight times the amount of the early thirties.

Scandinavia displays profound weaknesses in the relations between the needs of growing industries and the national resources of raw materials. For many years forest products have headed Norway's list of exports, but since 1955 processed ores and metals have taken their place [Fig. 111]. Aluminium stands in the lead, its output multiplying almost five times since the late thirties (1939 — 35,000 tons; 1961 — 167,984 tons). And yet this industry depends entirely upon imported raw materials — bauxite or alumina from France, Greece, or Canada. The refining of zinc, a lonely industry at Eitrheim on a branch of Hardanger fjord, rests upon imported ore, while the metallurgical plant at Kristiansand turns to Canada for the whole of its nickel matte [Plate 2]. The enlargement of Denmark's industrial base presents even greater problems of the supply of raw materials than in the other Scandinavian states. Her power stations, located in the chief ports, are fed from imported coal and oil, and she lacks all the raw materials to supply her varied engineering industries. Towards the end of the Second World War the Danes completed a blast furnace and rolling mill, producing 150,000 tons of pig iron a year, to strengthen the domestic foundations of her metal-working industries. But Denmark's predetermined weakness in raw materials was only uncovered at another level, because this plant uses imported scrap iron and coke.

Scandinavia's notorious weakness in the fuel minerals, principally coal and oil, is evident in a fresh way as the world enters the second half of the twentieth century. An absence of coal delayed the industrial revolution in these northern countries, but with the development of hydro-electric power in about 1900 they rose triumphant above the difficulties imposed by nature. In the past fifteen years a new dependence, paid for by precious foreign currency, has appeared in the rising consumption of fuel oil. Sweden, with the greatest number of cars on the road and the highest standard of living in northern Europe, displays this trend most clearly. In 1957 she imported almost ten million tons of oil, using it in ships and road transport and, increasingly, as a fuel for central heating systems. Imports of oil have quadrupled within a decade. Sweden, with many hydro-electric stations [Fig. 64] and great reserves of undeveloped water-power still left in the north, finds that half of her energy in the late fifties comes from imported fuels. No wonder that her engineers search for methods to use the power locked up in the peat-bogs — a source that would supply the equivalent of three decades of oil imports. Still more the Swedes look towards the oil-bearing shales of Ranstad as a source that will yield several hundred thousand tons of uranium, perhaps making her the richest Scandinavian country in the raw materials of atomic power.

As the nations of northern Europe survey their resources, they turn from their obvious riches in iron ore, timber, and hydro-electric power to face poverty in many other valuable commodities. The Norwegians, perhaps with a note of pessimism that seems to be part of their national character, point to the failing harvest of the whaling fleet in the Antarctic Ocean. At home their fish canneries rest upon the uncertainties of nature. For instance, the brisling fisheries failed completely in 1955 and 1956. The reserves of pyrites, the most valuable mineral resource of Norway at the moment, are rapidly decreasing. Behind the problems of feeding shipyards, foundries, forges, textile mills, and chemical plants with their raw materials lies the harder question of further industrial expansion. The capital costs of industrial growth have increased enormously in the middle of the twentieth century. For instance, the expenses of capital equipment in the chemical industry are five times higher than before the Second World War. A new cellulose plant in northern Finland today would cost 15 per cent of the country's annual revenue. If the post-war rate of industrial expansion is to continue into the 1960's it seems that capital, too, might become a necessary raw material to be imported from the world outside Scandinavia.

THE ORIGINS OF INDUSTRY IN NORTHERN EUROPE

Today, Sweden is the most industrialized of the Scandinavian states and since the early thirties industry has formed the largest sector of the national economy. Yet only a hundred years ago Sweden was on the brink of the economic transformations that were to change her into an industrial nation. For Norway, Finland, and Denmark in 1850 the dawn of industrialism was even more distant. Scandinavia has always been late in the acquisition of fresh ideas and techniques — a fact of history that is largely explained by the geographical isolation of this major region. The arts of agriculture reached the shores of the Skagerrak and the Baltic two thousand years later than the favoured loess lands of central Europe. Christianity took a thousand years to reach northern Europe, and the techniques of the industrial revolution suffered a delay of several decades before they took root in Scandinavia.

The late appearance of industry is partly explained by the almost complete lack of coal, the primary source of power for the first stage of the industrial revolution in western Europe. Denmark and Finland possess no coal at all, the one composed of Quaternary clays, gravel-spreads and sands, the other forming part of the Pre-Cambrian Baltic shield. Norway and Sweden are scarcely better off. Sweden's only coalfield lies in the south near Hälsingborg where poor coals of Liassic age yield 300 tons a year; in 1957 she imported almost six million tons of coal and coke. There are no commercially-worked coal deposits in Norway, but she receives almost half a million tons a year from mines in Spitsbergen. A colony of a thousand Norwegians operates these mines under the severest conditions in an Arctic climate and with export facilities by sea only from May until the middle of October. The Tertiary coal seams of Spitsbergen, too, lie a thousand miles from the briquetting plant at Trondheim, twice as remote as the coal staithes of Northumberland from the industrial centres of Oslo fjord. Spitsbergen's coal, the only important source of fuel in Scandinavia, stands as a symbol of Norwegian doggedness and a symptom of the poverty of northern Europe in the key mineral of the Victorian industrial revolution.

Scandinavian industry began to grow with the development of hydro-electric power towards the close of the nineteenth century. Norway's first electricity works was built at Skien in 1887, while the first municipal power station in the country opened at Hammerfest, the world's most northerly town, in 1891. But the first period for the continuous expansion of electric power in Norway lay between 1912 and 1920. The coming of electricity made possible the electro-chemical and electro-metallurgical industries, revolutionized the supply of power in all the workshop industries, and paved the way for fresh techniques and a relocation of plant in sawmilling and pulp manufacture. In Finland, too, the rise of industry is closely related to the building of hydro-electric stations. Between 1918 and 1940 the power capacity of the country increased ten-fold, and in these first decades of national independence there was also a rapid growth of manufactures.

The history of the development of hydro-electric power in Sweden resembles that of Norway. The first power stations appeared in the 1890's with the establishment of municipal and private plants to provide electricity for lighting. 1906 was a memorable year when the Swedish government financed a scheme to tap the energy of the Trollhättan falls on the Göta river. This act introduced a half-century of power development that revolutionized the nation's economy. Today, all but a few of the falls and rapids of southern Sweden have been harnessed. Nevertheless, two-thirds of the water power potential of Sweden awaits development, but most of this energy runs to waste in the rivers of remote Norrland and already the Swedes are considering the idea of atomic power as an economic alternative to hydro-electricity. This half-century of water power development is also the period of Sweden's industrial revolution. At the start of the twentieth century, more than half of Sweden's population was engaged in the traditional work of the land and sea, farming, timber-cutting, and fishing. Today these occupations claim less than a quarter of her population, and only 17 per cent earn their living from farming. Among the Scandinavian states Sweden today is the most deeply industrialized. Between 1950 and 1960 the agricultural population declined at the rate of 4 per cent per year, and up and down the country farmers abandoned the poorest and most marginal land.

Scandinavia's industrial revolution belongs to the twentieth century and depends upon the successful development of northern Europe's abundant sources of water power. But is it possible to explain the history of modern industry solely in the terms of an absence of coal and the discovery of the techniques of the water turbine? Sweden boasts an industrial history as long as that of any European state. The copper mines at Falun are among the oldest in Europe and were worked for an unbroken span of eight centuries. Methods of industrial organization were not unknown to medieval Sweden, and one of her greatest corporations today — the Stora Kopparbergs Bergslags Company — claims to be the oldest joint stock company in the world. Technical skill in metallurgy belonged to the forgemen of central Sweden more than a century before England showed signs of taking up her position as the leader of the industrial revolution. In the seventeenth century Sweden evolved techniques and standards of iron-working that led the world, and during the first half of the eighteenth century England imported half of her annual needs of bar-iron from Sweden. Some of the most important elements of the industrial revolution were present in eighteenth-century Sweden and yet she failed to achieve the transformations that affected the coalfields of western Europe in the Victorian age.

Scandinavia's relations to the states of the North Sea basin in the nineteenth century were as vital to the history of industrial expansion as the presence of thousands of sites for the development of water power. Often, northern Europe has stood in a colonial relationship to the rest of the continent. In the later Middle Ages, Scandinavia lay on the northern fringe of the Hanseatic League's commercial empire, sending its fish and furs, tar and timber, to the prosperous towns of central Europe. In return, the merchants of Bergen received corn and cloth from England and Flanders. Similarly, the nineteenth century witnessed relations of a semi-colonial character between Scandinavia and the industrially-developed nations of the North Sea basin. Raw materials such as fish, sawn timber, corn, meat, and butter played a large part in the traffic with Britain and Germany. Industrial goods — textiles, railway equipment, iron ships, and all kinds of consumer articles — formed part of the return traffic to the north. But this sphere of North Sea trade that enveloped Scandinavia, Westphalia and the

Netherlands, Belgium, northern France, and the British Isles was also an area where ideas and techniques circulated, if somewhat less freely and more slowly than goods. It was a region, too, through which capital was able to disperse itself from the capital-accumulating countries, such as Britain and France, to the capital-starved peasant economies of the north.

During the nineteenth century one is aware of the repercussion of political events and technical discoveries throughout the North Sea area. For instance, the feeble beginning of the industrial revolution in Norway dates back to the 1840's with the establishment of small textile industries in the eastern suburbs of Oslo and close to the port city of Bergen. One influence in the foundation of these small cotton mills was the removal of the ban upon the export of machinery from England in 1842. Other acts of English parliaments deeply affected the fortunes of industry in northern Europe. For instance, the repeal of the Navigation Act in 1849 introduced a new era of trade for the Norwegians that was to make the merchant navy the most vital part of the state's economy. Likewise, the first stage of nineteenth-century industrialism was ushered into Sweden by political and economic events in the British Isles. The establishment of free trade by Britain in the 1840's allowed the sawn timber of Scandinavia to enter a rapidly expanding market without hindrance. Between 1850 and 1880 almost every English town spawned off new streets and suburbs. Some towns, such as Barrow-in-Furness, sprang from nothing to populations of several thousand within a few years. The Victorian building industry had an insatiable appetite for Scandinavian softwoods, and it was out of the satisfaction of this demand that the Swedish sawmilling industry, steam-driven on imported coal, developed in the second half of the nineteenth century.

Apart from the stimulus of their own demands for timber and raw materials, the rich and densely populated countries of the southern part of the North Sea basin also contributed capital, ideas, and technical experts to the evolving industries of Scandinavia. Sweden exhibits this theme at an early date. The first half of the seventeenth century was a period of vigorous political expansion and economic growth. For a brief time, Sweden incorporated almost the whole of the Baltic coastline within her frontiers and many new towns were founded. Foreigners settled in Sweden to establish industries — Dutchmen, Scotsmen, Walloons, and Austrians. The most famous of these foreign industrialists was Louis de Geer, a member of a Liège family, who migrated from Amsterdam and built up for himself a vast range of industrial and commercial interests in Sweden. He became the greatest ironmaster of seventeenth-century Sweden. With Walloon smelting techniques and Swedish charcoal — the finest in the world — Louis de Geer was the chief pioneer of the expansion of Sweden's high-quality iron industry. He was an industrialist of many interests and his factories lay scattered about central Sweden, producing brass, tin, wire, paper, and cloth. This seventeenth-century industrial magnate also engaged in shipbuilding and built up a trading fleet.

Louis de Geer was the prototype of several industrialists in nineteenth-century Scandinavia. The shipbuilding industry of Göteborg illustrates the part played by foreigners in the economic development of northern Europe. The Götaverken, today employing nearly six thousand workers, sprang from the enterprise of a Scotsman, Alexander Keiller, more than a century ago. Collaborating with Alexander Gibson in 1832, he bought a water-driven sawmill and used the premises for the weaving of sail-cloth. Ten years later, Keiller set up as an engineer in the manufacture of steam engines. It is interesting that he imported his equipment from England — another instance of the transmission of one of the elements of the industrial revolution northwards from the British Isles. In 1850 Keiller turned his interest towards shipbuilding and built his first steamship. It is said that he wanted to exploit the fine estuary of the Göta river and Göteborg's position as a major Scandinavian port when he founded the shipyard that was to flourish in the twentieth century as the Götaverken.

As we have already noticed, a Scotsman was a leader of the industrial revolution in Finland. In 1828 James Finlayson built a cotton mill on a water power site at Tampere, acquiring from the Russian Tsar the right to import cotton and other raw materials free of duty. Today, Tampere is Finland's second largest city [Plate 34], maintaining an economic position first granted to it by the initiative of a foreigner and the edicts of a political system that vanished in 1917.

Besides initiative and industrial genius, the North Sea countries also fed Scandinavia with capital in the nineteenth century. By 1860, Britain, France, and the Low Countries were accumulating sufficient capital through trade and industry to be able to invest heavily in less developed areas. The growth of the Swedish economy before 1900 is especially indebted to capital from France.

The problems of industrial growth in northern Europe are most clearly illustrated in the realm of communications. As the England of the railway age clearly shows, the growth of industry and the construction of railways are related phenomena. It was no accident that the first successful public railway joined Liverpool and Manchester — the chief cotton-importing port and the metropolis of south-east Lancashire's textile region. The railway network of the British Isles, too, reflects the distribution of centres of industry and population. Scandinavia posed very different problems. Small populations scattered over wide territories with severe difficulties in terrain and climate did not open up a promised land to the nineteenth-century railway magnate. A lack of industries held out a gloomy prospect for traffic receipts, and yet factory industries, dependent upon markets stretching to the whole state and overseas, could not flourish without efficient communications. Even the Bergslagen, that ancient mining and metal-working district northward of the Swedish lakes, was hampered by its inefficient communications. Until the 1870's, the scattered forges and mines of Bergslagen relied upon a system of transport that had changed little since the late Middle Ages. In winter, their products reached the towns and the ports on the fringe of the region by 'winter' roads — snow tracks through the forests and across the frozen lakes. In summer, the routes leading out of Bergslagen presented a serious obstacle to its economic development. A maze of land portages connected by short sections along lakes and rivers formed the only means of communication in the summer months. Often goods had to be transhipped a dozen times. The emergence of this region as a major industrial area depended upon the creation of a railway system in the 1870's, mainly by private enterprise that used foreign capital. Ludvika, in remote, forested country on the northern fringe of the area, became the main railway centre. There the trunk line across the northern parts of central Sweden from Göteborg to Gävle threw off a railway southwards, joining a succession of mining centres to Oxelösund, a practically ice-free port on the Baltic. Railways transformed the economy of Bergslagen. The heavy products of her forges could be moved with ease at all times of the year. Previously, this type of trade had been restricted to the winter months. The export of iron ores, particularly the rich phosphoric

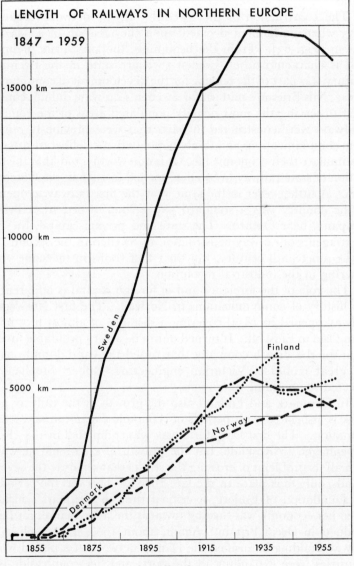

LENGTH OF RAILWAYS IN NORTHERN EUROPE

1847 – 1959

Fig. 63

In Denmark and Sweden the railway systems reached their greatest length in the late 1920's. The railways of Finland and Norway are still expanding. The graph for Finland shows the sharp loss of mileage in 1944 at the close of the war with Russia.

ore of Grängesberg, was added to the traditional trade in pigs and ingots.

The construction of the Swedish railway network began in 1855 when parliament decided upon the creation of a national system [Fig. 63]. From the beginning, the large-scale planning that is characteristic of Sweden's welfare state in the twentieth century was part of the scheme for the development of communications. Nils Ericson's pattern for Sweden's railways did not confine itself to serving the most densely populated areas of the country. Railways were constructed in parts that were previously remote from communications and thinly populated in a deliberate attempt to stimulate their economic life. It is noteworthy, too, that the first section of state railway in Sweden opened in 1856 in the Göteborg area. A little earlier in the same year the first railway to operate in the country was a standard gauge line, owned by a British company, near Örebro. The state and private capital, the two great agents of railway construction in Sweden in the second half of the nineteenth century, ran their first trains in the same year, ushering in the industrial revolution.

The rôle of the foreigner and of foreign capital is apparent in the history of communications in Norway. The first Norwegian railway opened in 1854, covering a distance of almost fifty miles from Oslo to Eidsvoll. It turned out to be a very profitable investment for the British company that raised the capital, and one of the great names of Victorian engineering, Robert Stephenson, directed the building operations.

In Denmark and Finland also the growth of the railway network is associated with periods of economic expansion and transformation. The first Danish railway was completed in 1847 from Copenhagen to Roskilde, but the growth of a national network, with all its problems of crossing the straits that separate the several islands, only took place in the late 1860's. This was the period of the foundation of Esbjerg, a critical time in Denmark's history when her economy was turning towards the huge market for farm products in Great Britain. Again, about 1900, a fresh phase of railway building intensified the Danish network at a period when industries were expanding in the ports and her countryside was becoming even more dependent upon an external market through its co-operative selling organizations.

The building of new railways continues in Scandinavia in the middle of the twentieth century. Above all, this is true of Finland

and Norway. At present the Norwegians are completing their costly project of a line into the thinly populated territories beyond the Arctic Circle. With the slogan of 'a kroner per millimetre', the Arctic railway was laid through the long, empty valleys of Nordland during the Nazi occupation of the Second World War. Today, the sinuous thread of embankments and shallow cuttings snakes its way along the northern shore of Saltfjord towards the projected terminus at Bodø. Railway building in Arctic Norway coincides with state planning and investment in the industrial development of the north.

Finland, too, proposes to build extensive additions to her railway system. Her motives for this surprising investment in new railways contain the deeply intermingled elements of strategy and trade. She aims to adjust her railways to the new post-war frontiers as well as to open up new areas to mining and forestry. Finnish transport statistics show that freight traffic accounts for the greater part of the railway's income, and timber constitutes more than half of the goods traffic on the railway system. Railway expansion seems to reflect the needs of the forest industries, Finland's major occupation. If Finland completes her proposed railway extensions in the second half of the twentieth century, she will be unique in a continent where railway construction has ceased almost completely.

Denmark and Sweden are comparable to the rest of western and central Europe in the present stage of railway development. Their railway networks have reached maturity and are in harmony with the industrial needs of the country; it is unlikely that fresh lines will be constructed in response to new economic demands. The astonishing rise of Swedish road traffic in the fifties and the extensive construction of new roads in the inaccessible forests of the north suggest that railway development is at an end. Denmark has reached a stage further in the history of railways. Since the Second World War many miles of branch line have been closed, and here the railway system is undergoing the painful adjustment to the competition of road transport that has afflicted the mature economies of other west European states.

The origins and progress of the industrial revolution in Scandinavia seem to be related to the presence and absence of fuel minerals and water power, the stimulus in ideas and capital provided by the economically mature nations of the North Sea basin in the nineteenth century, and the growth of the web of communications in the second half of the nineteenth century — a process that is scarcely finished in Norway and Finland. Beside these long-term factors, the speed and pattern of industrialization has been affected by the rhythm of political events both in continental Europe and the inner world of Scandinavia. Wars and the booms and slumps of international trade have left their mark on Scandinavian industrial history.

POLITICS AND WAR IN THE DEVELOPMENT OF SCANDINAVIAN INDUSTRIES

It is hard to weigh the effects of the Napoleonic Wars on the economic development of northern Europe. Industries and towns grew rapidly in the British Isles at this time. It is true, too, that important industrial techniques developed in England at the end of the eighteenth century and that they spread to continental Europe only in the period of peace that followed Waterloo and the Congress of Vienna. At this time Scandinavia was too remote from the southern parts of the North Sea basin to be deeply influenced by economic events there. Scandinavia's isolation broke down only in the second half of the nineteenth century. The first regular North Sea shipping services appeared in the 1870's, and it was not until 1904 that Sweden started her first trans-oceanic services to South America and South Africa.

The great European wars of the twentieth century had profound effects on industry in northern Europe. Wars choke international trade, and both the First and Second World Wars deeply affected the economies of Scandinavian countries. Northern Europe lay remote from the battles of the first war. The chief disturbance was in relations with England and Germany, established since the last quarter of the nineteenth century as the chief markets for Scandinavian raw materials and farm products. These countries, too, provided the main source of consumption goods for northern Europe. The First World War encouraged the growth of industries supplying the domestic Scandinavian market. In Norway, it stands out as the period of the first great development of hydro-electric power, a time when the foundations of the electro-metallurgical and electro-chemical industries were laid.

The period of the Second World War prepared far deeper

changes in the industrial geography of northern Europe. The neutral ideal that the Nordic world held up to itself proved untenable in the power relationships of World War II. Nazi Germany occupied both Norway and Denmark, while Finland became a battlefield for the armies of the U.S.S.R. The war uncovered deficiencies in the industrial structure of northern Europe, showing up its lack of important raw materials and its dependence for many manufactured goods upon the industrially mature nations of western Europe. Perhaps the most important development of the war years was the establishment in 1942 of an iron- and steel-works at Frederiksværk in Denmark. Today this rolling mill produces about a third of Danish needs in steel. For Sweden, the Second World War ushered in a long period of expansion in the output of hydro-electric power, especially through the construction of new power stations on the untapped northern rivers. As examples among several, the state-owned power station of Midskog was built between 1941 and 1944 on the Indals river [Fig. 65], and an additional power station came into service at Scandinavia's classic hydro-electric site, Trollhättan, in 1942.

Norwegian industry felt the direct effects of the German occupation. The rich power resources of her mountain lakes and waterfalls and her gloomy, cloud-enshrouded fjords encouraged the development of strategic industries. The Germans organized a company, A/S Nordag, to develop the aluminium industry in western Norway. At Årdal, sited on a deep arm at the head of Sognefjord, a power station, an aluminium plant, and electric smelting plant were partly constructed. The Norwegian government took over this half-finished aluminium plant in 1946, and along with the unit at Sunndal, another site chosen by German technicians for the development of aluminium smelting during the war, it has contributed much to the post-war expansion of the electro-metallurgical industries of Norway.

The two wars of this century left their mark on Scandinavian industries in a broadening of the range of products and industrial processes, but Scandinavia lies too close to the heart of Europe to escape the damaging effects of war upon the economy. In the graphs of industrial outputs the war years stand like a chasm between the gentle ups and downs of the twenties and thirties and the precipitously rising curves of the late forties and fifties. War hit northern Europe in three ways. Imported raw materials, upon which so many industries depend, became scarce. The export markets for timber, pulp, cellulose, and fish products were less certain and harder to reach with the broken North Sea communications. Lastly, the Second World War brought its own severe damage to the capital equipment of industry in Scandinavia. Submarine warfare crippled the merchant navies of all the northern countries. Norway, for instance, lost half of her merchant fleet between 1940 and 1945 [Fig. 74]. At the close of the war, Nazi scorched-earth policy in Finnish Lapland and Arctic Norway damaged industrial resources. The most notable, perhaps, was the destruction of the iron mines and concentrating plant at Sydvaranger in northern Norway. Despite the help of Marshall Aid funds, this Arctic source of iron ore was able to return to production only in 1952.

The stimulus of the Second World War to Scandinavian industry only becomes clear in the immediate post-war years. Perhaps the chief influence of the war was the temporary elimination of Germany as the main supplier of industrial goods to Scandinavia. Combined with the inability of Britain to supply the demands of foreign markets in the post-war years, this provided a healthy economic atmosphere for the growth of new industries in northern Europe. For instance, the expansion of Norway's electrical engineering industry illustrates the elaboration of an industry in the post-war period. Before the war, Norway imported three-quarters of her needs in electrical equipment from Germany. Today, this industry has grown many new branches, producing not only the equipment for power stations and transmission lines — dynamos, transformers, and oil-filled high-voltage cables for underwater transmission — but also the smaller commodities for domestic use that were largely imported in the 1930's. The Norwegians now make telephones, all kinds of electrical fittings, vacuum cleaners, washing machines and refrigerators, and of late she has produced radios and tape-recorders that have found a modest export market in western Europe. The same drive towards industrial self-sufficiency is apparent even more clearly in Sweden. Among the Scandinavian countries, Sweden has always possessed the most elaborate industrial structure, but the rapid growth of the car industry since the Second World War is symptomatic of a period of greater maturity that began with Germany's removal from the industrial field. Not that Germany's absence has had the permanency that was prophesied by some political and economic soothsayers. For instance, Western Germany has more than regained the Swedish trade of the larger pre-war Germany. The trade figures of 1958 show that Western Germany supplied Sweden with 23·3 per cent of the value of her imports. Twenty years earlier, in 1938, 21·8 per cent of the cost of Swedish imports went to Germany. Nevertheless, the abnormal circumstances of the late 1940's, a Germany damaged by war and paralysed by defeat, together with the preoccupations of recovery and reconstruction in the United Kingdom, forced the whole of northern Europe towards greater industrial maturity.

Fluctuations in international trade have deeply affected industrial history in Scandinavia. The boom of the post-war period, as we have already noticed, is connected with the most remarkable phase in the industrial history of northern Europe. But in this time of rising prosperity the months of minor crisis on the world's stock exchanges are reflected in Scandinavia's curves of trade and industry. The early fifties, the time of the Korean War boom, was one of steeply rising outputs from the Scandinavian industries; while the uncertainties of world trade and prices in 1957, the faintest cloud-shadow on the sunlit sea of the international economy compared with the darkness of the slump in the early thirties, foreshadowed unpleasant dislocations in the prosperity of northern Europe. Early in 1957, the Finns faced, for the first time, the problem of the overgrown engineering and shipbuilding industries, an expansion forced upon the country by the Soviet reparations demand. In the crisis of 1957, when a perilous level of inflation brought about a devaluation of the Finnish currency, workers were shifted from the uneconomic secondary industries to the basic wood and pulp industries of the country. But the minor slump in world trade was also sufficient to affect this basic sector of the Finnish economy. The world prices of sawn timber fell by 10 per cent and Finland was seriously injured by a loss of a quarter of her sales of this product. Costs of production in Finland's forest industries had been rising while world prices for timber and wood products declined. By the end of 1956 it was possible for a writer on Finland to say, 'it is now uneconomical to fell the more remote forests, especially the slow-growing timber of the far north'.[2] The limits of Finland's forest exploitation seem to be set by factors far removed from the province of physical geography.

The margins between profit and loss are always narrow, and

they are perhaps more critical in northern Europe than some other parts of the world. While the Finnish economy seemed to be drifting on the rocks in the early months of 1957, with the trade surplus of the early fifties transformed into a deficit, Denmark was suffering from difficulties resulting from low agricultural prices. The value of the chief agricultural exports, butter and bacon, fell by 12 per cent in 1956 and the first months of 1957, while the bill for imports of coal and oil into Denmark rose by 5 per cent. A slight shift in the terms of trade underlined the basic faults of the Danish economy, faults that spring from her geography. She lacks sources of power and her exports are too narrowly focused on one market, the British Isles, and confined within a narrow range of agricultural products.

The years since the Second World War have presented Europe with a period of prosperity and industrial expansion that is matched only by the episodes of vigorous economic growth in the Victorian epoch. On the other hand, the years before the war, especially the early thirties, were a time of severe industrial depression. Scandinavia reacted in two ways towards this slump in international trade, a slump whose causes lay beyond the ambit of the northern countries and whose course they were powerless to influence as small nations. Certain export industries, particularly those feeding the industrial plants of western Europe, were severely hit. In Norway the calcium carbide industry contracted sharply during the years of the world depression. Whereas there were eleven carbide factories in the 1920's, only four plants survived the slump.

The economic crisis of the early thirties also had the opposite effect. Besides damaging industries dependent on international trade, it could also stimulate the foundation of fresh industries to serve the domestic market. In such a manner this period left its mark on Danish industry. In 1933, a time when the drift towards economic autarchy was strong in Europe, the Danish government restricted the import of some types of manufactured goods and at the same time gave preference to the import of raw materials to stimulate the manufacture of similar goods in the home country. The result was that a varied range of industries, including textiles, boots and shoes, clothing, and furniture, flourished under these protective conditions and supplied the home market. The artificial isolation of the world depression, an isolation created by governments through tariffs, embargoes, and quota systems, caused new industries to germinate in Denmark, industries that were to flourish and expand in the real isolation of the Second World War, and to grow to maturity in the boom of the post-war years with the temporary elimination of Germany from the economic landscape of Europe.

CHAPTER 10

Hydro-Electric Power in Scandinavia

THE expansion of industry in Scandinavia since the Second World War, a growth that has changed the economic emphasis from agriculture to industry in each state, has been accompanied by the building of new power stations and the extension of electricity transmission lines. In Norway, the annual production of electricity multiplied three times from 1945 to 1959, rising from 10,000 million kwh. to 27,500 million kwh., and in the late 1950's the construction of new power stations reached a level unparalleled in the industrial history of Norway. There are many ways of expressing this remarkable development of Norway's chief natural resource. For instance, in the five years between 1953 and 1957 new generating capacity was installed at twice the rate of the previous half decade. Within this unrivalled period of growth, 1955 stands out as the best year when 567,000 kilowatts of fresh generating capacity were added to the national supply. One can only appreciate this achievement if one remembers that the first twenty years of power-station building at the beginning of the century only produced a total capacity of 200,000 kilowatts, and that an average of 140,000 kilowatts per annum was added between 1945 and 1950, the first post-war period of rapid development. The rate of growth in the late fifties is most graphically illustrated by the fact that during 1958 the Norwegians were at work on sixty-one new hydro-electric plants, and among these is the giant station at Tokke in Telemark which with its nine power units will have the biggest output in northern Europe.

Sweden, too, records the same immense expansion of electrical energy in the 1950's. In 1959 her power stations produced almost 30,000 million kwh. of electricity, an output that was double the figure of 1950. Finland also increased her ability to generate electricity at about the same rate as Norway and Sweden, adding 10 per cent to her capacity in each year since the end of the war. The incentives to producing more power have been especially compelling in Finland, where a war-damaged and impoverished nation had to replace power stations in territory lost to the Soviet Union, amounting to one-third of her generating capacity.

The link between industry and the generating capacity of the hydro-electric stations is particularly close in Scandinavia. Nearly two-thirds of Norway's output of electricity in 1959 was used by industry, while 45 per cent of the annual power production was consumed by the electro-chemical and electro-metallurgical industries alone. In Sweden, a national survey of power requirements between 1954 and 1961 anticipated that one-third of the projected increase in electric energy would be consumed by electric furnaces in the metallurgical and engineering industries.

A new feature of the geography of electric power in Scandinavia is the heavy increase of domestic consumption in the post-war years. The welfare states of northern Europe tacitly recognize electric power as one of the necessities of life. Consequently, at great cost of capital investment they aim to carry electricity to almost the whole of their small populations widely scattered over difficult terrain. By 1957 Norway could provide 98 per cent of her population with electricity. At the end of the war, in 1945, only 80 per cent of her people were within reach of an electric power supply. This notable achievement in the distribution of power to marginal districts beyond the hope of profits — to lonely farms and hamlets and by underwater cables to islands of the skerry guard — has been accomplished through one of the characteristic devices of the Scandinavian welfare state. In the post-war years the Norwegian government levied a tax on the consumption of power, using the profits of this levy to extend the nation's network of power lines. Sweden reaches an even higher percentage of her population than Norway with electricity supplies. Out of about two million households only 30,000 are without electricity; 98·5 per cent of the population is connected to the grid. Finland, the most backward of the northern countries, made similar great strides. Only half of her population used electric power in 1945, but by 1957 the grid had expanded in the southern and western parts of the country to feed 70 per cent of her people.

Geography places Denmark's power problems in a different context. Only 1 per cent of the national output of electricity comes from water-driven sources. Unlike their Scandinavian neighbours, the Danes cannot count off their untapped waterfalls and look across another three decades of expanding energy measured in the astronomical terms of thousands of millions of kilowatt hours. They must plan their future needs of electricity against the cost of imported coal and oil or the chance of laying an underwater cable that will make Jutland and the islands tributary to the power stations of the rainy fjords of south-western Norway. At present, Denmark aims to rationalize the production of power to eleven huge plants sited in the ports and fed with coal and diesel oil.

Scandinavia's water power resources are not unlimited. At the present rate of expansion Sweden will have harnessed all her hydro-electric power in the next thirty years. Norway possesses the greatest reserves of undeveloped water power in Europe, with only 23 per cent of the estimated hydro-electric potential tapped in 1958. Finland is the weakest of the north European nations possessed with water power. Her potential maximum seems to be about seventeen thousand million kwh. per year, a sum that equals about a third of the generating capacity of either Sweden or Norway at the close of the fifties. Today, Finland draws on about half of her calculated maximum. But time only shows that calculations in this particular field of economic geography are almost valueless. Technology changes so quickly that the power potential of a state within the next generation cannot be foreseen [Fig. 64].

Nevertheless, the limits to the development of hydro-electricity in Scandinavia seem to be clearly in sight. This coincides with a rising and changing demand in each of the northern countries. When the state aims to bring electricity to the smallest and remotest consumers it changes the nature of consumption. Until today the Scandinavian power plants have largely served the needs of industry. At lonely sites amid Finland's forests or under the frowning cliffs of some Norwegian fjord, a single power plant has given its whole output to either a pulp and paper mill or an aluminium refinery. Today, the domestic consumer is beginning to take more of Scandinavia's power and in the present decade has had an appreciable effect upon the pattern of production. Domestic heating accounts for the chief rise in the use of electricity in Norwegian homes. Sweden, the richest of Scandinavia's nations, shows a different trend, with a rising domestic consumption of electricity in refrigerators, washing machines, television, and the gadgets of the affluent society. There, domestic heating increasingly turns to the oil-fired central heating system and the electricity grid has not had to bear this burden. However, the margins are still wide and industry does not regard the domestic consumer as a serious rival for the power supplies of northern Europe.

In Norway, the increasing use of electricity for household heating may even benefit industry as the declining use of firewood in the home releases more timber for the pulp and paper mills, factories whose manufacturing capacity exceeds the annual supply of raw material.

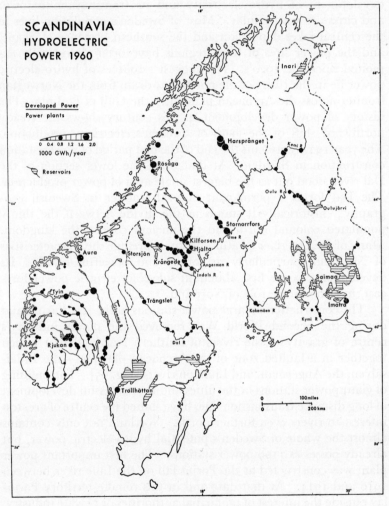

FIG. 64

The main sources of hydro-electric power are found in the isolated stations of Norway's western fjords and, above all, in the clustered power plants on the rivers of the Archaean Shield — the Indals and Ångerman in central Norrland, and the Kemi and Oulu of northern Finland. The adjustment of Scandinavia's rivers to post-glacial changes of sea level is noticed in the siting of power stations at knick-point rapids in the lower valley courses of the Glomma, Kymi, Dal, and Ume rivers.

HYDRO-ELECTRIC POWER IN SWEDEN AND FINLAND

For Sweden and Finland, the geographical problems of the development of hydro-electricity and its transmission to towns and cities are very similar. Most of Sweden's population lives in the central lakes depression and the southern province of Skåne, and the power sites of these regions have been almost fully exploited since the 1920's. Her biggest resources of hydro-electric power lie in the rivers of the north that drain from the Norwegian frontier across the Archaean plateau to the Gulf of Bothnia. The history of power development in this century shows the steady northward shift of the focus of Sweden's electricity production. The year 1922 represents the end of the first period of power-station construction in Sweden. At that time, the lower section of the Dal river stood out as the biggest single area of power production. The Dal forms a permanent natural frontier in Swedish geography; historically it stands as the divide between the thinly populated colonial north and the ancient core of the kingdom. Many of the Dal river's natural features presage the characteristics of Norrland, particularly its forests and powerful rapids. Its development as the first abundant source of electric power forecast, too, the future rôle of Norrland.

The construction of large power stations in the late thirties and during the Second World War removed the power industry's centre of gravity to the rivers of southern Norrland that bunch together in a faulted zone of the Archaean plateau — the Indalsälven, the Ångerman, and Ljungan rivers [Fig. 65]. The building of giant power stations in the fifties and the successful development of long distance transmission lines have shifted the centre of greatest interest to rivers even further north. Norrland not only contains almost the whole of Sweden's potential hydro-electric power, but already possesses 1100 power stations. The first important power plant was constructed at the Porjus fall on the Lule river between 1910 and 1914. At that date and in this remote territory Porjus lay outside the interest of municipal authorities or private industry. It was built by the state to provide power for the iron-ore railway between Gällivare, Kiruna, and Narvik. With a head of less than two hundred feet, Porjus harnesses a fall typical of the Baltic Shield country in both Sweden and Finland. Since this early foundation to supply Sweden's first electrified railway, the Porjus plant has been greatly extended; today it contains nine sets of turbines with a generating capacity of 140,000 kilowatts.

The early achievement of Porjus is dimmed by the enormous power plants constructed on the Lule and Ume rivers in the fifties. Harsprånget power station on the Lule älv took five years in building between 1946 and 1951. Harnessing a three-hundred-foot head of water, Harsprånget has a capacity of 350,000

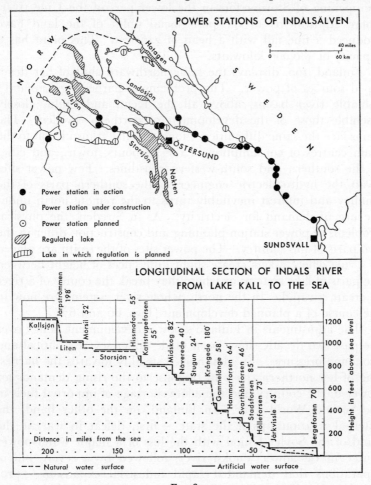

FIG. 65

Since 1940 Sweden has had to turn to the rivers of Norrland as her chief source of electricity. The Indals valley is now one of her most developed sources of power, and the river is transformed into a succession of steps at each of which stands a power-plant. A number of regulating lakes helps to control the flow of water.

kilowatts in its three generating units. It is notable, too, as the starting point of Sweden's first six-hundred-mile-long high tension cable carrying an enormous current of 380,000 volts. The Swedish state built Harsprånget with the chief aim of feeding the national electric grid and the distant towns and industries of the midlands. For a decade Harsprånget remained the biggest hydro-electric plant of northern Europe, but in 1959 its place was usurped with the opening of Stornorrfors in the lower part of the Ume river, where adjustments to the post-glacial uplift of the land have produced a fine fall with a head of 246 feet. This plant has a capacity of 380,000 kilowatts.

Finland, too, displays the same northward shift of her developed sources of power. The problems of harnessing Lapland's valuable river basins, above all the Kemi and Oulu, closely resemble those of the development of northern Sweden. The Finns face the same difficulties of long distance transmission to the main centres of consumption in the harbours, towns, and cities of the southern and south-western coastlines. Few power sites await the hydro-electric engineer in the southern parts of the country and interest inevitably turns to the remote north under the urgent demand for electricity. As in Sweden, the physical problems of power station planning and construction differ in the two parts of the country. The power sites of the south are placed as a rule where eskers create slight differences of height between the parts of lake systems or where they break the course of a river to create a rapid. In the north, whole river systems are now in the course of a planned development [Figs. 66 and 67].

The adjustments in Finland's power development policy over the past two decades have been made under severe political and economic pressures. Sweden moved steadily towards the harnessing of her northern rivers in response to the rising demands for power in the country and the acute shortage of imported fuels in the Second World War. In Finland, on the other hand, the external relationships of the state — first, defeat in war at the hand of the Soviet Union with the loss of a major water-power source in the lower Vuoksi river, followed by a severe bill of reparations that demanded rapid industrial expansion — provided the harsh stimulus to the development of her northern rivers. In the reorientation of hydro-electric sources in the post-war years Finland was not unconscious of the strategic weakness of her pre-war centre of primary power production in the south-eastern

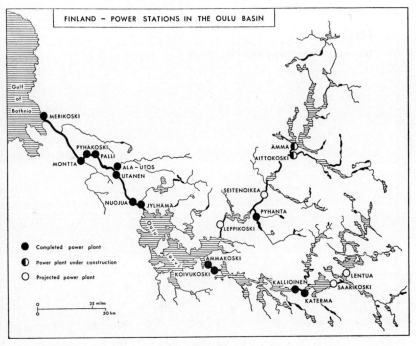

FIG. 66

Since the Second World War the centre of hydro-electricity production in Finland has shifted to the northern rivers, Kemi and Oulu. A chain of power plants has been under construction in the fifties that will harness the whole river-basin of the Oulu, using its lakes as storage basins.

sector of the country. The peace treaty with the U.S.S.R. deprived Finland of a third of her hydro-electric power as a result of the shifting of the frontier in Karelia. Since 1945 the demands of nature and policy have directed the chief centres of power production to the north and west in Finnish Lapland at the opposite pole to the long-disputed region of Karelia.

Two stages of power development may be distinguished in post-war Finland. The period from 1941–57 witnessed the completion of a series of power stations on the Oulu river. The lower section of the river between the large lake of Oulujärvi and the Gulf of Bothnia had been harnessed at seven power stations in 1957. In the upper reaches and tributaries of the Oulu another dozen plants had been finished or were approaching completion [Fig. 66]. By 1957, only one major potential source of hydro-electric power awaited exploitation in Finland — the Kemi river

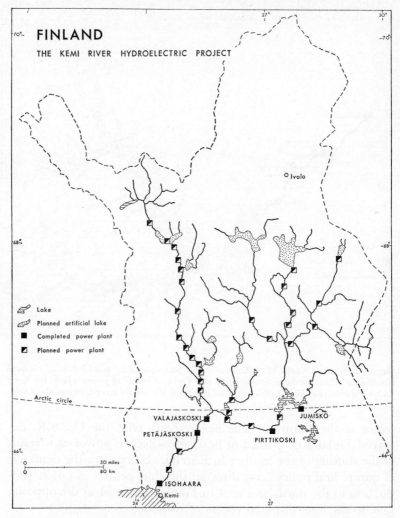

FIG. 67

The years since the Second World War have seen a transfer of the chief centres of electricity production from the south-eastern border to the great river basins of the north. The construction of the chain of power plants in the headwaters of the Kemi is Finland's main capital project of the sixties.

and its tributaries. The development of the Kemi basin promises to be the chief power engineering project in the sixties [Fig. 67]. The first power station on the Kemi was built at the mouth of the river between 1945 and 1950 — the Isohaara plant. The first work by the Kemijoki Corporation, founded in the fifties, was the Petäjäskoski power plant on the lower section of the river. It took four years to complete between 1953 and 1957 and has a generating capacity of 150,000 kilowatts. Petäjäskoski acted as the key to the next stage of development on the Kemi, a stage with the simultaneous construction of several large power stations. Besides possessing the biggest power output in Finland, the Petäjäskoski hydro-electric station is also the northern terminal of the 400,000 volt transmission line that carries the current of the north to the towns and industries in the south of Finland.

Inside two decades, the chief centre of power production has shifted from the south-eastern boundary of Finland towards her north-western frontier. The Vuoksi river and Imatra rapids of Karelia spelt out for the geographer of the late thirties the chief source of hydro-electric power in Finland; by the early fifties it had been transposed several hundred miles to the north-west — to the Oulu river and its tributaries. In 1960, the Kemi river, further north still, emerged as Finland's chief source of power. A mere twenty years earlier, its five-hundred-mile course through unmapped country could only be surmised as a great potential source of energy. The detailed mapping of the Kemi's falls and rapids, the geological prospecting of its power sites for the blasting out of tunnels, generating chambers, and sluices, and the measurement of the variations in the river's annual flow only started in 1951.

Finland has one remaining untapped source of major importance for her hydro-electric supplies — the Torne river. Like those other Lapland rivers, the Tana and the Pasvik, the Torne marks an international frontier. Up to now its political status has sterilized the germination of its capacities for hydro-electricity. It is not unlikely that the next two decades will witness a Swedish-Finnish development of the lower Torne and its long tributary, the Muonio river. Such a co-operative action was foreshadowed in 1959 when a 220,000 volt transmission line was completed between the Kemi river plants and the Kalix river in Swedish Norrland. Once again the geography of Finland's main power resource seems likely to involve her in relations with a foreign power, but with the certain prospect of a far happier outcome than when her main power supplies depended upon a Karelian river draining to a Soviet lake.

THE DEVELOPMENT OF HYDRO-ELECTRICITY
IN NORWAY

The geographical pattern of hydro-electric power differs in Norway from that of Sweden and Finland. We have noticed that the power centres of the latter lie in the thinly populated northlands that stretch across the Arctic Circle. Four-fifths of Norwegian power resources, existing and potential, are found south of Trondheim fjord [Figs. 68 and 69]. Because the water parting between the Atlantic and Baltic drainage systems lies close to the western coastline, Arctic Norway lacks the immense river systems of Swedish Norrland. Her rivers tumble to the sea within a few miles and fail to provide the succession of sites that can be organized into an integrated system of hydro-electric stations. The immense extent in latitude of northern Norway, combined with a landscape of harsh, glaciated mountains and wide, penetrating fjords, presents problems too in the laying of transmission lines. Even if Arctic Norway presented better prospects for the development of hydro-electric power, it lies a long way from the chief area of consumption around Oslo fjord. The capital city and the small industrial towns of southern Norway are as close to central Italy as to the empty tundras of Finnmark province.

Distance and the mediocre prospects for the development of hydro-electricity suggest that Arctic Norway will never be joined to the towns and industrial centres of Oslo fjord in a national power grid. At present, northern Norway is served by a number of isolated electricity grids. For instance, Varanger fjord, with its iron mines and the town and port of Kirkenes, is supplied by a 220,000-volt transmission line that collects its power from five plants, including a 12,000-kilowatt steam-driven power station. Farther south the coastal district of Troms draws its power from a half-dozen small hydro-electric stations joined together in an isolated regional grid. Again, the larger islands of the Lofoten and Vesterålen group are today fed from a dozen power stations. Submarine cables cross the interlocking arms of sea, while the pylons of transmission lines stand gaunt amid the scented birch scrub beneath the naked, granite peaks of Lofoten. The total generating capacity of the islands' power stations is only 26,000 kilowatts — less than a quarter of the output of the normal power station in northern Sweden.

Hydro-Electric Power in Scandinavia

Southwards of Bodø and the wide barrier of Saltfjord that stretches almost to the Swedish frontier lie Helgeland and Nordland, provinces that hold out the highest prospects for hydro-electricity in northern Norway. Two major power stations have been built here since the Second World War, and both are designed to supply metallurgical industries. The first stage of the

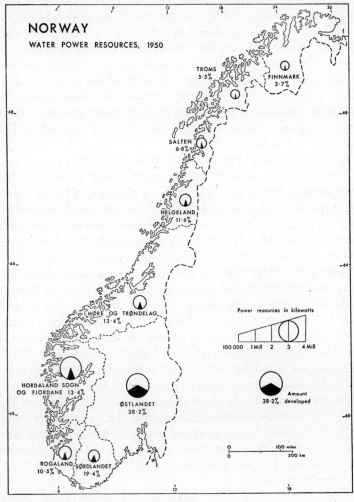

FIG. 68

Norway's greatest sources of water power lie in the rainy fjord region of Vestlandet and in the long valleys of the south-east. The resources of Arctic Norway are limited and poorly developed.

Røssäga power station has a capacity of 100,000 kilowatts and supplies the iron and steel plant and its satellite town at Mo i Rana. Electricity from this centre is also carried southward to Mosjøen, where a freshly constructed aluminium works has brought another transformation to the wilderness of northern Norway. A similar plant, with a 100,000-kilowatt capacity, has been erected on Glomfjord and feeds an electro-chemical plant. Nordland's potential riches in water power are now being tapped for the energy-greedy industries that Norway's abundance of cheap hydro-electricity has always favoured. Within the next two decades, this region to the south of Saltfjord may become tributary to the populated and industrialized south of the country. It lies within a hundred miles of the network of transmission lines focused on Trondheim fjord, and already there are plans to connect this region with the country's premier grid centred on Gudbrandsdal and Oslo.

Norway's greatest reserves of hydro-electric power belong to the region of the western fjords that extend southward from Trondheim to Stavanger [Fig. 68]. This zone of heavy rainfall where glaciers and snowfields glint above the deep, sheer-walled troughs of the fjords forms one of the richest areas of hydro-electric power in the world. The physical conditions for the development of power in western Norway are very different from those in Swedish Norrland. Here there is no single river system whose nickpoints, faults, and glacial diversions provide a series of falls and rapids for systematic harnessing. Instead, the short and powerful rivers fall through hundreds of feet to the fjords from a plateau dotted with scores of lakes fed by snowfields and glaciers. Norway's fjord power centres all depend upon high heads of water. She has more than six hundred falls of over a thousand feet, and 60 per cent of Norway's hydro-electric stations tap sources with a head between a thousand and three thousand feet. The highest head of water in Norway has been harnessed at the hydro-electric plant that feeds the aluminium smelting works at Årdal in Sogn where Lake Tyin, three thousand three hundred feet above sea level on the western flank of the Jotunheimen, provides the static head of water for its turbines.

The thousands of lakes scattered across the high plateaus above the fjords and the forbidding sheets of water in ice-scoured basins provide a unique physical element among the resources of hydro-electric schemes in western Norway. They form natural storage basins to maintain flow through periods of drought. The chief cause of reduced supply comes from severe spells of winter cold when the discharge of water to the turbines may fall to as little as 10 per cent of the normal flow. Storage in lakes can help to offset such shortages, especially now that it has become the

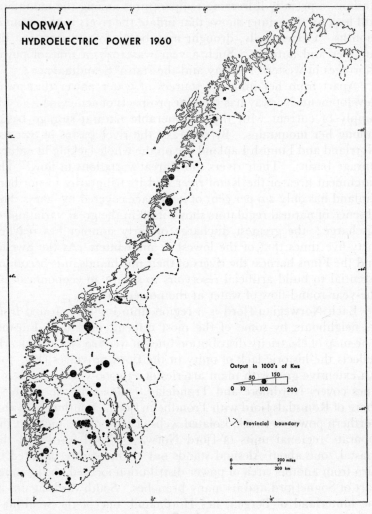

FIG. 69

Norway's largest number of power stations is clustered in the valleys of the south-eastern part of the country, serving her main centres of population and industry. Large isolated power units supply the chemical and metal-refining plants of the fjords and the north.

practice to build deep, underground power stations with long intake tunnels cut through rock to the turbine sets. But drought can afflict the normally rainy south-western flank of Scandinavia at other seasons. Late spring and early summer display the lowest precipitation figures. This may be a time of shortage at the power stations, especially if freezing temperatures among the mountains still lock up the winter snows that inflate the rivers in the summer months. Occasionally, drought may be prolonged late into the summer and autumn. Such a year was 1947, a time of power shortages in western Norway and the rest of Scandinavia.

Apart from her immense sources of water power that await development, Norway has the best prospects of achieving a steady supply of current with the innumerable natural storage basins among her mountains. By contrast, the river basins of Swedish Norrland and Finnish Lapland are on the whole lacking in natural storage basins. Their rivers show great variations in flow. The catchment area of the Kemi river and its tributaries in northern Finland has only 2·9 per cent of its surface covered by lakes. This absence of natural regulators shows itself in the great variations of discharge; the greatest discharge of early summer has reached forty-five times that of the lowest in midwinter. As the Swedes and the Finns harness the rivers of their northlands, it is becoming essential to build artificial reservoirs to secure an economical all-the-year-round flow of water at the power stations.

Each Norwegian fjord is a region unto itself, separated from its neighbours by some of the most difficult terrain in Europe. The map of electricity distribution lines in western Norway clearly reflects the historic lack of unity in the fjord provinces [Fig. 70]. An extensive grid with main arteries of 220,000-volt transmission lines covers Nordmøre and Trøndelag, connecting the northern shore of Romsdals fjord with Trondheim fjord. Southward of this northern power network, isolated webs of power lines pick out the separate regional units of fjord Norway. Nord fjord and the coastal zone about Ålesund stands out as one centre, isolated in turn from another area of power distribution focused on the inner part of Sognefjord and its many branches. Southwards again, in the hinterland of Bergen, lies Hordaland, one of the wealthiest districts for hydro-electric power in the whole country. Here twenty-five power stations have an installed generating capacity of more than 300,000 kilowatts. On the southern fringe of Norway's fjord province, another high-tension line and its branches

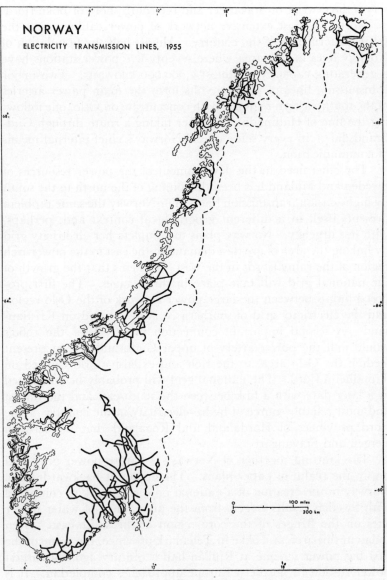

NORWAY

ELECTRICITY TRANSMISSION LINES, 1955

FIG. 70

The isolation of Norway's regional cores is illustrated in this map of electricity transmission lines. Along the Atlantic coastline each group of fjord communities is defined by its own power network. The most extensive grid centres upon Oslo and the south-eastern region, drawing upon power stations deep in Gudbrandsdal and Hallingdal as well as many local centres.

serves the district of Stavanger and the south shore of Bokn fjord.

Norway's most extensive network of power cables covers the south-eastern part of the country. Almost half the population of Norway lives in this area where seventy-five power stations have a generating capacity of almost 2,000,000 kilowatts. Two major transmission lines of 220,000 volts form the main power arteries of the south-eastern region. Both concentrate on Oslo, one following the line of Hallingdal, the other taking a route through Gudbrandsdal — in every sense one of Norway's chief internal means of communication.

The chief need in the development of the power resources of Sweden and Finland has been the joining of the north to the south by high-tension transmission lines. For Norway the same problem presents itself in a different geographical context and, perhaps, with less urgency. Norway plans to complete her electricity grid by linking the area of greatest demand in the east to the power-rich region of the rainy fjords in the west. It seems that the growth of the national grid will take place in three stages. The first proposed link is between the large power network of the Oslo region and the electricity grid of southern Norway centred on Kristiansand. A second important connection proposed for the 1960's would join the power artery of upper Gudbrandsdal, at present feeding the Oslo area, to the rich and extensive grid centred on Trondheim fjord. The national grid will probably be completed at a later date with a link between the south-east and the richest and most reliable source of hydro-electricity in the country — the fjord provinces of Hordaland and Rogaland that lie between Bergen and Stavanger.

The knitting together of Norway's separate power grids still lies in the realm of paper plans. The apparent backwardness of Norway in the creation of a national power network as compared with Sweden results largely from the abundance of water power sites on the fringes of the core region of the south-east. Even today in this area at Tokke in Telemark province, the scene of the first big power scheme at Rjukan half a century ago, the largest power station in northern Europe approaches completion. It is forty years since the Swedes turned seriously to the problem of drawing electricity from beyond the core-area of the lakes depression. The joining of the western fjords to the eastern valleys foreshadows a more economical use of Norway's greatest natural resource. From year to year, the distribution of rainfall in the three areas of Trøndelag, the south-western fjords and the eastern valleys is markedly different, apart from the permanent contrast between the more continental climate of the east and the deeply oceanic climate of the west. A joining of the three major areas would help to eliminate the restrictions imposed by phases of drought, restrictions that have made steam-driven power stations a necessary supplement during dry years in the south of the country.

ALTERNATIVES TO HYDRO-ELECTRIC POWER

During the winter of 1959–60 Sweden and Norway took an unusual action to offset the power shortage that resulted from the drought of the previous summer. In south-eastern Norway and central Sweden less than half of the expected annual total of rainfall had fallen by the end of September — a deficit that could only have severe effects on the output of electricity in the early weeks of winter. To help overcome this shortage the Norwegians moored a particular type of oil tanker with a turbo-electric engine in some of the ports of Oslo fjord. The power from the ships' main generators was coupled to the public electricity network or else fed into the power house of an industrial company. At Drammen, for instance, two such oil tankers were moored. The *Asato* contributed power to a pulp mill, while the *Beaver Dam* was used to boost the public supply of the Drammen power board. The Swedes, suffering from the same drought, took up the idea from Norway and electric generating ships were moored at Stockholm and in some of the timber-processing ports of the Baltic. The amount of power produced by these ships was minutely small when set against the hydro-electricity outputs of the Scandinavian countries. During twelve weeks, eleven ships in Swedish harbours generated 1·2 per cent of the total output of Sweden's thermal power stations in the same winter. Nevertheless, they added current at its heaviest points of consumption when the government seriously considered the rationing of electricity. This extraordinary experiment of the winter of 1959–60 is unlikely to be repeated. The oil tanker with a turbo-electric engine was of an uncommon design built in the United States in the Second World War as part of a fleet to import oil to the European battle fronts. The design has been obsolete for nearly twenty years and already these vessels are disappearing rapidly in the world's scrapyards.

Some Facets of Scandinavian Geography

Although Scandinavia ranks as one of the world's primary sources of hydro-electric power, the region also produces considerable quantities of electricity in steam-driven power stations using coal and oil as fuel. Denmark depends entirely upon her thermo-electric plants located in the ports, apart from a small amount of electricity imported by submarine cable from the grid in southern Sweden. Finland, surprisingly enough, reckons a third of her generating capacity in steam-driven plants. This fact reflects the severe reductions of hydro-electric power in the freezing time of late winter. Some hydro-electric stations possess an auxiliary steam plant, and the large pulp factories accumulate stocks of coal in the summer to feed their auxiliary thermo-electric stations through the harshest weeks of the winter.

In Sweden, too, a small but important fraction of the total supply of electricity is produced in steam-driven plants. Before the Second World War it amounted to 10 per cent of her annual total, but during the 1950's it dropped to less than 3 per cent, largely due to the building of vast new hydro-electric stations in the north. Today, the generating capacity of the thermal power stations in Sweden is about 800,000 kilowatts or little more than the equivalent of two of her biggest hydro-electric stations. The steam-driven stations are all located in the cities and ports of southern Sweden. Västerås, the birthplace and chief centre of the electrical engineering industry on Lake Mälaren, has one of the oldest and biggest thermo-electric stations in the country — a plant that performed vital services for Sweden's power supplies in the drought year of 1947. Stockholm, too, possesses a thermo-electric power station and Malmö contains two coal-fed power stations. The thermo-electric capacity of Sweden was extended in 1960 with the opening of a 300,000-kilowatt plant in western Sweden. The Swedes experimented in the post-war period with fresh varieties of fuel such as pulverized coal, the carboniferous shales of central Sweden, and the low-grade coals of Skåne's tiny coalfield. A small amount of thermo-electricity is produced as a by-product of industries that require large quantities of steam in processing. For instance, some of the larger cellulose factories possess back-pressure units that produce electricity, the total output of the country in this form being about equal to a large hydro-electric plant.

TECHNOLOGICAL DEVELOPMENTS AND THE FUTURE OF HYDRO-ELECTRICITY IN SCANDINAVIA

Sometimes we make the mistake of thinking of the industrial revolution as a piece of history, a useful label for much that happened in the nineteenth century. The truth is that, in the middle of the twentieth century, applied science has entered an even more complex phase of rapid development. In the narrow field of hydro-electric power, fresh discoveries and changes in techniques are having profound effects on the geography of the industry. The main trends, as the foregoing pages show, are towards bigger power stations, the transmission of power over longer distances, and the organized development of whole river basins.

Since the end of the Second World War, power station design has changed radically. The greatest of these recent changes is the construction of underground hydro-electric plants [Figs. 71 and 72]. The cutting of underground turbine and generating chambers and the driving of channels and tail-races through miles of solid rock has become economically feasible through developments in other industries; for example, the discovery of new compressed-air drilling techniques and the production of tougher steel alloys for drills in Sweden. Less than twenty years ago the underground power plant was the subject of discussion in technical journals, and the novelty of the popular press. Today it is the accepted norm in the planning of Scandinavian power stations. 40 per cent of Norway's generating capacity was underground by 1959.

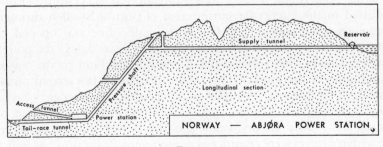

FIG. 71

This power plant in Valdres, south-eastern Norway, was completed in 1951. With its turbine intake, power plant, transformers, and switchgear completely underground this station follows the trend of post-war design in northern Europe.

Although the strategic motive is important in this new trend, it is not uppermost in these developments. The chief gain is a steeper fall of the intake pipes to the turbines, which provides a more powerful head of water. In the end, it is more economical to bring the flow of water to the power plant through steel-lined tunnels than to construct the familiar pipe-line down an open valley-side. Hydro-electric stations that lie deeply underground are protected from the severe cold of the northern winter, and in some of the power stations recently constructed in northern Sweden there are arrangements to heat the water before it enters the turbines.

Although the underground power station would seem to be best adapted to the topography of western Norway where the latest equipment is buried in the depths of mountains, similar installations are being built in the shallow valleys of Norrland and northern Finland. Pirttikoski power station on the Kemi river is entirely underground [Fig. 72]. Its machine chamber was blasted out of solid rock, and the tail-race tunnel, returning the water from the turbines to the river, penetrates a rocky spur for one and a half miles. Stornorrfors, too, Sweden's biggest power plant on the Ume river, is entirely underground, carved out of the rock on the banks of the river.

Another important development of the post-war period is the successful transmission of power over long distances. Among the Scandinavian states Sweden first felt the need to transmit electricity in bulk over hundreds of miles. The joining of Norrland to the central lakes depression took place in two stages. The first phase occupies the forties, when the surplus of power in the valleys of the Ångerman, Indals, and Ljungan was successfully transmitted to the energy-devouring area of central Sweden through 220,000-volt cables. The first high-tension line was opened in 1939 between the two regions, and ten years later, six power arteries using this voltage joined central Norrland to the towns and cities of the south. The 1950's introduced the second phase in the long-distance transmission of electricity in Sweden. Technical developments since 1950 have eliminated the problem of distance. Only twenty years ago the power sites of northern Sweden's rivers were considered as too remote from the consuming areas for their proper economic development. Within the past ten years Sweden has constructed a power grid that enables current to be exchanged from end to end of the country. In 1952,

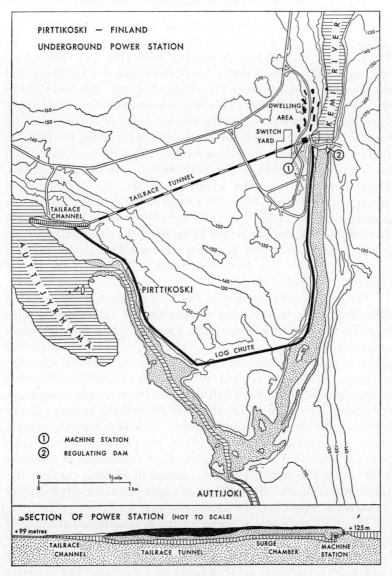

PIRTTIKOSKI — FINLAND
UNDERGROUND POWER STATION

KEMI RIVER

DWELLING AREA

SWITCH YARD

① ②

TAILRACE TUNNEL

TAILRACE CHANNEL

AUTTIJYRHÄMÄ

PIRTTIKOSKI

LOG CHUTE

① MACHINE STATION
② REGULATING DAM

0   ½ mile
0   1 km

AUTTIJOKI

SECTION OF POWER STATION (NOT TO SCALE)

+99 metres   + 125 m

TAILRACE CHANNEL   TAILRACE TUNNEL   SURGE CHAMBER   MACHINE STATION

FIG. 72

The power station at Pirttikoski, on the Kemi River, was completed in 1959 and it is
the fourth largest in Finland. It illustrates the use of underground plans and methods
of construction in the shallow valleys of the Archaean Shield. Pirttikoski stands on a
chain of rapids, ten miles in length, below lake Juujärvi, of which the total fall is only
seventy feet. The turbine and generator plant are entirely underground and the
tailrace tunnel runs for one and a half miles through a rocky spur. Note the log
chute for the timber floating of the Kemi River.

the first 380,000-volt power line was completed between Hars-prånget, at that time the country's largest power station, and Hallsberg — a distance of six hundred miles [Fig. 73]. Since then this high-tension power artery has been extended to Göteborg and southwards to Hälsingborg, the industrial city that looks across the Sound to Denmark. This first 380,000-volt line could carry four times as much power as the 220,000-volt cables erected in the forties, but already technical developments involving the installation of series-capacitator plants have doubled the load that could be borne by the grid of the early fifties. As already noticed, Finland was able to take advantage of the new techniques of power transmission. With the loss of the power stations in the Karelian border country she was forced to turn to her only substantial reserves of water power in the northern rivers and the bulk transmission of electricity has been achieved through the building of a 400,000-volt line from the Kemi and Oulu rivers to the populated centres of the south.

The recent achievements in the long-distance transmission of electricity bring to the front the problem of international links between the countries of northern Europe. Here the difficulties of the world of technology give way to the problems of international politics, problems that are not solved by the tools of scientific method. Norway, possessing in her western fjords Scandinavia's greatest potential source of hydro-electricity, is deeply involved in the question of the future development of northern Europe's power resources on an international scale. Already Norway exports about 300 million kwh. of electricity per year to Sweden. The power is generated on the Nea river near Trondheim at a station built in 1955 as a result of loans raised in Sweden through the International Bank. Stockholm consumes this electricity from the Trondheim region and the agreement runs for fifteen years.

The more ambitious schemes for the international exchange of power depend upon the recently developed techniques for the bulk transmission of electricity beneath the sea. The opening in 1954 of the underwater cable to Gotland, a sixty-mile link between Västervik on the Swedish mainland and Visby, foreshadows an even more vital connection between Norway and Denmark across the Skagerrak. Denmark, dependent upon expensive imported fuels, might turn a substantial part of her demand to Norway, the cheapest producer of electricity in the world after Canada. What is today a technical possibility is hindered by political argument.

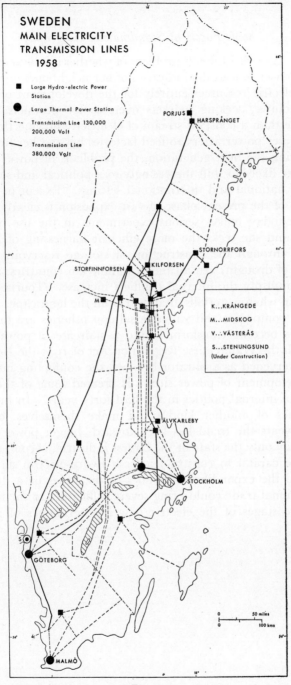

SWEDEN
MAIN ELECTRICITY
TRANSMISSION LINES
1958

■ Large Hydro-electric Power
  Station

● Large Thermal Power Station

---- Transmission Line 130,000
     200,000 Volt

—— Transmission Line
     380,000 Volt

K...KRÅNGEDE
M...MIDSKOG
V...VÄSTERÅS
S...STENUNGSUND
(Under Construction)

PORJUS
HARSPRÅNGET
STORNORRFORS
KILFORSEN
STORFINNFORSEN
M
K
ÄLVKARLEBY
V
STOCKHOLM
S
GÖTEBORG
MALMÖ

0   50 miles
0   100 kms

FIG. 73

Two clear stages are noticed in the development of hydro-electric power and its transmission in Sweden. Cables with a maximum capacity of 220,000 volts were erected between 1939 and 1952, bringing power from southern Norrland to the central lakes depression. Since 1952 a new high-tension grid of 380,000 volts has joined the power stations of the far north with the towns of southern Sweden.

Norway faces the difficult problem of whether it is better to export cheap power to feed the industries of her neighbours or to use her hydro-electric resources entirely for the development of her own manufactures, seeking markets overseas for products far more valuable than a constant stream of electricity flowing through an underwater power artery to feed factories beyond her frontiers.

During the next generation, the problems of power development are likely to shift increasingly to a political and social level in both national and international settings. Except in Norway, the end of the present phase of vast expansion is clearly in sight. Sweden today makes serious experiments in the use of atomic energy and she seeks the more efficient harnessing of her river systems through the construction of storage reservoirs to offset periods of drought. In all the Scandinavian countries, as power plants multiply the internal conflicts increase. Tourist interests complain when waterfalls disappear from the landscape. Timber-floating companies and valuable salmon fisheries are threatened as rivers become transformed into a staircase of power plants. Through the Watercourse Regulation Act of 1917 the Norwegian state intervened as arbitrator between the conflicting interests in the development of power sites. It created some of the biggest battles of internal politics in the past forty years. In the future, difficulties of another kind could make themselves felt. For twenty years the trend has been towards bigger power units so that today only the state or the largest industrial corporations can raise the capital to construct a fresh hydro-electric station. A check to the expanding economies of the fifties or a decline of international trade could bring severe difficulties to the financing of future stages of the electric power programmes of northern Europe.

25. SCENE IN NORRLAND.   Bogs, lakes, and, above all, coniferous forest make up most of the landscapes of northern Sweden.   In southern Norrland more than three-quarters of the total land area is forest covered

26. THE LJUSNAN VALLEY, HÄLSINGLAND, NORTHERN SWEDEN. The valleys that cross the Archaean plateau of northern Sweden to the Gulf of Bothnia form corridors of cleared land and farms, based on the recent sands and clays of terraces

27. THE INDALS RIVER, in southern Norrland, ranks among the most important of Sweden's natural floatways

28. A *FÄBOD* IN THE FORESTS OF DALARNA, SWEDEN. A cluster of huts in a forest clearing make up the summer settlement to which cattle were formerly driven for many miles. This type of transhumance has now almost disappeared from Sweden and may be found rarely in the northern parts of the country. In the past, the temporary summer settlement frequently represented the first stage in the creation of a permanent village

29. ARESKUTAN MOUNTAIN, JAMTLAND, SWEDEN is carved out of the granites of a Caledonian *nappe* overthrust on to the Archaean shield. Its long slopes are one of Sweden's most popular spring skiing grounds

30. KALMAR CASTLE, SWEDEN. Kalmar looks across a strait to the island of Öland, source of much of the limestone in the buildings of this town. The castle, an island fortress, founded in the twelfth century, dates mainly from Sweden's period of political dominance in northern Europe in the early seventeenth century

31. VISBY, GOTLAND. In the geography of the Baltic in medieval times Visby held a key position. Like Bergen, it was one of northern Europe's most powerful members of the Hanseatic League. Today it lives entirely within its medieval wall, containing within its compass a half-dozen ruined gothic churches. Visby is now a neat and prosperous tourist town and its countryside sends market garden produce to Stockholm

32. ISLAND OF VEN. This Swedish island stands in the Øresund between Sweden and Denmark. The distant view shows the narrowest part of the strait with the shorelines of Skåne and Zealand. The island is typical of the landscapes of Zealand. Low chalk cliffs in the foreground expose rocks of Cretaceous (Danian) age. The geometrical pattern of rectangular fields, the scattered spinneys and neat lines of planted trees display a landscape of enclosure. The village nucleus of St Ibb (*centre left*) disintegrated as farms moved out to sites in the former open fields. The huge fields in the left foreground are a former common grazing ground situated on a chalk downland

33. HELSINKI IN THE GRIP OF WINTER. This picture, taken on Finland's Day of Independence, December 6th, shows the Great Church and the classical elegance of the architecture in the part of the capital that was replanned under the guidance of Ludvig Engel in the first years of the nineteenth century

34. TAMPERE, one of Finland's greatest industrial centres. It manufactures textiles, boots, and shoes, and is important in the engineering and rubber industries

35. MELAVESI, FINNISH LAKES PLATEAU. Within the northern part of the eastern lakes system this picture is typical of the intermingling of lakes, forests, and, more rarely, farmlands, in the interior of Finland. The even surface of the Archaean plateau is seen in the distant skyline

36. PUNKAHARJU, esker in lake Puruvesi, part of the lake complex of eastern Finland. The steep-sided winding ridges of eskers are one of the characteristic features of the Scandinavian landscape. Occasionally they stand out as natural causeways, dividing one part of a lake from another. Here the Punkaharju (*harju*, Finnish for esker) is followed by both road and railway to Savonlinna

37. KAUKOPÄÄ SULPHATE PULP MILL, FINLAND. This is an example of the modern integrated plants that are becoming characteristic of the forest industries in Finland. Kaukopää stands on the southern shore of lake Saimaa with access to an immense hinterland of timber resources. This factory, the biggest industrial plant in Finland, produces pulp, cellulose, cardboard, and paper. The company that owns Kaukopää (Enso-Gutzeit Oy) operates a fleet of 40 tugs and 60 barges on lake Saimaa and employs 12,000 in its company forests during the winter season

38. SAVONLINNA. At a strategic point in the eastern lakes system of Finland. The fortress of Olavinlinna (*centre*) symbolizes Sweden's thrust into Karelia at the end of the fifteenth century. In 1639 Savonlinna achieved borough status at a time when many towns were created by the Swedish crown. The railway (*middle distance, right*) was built by Russia as part of a strategic line across central Finland from St Petersburg to the Gulf of Bothnia. Today Savonlinna is important as a lake resort and tourist centre

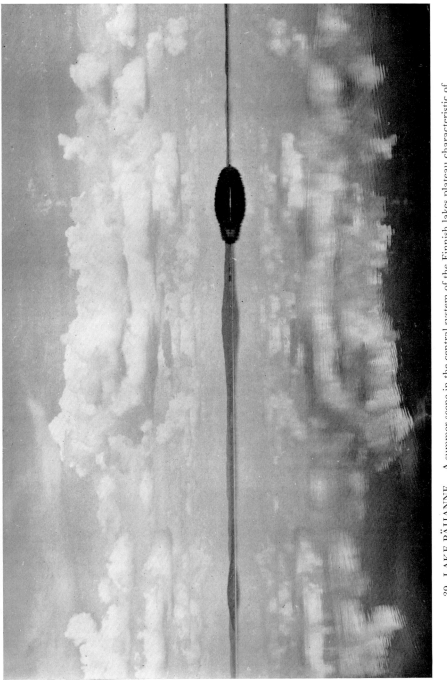

39. LAKE PÄIJÄNNE. A summer scene in the central system of the Finnish lakes plateau characteristic of this region of unexciting landforms, extensive lakes, and forests. Here also a typical summer sky of fine-weather cumulus clouds and immense visibility

40. ROVANIEMI, a township of northern Finland on the Kemi river. Communications have been important in its growth. It stands on the Arctic highway that runs northward across Lapland to the Inari basin. It is on a railway that runs eastward from Kemi across the Soviet frontier. Rovaniemi is a raw northern town that has been largely rebuilt since its destruction in the closing months of the Second World War

41. PALLASTUNTURI. This rounded mountain is typical of the northernmost parts of Finland. Here at 68 degrees latitude north the stunted coniferous forests find a frontier against the bare tundra. Pallastunturi reaches 2700 feet above sea level, and the valley in the distance leads to the Muonio river that marks the frontier between Sweden and Finland

42. AHVENANMAA (ÅLAND) ARCHIPELAGO. Countless flat islands and intricate straits and channels make up the scenery of Finland's south-western archipelago. Ice-scraped granite hummocks are a characteristic element. Woodland is sparse and stunted. Fields are tiny and scattered, and fishing is as important as agriculture

43. THE LITTLE BELT BRIDGE. The Little Belt between Jutland, in the distance, and Funen provides an important link in the communications of Denmark. The bridge carries both road and railway. Before the sea flooded the Little Belt in Littorina times, this was a meandering river valley ; earlier, in the closing phase of the Ice Age, it was occupied by an ice lobe. Wooded hills in the distance are characteristic of the morainic country of eastern Jutland

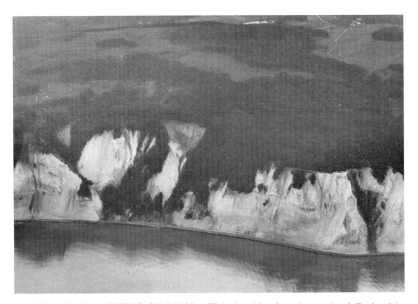

44. THE CHALK CLIFFS OF MØN. This tiny island to the south of Zealand is notable for its fine cliff scenery composed of the Senonian limestone. The chalk surface is largely covered by morainic deposits (*see exposure in gully to left, and centre*). The hummocky morainic landscape may be seen clearly at the top of the picture, including a small kettle-hole lake. On the cliff-top the glacial deposits support deciduous woods, mainly beech. Note the forest growing down the cliff-face that indicates slumped masses of boulder clay

45. HELSINGØR, DENMARK, at the narrowest part of the Øresund and an important rail ferry port for Sweden. In the centre the Kronborg Castle, a name made famous by Shakespeare's Hamlet. Its former chief function was to guard this strategic entrance to the Baltic (cf. Nyborg in relation to the Great Belt). In the background across Øresund is Hälsingborg, the Swedish counterpart of this Danish port

46. ESBJERG, founded in 1869, became the chief port of Denmark for the trade in dairy products with the British Isles. Esbjerg, too, is an important base of the North Sea fishing fleet

47. ROSKILDE, DENMARK, was the first capital of Denmark until it was eclipsed by Copenhagen in 1443. The cathedral, built in brick, dates from the early thirteenth century. Here are the tombs of Danish kings, and in the geography of the country it is the equivalent of Sweden's Uppsala and Norway's Trondheim

48. COPENHAGEN. The core of the Danish capital with the Christianborg palace in the foreground. On this island site the first castle of Copenhagen was built in 1167. The Christianborg was built early in the eighteenth century and destroyed by fire in 1884. The present building dates from 1903 and is now the meeting-place of the Danish parliament. The huddled buildings and narrow streets beyond the Christianborg point to the medieval core of Copenhagen. Top left is the City Hall, and beyond that the wide streets and grid-iron plan of the nineteenth-century town

CHAPTER 11

Merchant Navies and Fishing Fleets

NORTHERN Europe's rivers and lakes form the background to the development of power in the Scandinavian countries. Similarly, the encircling seas and oceans contribute valuable items to the economies of each of these northern states. Sea transport dominates their relations with the world outside northern Europe.

Norway, whose coastline has a length of half the earth's circumference, is more deeply engaged in the surrounding seas than any other Scandinavian country. The rich fishing grounds of the Norwegian Sea and the Skagerrak still contribute a fifth of the value of her annual exports, a share that was considerably greater only a decade ago [Fig. 77]. Norway's close bond with the enveloping ocean is displayed perhaps even more clearly in the size and currency-earning capacity of her merchant fleet. In 1959, after a decade of feverish expansion, the Norwegian merchant navy had achieved ten million gross registered tons and was bigger than at any other time in its history, holding third place among the fleets of the world. Only one-tenth of Norway's shipping calls at Norwegian ports, the rest carrying oil, grain, iron ore, sugar, timber, and coal between harbours scattered up and down the coastlines of the five continents. Sixty per cent of Norway's merchant navy today is composed of oil tankers, and yet one modern tanker could keep Norway supplied with all her needs in petroleum and diesel fuel.

The rôle of Norway's merchant navy as an international carrier has given it a crucial position in the nation's economy. During the fifties, the merchant fleet's earnings of foreign currency have balanced the nation's trading accounts, making up the broad gap between the high bill of imports and the takings of the export trade in refined metals, timber, paper, pulp, fertilizers, and the products of the fishing industry. The Norwegian shipowner views his spruce and gleaming fleet of motor vessels in a different rôle *vis-à-vis* the state. Since the Second World War, the heavy taxes of Norway's welfare state have placed a large burden on the wealthiest members of the community, the shipping companies and shipowners. With a certain amount of envy they can look to the ships of Panama and Liberia, whose vessels compete for the world's trade unhampered by strict union regulations and utterly free from financial responsibilities to the state.

In a lesser way, the sea forms part of the life and the economy of the other Scandinavian states. Sweden, although joined in the north to Finland and possessing a long land frontier with Norway, is virtually an island from the point of view of trade relationships. The bulk of her international trade in iron ore, pulp, paper, and the varied commodities of the engineering industry, passes to western Europe and the rest of the world across the quays of the several ports of the Gulf of Bothnia, through Norwegian Narvik, or by the wharves and warehouses of Göteborg, Stockholm, and Malmö. With 3·3 million gross registered tons, Sweden's merchant fleet reached one-third of the size of Norway's in the late fifties, and the general features of its trade and activities are not unlike those of the Norwegian merchant marine [Fig. 75]. The large oil tanker, chartered by the great petroleum companies, on journeys between the Middle East and the oil refineries of western Europe and the eastern United States, forms about a third of the Swedish merchant navy today. Again, a rising proportion of the trade — 71 per cent in 1958 — of Sweden's merchant fleet lies between foreign ports outside the realm of northern Europe.

The sea, too, has an important, though not a dominating rôle, in the economies of Denmark and Finland. Denmark possesses many of the qualities of an archipelago. It contains 280 ports, and a large part of the trade and travel within the country goes by sea. The Danish merchant navy expanded rapidly in the boom period of the fifties. In 1959 she possessed 2 million gross registered tons, double the size of the Danish merchant fleet of 1939. Denmark, too, has moved towards a great expansion of her fleet of oil tankers. In the late 1930's, tankers formed barely 10 per cent of the Danish merchant navy. By the end of 1958, oil tankers took up 35 per cent of the total tonnage, and a more alarming sign of this trend towards a highly specialized type of ship and restricted branch of trade appears in the fact that two-thirds of the Danish building programme for the early sixties is occupied by oil tankers. Since the war, the merchant navy has taken a vital position in Denmark's national economy. As in Norway the earnings of the fleet in the traffic of the high seas have filled the deficit in the annual budgets of the fifties between the earnings from exports and the heavier bill of imports. Denmark's other interest in the sea belongs to her fishing fleet. In 1958, with 15,000 fishermen and a fleet of 8,000 motor vessels, she stood second to Norway among the Scandinavian nations.

Measured by the size of her merchant navy, Finland's interest in the sea would seem to be least among the nations of northern Europe. At the end of 1958 her merchant navy totalled three-quarters of a million gross registered tons. The peculiar political problems that beset Finland in the past two decades have influenced the composition and expansion of her merchant fleet. The peace treaty that followed her defeat in the war with Russia added to the heavy losses of shipping in the early forties. Russia claimed 105 of Finland's remaining ships as reparations, leaving some of the oldest vessels as the nucleus of her post-war fleet in 1945. At that time, Finland's merchant navy stood at less than 40 per cent of its pre-war size. Post-war rebuilding has been severely hampered as compared with her Scandinavian neighbours. Until 1952, Finnish shipyards and marine engineers directed most of their energies towards fulfilling the annual quota of reparations to the U.S.S.R., and a lack of foreign exchange for the purchase of ships abroad also restricted the renewal and expansion of the merchant navy. Consequently, Finland's commercial fleet differs in age-structure and composition from those of the other Scandinavian countries. Denmark boasts that 93 per cent of her merchant navy consists of motor ships, and at the end of 1958 statistics showed that half of the fleet had been built in the previous five years. Nearly half the Norwegian fleet, too, is less than five years old — a result of the energy that has ever characterized her shipowning families and their ability, against restrictive legislation from the state, to raise loans in foreign countries, especially Sweden, for the laying down of fresh keels in shipbuilding yards outside Norway. In the late fifties, the Finnish merchant navy was still composed almost equally of steamships and motor-driven vessels. The oil tanker, too, has not assumed the rôle among Finnish ships that it has found in the merchant navies of the other Scandinavian countries.

The hard facts of geography rule in northern Europe. Norway is blessed with an outlook on ocean waters rich with oxygen and plankton, where herring gather in the depth of winter and cod assemble in the lighter days of early spring for spawning. Finland, on the other hand, is deprived of this easy access to a natural wealth that forms the foundation for an ancient industry in Norway. Despite her far reaching coastline, sixty thousand lakes, and the salmon and trout rivers of Östterbotten, fisheries play a negligible part in the economy of the country. The Baltic is a poor sea for fishermen, with its low salt content and scarcity of plankton. Off the coasts of Finland the abundance of fresh water reduces salinity below the average, and even in the south-western archipelago it reaches only 0·5 per cent. The most adaptable of sea fish, such as the Baltic herring, alone can flourish in the tideless, brackish gulfs of the Baltic. This fish comprises three-quarters of the annual catch of Finland's fishermen, a harvest whose sum total ranges between 1 and 2 per cent of the annual haul of fish captured by Norwegian seamen. Fishing, too, has felt the impact of Finland's stormy relations with the U.S.S.R. in the past two decades. Until the outbreak of the Winter War with Russia at the close of 1939, Finland had slowly nurtured a deep-sea fishing fleet based on the Arctic port of Petsamo. From the dark waters of the Arctic Ocean, rich with fish, the interests of the three Petsamo fishing companies had stretched to Iceland. The loss of Petsamo and the Arctic corridor by the armistice agreement of 1944 snuffed out this interest of Finnish fishermen in the fishing grounds of the furthest north. In the post-war years, the rapid expansion of Norwegian and Russian cod fisheries in the Barents Sea suggests that if Finland had retained control of a strip of the Arctic coastline, her northern sea fishing would have entered a similar period of growth. Instead, she has returned in a modest way to the herring fisheries off Iceland from her south-western ports in the land-locked Baltic.

The relationship between the Scandinavian states and the sea declines from the exposed Atlantic and North Sea façade to the enclosed gulfs of the Baltic. The vast merchant fleet of the Norwegians and the huge harvest of fish from near-by banks and remote Antarctic whaling grounds speak of the dependence of the economy upon the exploitation of the seas. Finland, on the other hand, turns inward to its monotonous boreal forests to find its main source of wealth. It remains now to discuss some of the current trends and problems in this economic relationship of northern Europe with its surrounding seas.

TRENDS IN THE GROWTH OF SCANDINAVIAN
MERCHANT FLEETS

A glimpse of the history of the Scandinavian merchant navies over
the past century reveals few static or even stable features. The
industrial revolution that we so often relegate to the Victorian
epoch is still very much with us; and technical changes more
radical than those which gave confidence to our Victorian fore-
fathers follow upon each other at alarming speed in the middle of
the twentieth century. The merchant fleets of the Scandinavian
countries have changed in size, composition, and types of ships,
and in the organization of their traffic.

The first great revolution, the changeover from sail to steam,
was accepted and accomplished with reluctance by the northern
countries. Norwegian shipping magnates bought their first
steamers in the 1860's and began to usher in a change of revolutionary character — all-the-year-round services on the high seas.
But the revolution of the steamship spread slowly. Forty years
later, in 1900, two-thirds of the Norwegian merchant fleet still
consisted of sailing ships. In Finland, the sailing ship survived as
a remnant of the active merchant fleet into the 1950's. The
changeover to coal-fired, steam-driven ships was accomplished
slowly and with difficulty in all the Scandinavian countries.
Sweden, like Norway, started the painful process of re-equipment
about the turn of the century when she began to buy secondhand
steamships, the 'cast-offs' of Britain's huge merchant fleet.

Scandinavia's reluctance in the acceptance of steam power,
explained by the lack of coal in the northern environment, a
shortage of capital to finance change and growth, and the psychological inertia that seems to be part of the process of change and
transformation, is surprisingly absent from the later history of the
merchant navies of northern Europe. Diesel power appeared soon
after the First World War. By the thirties, Norway's merchant
navy consisted predominantly of motor ships that cut the cost of
fuel by more than a third when compared with the coal-fired
steamer. In Denmark, the engineering firm of Burmeister and
Wain were pioneers of the diesel engine and remain at the front
of developments in this line, producing in 1959 a turbo-charged
diesel unit of immense power. Just as the age of coal provides a
prelude to northern Europe's industrial revolution based upon

hydro-electricity, so the steamship forms an interlude between the periods of sail and oil in the history of the Scandinavian merchant navies.

The period since the end of the First World War has been one of great energy and constant transformation in the merchant navies of the Scandinavian countries [Figs. 74 and 75]. During the inter-war period between 1918 and 1939, the Norwegian merchant fleet almost doubled in size as well as changing its motive power from coal to oil. The Second World War was a catastrophe for Norwegian shipping because it caused the destruction of half her tonnage. In 1945, she emerged with a merchant navy of only two and a half million gross registered tons, about the same size as the fleet of 1914. The period since the Second World War has witnessed a more rapid transformation and expansion than at any previous time in Norway's history. By 1959 the merchant navy was more than double its size of the late 1930's, with ten million gross registered tons. Similar rates of expansion are apparent in the merchant fleets of Denmark and Sweden in this post-war epoch

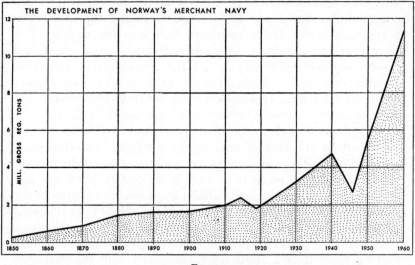

FIG. 74

In the history of Norway's merchant navy the most striking fact is the period of soaring tonnage since the end of the Second World War, reaching a peak of almost 12 million g.r.t. in 1960. The periods of sharp decline from 1914 to 1918 and from 1940 to 1945, when Europe was at war, are equally evident. Less spectacular phases of growth appear in the 1870's and immediately before the First World War.

of high prosperity. The Danish fleet has doubled in size since 1939, while the Swedish merchant navy with an increase of 105 per cent since 1938 displays a similar capacity for change and growth.

Since 1945, several other changes, apart from an astonishing increase of tonnage, have overtaken the Scandinavian merchant fleets. For instance, the participation of Denmark and Sweden in the North Sea trade declined sharply, and the number of small ships between 500 and 2000 tons that used to carry timber, pulp, coal, and coke between the Baltic lands and the North Sea countries has fallen heavily. The causes of this change, as in all economic matters, are many and subtle. For several years since the

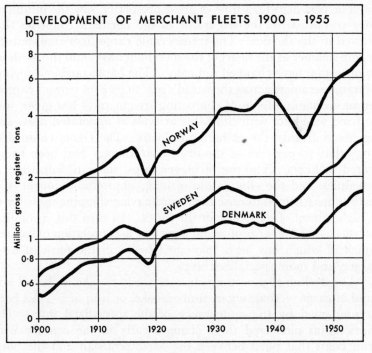

FIG. 75

The general trend in the growth of the merchant navies of these three Scandinavian countries is the same since the beginning of the century. The steady expansion of the years before the First World War, the stagnation of the early thirties, and the recent rapid growth are imprinted on each graph. Norway's severe losses in two world wars reflect her world-wide shipping interests. Sweden's neutrality in the Second World War is noticed in the expansion of her merchant navy in the early forties.

war, Britain and Germany had little coal or coke to sell to Scandinavia, so the pattern of pre-war trade was slow to re-establish itself. The timber and pulp of the northern countries, in heavy demand in western Europe, sought transport in greater bulk and used cargo liners to reach its markets. The final blow to Scandinavian participation in the traffic between the innumerable North Sea harbours was the severe competition in the fifties from German and Dutch coasting vessels. The inability of Sweden and Denmark to re-enter the North Sea trade is explained, too, by the regulations for working ships and the wage-scales imposed by the state. Germany and the Netherlands, with less stringent rules upon the manning of ships at sea and lower wages, were able to offer more competitive terms.

The past decade, a time of great prosperity, saw the fulfilment of a revolution in the sea traffic of the northern countries that started in the thirties. The transoceanic cargo liner replaced the tramp steamer as the heart of the merchant navy, and the methods of operation have changed radically. The haphazard journeyings of tramp steamers across the world's seas to pick up various cargoes in an economic jungle of competing freight rates has given way to fixed schedules with timetable arrivals at appointed ports and agents to arrange the gathering of loads. The Danes claimed in 1957 that 70 per cent of the dry cargo tonnage had been transferred to liners. The use of bigger ships, the rationalization of schedules, and the elimination of long, unprofitable journeys in ballast have helped to raise the Scandinavian shipping industry to a higher level of efficiency in the fifties. In turn this revolution is reflected in higher profits and a greater accumulation of capital, much of which has been 'ploughed back' in the form of new, larger, and more specialized ships.

The decline of the tramp steamer ready to take on board any kind of cargo — coal, sugar, timber, coke, or iron ore — has been accompanied by the appearance of the specialized ship. The Norwegians pioneered these changes early in the century with fruit boats that plied between the Mediterranean and the ports of western and northern Europe, as well as banana boats running from the Caribbean to the harbours of the North Sea and the eastern United States. Another line pursued with great success by the Norwegians since the war is the construction of large ships with cranes and specialized lifting gear capable of handling bulky and heavy cargoes such as locomotives and engineering equipment.

Some of these ships reach 10,000 tons and concentrate upon the transport of heavy industrial cargoes between western Europe and the tropics. Sweden, too, introduced an interesting rationalization of ship design at the end of the Second World War. The Gränges-berg Company built a fleet of large ore-carrying ships that could return to Sweden with specialized cargoes. One type of ship combined the transport of iron ore with a return cargo of oil, while another displayed a return to the pattern of a general ocean tramp steamer with a revolutionary lay-out of ore-holds along the centre-line of the ship, surrounded by compartments for grain and coal.

The most specialized of the post-war developments is the giant oil tanker. By the close of the fifties, tankers formed a substantial part of the tonnage in the merchant navies of Norway, Sweden, and Denmark. This trend reached its furthest extreme in Norway, where nearly 60 per cent of the tonnage in 1959 was composed of oil tankers. Norway's specialization in the oil trade is apparent in the distribution of ships bearing the Norwegian flag across the oceans of the globe at any moment of time [Fig. 76]. A map of the positions of Norwegian vessels on any particular day reveals that they swarm in the areas of the Caribbean, off the Gulf coast of the U.S.A., in the Red Sea and the Persian Gulf, and about the narrows of the North Sea and the English Channel — the focal points of the world's oil routes. Experts in Scandinavian shipping have looked with some alarm upon the rise of the oil tanker. Swedish experts forecast the replacement of the fast cargo liner by the oil tanker as the most important sector of the merchant navy in the sixties. But already in 1960 an air of uncertainty hangs over the rapid growth of the tanker fleet in the future. The extension of oil pipe-lines will have a radical effect on tanker routes. For instance, the completion of a Russian pipe-line to the Baltic coast has profoundly affected the Norwegian tanker routes between the Black Sea and the oil ports of northern Europe. Perhaps a disturbing phase of readjustment from this overspecialization may be forecast for the sixties, when one remembers that a large share of the ships on the order books of the yards consists of tankers. It is calculated that seventeen million gross registered tons of oil tankers will be delivered from the world's shipyards before 1963, a sum equal to half the present world fleet of oil-carrying ships. But in the first months of 1960, 15 per cent of the world's oil tankers were already without cargoes and laid up.

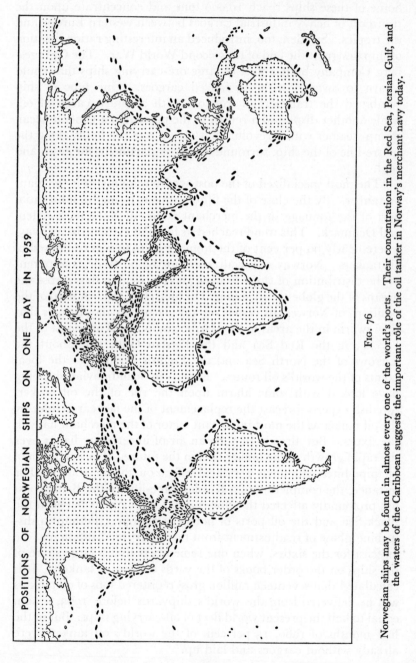

FIG. 76

Norwegian ships may be found in almost every one of the world's ports. Their concentration in the Red Sea, Persian Gulf, and the waters of the Caribbean suggests the important rôle of the oil tanker in Norway's merchant navy today.

Periods of prosperity and over-specialization inevitably bring in their train phases of harsh adjustment and realignment to new conditions. Norway, above all, has benefited from the long charter agreements — sometimes as long as ten years — with the oil companies. She may find it hard to adjust to fresh economic facts and changing geographical values.

SCANDINAVIAN FISHERIES

The merchant fleets of Scandinavia are focused on the great ports of northern Europe, and their flags are seen in the harbours of every continent, participating in trades utterly foreign to the Baltic world. Nearly half of Norway's merchant tonnage is registered at Oslo. Stockholm, Göteborg, and the ports of the Sound account for much of Sweden's merchant fleet, while Copenhagen takes a large share of the merchant tonnage of Denmark. The chief centres of the fishing industry, on the other hand, are focused on different sections of the long and intricate coastline of Scandinavia. Apart from the specialized Norwegian whaling fleet that searches the Antarctic seas through the long daylight hours of the southern summer, the Scandinavian fishing fleets cast their nets scarcely more than a hundred miles from the mainland. Fishing settlements and processing centres occur in regional clusters, each deriving some special characteristic from the dominant type of fish, the season of high activity, the techniques of fishing in vogue, and the attendant processing industries that have developed [Fig. 77].

Norway's two chief fishing areas belong to Vestlandet and extend from the Arctic Circle to the bleak coastline of Finnmark. Although it has been said that 'northern Norway would be practically uninhabited without its rich resources in fish',[1] and every farm and settlement on the hundreds of miles of strandflat northward of Trondheim fjord gains its living as much from the sea as the land, it is true that the focus of Arctic fisheries lies in Vestfjord and the Lofoten islands. The mature cod congregate on this spawning ground in spring, gathering in vast shoals after their long, blind journey from the Arctic Ocean. The open jaw of Vestfjord, more than a hundred miles wide at its mouth and screened from the open sea by the jagged, ice-scarred mole of the Lofotens, seems to have been chosen by Nature's mysterious forces

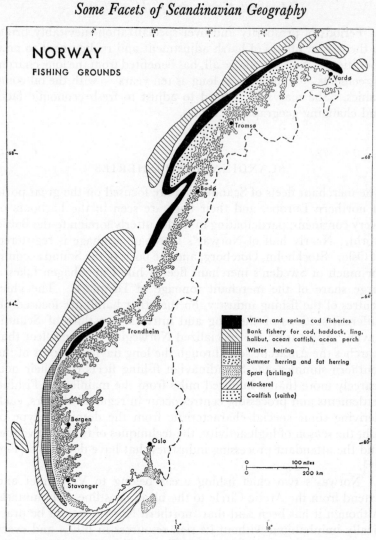

Fig. 77

Norway's chief fishing grounds belong to the Arctic north and to the coastline of Vest-landet. Cod dominates the northern fisheries in the Barents Sea and off the Lofoten islands whose main season is in late winter and spring. Herring and cod abound in the fishing of the extensive banks that lie off the north-west coast of Vestlandet. The south coast fisheries concentrate on the summer catch of mackerel in the Skagerrak.

as the chief spring breeding-ground of the codfish. Here the cold coastal current that flows along the shores of Arctic Norway mingles with the warmer, saline waters of the Norwegian Sea and provides the perfect temperature conditions for the spawning fish.

The shoals enter Vestfjord about the beginning of February and, to judge from the rising weekly catches of the thousands of fishermen, reach their peak during the last two weeks of March. The Lofoten fishing season begins at the end of January and finishes abruptly in the middle of April. For the Norwegian, these spring cod fisheries of the north constitute one of the several elements in his romanticized picture of the nation's life. Nearly every book that tries to conjure up the essence of Norway contains a photograph of the spring fishing season in Vestfjord, the sea hidden beneath a carpet of small fishing boats and the spectacular background of Lofoten peaks half-wrapped in a passing snowstorm.

Fishing off the Lofoten islands is carried out by small groups of fishermen; so often the unit is the family boat. Some of the methods of fishing by hand-line date back to the Middle Ages and perhaps even further into the unrecorded centuries of prehistoric northern Europe. Although the metropoles of the Lofoten cod fisheries — Stamsund, Henningsvær, and Svolvær — contain modern freezing and processing plants, the landscape of the strand-flat is still littered with the gaunt, wooden frames whose springtime burdens of salted, drying codfish may each be worth a thousand pounds [Plate 15]. The Lofoten fisheries possess dramatic qualities that are absent from this industry in other parts of northern Europe — a drama set against a backcloth of snowy needles, pinnacles, and giddily-poised cones of granite.

The cod is caught all along the coasts of Norway, particularly in the fjords, at any season; but the spring fisheries of Vestfjord produce the greater part of Norway's annual catch. Statistics show an ominous decline in the yield of the fisheries of the Lofoten islands [Fig. 78]. The average annual catch of Lofoten cod between 1930 and 1939 was 86,000 tons. The decade of the fifties reveals a fall to 58,900 tons, and the annual variations display wide extremes. For instance, in 1951 the yield was 115,964 tons of gutted cod, while in 1957 the output of the spring fishing season in Vestfjord fell to 23,043 tons.[2]

Lofoten fisheries and the trade in dried fish are at least eight centuries old. Archaic techniques and customs lend colour to the economy of these islands. But farther north a new centre of cod fishing has emerged along the coast of Finnmark in recent years. Already before the Second World War, Norwegians, Finns, and Russians were fishing for cod from the banks along this coastline and far out into the Barents Sea. There is a winter season, when

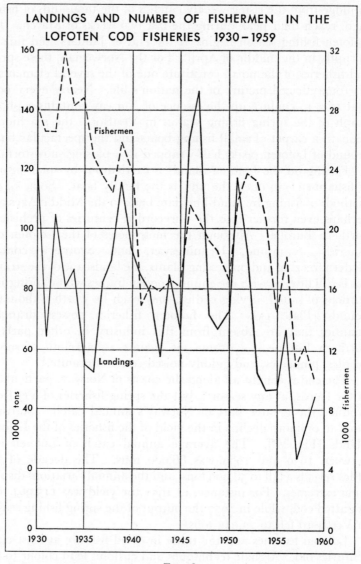

LANDINGS AND NUMBER OF FISHERMEN IN THE LOFOTEN COD FISHERIES 1930-1959

Fishermen

Landings

1000 tons

1000 fishermen

FIG. 78

The spring cod-fishing season of the Lofoten islands displays great variations in landings from year to year. There is an evident decline in the importance of the industry — at least measured in terms of its labour force — over the past three decades from a peak of 32,000 fishermen in 1933 to a third of this figure in 1959.

the mature fish are caught in this dark northern ocean as they make their way southwards to the Lofoten spawning ground. In summer, the seas off Finnmark abound in immature fish. It has been suggested that this bleak, remote northern coastline of Norway might emerge in the next generation as the nation's greatest fishing region. Since 1945, the new processes for the quick freezing of fish have been established in this region that lies so far from markets. Twelve preserving plants have been built, and Vardø, at the mouth of Varanger fjord, may now be listed among Norway's important fishing ports. The rise of Finnmark's cod fisheries is likely to have a deep influence on the older fishing centre of the Lofoten islands. The decline in the yields from Vestfjord since the war has been blamed on the rise of codfishing further north, particularly by foreign trawlers, whose activities in the Barents Sea have tripled during the decade of the fifties.

The second great fishing region lies off the fjord coast of western Norway. From Egersund to Kristiansund a string of strandflat ports concentrates on the winter herring fisheries on the submerged banks of this coastline. If they lack something of the romantic qualities of the Lofoten cod fisheries, nevertheless they contribute more to the economy. Herring form three-quarters of the annual catch of Norwegian fish, and the huge harvest of the winter herring season in the early fifties largely accounts for the doubling of the quantity of fish landed as compared with the years before the war [Figs. 79 and 80]. Like the spring cod fisheries of Vestfjord, the winter herring season is confined to a few weeks. Early in the year, at the end of January or the beginning of February, the herring approach the submarine banks and coastline of Vestlandet from the Norwegian Sea for spawning. One of the attractions of this area may lie in the oxygen-rich water that occurs in the depths. The winter anticyclone that settles over Scandinavia early in the year encourages the severe cooling of the surface layer of the sea. The cold surface waters, made denser by the cooling process, cascade down the slopes of submerged banks and slide into the depths of the sub-Norwegian trench.

Formerly, fishermen watched for the approach of the herring towards this sea rich in oxygen and plankton, where the warm waters of the North Atlantic Drift mix with the cold current that flows along the Norwegian coast. Today, the period of anxiety and anticipation that signalled the approach of the herring season has given way to the more orderly regime of science. For the first time, in 1951, a Norwegian research vessel was able to track the journey of the herring shoals from the wide spaces of the North Atlantic to their coastal spawning grounds by the use of echo-sounding apparatus. Today, the course of the migrating fish is known from the end of November and science is able to signal exactly the start of the fishing season.

The peak of the winter herring fisheries is confined to a period of about twenty days in February when the bulk of the catch will be taken. Thirty-five thousand tons of herring have been hauled from the sea in a single day, a glut that taxes the capacities of a chain of processing plants extending from the southern tip of Norway to Trondheim fjord. The heavy fish yields of the early 1950's reflect not only the abundance of nature, but point to improved fishing techniques and better methods of distribution. The purse seine net that can entrap a hundred tons of herring in one operation has become a common implement. The radio telephone now directs the movement of vessels towards prolific shoals, and at the height of the season transport ships move between the fisheries and the processing plants so that the fishing fleets can work continuously.

Herring and cod together account for nine-tenths of the annual catch of Norway's fisheries, a harvest that in the best of the post-war years has reached two million tons. The remaining tenth is largely explained by the fisheries of Norway's southern coastline and Oslo fjord. They stand apart from the spectacular herring and cod fisheries of Sunnmøre and Nordland because they are limited largely to the summer season. The mackerel fishing of Sørlandet starts in high summer at the beginning of June on the open waters of the Skagerrak, and later moves towards the land to the mouths of fjords and the skerry-guard [Fig. 79]. Sprats are caught in the early autumn in Oslo fjord and along the south-western coastline, providing the best material for Norwegian sardine canneries.

Apart from its local fisheries, Oslo fjord assumes a special place in the Norwegian economy as the centre of the whaling fleets. Their activities focus on the ports of Sandefjord, Tønsberg, and Larvik in the tiny county of Vestfold. For half a century Norway has played a dominant rôle among the whaling fleets of the Antarctic. In the peak season of 1930–31 she sent twenty-seven factory ships to the Antarctic. During the past decade the whaling ports of Oslo fjord sent nine floating factories to the seas of the southern hemisphere. Since the war an international convention has limited the annual catch of whales to less than a half of the bumper harvests of the early thirties. Despite the intrusion of several countries into the whaling industry, Norway still takes

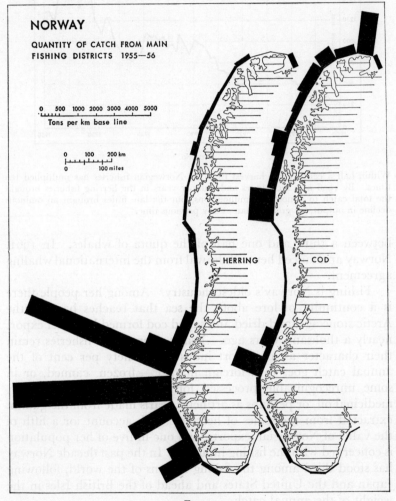

NORWAY

QUANTITY OF CATCH FROM MAIN
FISHING DISTRICTS 1955—56

0   500 1000 2000 3000 4000 5000
Tons per km base line

0   100   200 km
0   100 miles

HERRING   COD

FIG. 79

The map of herring fisheries shows the great concentration of this industry in the ports of northern Vestlandet, particularly about the mouth of Nordfjord and at Ålesund. The cod fisheries, notably less in quantity, belong to the Lofoten islands and the far north. The base-line of the columns is the present fishery limit, four miles from the outer skerries, within which most of the fish is caught. The total catch for each district is obtained by multiplying figures read off on the two scales.

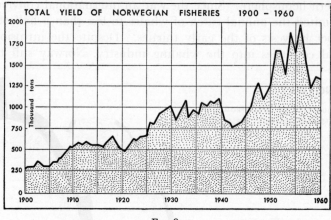

FIG. 80

Within half a century the harvest from the Norwegian fisheries has multiplied ten times. By 1956 new techniques and bumper years in the herring fisheries brought the total catch to almost two million tons, but the late fifties brought an ominous decline in output, far greater than at any previous time.

between a third and one half of the quota of whales. In 1961, Norway announced her withdrawal from the international whaling agreement.

Fishing is Norway's oldest industry. Among her people there is a continuity of lore about the sea that reaches back to the Arctic stone age, and dried and salted cod formed her chief export nearly a thousand years ago. Today, Norwegian fisheries retain their character as an export industry. Ninety per cent of the annual catch goes to a foreign market — frozen, canned, or in some unrecognizable processed form as cattle food, fertilizer, medicinal oil, or perhaps as artificial pearls made from the guanin extracted from the scales of herring. Fish account for a fifth of the value of Norwegian exports, and one in five of her population is concerned with the fishing industry. In the past decade Norway has stood third among the fishing nations of the world, following Japan and the United States and ahead of the British Isles in the weight of the annual catch.

Denmark, Sweden, and Finland fall far behind Norway in the importance of their fishing industries. The Danes hold second place among the North European states with between a quarter and one-sixth of Norway's average yearly catch. In each country, the westerly location of the main fishing harbours is notable.

Denmark's chief fishing grounds lie in the Skagerrak and the North Sea, and her main fishing ports stand on the Jutland peninsula strung out between Frederikshavn in the north-east and Esbjerg [Plate 46]. More than half of Denmark's total catch comes from the North Sea fishing grounds, and the importance of this area is reflected in her plans for a new deep-water harbour at Hantsholm on the north-western tip of Jutland, facing both the Skagerrak and the North Sea. It is expected that this will develop as a centre for the expanding deep-sea fishing fleet. Denmark's fisheries are remarkable, too, for the high market value of their catch. The figures for the years 1955 and 1956 show that the Danes netted about a fifth of the Norwegian catch by weight, but its value was somewhat more than a third of Norway's much larger harvest. The explanation of the value of Denmark's catch lies in the high proportion of halibut and plaice caught on the fishing banks of the North Sea. A large part of the catch of these valuable fish is taken directly to the markets in the British Isles. Denmark benefits, too, from the fact that she is the only Scandinavian country endowed with direct rail connections to Germany and the other states of central Europe.

Sweden's fisheries are less important than those of Denmark, the annual catch amounting to less than half of that brought in by Danish fishing boats. The geographical and economic pattern of the Swedish fishing industry possesses several features in common with that of Denmark. Again her chief fishing grounds are in the North Sea and Skagerrak, and her main harbours stand on the exposed coastline of Bohuslän [Fig. 81]. The fishing ports of Bohuslän lie along this red, granitic, ice-shaped coastline from Göteborg northwards to the Norwegian frontier. Central Bohuslän, and above all the harbour of Smögen, formed the main base of the fishing fleets forty years ago. Today it is displaced southwards to the cluster of islands that guards the northern entrance to the harbour of Göteborg. This shift in location to the precincts of Sweden's greatest port was determined by the modern fisherman's growing dependence on processing and quick-freezing plants, together with the need for effective communications with Sweden's domestic market. Göteborg's fish market has achieved a dominant position in the fishing industry of western Sweden. The large trawlers and motor ships, based on the fishing port of Hönö Klova, bring their catch from long distances to the Göteborg fish market, which, through its fast rail communications, commands most of the

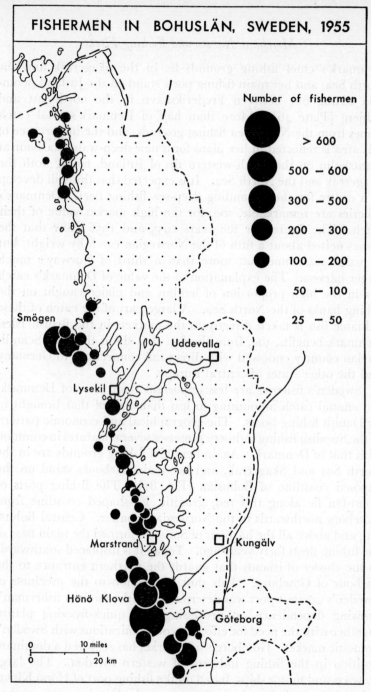

FISHERMEN IN BOHUSLÄN, SWEDEN, 1955

Number of fishermen

> 600

500 — 600

300 — 500

200 — 300

100 — 200

50 — 100

25 — 50

Smögen

Uddevalla

Lysekil

Marstrand

Kungälv

Hönö Klova

Göteborg

0   10 miles
0   20 km

FIG. 81

Sweden's chief fishing ports lie along the westward-facing coast of Bohuslän. Recently
the industry has become focused on the approaches to Göteborg where Hönö Klova
is Sweden's greatest fishing port.

interior of Sweden. Meanwhile, the picturesque small ports of Bohuslän's intricate and indented coastline have declined in importance, a decline that has been hastened by the replacement of the regular coastal steamer services by bus routes.

Swedish fishing in the North Atlantic and on the North Sea fishing banks takes place mainly from large, well-equipped trawlers, manned by crews for whom fishing is a full-time occupation. During the fifties the labour force of the Swedish fishing industry fell from 14,000 to 10,000. Nevertheless, technical improvements have raised the annual catch and the small, effective labour force is devoted entirely to fishing. On the other hand, Norway's fishing industry still remains diffuse in its organization, despite the widespread introduction of many mechanical and technical devices, and the creation of effective selling bodies. Fishing, especially in the north, is still joined to farming as a part-time occupation [Plate 13]. In 1956, Norway's fishermen numbered 90,000, but only a third of these were occupied solely in fishing. Sweden and Denmark strongly resemble each other in the structure of their fishing industries with small, effective labour forces, the widespread use of the trawler with its heavy hauls, and the concentration of the catch on a few ports possessing efficient processing plants, good rail communications, and effective marketing facilities.

Sweden and Finland share the poorer fish resources of the Baltic Sea. This brackish sea contains the smaller Baltic herring, eels, salmon, and cod. About a third of the total Swedish catch comes from the Baltic, and among the nations that look out to this sea her south-eastern fishing ports are the most active. Of all the Scandinavian countries Finland has the least contact with the sea. Her annual catch was about a thirtieth of that of Norway in the 1950's. Finland's fisheries bear some likeness to those of Norway in the persistence of archaic elements. The south-western archipelago and the Replot skerries in the Gulf of Bothnia form the two chief fishing districts, although this is an occupation that belongs to almost every part of the Finnish coastline. As in Norway, fishing frequently forms a part-time task in association with farming. Baltic herring make up three-quarters of Finland's annual catch. They are caught at every season of the year and from all parts of the coastline, though the most rewarding areas for the open-water fisheries seem to be in the south-western archipelago and from the waters at the mouth of the Gulf of Finland.

An archaic element of the Baltic herring fisheries is the winter fishing of the archipelago, carried on from shelters built by the fishermen on the ice. Like the intrepid seal hunting among the ice floes at the head of the Gulf of Bothnia in the depths of the Finnish winter, the winter herring fisheries of the south remind one of a time when Finland's remoteness turned her to exploit every food resource, even under the most trying conditions of the environment. Today, such activities form picturesque shreds of a way of life that is fast disappearing, and they make little or no impression on the national production figures of the fishing industry.

THE PROBLEMS OF CHANGE IN THE SCANDINAVIAN FISHING INDUSTRY

At the present time Scandinavian fisheries display a remarkable variety of features, a variety determined by the distribution and character of the abundant fish resources of the northern seas, and the historical development of an industry that has been in existence since the first Mesolithic fishermen and gatherers of shell-fish left their kitchen middens on the shorelines of the southern Baltic. Today, the technological revolution that engulfs the world is changing the character of fishing in Scandinavia, but the changes often come slowly, halted and resisted by the innate conservatism of men whose lives have been scarcely touched by the ideas and outlooks of the industrial revolution. Denmark and Sweden, as we have noticed, have moved towards a capitalistic structure in their fishing industries. Fleets of large trawlers are centred on a few efficiently organized harbours. In Norway, an older social structure persists in the fishing industry, but under the guidance of the state and voluntary organizations of fishermen it begins to adopt new economic ways.

The equipment of the fishing industry has changed continuously during this century. Perhaps the first and greatest revolution in Norwegian fisheries was the adoption of the petrol and diesel engine in small and medium-sized craft. This began about 1900, and thirty years later Norway's vast fishing fleet was almost completely motor-driven. Machinery has replaced manpower in many fishing operations. For instance, powered gurdies and rollers have become common for the drawing-in of long lines and nets. Since 1930, and particularly with the reconstruction of the fishing fleets after the Second World War, the instruments and devices of the electronics industry have come to the aid of the fishermen. Echo-sounding apparatus is now a common instrument in the equipment of the Lofoten codfishing fleet, and yet this magic device of the electronics laboratory here fits into an industry whose customs, regulations, and style of equipment often date from the medieval period. Radio telephones, especially in the herring fisheries, allow the co-ordination of fishing boats and transport craft in the areas of the richest shoals, and improved meteorological services have added to the safety and efficiency of the fishing industry.

In Norway, certain technical changes have been the subject of controversy and prohibition. For example, the purse seine net that has contributed so much to the increased catch in the winter herring fisheries off western Norway still remains a deeply controversial topic among the fishermen of Vestfjord.

It is no easy task to introduce a new technique or revolutionary implement into these northern fisheries whose complex regulations and methods have all the beauty and rigidity of a highly stylized art form. At the height of the spring codfishing season in the Lofoten islands, it is estimated that 70,000 nets and 14,000 handlines are cast into the waters of Vestfjord. Fishing is forbidden at night, and the little craft leave the crowded harbours of Svolvær and the other fishing settlements at a given signal after sunrise. Nets and lines are set and hauled at fixed times through the day, and the wide waters of the Vestfjord are divided into fifty separate territories, each allotted to a certain style of fishing [Fig. 82]. Such a system, deriving its energy from customary regulations accumulated over the centuries, stoutly resists changes of any kind. The purse seine net was first tried in the 1860's and then forbidden. It made a more successful re-entry into the closed circle of Lofoten fishermen after the Second World War. In 1950, more than a hundred boats took to seine fishing; two years later the revolutionary technique seemed to be on the verge of adoption in this area that lives by its traditions, when 1657 boats used purse seine nets and more than 12,000 fishermen were engaged with this new method. But the argument still rages in the little harbours that lie two hundred miles north of the Arctic Circle under the shadow of those gaunt, unchanging mountains. It is contended that the new net, taking thirty tons of cod at a single haul, has disturbed

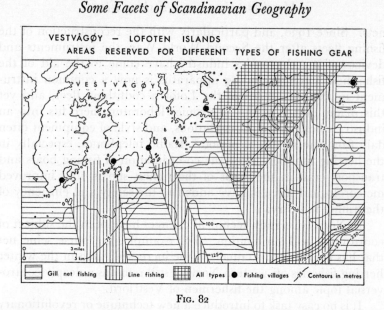

FIG. 82

The fishing grounds of Vestfjord that stretch out across the submerged parts of the strandflat are strictly divided into territories according to the different types of gear and fishing techniques.

the spawning fish in the inky waters of Vestfjord and, according to this argument, the worst result is the depleted harvests of the post-war years. Meantime, the debate hangs suspended, a topic for idle discussion and deep research, while the Norwegian parliament has prohibited the use of the purse seine net in the Lofoten fisheries during the fishing seasons of 1959 and 1960 to enable information to be collected on the effect of this revolutionary device upon the movements of the codfish.

The trawler, too, makes little headway among Norwegian fishermen, although it has become the basis of the Icelandic fishing fleet and the chief component in the fisheries of Sweden and Denmark. For long, the trawler was outlawed from the Norwegian fisheries because of the danger to the democracy of the small boats, where each independent unit is the property of the family or held jointly by a small group of men. A trawler fishing in the same grounds would steal the resources of the small boats, while the organization of fishing trawlers into large companies spelt out 'capitalism' in a community that leans far to the left in its politics. Since 1946 the trawler has been accepted with some reluctance as a small element in the Norwegian fishing industry.

In that year, Norwegians took up herring trawling in the North Sea for the first time. Today, the industry and the Norwegian government have accepted the idea that the trawler is a suitable instrument for fishing in international waters. By 1959 her fleet of 41,000 fishing vessels contained thirty modern deep-sea trawlers.

If the Norwegian fishing industry has been reluctant to introduce new techniques to the rich fishing grounds of the skerryguard and the Atlantic coastline, it has displayed remarkable flexibility in the organization of its markets and the growth of the processing industry. Each of the main fisheries — cod, herring, and mackerel — has its own sales organization acting as a compulsory intermediary between the innumerable small groups of fishermen and their market. They have secured even prices and a smooth flow of this perishable commodity to the freezing and processing plants. During the past thirty years these co-operative organizations have got rid of the chief causes of insecurity and poverty in this hazardous occupation.

Some notable changes have overcome the disposal and processing of fish since the beginning of this century. The Norwegian fisheries have always lain at a great distance from their chief markets. During the Middle Ages, the dried and salted cod of the north reached markets in central Europe and the Mediterranean through the medium of the Hanseatic trading empire. Today, too, the *klipfisk* from Arctic Norway is still exported to Spain and Portugal, and, in rising quantities, to Brazil. The first revolution in the preservation of Norwegian fish for distant markets appeared with the rise of the canning industry in Stavanger about 1880. Since that time several important developments have affected this industry. The aluminium can was introduced in the 1930's and, since the war, highly refined Norwegian sild-sardine oil has replaced imported olive oil as a packing material.

Two important developments have influenced the fisheries of northern Europe since the Second World War. First, the export of fish in the form of frozen fillets has greatly increased. By 1951 the quantity of Norwegian fish used to produce frozen fillets had trebled. The new refrigeration plants are located in the north and plainly illustrate the value of a new industrial technique in changing the market relations of this remote area. A second change of the past decade is the steep rise in the amount of herring consumed by the oil and meal plants distributed along the coastline of southwestern Norway. The processing plants used 58 per cent of the

Norwegian herring harvest in 1946. By 1951 the oil and meal factories were taking 81 per cent of a greatly increased catch. With their output of solid fats for margarine production and valuable, protein-rich cattle foods, the processing plants provide Norway with commodities capable of earning far more foreign currency than fish exported in a salted, frozen, or canned state. Early in the fifties the herring fisheries adopted a technique from the Antarctic whaling industry, the fitting out of a ship for the processing of herring at sea. The *Glupea*, the first floating oil and meal plant, gathers its raw material fresh from the most prolific shoals and represents a radical development in an industry that seems so slow to accept change.

No industry remains for long without change. Even when technical developments are resisted and inventions outlawed, the realm of politics and the capricious world of fashion can impose changes upon a rigid industrial structure. For instance, Norway's oldest export commodity, the *kilpfisk*, is still subject to the vagaries of world politics. The Hansa League that once monopolized the fish trade of Atlantic Norway is only remembered in the pages of history books and the topography of the German merchants' quay at Bergen. Today, the profits of Lofoten fishermen depend upon political events in faraway Latin America. Since 1956, the exports of dried and salted cod from Arctic Norway have increased sharply as a result of the opening up of the market in Latin America. By 1960 Brazil had become the largest importer of *klipfisk*, largely the result of the creation of favourable currency regulations. On the other hand, the fishing fleets of Spain and Portugal grew over the past decade and the traditional Catholic market for the dried fish of Scandinavia has declined. An interesting result of the rising market for dried cod in South America is a marked change in the proportions of the Lofoten catch absorbed by the different processes between the beginning and end of the decade of the fifties. In 1952, less than 30 per cent of the catch from the spring fisheries in Vestfjord went to the drying frames; by 1959, largely as a result of the expanding market in Brazil, 78 per cent of the cod were preserved by this traditional method. The change was mainly at the expense of salted cod. The proportion taken by the refrigerator plants in the Lofoten islands has remained stable through the fifties, at between 8 and 15 per cent of the total catch. The world of politics, apart from discouraging or developing markets or framing regulations for the operation of an industry, occasionally makes an even more direct impact. For example, the declaration of a twelve-mile limit to territorial waters by the U.S.S.R. has closed the entrance of the White Sea to Norwegians. As a result, her sealing fleet has had to abandon this traditional sealing ground and to re-centre the industry among the drift ice off eastern Greenland.

Behind the changes that technology and man's habit of making regulations impose upon the fishing industry of northern Europe lie the deeper transformations engineered by nature. The history of Scandinavia's coastline abounds with evidence of famines and gluts. The herring has a fickle history in Sweden's chief fishing district, Bohuslän. Since the tenth century nine periods of abundance have been recognized. The last quarters of the eighteenth and nineteenth centuries were times of bumper catches, but since 1906 the herring seems to have avoided this coastline. The history of Norwegian herring fishing reveals a similar cyclical pattern. Records of the industry since 1500 suggest that periods when fish are abundant close to the coast last between a half and three-quarters of a century, while the intervening times of poor catches may run between thirty and sixty years. It is certain that the rich harvests of the winter herring fisheries off Vestlandet in the 1950's result from the prolific shoals that have come close to the Norwegian coastline, as well as the improved nets, transport boats, and the revolutionary detection gear. Behind the broad changes in the North Atlantic fisheries during the past two decades there seems to lie the marked climatic amelioration of the northern latitudes, with its slow, deep influences on temperature, salinity, and the movement of ocean waters. The rise of temperatures along the coast of Greenland has shifted the centres of codfishing some three hundred miles to the north. Hydrographic changes, too, have brought a new fishing area into being off the coast of western Spitsbergen. The chief centres of the prolific winter herring fisheries of western Norway show a distinct change of location between the decades of the thirties and the fifties, shifting from the southern coast of Vestlandet to the northern coast seaward of Ålesund.

The relationships between a nation's political and social institutions, the changing technology of a period, and the resources of the natural environment are always complex. In the fishing industry of northern Europe, many aspects of the natural resource still remain a mystery and today provide a subject for intensive research. On the other hand, some of the social features of this industry are equally difficult to forecast and control. For example, in the years since the war, when the economies of the Scandinavian countries have been expanding rapidly, the fishing industry has suffered from a declining labour force. Most serious perhaps is its failure to recruit young people. Between 1949 and 1957, the number of Swedish fishermen fell from 14,000 to 10,000. The spring codfishing season in the Lofoten islands has experienced an even more serious decline in its labour force. In the decade of the thirties an average of 26,744 men took part in the Lofoten fisheries. The average for the decade 1950–60 is 17,000, and the closing years of this period, 1957–59, reveal a much lower figure of only 10,919 fishermen in Vestfjord. The waning labour force of the fisheries is not apparent in the output figures of the northern nations. On the contrary, improved techniques have produced notably higher yields in the post-war years [Fig. 80]. But manpower is not yet a dispensable factor in any industry and, in the dangerous, individualistic tasks of the deep-sea fisheries, never likely to be. Within the next few years the ageing labour force of the Scandinavian fisheries is likely to present a problem at present concealed by the achievements of technology. It remains to be seen whether the welfare state will find the right incentives to direct labour back towards an essential industry when this is wanted.

CHAPTER 12

Forestry and Timber Industries

FORESTS of coniferous softwoods form the greatest natural resource of Scandinavia. They cover 55 per cent of the Swedish landscape, and timber products provide two-fifths of the nation's exports. Statistically, forests seem less obtrusive in the Norwegian scene, where only a quarter of the country is timber-covered [Fig. 83]. Some major features of her regional make-up discourage the dark garment of spruce and pine that meets the traveller almost everywhere in Sweden or Finland. Altitude and high latitude exclude much of northern Norway from satisfactory colonization by coniferous trees, although the temperature anomalies of this Atlantic seaboard allow slow-growing stands of pines to survive at more than 70° north. Further south, the bare islands and strand-flat bench bear witness to the power of Atlantic gales in preventing the growth of trees, though the exorbitant demands of the medieval fishing industry for fuel, boat building, and packing materials is partly responsible for the naked condition of this coastal fringe in recent centuries. Lastly, much of Norway southward of the fertile lowland of Trøndelag lies high above the limit of tree growth in northern Europe. Here the empty expanse of the *vidda*, with the glint of light from some distant snowfield, symbolizes Norway's comparative poverty in the most plentiful commodity of the Scandinavian states. Despite the fact that Norway's timber resources are restricted and her wood-processing plants operate below their full capacity from a shortage of raw materials, the products of her timber industries make up a third of the value of her exports.

In contrast to Norway, the forest wealth of Finland reflects her interior continental position among the Scandinavian states as well as the favourable topography of the low Archaean peneplain, liberally plastered with the waste of the Quaternary ice-sheets. Nearly three-quarters of Finland's area is forest-covered, a proportion greater than that of any other European country [Figs. 84 and 85]. The monotonous, silent shadows of her pine forests

333

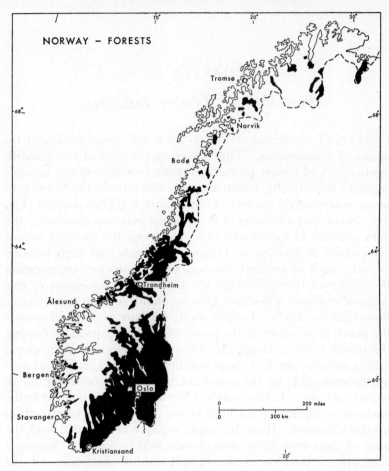

FIG. 83

Norway is the least wooded of the Scandinavian countries with only a quarter of her area covered in forest. The main forest districts centre on Trondheim fjord and the plateaus and valleys of the south-east. There are scattered stands of timber in the western fjords and the most extensive forests of Arctic Norway lie in the longitudinal inland valleys sheltered from North Atlantic gales and the depredations of coastal farmers and fishermen.

represent one of the popular images of Finland. Her national culture, perhaps even more than those of the other Scandinavian states, has been shaped in wood. The churches of her countryside, farm-buildings, implements and domestic utensils, the huge piles of winter fuel stacked in every village, and the fast-disappearing timber-fired locomotives with their bulbous smoke-stacks that

334

look like some utilitarian resurgence of the baroque style in an industrial age, all speak of a culture and an economy founded on the immense wealth of the softwood forests. The export figures speak even more plainly of Finland's forest background. Ever since she gained her independence after the First World War, timber products — ranging from sawn timber to plywood, furniture, prefabricated houses, paper, pulp, and wallboard — have formed between 80 and 85 per cent of Finnish exports.

THE GEOGRAPHY OF SCANDINAVIA'S FORESTS

The whole of Denmark lies beyond the southern limit of the boreal coniferous forests within the realm of the deciduous woods [Fig. 84]. Forests cover only 10 per cent of the country and stands of natural self-seeding trees disappeared from the Danish landscape long ago. Today, the orderly copses and spinneys of beech, elm, lime, and oak are mainly the result of deliberate planting, and in the past three-quarters of a century the applied science of forestry has caused the spread of pine and spruce in the interior of Jutland.

The boreal coniferous forest covers the greater part of Scandinavia. Northward of latitude 68°, the seemingly limitless woodlands of Scots pine and Norway spruce give way to the open sub-Arctic zone, treeless apart from extensive stretches of sparse, low-growing birch woodland. At latitude 60°, almost six hundred miles to the south of the forests' northern frontier, the southern boundary of the boreal forest belt is announced by the appearance of the oak, elm, ash, and hazel. To the unpractised eye, the mixed forest region that borders the monotonous empire of the pine and spruce looks hardly different, a fact that is not surprising when one remembers that three-quarters of the trees in the mixed forest belt of southern Scandinavia are conifers. In Finland, the mixed forest belt, the zone where deciduous specimens survive, is confined to the south-western fringe of the country. Here the boundary with the zone of pure coniferous forest that covers most of the country demands the skill of the botanist for its identification rather than the eye of the geographer. The conventional boundary of the mixed forest region and the boreal coniferous forest is determined by the northern limit of the oak. Other species of deciduous trees grow far to the north of this limit in Finland, where the great sheets of inland water tend to blur the latitudinal differences of climate. Thus the lime tree is known in central Finland, and the alder finds its northern frontier beyond the head of the Gulf of Bothnia.

Central and southern Sweden belong largely to the mixed forest belt, but here once again the dark conifers play a predominant rôle in the landscape and the economy. Deciduous trees flourish in the countrysides of the low-lying, rich clay plains, but they only properly come into their own in the parks of central Sweden's country mansions. Here the pale greens of broad-leaved trees are highly valued for the impression of the south which they create in these artificial landscapes of the gardener and the planting forester. On the fault-bounded hills that rise from the plains of Midland Sweden and in the bleak upland of Småland the great forests seem to be filled unendingly with pine, spruce and birch — islands of the vast northern woodlands that lie south of the conventionally accepted boundary of the boreal coniferous forest.

A third major forest type — the north European deciduous forest — makes its appearance in a narrow belt of country that stretches from southern Sweden to Oslo Fjord and westward along the sheltered shores of the great fjords of Vestlandet. The fine beech woods of Denmark and southern Sweden belong to this belt, but geographically the zone of the north European deciduous forests is most notable for the amount of clearing that has been accomplished over the past four thousand years. Here the first farmer-settlers of the Neolithic period found the only tolerable setting for their way of life.

The frontiers between the three great forest types — the deciduous, mixed, and coniferous — become pinched together in Norway and contribute a variety to her landscape that is absent from the monotonous tracts of Swedish Norrland and the interior of Finland. The major vegetation boundaries depend upon the almost imperceptible changes of climate brought about by increasing latitude in the flatter lands around the Baltic Sea. The boundaries between the chief forest zones lie hundreds of miles apart. In contrast, the landscapes of south-western Norway's fjords display a vertical zonation of the main vegetation belts. A half-day's walk will take one from deciduous trees along the sheltered shore of a fjord through mixed and coniferous woods to the high slopes where the open, scrubby birchwoods give way to vegetation and landscapes scarcely distinguishable from those of sub-Arctic Lapland. Fjord Norway owes much of its attractiveness for tourists to the vertical zonation of the vegetation belts brought about by this high, dissected plateau penetrated by deep, glaciated valleys and drowned by the sea.

The vast coniferous forests of Scandinavia form the western extension of the even vaster belt of woodland that encompasses the northern parts of the whole Eurasian continent [Fig. 84]. A traveller through Swedish Norrland remains impressed by the monotony of the boreal coniferous forests, where the dark blue-green of tree-tops clothes every topographical feature and stretches like some immobile sea to the furthest horizon [Plate 25]. The monotony of these forest landscapes extends to the variety of species growing there. North-western Europe's forests may be summed up in the terms of three species — the Scots pine,

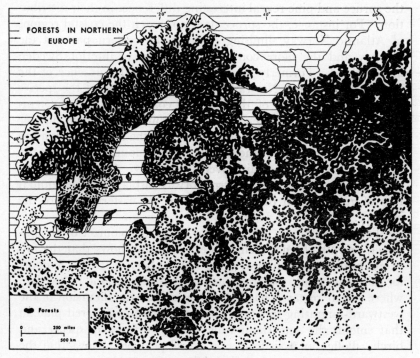

FIG. 84

Scandinavia forms the western limit of the coniferous forest belt that extends across the Eurasian continent. Denmark and Skåne belong to the lightly forested north European plain. In the rest of Scandinavia, only the high treeless plateaus of Norway, the bare Atlantic coastline, and parts of the closely settled Swedish midlands stand clear of the enveloping woodland.

z

the Norway spruce, and the birch. These forests owe their botanical poverty to the Quaternary ice age. Only a few thousand years have elapsed since the disappearance of the ice that accumulated over Scandinavia. In the recolonization of Europe vegetation reached northern Sweden and the interior of Finland at a late date. It has not achieved the balanced richness that is possible in areas saved from glaciation or but mildly affected by this natural catastrophe on a grand scale. But the poverty that depresses the collecting botanist represents easily exploitable wealth for the economic geographer and the industrialist. The vast forest industries depend upon the limitless abundance of pine and spruce, and the monotonous uniformity of species across large tracts of country aids their rational cutting.

Within the large region of the Scandinavian coniferous forests the spruce and pine reveal interesting differences in their distribution. For instance, the spruce does not reach the coastal regions of Atlantic Norway, limiting itself to the eastern parts of the country and the more continental climates of interior Sweden and Finland. Formerly it was believed that this absence of the spruce from western Norway reflected the hostility of the species to the moist climate of the Atlantic coastline, where the temperature contrasts between winter and summer are much slighter than in the rest of Scandinavia. However, the successful planting of spruce seedlings from the German Harz mountains among the fjords of Vestlandet has disproved this theory. On the contrary, the plantation spruces of western Norway display a higher annual rate of growth than the native trees in the eastern parts of the country.

Today, the spruce is believed to be a late colonizer of Scandinavia, and its absence from western Norway shows that the full extent of the spruce migration has not yet been reached. Support for this view comes, too, from the province of Jämtland in Sweden, where recent research has been able to date the incursion of the westward-migrating spruce. There the moraine-covered plateau that enfolds the Ångerman valley carries a forest of spruce and birch. Pollen analysis from prehistoric peat beds shows that the spruce entered this region about three thousand years ago, and since the late Bronze age spruce forest has formed the natural climax vegetation of this area. The slow migration of the spruce towards Scandinavia's western seaboard is now likely to be achieved much more rapidly with the helping hand of man.

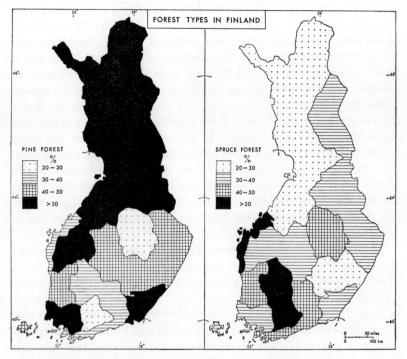

FIG. 85

Pine forests predominate in the north of Finland where they take up almost two-thirds of the productive woodland. The spruce is the characteristic tree in the more quickly maturing forests of southern Finland where it forms more than half of the productive woodland in southern Östterbotten and on the western fringe of the lakes plateau.

Spruce is the most favoured species in the forest replacement programme of western Norway, so former stands of deciduous forest are giving way to conifers. Man, too, has enriched the forests of Scandinavia with species from overseas. Alongside central European species, trees from the humid Pacific coast of North America, such as the Sitka spruce and Douglas fir, thrive in the plantations of western Norway.

Within Scandinavia, the main species of the boreal coniferous forest each possess a marked distribution pattern. As a result of its late migration history, the spruce fails to reach Scandinavia's Atlantic seaboard and there gives way to a predominance of pine. On their northern fringe, the spruce and pine forests are succeeded by landscapes dominated by the birch. But a local view of almost any tract of the great forest belt in these northern countries reveals an intricate mosaic of the main species. In the harsh conditions of soil and climate that reign over northern Europe, the pine seems to be more tolerant than the spruce. The spruce demands a heavier, moister, richer soil than the pine tree. Consequently, in Sweden's central province of Jämtland it is usual to find a spruce forest dominant on the boulder clay and moraine-strewn inter-fluvial plateaus, while pines have colonized the arid gravels and sands along the river valleys. In far northern Finland, the same relationships prevail in the local distributions of pine and spruce. The forests of the long valley of the Ounas, a tributary of the Kemi draining into the head of the Gulf of Finland, show that the spruce dominates the moister, heavier boulder clays, while the Scots pine is associated with sandy, gravelly deposits and a heathland type of vegetation.[1]

The birch is another major element in the mosaic of the northern forest. Stands of pine and spruce often give way to tracts of birch forest. Within the main forest belt this is almost inevitably a result of clearance at the hand of man. Birch is the first colonizer of land that has been burnt over or cleared of timber. It survives throughout the woodlands of Scandinavia and Finland, a symptom of man's perpetual interference with the climax forest through unregulated cutting or the regular burning of the timberlands that was once part of the peasant economies of the north. Today, the birch seems about to be revalued in the commercial life of Scandinavia's boreal forests. Until lately it has had little economic value, apart from the manufacture of plywood and spools in Finland, and has been regarded as the product of mismanagement and archaic systems of land-use. Nowadays, however, the birch has been discovered as a raw material in the manufacture of pulp, and at the same time the scientific forester has come to realise that the tree plays a part of some value amid the tall conifers. Its leafless state in the early spring permits sunlight to penetrate to the forest floor, and soils warm up more quickly than in the unbroken shade of the tall softwoods.

PROBLEMS OF FOREST EXPLOITATION

The exploitation of the northern forests is deeply affected by the timber's age and rate of growth, the question of ownership, and the accessibility of a cutting area to effective means of communication and processing plants. It is a rule of good forestry that the annual growth of timber determines the amount of the annual cutting. In Finland, the forests of the north take three times as long to reach maturity as those of the south [Fig. 86]. As a result, Finland's oldest forests lie in the northern parts of the country. More than half the trees of the timberlands in the Kemi valley are older

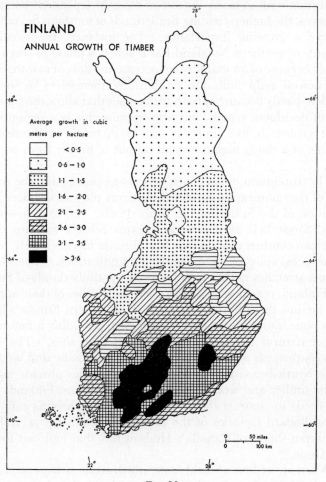

FINLAND

ANNUAL GROWTH OF TIMBER

Average growth in cubic
metres per hectare

	< 0·5
	0·6 — 1·0
	1·1 — 1·5
	1·6 — 2·0
	2·1 — 2·5
	2·6 — 3·0
	3·1 — 3·5
	> 3·6

0   50 miles
0   100 km

FIG. 86

The rate of growth in Finland's coniferous forests deeply affects the economics of the timber industry. The most rapid rate of increase is found in the woodlands of the south-western fringe of the lakes plateau. In the harsh climates of the north annual increment of timber is only one-third that of the south.

than a hundred and fifty years. Their wood, too, has a different quality, because the slow annual increment gives rise to thin rings and a hard, dense wood. The Swedish forests display an even wider range in the rate of annual increment. From the north in Lapland to the southernmost province of Skåne it increases from 1·9 m³. per hectare to 8·2 m³. per hectare. At a time when the word 'conservation' begins to replace the term 'exploitation' in connection with so many industries directly dependent on natural resources, the higher-yielding timberlands of southern Scandinavia achieve a growing importance. For instance, the wood-pulp industry of southern Norrland has reached a phase of stagnation, largely because of an inability to increase the flow of raw materials. The newest pulp mills are establishing themselves in southern Sweden, partly because of fresh techniques that allow the consumption of deciduous woods, but also because this is a region where forest growth is five times as fast as in northern Sweden and capable of a much higher annual output of timber from an equal area.

The disposition of harbours, processing plants, and the natural lines of communication provided by rivers play a vital part in the evolution of the Scandinavian timberlands. A world view of the boreal forest belt as it stretches across Siberia and the North American continent shows that Scandinavia has been well blessed in the geography of its natural communications. The Gulf of Bothnia stretches northwards between the timberlands of Sweden and Finland, reaching to within a few score miles of their northern limit against the sub-arctic wilderness. Northern Europe's largest rivers pour into this arm of the Baltic Sea, providing a fine succession of natural floatways and hydro-electric sites. The Baltic leads southwards to the ports of northern Germany and westward to the North Sea, where industrial communities provide markets for the timber and wood products of Sweden and Finland. One only needs to contrast the scores of ports and thriving pulp mills and wallboard factories of the Bothnian coastline [Fig. 91] with the barren shores of Canada's Hudson Bay that look out towards the Arctic.

When viewed on a world scale, north-western Europe is richly endowed by nature for the growth of its timber industries. A nearer prospect, however, shows that the factors of distance and ease of communications are still vitally important for the stable and prosperous development of a forest economy. Among the

Scandinavian countries Finland lies furthest from the timber-hungry lands of the North Sea. This simple geographical fact makes itself felt in the history of the development of the timber industries. The accessible coastline of south-eastern Norway was already exporting timber in the seventeenth and eighteenth centuries, and the city of Amsterdam grew across its marshland site on piles cut from the forests of Sørlandet. Early in the nineteenth century, the more remote forests of Baltic Sweden began to enter the European market, and Finland made an even later entry into the timber trade towards the close of the last century.

Accessibility to markets is an apparent factor in the economic geography of forestry within each of the Scandinavian states. For instance, the forests of Finland's eastern border, particularly in the north, lie beyond the reach of profitable exploitation at the present time [Figs. 92 and 94]. This tract of frontier country stretches beyond Finland's main watershed and streams drain eastward to cross into the Soviet Union. In recent years there has been a drive to build roads into this remote marchland, so that industry may begin to tap the resources of these ancient woodlands where the last extensive stands of virgin forest remain in Europe. The distant interior of Swedish Norrland also forms a marginal region for the forest industries. For instance, the wooded plateaus of Jämtland lie a long way from the timber-processing industries along the Baltic coastline. At times when trade is poor and prices fall, the timber-cutters of Jämtland are the first to feel the recession.

The type of forest ownership is as important a factor in the development of timber industries as the species and quality of tree and the ease of communications with the processing centres. The timberlands of the Scandinavian countries belong either to the state, the large companies, to the community in the form of shared parish woodlands, or else in the form of countless patches and small tracts to individual farmers. Today, the type of ownership is the most powerful factor in the rational development of the north European forests.

Norway's forests are predominantly in the hands of her small farmers, 71 per cent of the woodland area belonging to private farmers. The majority of the holdings are tiny and impede the spread of the techniques of scientific forestry. The state possesses only 17 per cent of the Norwegian forests, and unfortunately this represents a resource of mediocre value. Many state forests lie in the far north where the annual increment of timber is very low;

others, in eastern Norway, occupy high ground close to the tree line and are excluded from the axe of the wood-cutter to preserve the quality of forests at lower levels.

Finland stands at the opposite extreme from Norway [Fig. 87]. There, the state owns more forest land than any other Scandinavian government with a third of the total area of woodland. As in

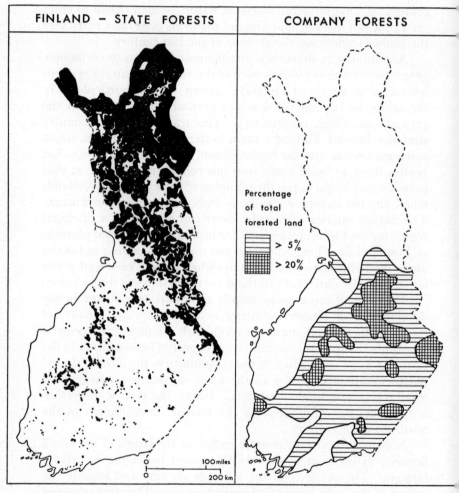

FIG. 87

Finland's state forests lie mainly in the remote unpopulated northern parts of the country where timber grows more slowly than in the south. The heavily exploited domains of the pulp and paper corporations are concentrated on the lakes plateau.

neighbouring Sweden and Norway, much of the state-owned forest lies in the more isolated northern parts of the country. The thinly populated and inaccessible basins of the Kemi and Oulu rivers find three-fifths of their woodland in the possession of the state. Towards the coastline of the Gulf of Bothnia and in southern Finland, areas of early and continuous settlement, the government gives way to the private farmer and local community in the ownership of forested land. For instance, state forests take up less than 7 per cent of the wooded area in southern Finland. On the Finnish lakes plateau a third type of ownership becomes dominant. There it is common for the big pulp and paper companies whose plants are located on the southern fringe of the lakes to own as much as a half of the woodland in the parishes at the lake-heads.

Sweden displays some of the ownership traits of both Norway and Finland [Fig. 88]. For example, the small farmer still possesses a half of the country's total area of timberlands. In her southern provinces, Skåne, Blekinge, and Halland, nearly 90 per cent of the forest is in the hands of farmers. Again, in the old farming districts further north, for instance around Jämtland's great lake of Storsjön, the small farmer is the predominant owner of forest land. But amid the wilds of Norrland 60 per cent of the forests belong to the great industrial concerns and the state.

The outstanding feature of forest ownership in Sweden is the part played by the industrial corporation. Many of the company forests, particularly to the north of lake Vänern, are inherited from an earlier industrial age of countless scattered forges and smelting mills. Firms that formerly produced iron have now entered the field of pulp and paper manufactures. The woodlands that were carefully tended as a source of charcoal now form the company forests of the new industries. Further north, vast estates were carved out of the timberlands by the wood-processing firms situated along the coast of the Gulf of Bothnia. The biggest of these, the Swedish Cellulose Company, controls more than five thousand square miles of forest, and several other corporations possess territories larger than an English county.

The aggrandizement of company forests was at its height in the last decade of the nineteenth century, the result of a law passed in 1889 that restricted the purchase of timber-felling rights to a maximum period of twenty years. Before that time, the coastal sawmilling companies bought the rights of timber-felling from farmers, making contracts that ran for as long as half a century. The reduction of the contract periods by state legislation drove the large companies to seek permanent supplies of softwood from their own forests, a trend that was stimulated by the rapidly

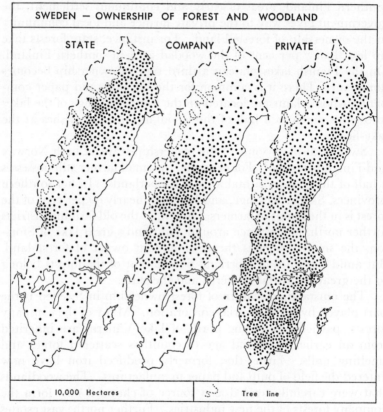

FIG. 88

The state owns 18 per cent of Sweden's forests, mainly in Norrbotten and among the hills of Dalarna. Twenty-five per cent of the woodland belongs to joint-stock companies and it lies in the valuable timber-producing provinces to the north of the central lakes depression. The greater part of the forests, 51 per cent, is still in the hands of private owners, either farmers or the landed gentry who exploit their timber resources as a support to agriculture.

expanding traffic in sawn timber towards the end of the century and the appearance of the pulp industry. The Swedish parliament intruded even more dramatically in the economic geography of Norrland in 1906, when it passed a law prohibiting the purchase of land by companies or associations. To protect the interests of the small farmer the state put an end to the timber companies' empires in northern Sweden. The company forest in Sweden is the product of a brief period of history, a product of society and the laws that are devised for its government.

The various types of ownership in the Scandinavian woodlands represent different attitudes to forestry, standing for different aims and techniques in the management of this great natural resource. At one extreme, the small farmer, with his narrow slip of woodland leading back from some river terrace or valley road, looks upon his timber as a source of fuel in the long, hard Scandinavian winter, a lavish supplier of building material for barns, houses, and fences, and an occasional source of ready cash. Remote from this ancient attitude to the coniferous forest stand the intentions of the timber company. Foremost in the mind of the modern pulp and paper combine is the acquisition of a regular supply of raw material to serve the annual needs of the plant. The smooth flow of timber to the processing factories has only been achieved through the construction of floatways, the making of roads to logging camps far from rivers, the organization of labour, and the application of silvicultural techniques.

The great corporations have now left behind them the brief period of destructive exploitation that characterized their first attacks on the virgin forests. Today, their methods are turned towards the conservation and improvement of timber resources to ensure a rising supply of raw material for an expanding industry. The company forest, particularly in Sweden, has become the centre of a technological revolution. Methods of timber-cutting are adapted to the topography, climate, and soil qualities of the site. On cleared land the choice of seedlings, methods of sowing and planting, and the protection of the young forests against disease and other calamities have become subjects of deep research. Changes, too, have overcome the systems of transport. In Sweden, many of the smaller streams have fallen out of use as floatways, being replaced by roads with tractor haulage and lorries. The romantic picture of timber-felling in the short days of winter, when logs were hauled to river banks across the frozen snow to await the spring thaw, has given way to the rational management techniques of the applied economist. In the company forests timber-cutting goes on throughout the year, and a permanent labour force is supplemented by casual workers from the farms during winter. Forestry in Sweden is a highly specialized occupation that now bears all the marks of the welfare state with trade schools, research institutes, subsidized houses for its workers, company-owned holiday chalets on the beaches of the Gulf of Bothnia, and state-directed life insurances and pensions.

The problems that belong to the peasant ownership of forests are illustrated most clearly in Norway. In recent years, her wood-processing industries have failed to run to their full capacity through a shortage of raw material. Many of Norway's difficulties in achieving higher outputs of timber arise from the small units of forest property and the attitudes of her peasant farmers. Timber-cutting for them is only a part-time occupation, an adjunct to farming. It is difficult to introduce rational methods of clearing and replanting when every man is the master of his own tiny strip of forest. For instance, soon after the Second World War the Norwegian government tried to introduce motor-driven saws among its farmer foresters, but found it hard to engineer a minor technical revolution of this kind in a conservative country. Apart from the reluctance of the Norwegian countryman to accept technical changes, the scientific cultivation of forest land demands the larger unit. Norway is hampered by the minute divisions of woodland ownership that are absent from the scientifically managed state and company forests of northern Sweden. The effect of a social factor, in this case land-ownership, upon the development and running of an industry is strikingly illustrated in the quality of Norway's forests. A post-war forest survey showed that in Norway's various forest districts only between five and ten per cent of the timber was of the highest quality.[2] The country suffers from too many stands of old and thinly spaced trees, whereas a rational policy of forest management aims at close-growing plantations of young and mature timber. Norway's recent survey revealed, too, that the annual increment of wood by growth clearly exceeds the loss by cutting, and many tracts of forest are past their prime from an economic point of view. The Norwegian peasant farmer regards his strip of woodland as a reserve to be drawn upon in times of need or when timber prices are high enough to make this part-time occupation worth-while, but at the board meeting of a pulp and paper company, the forest is cherished as the first and essential stage of a complex industrial process whose products have found a steadily expanding market ever since the beginning of the century.

The relationship between man and nature on the face of the earth is complex and ever changing. Scandinavia's boreal forests, empty and but thinly populated in the eyes of a demographer, illustrate some of the features of this delicate relationship. Forests respond to the slow changes of other elements in the physical environment. The notable amelioration of Scandinavia's climates in the past three decades finds its response in the vitality of her coniferous forests. In Swedish Jämtland, the botanist Tore Arnborg has noticed an upward movement of the higher limit of the birch forest in recent years.[3] The same climatic improvement that is more strikingly demonstrated by the shrunken glaciers of western Norway has encouraged the active colonization of the lower edge of the birch forests by the spruce. Again, Norwegian silviculturists have noted an increase in the annual growth of timber over the past decades that seems to be due to the climatic improvement in these northern lands.

Man himself exercises an infinitely more powerful influence upon the forests of Scandinavia than the slow revolutions of climatic change. For centuries, his burning and clearing reveal the peasant farmer as a destructive agent, substituting a birch scrubland for the tall earth-red trunks of conifers. The selective desires of industry are plainly changing the composition of forests over large areas. The two forest surveys of Finland, taken in the early twenties and the early fifties, show that the area of spruce woodland has extended considerably.[4] In the south of the country, where the timber industries have made their greatest impact, the spruce has visibly conquered the territory of the pine tree within the space of a generation. Forty years ago the spruce covered 27 per cent of the forest area in southern Finland. The survey completed in 1953 showed that it then occupied 35 per cent of the southern woodlands. Developments in Sweden point to an even more radical relationship between men and the forests in the near future. The Forest Tree Breeding Association has selected fine specimens of trees from different parts of the country for the production of seeds to be used in the plantations of the future. It is conceivable that the Swedish forests of the next century will be the descendants of a handful of fine breeding specimens selected by the silviculturists of today.

THE EVOLUTION OF THE SAWN-TIMBER TRADE

The Scandinavian woodlands feed two markets [Fig. 89]. One serves the slowly changing local needs of farm, hamlet, and small town in every part of northern Europe. This satisfies the age-old requirements of fuel for heating and wood for fencing and building-

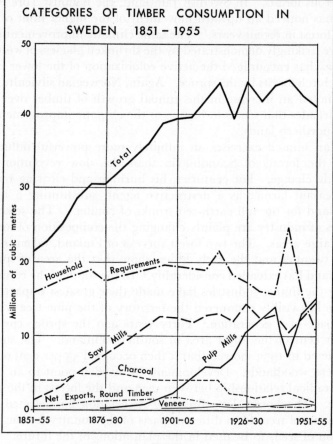

FIG. 89

Within the past century the consumption of timber, calculated in five-year periods, shows important changes in the Swedish economy and society. The household use of wood has declined sharply since 1945 with the widespread consumption of electricity and oil in domestic heating. The period of the Second World War is evident in the sharp rise of timber for household use and the contraction in the production of pulp. Charcoal has declined over the years; pulp, the most valuable export product, has advanced strongly.

techniques that have changed little through several centuries. Almost a half of the annual cut from Finland's forests goes to satisfy this primitive local demand. The second outlet for the products of the forests leads to distant markets overseas. Today, the bulk of the timber that takes this route reaches its destination only through the medium of elaborate transforming industries as pulp, paper, wallboard, plywood, furniture, and cellulose. The development of the boreal coniferous forests during the past century results from a revolution, or, to express it more correctly, a series of revolutions in the demands of overseas markets.

The middle of the nineteenth century was a critical time for Scandinavia's forest industries when England removed the restrictions and import duties on timber — timber that was an essential building material in the rapid expansion of the Victorian industrial town and suburb. Ports such as West Hartlepool and Hull began to play a great part in the traffic with the Baltic countries in deals and planks. Western Europe's industrial revolution not only provided an expanding market for the sawn timber of Scandinavia, but gave the steam-driven sawmill to the Baltic countries as a means of satisfying their growing demands. An act of an English parliament and the introduction of one of the many inventions of the industrial revolution began a century of continuous change and growth in the Scandinavian timber industries.

Before 1850, the external stimulus had been insufficient to awaken the forester and the industrialist to a period of change and economic expansion. Until that date the narrow domestic market dominated the economic scene, and only in limited and favoured areas was there a demand for timber as an export commodity. From the sixteenth century to the middle of the eighteenth century a narrow strip of southern Norway, accessible to the coastline of the Skagerrak and Oslo fjord, dominated the timber trade of the North Sea. Primitive, water-driven sawmills grew along this shore and Dutch merchants developed a profitable traffic in timber with the British Isles. By the middle of the seventeenth century the timber exports to North Sea countries formed the largest item in Norway's export trade.

At this time, Sweden and Finland, under the same crown and sharing an outlook on the Baltic Sea, lay too remote from the markets where Norway's Atlantic façade gave her a notable advantage. The chief fame of the Gulf of Bothnia in the seventeenth and eighteenth centuries was for its exports of tar. It ranked next

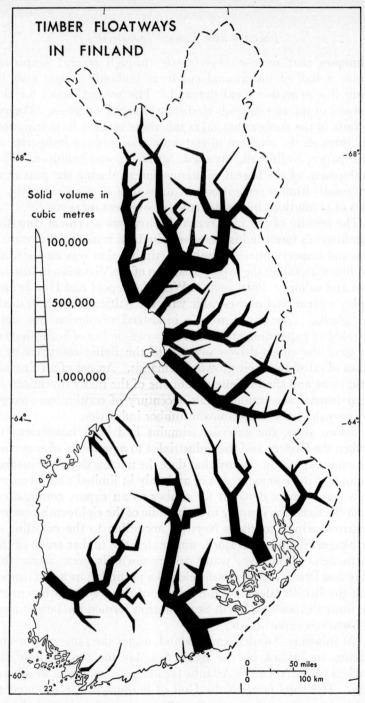

TIMBER FLOATWAYS
IN FINLAND

Solid volume in
cubic metres

100,000

500,000

1,000,000

FIG. 90

The Kymi River of south-eastern Finland and the Oulu and Kemi rivers of the north
are outstanding as timber floatways. The blank areas of the south-west and in
Östterbotten show the decline of timber-floating on smaller rivers and its replacement
by rail and, above all, road transport.

to iron among the exports of seventeenth-century Sweden and was one of the chief reasons for the prosperity of Norrland's ports at that time. The forests of central Sweden found themselves deeply affected by the economic demands of the world outside northern Europe through the supply of vast quantities of charcoal to the iron industry. The need for charcoal introduced a system of regular cutting and woodland management to the forests of Värmland and Bergslagen generations before such conservation techniques spread to the timberlands of the north.

The traffic in sawn timber, as we have already noticed, began the economic revolution in the forest industries. The century since 1850 has witnessed a succession of deep changes in the timber belt of northern Europe — changes of location in the areas of intensive timber-cutting, the development of communications, and the appearance of radical transformations in the processing industries. The coming of the steam sawmill in the 1850's focused the industry close to the coastlines within reach of imported coal, and in a convenient place to export its planks and boards. The ever rising demands of the sawmills for raw materials widened the area of tributary forests. Each of the Scandinavian states developed its great rivers as floatways for timber to the coastal industrial plants [Fig. 90]. Although the economics of timber floatage are today very much in question and a considerable amount of wood reaches the factory by rail and heavy lorry, the Scandinavian rivers — Kemi, Ångerman, and Glomma, to mention only the greatest, still bear witness to this first radical change that the industrial revolution wrought on the landscapes of northern Europe.

Hydro-electric power appeared at the close of the nineteenth century, with the possibility for the timber industries of freedom from their location close to a coal-importing water-front. But the power of capital already invested and the rigid need for export facilities maintained the industrial pattern that had evolved over the previous half-century. Southern Norrland, where the Ångerman and Ljungan rivers empty into the Gulf of Bothnia, and the northern shore of lake Vänern have remained outstanding centres of the timber-processing industries [Fig. 91]. Likewise, the last few miles of the Glomma, Norway's biggest river, and the wooded shores of Drammen fjord perpetuate a geographical design of the timber-processing industries that was first sketched about the middle of the nineteenth century.

If the geographical aspects of the timber industries reveal a steadiness of outline, the industry itself seems to be in a continuous flux. In Sweden, the output of sawn timber reached its peak in 1900. Since then its position as the chief product of the softwood forests has been steadily usurped by the pulp and paper industries [Fig. 89]. Today, at the outset of the sixties, the prospects of the timberlands are turned even more towards the highly changed products of pulp, paper, and cellulose. As Sømme, the Norwegian economic geographer, has written, 'the Norden wood-processing industries show all the signs of developing into chemical industries'.[5] This latest stage in the growth of the industry is clearly illustrated by the expansion of the Borregaard plant at Sarpsfoss, sited on the Glomma some fifteen miles from the sea. This largest of Norway's wood-processing plants produces sulphite cellulose, rayon fibres, alcohol, and many other chemical by-products.

The steam-driven sawmill introduced the industrial revolution to Scandinavia. In northern and central Sweden, the social and economic implications of the first steam-driven sawmills are particularly clear. Large units of industry became concentrated on shorelines such as the north of Lake Vänern and the Gulf of Bothnia, accessible to fuel and open to export facilities. These growing coastal communities attracted labour from distant parts of the country and demanded the tribute of an ever-widening area of forest for their raw materials. The social problems of the rootless industrial community first made themselves felt in the sawmill settlements. Periods of unrest accompanied the spells of depression in the export trade. As late as 1931 a collapse in the world prices of timber commodities, a depressed export market, and the closing of several plants that has been nicknamed 'the sawmill black death', started riots among the communities of the Ångerman estuary that ended in conflicts between workers and Swedish troops.

The production of sawn timber occupies a different position in the structure of the forest industries in each of the Scandinavian countries. The outputs of the Norwegian and Swedish sawmills rose to a climax at the end of the nineteenth century. The year 1900 represents a peak year for the Swedish exports of sawn timber after a half-century of expansion. Then she exported a million standards of sawn and planed wood, a figure that seems to mark the limit of the industry's growth because it has been equalled on only two occasions in the succeeding half-century, in 1929 and again in 1955. Soon after 1900, the trade in sawn timber ceased to dominate the forest industries of Norway and Sweden, its place being

taken by the more elaborate and lucrative processing of pulp and
the manufacture of paper. Today, the export trade in planks and
boards and wooden building materials plays scarcely any part in

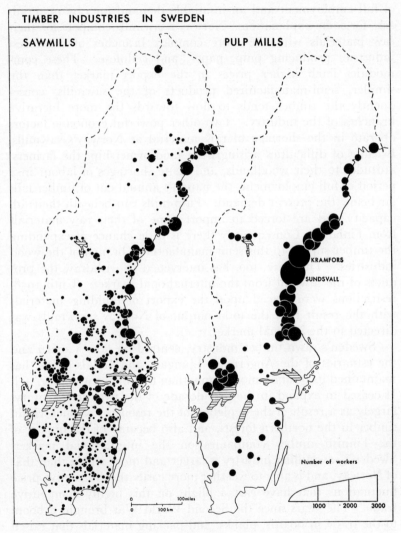

FIG. 91

The production of sawn timber, the earliest of the forest industries, is scattered widely
over Sweden. The largest plants, supplying the export trade, are located along the
coast of the Gulf of Bothnia and on the northern shore of Lake Vänern. The pulp
industry is concentrated in the large factories of central Norrland and Lake Vänern.

the economy of Norway. Her eight thousand sawmills, most of them tiny plants that feed only the local needs of farm and hamlet, produce less than two-thirds of the output of the sawmills of 1870.

Norway's reduced output of sawn timber in the post-war years of full employment and an insatiable demand for raw materials asks for some explanation. Norway's sawmills compete for their raw materials with the more complex branches of the forest industries producing pulp, paper, and cellulose. These commodities fetch higher prices in the export market than the simpler, semi-manufactured products of the sawmills, consequently the timber tends to flow towards the more lucrative branches of the industry. Two other powerful economic factors operate in the shortage of raw material at Norway's sawmills. Because of difficulties arising from land-ownership, the farmers' attitudes to their woodlands, and acute shortages of labour in a period of full employment, the nation's annual cut of timber falls far below the present demand. Pulp mills run beneath their full capacity and are forced to import some of their raw materials from Finland. Consequently there is little chance of expanding the timber supply to this semi-manufactured branch of the wood industries. The state, too, has intervened to withdraw the products of the sawmill from the international market. Until 1958, restrictions were placed upon the export of building materials with the result that the total output of Norway's sawmills was directed to the internal market.

Sweden's sawn-timber industry, centred on lake Vänern and the estuaries of the Ångerman, Ljungan, and Indals rivers, has maintained its position more firmly than that of Norway [Fig. 91]. It ceased to expand in the first decade of the twentieth century, largely as a result of the depletion of the resources of thick virgin timber in the northern forests, and also because of the impact of the Finnish timber companies on the international market. Sweden's sawmilling industry is larger and more viable than that of Norway, and is able to weather more easily the destructive price fluctuations that have cast a blight on this highly competitive trade. The years since the Second World War brought a boom to the trade in boards, planks, and packing materials that raised Sweden's export trade in semi-processed timber to the high level achieved at the beginning of the century. A hungry demand in western Europe and overseas, in the tropics and South Africa and Australia, combined with the disappearance of the Soviet Union

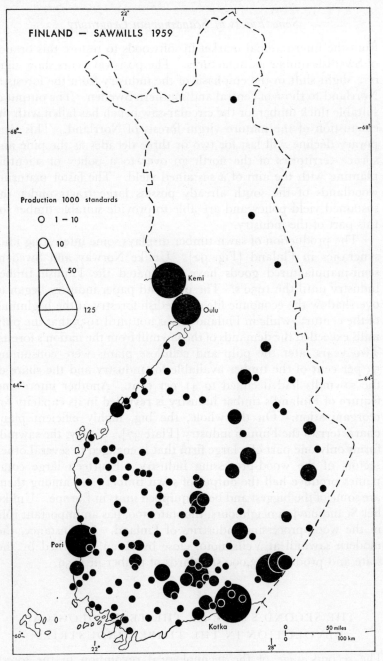

FINLAND — SAWMILLS 1959

Production 1000 standards

○ 1 – 10

○ 10

○ 50

○ 125

Kemi

Oulu

Pori

Kotka

0   50 miles
0   100 km

FIG. 92

The largest of Finland's sawmills are concentrated along the coastline, particularly
in the exporting ports of Kemi, Oulu, Pori, and Kotka. Widely scattered plants
with large outputs predominate in the lakes plateau of eastern Finland, while smaller
sawmills line the valleys that lead to the south-western coast.

from the international market in softwoods to restore this branch of Swedish timber manufactures. The post-war years show signs of a slight shift in the emphasis of the industry from the forests of Norrland to those of central and southern Sweden. The output of suitable thick timber for the circular-saw bench has fallen with the exhaustion of the mature virgin forests of Norrland. This temporary decline will last for two or three decades as the pine and spruce territories of the north go over to a policy of scientific planting with the aim of a sustained yield. The faster maturing woodlands of the south already possess large tracts under the sustained yield policy and are able to provide suitable timber for this part of the industry.

The production of sawn timber displays some interesting idiosyncrasies in Finland [Fig. 92]. Unlike Norway and Sweden, semi-manufactured goods have dominated the Finnish timber industry until the 1950's. The pulp and paper industry began to overshadow the economic life of Swedish forestry at the beginning of the century, while in Finland it was not until 1955 that the pulp mills exceeded the demands of the sawmill from the nation's forests. Two years later the pulp and cellulose plants were consuming 53 per cent of the timber available for industry and the share of the sawmills had declined to 41 per cent. Another interesting feature of Finland's timber industry is revealed in its capacity for reorganization. On the whole, the big, highly efficient plant characterizes the Finnish industry [Plate 37]. Today, the sawmill forms only one part of a large firm that is engaged in several other sectors of the wood-processing industry. Fourteen large companies produce half the output of sawn timber, and among them are some of the biggest and best-equipped units in Europe. Unlike her Scandinavian neighbours, the state, too, has an important rôle in the wood-processing industries of Finland. For instance, the modern sawmill at Veitsiluoto, close by Kemi, is owned by the state and produced 43,000 standards of timber in 1959.

THE SECOND STAGE OF THE TECHNOLOGICAL REVOLUTION IN THE TIMBER INDUSTRIES

The second stage of the technological revolution in the forest industries appears with the manufacture of pulp and paper. This trend towards a more highly refined and valuable end product, a sign that is welcomed in any evolving economy, appears at different times in the Scandinavian countries. For both Sweden and Norway the turning point was reached at the beginning of this century. In Finland, as we have already noticed, the pulp and paper mills only became serious competitors for the timber supplies of the country after 1920. But the foundation of these important branches of the wood-processing industries took place in all the Scandinavian states at a much earlier date in the nineteenth century. Sweden assumes her accustomed rôle as the industrial pioneer of northern Europe with the construction of the first mill for the manufacture of mechanical pulp in 1857. A few years later, in 1863, Norway's first mechanical pulp mill was opened near to Oslo. Finland was not excluded from this early history of the pulp industry because the first mechanical pulp mills appeared in the interior of the country during the 1860's.

The first stages of an industry's growth scarcely ever leave any mark on the economy of a state. The crucial period from the point of view of the national economy arrives with the expansion of an industry into the export market, and at the time when it begins to make a noticeable claim upon the natural resources of the state and to employ a significant part of its labour supply. This happened in the pulp and paper industries of Sweden and Norway between 1900 and the outbreak of the First World War. At the beginning of the century, the Norwegian sawmills consumed three-quarters of the timber available for industry. By the early 1920's, the pulp mills and their close allies, the paper factories, were taking the lion's share from the pine and spruce forests of both Sweden and Norway.

The Finnish pulp industry was a creation of the decade after 1920, and it was only in the 1950's that this more elaborate stage of the wood-processing industries overtook the sawmills in its consumption of timber [Fig. 94]. No satisfactory single explanation exists for Finland's backwardness in this and many other aspects of the industrial revolution. Her landlocked position within the Baltic Sea and a comparative remoteness from the essential markets in western Europe offers some explanation of Finland's late development. The history of every Scandinavian industry uncovers the chief internal weakness of these northern countries; none has possessed at any time in its history a home market sufficient for industrial growth. For instance, the Norwegian fisheries of the late Middle Ages and the Swedish iron industry of the eighteenth century both depended upon a substantial market beyond their homeland. Similarly, the forest industries were stimulated by their access to markets in the timberless and densely populated countries of the North Sea basin. In this, Finland was placed at a disadvantage. Only as demand expanded, bulk transport cheapened, and the virgin forests of Sweden and south-eastern Norway became exhausted in the late nineteenth century did Finland step into a dominant position in the sawn timber trade.

Finland's political orientation, too, in the nineteenth century, influenced her industrial history. As part of the Russian imperial domains, she turned away from western Europe, and precocious industrial adventures such as the cotton and woollen mills at Tampere were directed towards the Russian market. The manufacture of chemical pulp and paper represents a more sophisticated phase of the industrial revolution and it was unlikely to find a healthy setting in the economic environment of Tsarist Russia. In the first period of national independence after 1917, Finland turned towards the west, and it is no accident that the pulp and paper industries expanded as a result of these new political relationships. Their markets lay in western Europe, and even the United States, until the outbreak of the Second World War. Politics and the elemental facts of geography help to explain the time-lag in the eastward spread of the second phase of the revolution in the forest industries across Scandinavia.

A more detailed examination of the pulp and paper industries shows a continuing process of technological changes. First, the pulp is produced mechanically by the grinding-up of the wood, a technique that demanded a good supply of water power before the age of electricity, and resulted in the location of the mechanical pulp mills at waterfalls on the rivers of south-eastern Norway and inland from the shoreline of the Gulf of Bothnia, where Norrland's rivers pass by rapids to the narrow plain of post-glacial marine clays [Fig. 91]. A later revolutionary change in the manufacture of pulp was the discovery of methods of reducing the pine and spruce by the boiling of wood-chips in a chemical liquid. Chemical pulp is produced by two processes. In the older method — the sulphate process — the wood is cooked for several hours in a solution of sodium sulphate. In 1872 Sweden gave the world a lead in the manufacture of chemical pulp, when Carl Ekman developed the sulphite process. This uses calcium bisulphite as its chief chemical solvent and yields papers of a high quality. The earlier technique for the manufacture of chemical pulp — the sulphate process — is used for newsprint, cardboard, and the coarse wrapping papers that form some of the chief exports of the northern countries to the rest of Europe.

Although the main processes for the manufacture of pulp appeared at different moments of time since the middle of the last century, none has yet suffered extinction at the hand of its later competitors. It is true that between 1870 and 1890 the infant Swedish pulp industry changed its emphasis towards the chemical processes and that in Finland the output of sulphate pulp doubled from the late 1930's to the mid-fifties. Nevertheless, each of the chief processes serves different parts of the complex and varied paper industry. Mechanical pulp still forms the chief basis of newsprint, the sulphate process produces the raw material for cardboard and many coarse papers for wrapping and packing purposes, while the sulphite technique yields high-quality papers and the highly refined cellulose used in the manufacture of rayon. This wide range of commodities keeps alive each branch of pulp manufacturing. For instance, the Norwegian mechanical pulp mills, largely centred at inland water power sites to the westward of Oslo fjord from Hønefoss to Skien, have re-equipped themselves with modern ring-grinding plant since the end of the war [Fig. 95]. In Finland, too, the output of mechanical pulp rose slowly between 1938 and 1959 by almost 100,000 tons, but over the same period the production of sulphate pulp increased by half a million tons. There the centre of the mechanical pulp mills is focused on the south-east of the country, along the Kymi river with its prodigious supplies of soft water.

Complex factors of raw materials and markets enter into the choice of a particular process for pulp making. For instance, at Kemi, port and chief centre of the timber industries at the head of the Gulf of Bothnia, the manufacture of pulp was introduced to increase the profits of the sawmills, some of which had been founded in the 1870's. [Fig. 93]. The first pulp mill, using the sulphite process, was constructed in 1919 to consume the waste of the sawmill on Pajusaari island in the manufacture of sulphite cellulose. Ten years later, the industrial complex on this island at the mouth of the Kemi river became more elaborate with the establishment of a sulphate pulp mill.

The great phases of expansion in the Scandinavian pulp industry during the twenties and again in the decade of the fifties

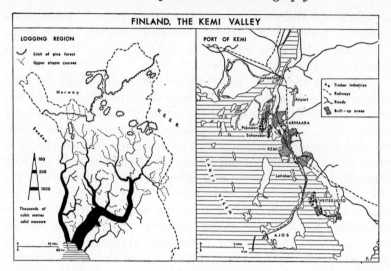

FIG. 93

The Kemi valley possesses Finland's most northerly timber resources, predominantly slow-growing pines. Three-quarters of the wood cut in this region is exported as round timber. The port of Kemi is expanding as a centre of the timber-processing industries. The state-owned Veitsiluoto plant is one of the largest in Europe and the northern ports of Oulu and Kemi produce together a quarter of Finland's total output of chemical pulp.

have been accompanied by a rationalization of plant distribution. Large modern factories have chosen sites, served by extensive, forested hinterlands and equipped with effective water communications. For instance, the Uddeholm group of central Sweden, an industrial empire specializing in high-grade steel, pulp, cellulose, paper, and electro-chemical products, has concentrated its pulp and paper interests at one point on the northern shore of Lake Vänern [Fig. 103]. Skoghall stands on Hammarö island where the Klar river empties into this inland sea. It is an industrial complex that represents every branch of the forest industries and employs 2500 workers. Apart from a sawmill capable of producing 30,000 standards of sawn timber a year, there are plants producing pulp by the sulphite and sulphate processes. The by-product industries, too, have been fully exploited at Skoghall, where a plant recovers one and a half million gallons of alcohol per year from the sulphite process. The first rationalization of the Uddeholm interests on the island-site at Skoghall took place during the years of the First World War. In 1930 a paper mill was added to this industrial complex, producing mainly kraft paper (brown wrapping paper), but separate plants specialize in gummed paper and multiwall bags for packing cement. An electro-chemical plant completes the wood-processing industry at Skoghall, producing chlorine and alkali — some of the raw materials needed in the reducing, bleaching, and paper-making processes. Skoghall, active and gigantic, is the only remaining unit of the wood-processing industries in the economic empire of Uddeholm. It is the logical conclusion to a plan of rationalization that recognizes the economic values of site and regional relationships. The Klar river focuses on Skoghall all the resources of its extensive, forested hinterland that reaches beyond the Norwegian frontier. From the wharves of Skoghall a waterway leads directly to Göteborg and the North Sea across Lake Vänern and through the Göta river. This is especially important for the paper industry whose products find their greatest market overseas as liner cargo in ships that operate from Göteborg.

Sweden, too, provides an interesting example of a pulp mill that changed from the newer chemical techniques of pulp manufacture to the older process of grinding the wood mechanically. In 1957, the sulphite mill at Göta, on the Göta river to the south of Trollhättan, was destroyed by a landslide in the late glacial clays of the valley floor that are frequently unstable as a result of rapid excavation by the river. When the pulp works was reconstructed, a mechanical pulp mill replaced the former sulphite plant.

The industrial revolution introduced technological changes and expanded outputs in the primitive industries of northern Europe after the middle of the nineteenth century. The continuing technological revolution of the twentieth century is characterized by a rising tempo of change that largely results from highly organized research. The chemical processes for the manufacture of pulp received the stimulus of fresh discoveries in the past decade that could result in important adjustments on the geographical plane. For instance, until a few years ago the sulphite technique of pulp manufacture was able to use only spruce as its primary raw material; now it has been extended to the consumption of pine. An even more revolutionary widening of the basis of raw materials for the manufacture of chemical pulp is the recent success in the use of birch and deciduous woods in the sulphate process. Above all, this discovery could change the value of the comparatively unexploited tracts of birchwood in northern Sweden and Finnish Lapland. An increasing use of birch and the deciduous hardwoods of southern Sweden and Norway might induce an adjustment in the transport geography of the pulp industry. These woods float less easily in water than the long, bark-stripped trunks of pine and spruce. Already, the building of forest roads and the use of bigger timber lorries has cheapened the cost of overland transport. The margin between land and water transport has been narrowed even further by the rising cost of labour to the floatage companies. A shift of emphasis towards the birch woodlands of the north or the mixed forests of southern Scandinavia could widen the net of overland communications for the timber industries.

Among the states of northern Europe Sweden holds a leading position in the timber industries — a reflection of the extensive natural resources of Norrland, her early engagement in the expansion of the timber-processing industries after 1850, and the genius of Swedish industrialists and research workers in technological developments. But today Finland runs close to Sweden in the development of the timber industries. The prosperous decade of the 1950's brought her to maturity in the wood-processing industries. The export figures from the northern countries show that Sweden led in the category of sawn timber and pulp with 55 per cent of the value of Scandinavian wood exports in 1957. Finland, on the other hand, drew ahead of Sweden in the same year, when she topped the list for her exports of paper, hardboard, and plywood with 45 per cent of the value of the total overseas sales of the Scandinavian countries in this group of commodities. Her predominance in this branch of the industry is largely explained by Finland's huge output of newsprint, half a million tons in 1957 and slightly more than double the production of Sweden.

SWEDEN'S PULP AND PAPER INDUSTRIES AND THE PROBLEMS OF EXPANSION

The production of pulp and the manufacture of paper represent two stages in the timber-processing industries. At several Swedish sites, the two branches of the industry lie side by side under the wing of the same company. Nevertheless, a general view of the distribution of pulp mills and paper factories across the landscape of Sweden reveals two different patterns of distribution. The chief centres of the paper industry lie in Midland Sweden and the south, while the pulp mills find their greatest concentration in the same two regions as the sawmills — along the coastline of the Gulf of Bothnia in central and southern Norrland and fringing the northern shore of Lake Vänern [Fig. 91]. The different patterns of distribution are explained partly by the physical and resource requirements of the early stages of industrial growth and, above all, by the marketing demands of the two commodities.

The foundations of the paper industry date back to the seventeenth and eighteenth centuries, when rags provided the chief raw material. Then the paper mills, working only for the Swedish internal market, lay in the south and centre of the country, close to the towns and cities. When wood-pulp displaced rags as a raw material, the paper industry suffered no severe dislocation in its general distribution. As commodities become more highly refined and removed from their original basis of raw materials, so the factors of labour and ease of marketing play a predominant part in determining the sites of industrial plants. The modern Swedish paper industry demands easy access to the major ports and asks to be within reach of the chief internal consumer of paper, Stockholm, where the national press and book publishing trades are concentrated. Consequently, some of the biggest newsprint mills lie within the orbit of the Stockholm region at Hallsta, only sixty miles from the capital, and at Norrköping and Borlange. The paper industry has to export its products in bulk and all the year round. As a result, the frozen harbours of the Gulf of Bothnia impose a great handicap upon the establishment of paper mills in northern Sweden. The shores of Lake Vänern benefit particularly in the realm of market facilities with both rail and water communications to Sweden's greatest port and North Sea outlet, Göteborg.

The pulp industry, on the other hand, grew in response to a different set of stimuli. As a semi-manufactured commodity, it lies closer to the raw material base in the spruce and pine forests than the products of the paper mills [Fig. 91]. One of the chief factors in the siting of pulp mills has been the need for a continuous and large supply of wood. The distributional pattern of the modern pulp industry reveals a strategic location in relation to floatways and hinterlands rich in coniferous softwoods. Outstanding is the coastline of the Gulf of Bothnia, between the estuaries of the Ljungan and the Ångerman — rivers that serve southern Norrland's richest forests. Here the Ångerman river forms Sweden's biggest floatway, bringing twenty million logs of pine and spruce in a season to the half-dozen huge pulp mills sited on the forest-fringed inlets of the southern shore of the estuary.

A second focal zone of the pulp industry belongs to the northern shore line of Lake Vänern, with a rich hinterland of softwoods in the province of Värmland. Although both areas suggest the presence of some of Sweden's finest forests in their locations, the historical factor, the impress given by the first stage of the timber industries a century ago, is not lacking in an explanation of the present pattern of the Swedish pulp industry. The pulp mills have grown alongside or else supplanted earlier sawmills. Both the Gulf of Bothnia and Lake Vänern with its inland water route to Göteborg were well placed for the export trade in boards and planks with the North Sea countries. An even earlier industrial transformation needs to be considered in an account of the wood-processing industries of Värmland. There, the many small ironworks scattered through the forests abandoned metalworking as the industry languished after the middle of the nineteenth century. Their chief capital investment, the charcoal-yielding forests, was turned to other more profitable purposes — the provision of timber for sawmills and later pulp mills on the sites of the former ironworks by falls and rapids.

At the present time, there are clear signs of important changes in the distributional pattern of Sweden's pulp and paper industries. During the past decade the pulp industry has grown vigorously in southern Sweden, attracted there by increased supplies of timber at a period when the output of the northern forests is temporarily restricted. The south of Sweden benefits notably by its more quickly maturing forests, and in the post-war years earlier plantations on poor pastures or abandoned agricultural land have become ripe for the woodman's axe and the mechanical saw. Southern Sweden, too, has attracted the pulp manufacturer for the scope it offers in the use of the new processes that involve hardwood timbers. On the other hand, the geographical frontier between the paper and pulp industries has been blurred of late by the construction of fresh paper mills in the north of Sweden. In the past, this more elaborate stage of the wood-processing industries was excluded from Norrland not only on account of natural factors — distance from markets and the winter freezing of ports for several weeks — but also because many of the northern saw-mills and pulp manufacturers lacked the capital to float a new and more elaborate stage of the industry. The inter-war years, a time of important technical changes in the pulp, cellulose, and paper trades, were a period of severe economic distress in the sawn-timber industry. During the harsh economic depression of the early thirties many of Norrland's sawmills disappeared. It became an axiom that only those sawmills could survive that were part of larger industrial structures and attached to pulp factories. And even these larger units had little capital for expansion or fresh industrial adventures. The post-war years have been character-ized by an unbelievable industrial growth, and in this period of high prosperity the Norrland timber firms have accumulated enough capital for investment in the fresh field of the paper industry. They have also been encouraged by the Swedish government's generous attitude in its taxation policy towards industrial expansion and re-equipment. In one of the most heavily taxed states in the world, it has seemed better to the industrialist to turn his profits into the expansion and improvement of his own factories rather than allow them to be drained off into the apparently sterile exchequer of the government's tax collectors.

Lately, the paper industry has intruded among the sawmills, wood-grinding mills, chemical pulp plants, and wallboard factories of the Ångerman estuary. Apart from a small kraft paper factory that was founded in the First World War, the paper industry had avoided this industrial complex at the mouth of Sweden's richest timber floatway. Distance from markets and a waterway that was frozen for five months of the year, until powerful icebreakers managed to keep an open fairway for all but six weeks, acted as passive deterrents to this more elaborate stage of industrialization. Apart from the hard times of the thirties and the financial inability of the timber firms of the Ångerman estuary to float a new group of industries, paper-making in this area also suffered from a potential shortage of fresh water which it needs in vast quantities. The thirty-mile-long estuary of the Ångerman river is subject to invasions of brackish water from the Gulf of Bothnia, especially in autumn when river discharge may be low and prevalent east winds sweep the surface waters from the sea to the head of the estuary. Despite the unfavourable elements in the environment of the lower Ångerman river, a modern paper industry has taken root as a result of the sunny economic climate of the fifties. A factory, specializing in the making of paper sacks, opened at Väja in 1959 and has a capacity of 50,000 tons per year.

It seems likely that the paper industry will extend into Norrland during the decade of the sixties. A long spell of prosperity and expanding outputs since the Second World War means that the wood-processing industries have the resources for further growth. Still more important, the world demand for paper has risen astonishingly in the past fifteen years. There has been a steep rise in the consumption of newsprint. A still more surprising increase of paper consumption results from the packing of foodstuffs in small quantities before they reach the shops. It is believed that new habits in the sale of foodstuffs and the widespread use of pre-packed frozen foods in the fifties has doubled the world consumption of paper. Specialized papers are also finding uses in unexpected fields of industry. For instance, paper sacks are used for bulky commodities such as cement and seeds, and insulating paper strip is used in the manufacture of electric cables. Sweden's paper production and exports have increased in the past ten years. From 1950 to 1957 the output expanded by half a million tons, and in the latter year 60 per cent of the national production, more than a million and a half tons, went for export.

Sweden's chief market for paper lies in western and central Europe. Two-thirds of her paper exports are sent to Britain, though western Germany became a large importer of kraft paper and newsprint in the late fifties. The paper industry will doubtless be deeply affected by future political and economic agreements in western Europe. Up to the present time, tariffs and import quotas have shaped the pattern of trade with west European countries. For instance, Swedish paper exports to western Germany, the Netherlands, and Belgium have faced heavy import duties. Great Britain, the largest market for Swedish paper, strictly limited imports for several years during the fifties as well as collecting a duty from all imported paper. As a result, the Swedish paper trade feels that its potential market in Europe would be much greater than the real market but for the political and economic acts of the importing states. This artificially restricted market for paper commodities is reflected in the immense sales of pulp from the north European countries. Pulp from Scandinavia feeds the paper mills of the industrialized North Sea countries and forms one of the large items in Sweden's list of exports. Nearly half of her output of pulp goes abroad, and the Swedes believe that it would be healthier for the economy if some of this pulp could be exported as the more highly refined products of the paper mills with their higher currency-earning capacities. If any of the schemes in the realm of international politics for lowering tariff walls and creating free trade areas in western Europe emerges successfully, Sweden hopes for a rapidly enlarging market for the paper industry. Such a stimulus, inspired by political action, could start another phase of growth in this industry and it is not unlikely that Norrland would see the foundation of new paper mills. The old division between the south and north of Sweden in the distribution of pulp and paper mills promises to disappear — a reminder that the rigid controls of the environment become flexible in the rapidly changing world of technology and politics.

THE PULP AND PAPER INDUSTRIES IN FINLAND AND NORWAY

In Finland the period since the Second World War has been one of industrial reconstruction and expansion, an expansion that reflects the nation's dual outlook towards the east and west. The pressure of reparations payments to the Soviet Union in the early fifties forced the growth of Finland's shipbuilding yards and the electrical and mechanical engineering industries. Towards the end of the decade, the emphasis in industrial growth turns towards the wood-processing industries that find their markets mainly in western Europe.

In Finland, the state's employment policies turn around the forest industries. With the threat of unemployment and industrial stagnation brought by the minor trade recession of 1956–57, the Finnish government deliberately planned a further phase of growth in the wood-processing industries to absorb the larger groups of young workers that would be turned into the employment market of the early sixties. By 1964, Finland expects to produce another million and a half tons of pulp and 800,000 tons of paper and board above the output of 1957. The distributional pattern of the industry is not likely to suffer any radical change, because the new units are mainly to be added to existing plants in the southern parts of the country. The immensely powerful factors of the established site — power, boundless quantities of fresh water, a network of communications serving a developed hinterland of softwood forests, and long-settled marketing arrangements — largely determine that there shall be no revolution in the geography of Finland's forest industries.

This latest phase of expansion in the forest industries provides a hint of Finland's wealth of timber resources and underlines the sharp contrast with Norway, where the pulp mills run below their full capacity on account of shortages of wood. It is believed that the new phase of growth in Finland's wood-processing industries will demand an increase of 40 per cent in the supply of timber to the pulp mills. This will be met by a diversion of wood from the export trade in round timber, the exploitation of isolated sites that come within reach of the timber-cutter through the building of forest roads, and the use of thin and low-quality trees. Finland, like Sweden, can look forward with optimism to the next two decades, when the spread of scientific policies of cutting and planting and the marked climatic amelioration that has affected Scandinavia should increase the annual yield of her forests.

The siting of the pulp and paper industries of Finland does not reveal a divergence between the locations of the two manufacturing processes such as occurs in Sweden. Pulp mills and paper factories belong clearly to three regions [Fig. 94]. In the south and the south-east, they lie along the banks of the Kymi river and gather along the southern shore of Lake Saimaa. In fact, the short Kymi river, draining the central lake system, leads the country in the output of wood products. Two-thirds of the national output of mechanical pulp, a fair proportion of the chemical pulp, and two-fifths of Finland's paper come from this small region at the head of the Gulf of Finland. This river is the Finnish counterpart of the Klar and Ångerman in Sweden, the equivalent of the lower Glomma in Norway. Finland's second zone of pulp and paper mills stretches across the middle and southern parts of the lake systems to reach the coast of the Gulf of Bothnia between Pori and Rauma. Remote outposts of these industries cluster around the mouths of the Kemi and Oulu rivers tapping the resources of the northern forests [Fig. 93]. Northern Finland suffers the same disadvantages as Swedish Norrland. Costs of production are greater than in the south because of the long winter freeze in the harbours and the higher cost of living that is reflected in the price of labour. Distance to markets is greater, but the rising demands for pulp and paper in western Europe are likely to expand the output of this marginal region.

The coincidence of the patterns of pulp mills and paper factories in Finland is largely explained by the late date and rapid progress of the modern wood-processing industries. The pulp and paper industries grew together after 1920, and their development was largely in the hands of big companies that favoured the placing of the several manufacturing units on the same site. Vertical integration has been the order of the day in Finland's national industry, and she escaped the disparities in the distribution pattern that history has given to the pulp and paper industry of Sweden.

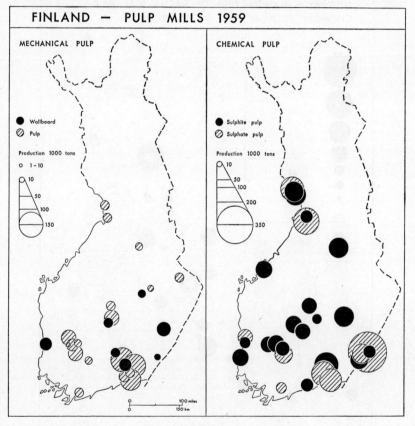

FIG. 94

The older mechanical pulp industry is located in the south of the country where it was first established at sites with water-power along the Kymi River and at Tampere. Chemical pulp is produced at large integrated plants in association with saw-milling and paper manufacture. Particularly important sites are along the south-eastern shore of Lake Saimaa, by the Kymi River, and in the northern ports of Kemi and Oulu.

371

Norway lacks the boundless forest wealth of both Sweden and Finland. Consequently her pulp and paper industries have achieved a more modest scale of development. Apart from some small outliers of the pulp industry around Trondheim fjord, her timber-processing plants are concentrated in the south-east. Here, rivers such as the Glomma and the long valleys that gather together at Hønefoss carry a good deal of the wood cut in Norway's forests.

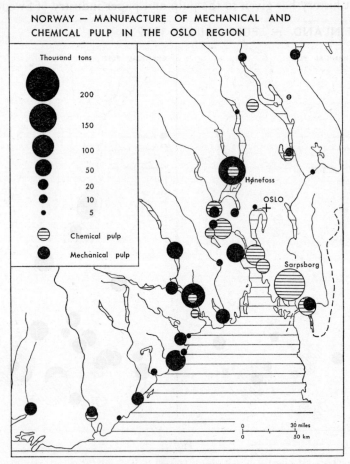

FIG. 95

The mechanical pulp industry, whose products are largely used for newsprint, is located mainly at inland sites, determined at first by the presence of water-power, on the western side of Oslo fjord. The later chemical pulp industry has grown chiefly in coastal locations in the province of Østfold on the eastern shore of the fjord.

The history of the Norwegian pulp industry is longer than that of Finland. The first mechanical pulp mill was constructed near Oslo in 1863, and by the end of the century the industry had gone through an important period of growth when there were fifty-nine mills producing mechanical pulp in Norway. As a rule, these mills were placed at water-power sites on falls and rapids inland from Oslo fjord. Today, the mechanical pulp industry still reveals an inland distribution, its chief centres lying away from the coast on the rivers that enter the Skagerrak [Fig. 95]. Particularly, the pulp mills follow a line from Skien fjord towards Hønefoss and thence to Lillehammer at the head of Lake Mjøsa. The same pattern of distribution, inland and located to the west of Oslo fjord, is apparent in the newsprint industry — a fact that becomes explicable when one remembers its close association with the production of mechanical pulp. By contrast, the Norwegian paper industry and the manufacture of chemical pulp display a remarkably different pattern of distribution. The plants stand close to the eastern shore of Oslo fjord, extending from the Swedish frontier near Halden through Sarpsborg and Drammen to the lake of Tyrifjord. The later growth of the paper and chemical pulp industries in Norway, largely within the twentieth century, gave them a greater freedom of location than the earlier mechanical pulp mills. The chief determining factors in the siting of these larger industrial units were the need for a large and constant supply of timber and effective exporting facilities. The River Glomma, emptying into the sea on the eastern shore of Oslo fjord, serves the biggest hinterland of softwood forests in Norway. The Dramselva, finding its mouth at the head of Oslo fjord, also drains a rich area of forests in Hallingdal. Some of the latest pulp mills stand on the peninsula between Drammen and Oslo, taking advantage of their coastal sites for export, and drawing timber not only from the Dramselva but also rafted across the fjord from the mouth of the Glomma river.

RECENT TRENDS IN THE TIMBER INDUSTRIES

Since the end of the Second World War, the wood-processing industries in all the Scandinavian countries reveal similar trends. The output of the high-quality bleached pulps grows rapidly. The wallboard industry, using the waste of sawmills, was founded in the 1930's and grew quickly in the late forties, encouraged by the post-war shortages of raw materials and the great needs of the building industry. Today, there are five factories in Norway making hardboard and porous boards with an output of 100,000 tons per year, enough to supply the domestic market and to leave some over for export. But the expansion of the timber industries in Norway is hampered by a dearth of raw material; further growth awaits the slow harvests of vigorous planting policies in the post-war years and the results of education in better forest management.

In Sweden, too, the making of hardboard appeared as a late entrant in the wood-processing industries. As in Norway, the first plant opened in the thirties, and the boom years of the building trade since the war produced a rapid expansion of output, so that Sweden with 450,000 tons in 1956 surpassed the Norwegian figure by almost five times. Sweden's wallboard plants are mainly attached to the sawmills and pulp factories along the coast of Norrland. In Finland, as one might expect, the hardboard industry developed at a later date and more slowly than with her Scandinavian neighbours. There was a small output just before the war, but its first phase of expansion, reaching 165,000 tons in 1959, belongs to the prosperous decade of the fifties.

Finland holds a unique place among the wood-processing industries with her production of plywood. This branch of the industry appeared at an early date when the first plywood factory opened at Jyväskylä in 1913. The industry grew quickly in the late twenties, as a number of large plywood factories began to tap the extensive birch forests of the eastern part of the lakes region. Today, her plywood output is four times greater than that of 1930 and the bulk of it goes towards Finland's export trade.

In the past decade, the wood-processing industries of northern Europe entered a fresh stage in their evolution, with the commercial development of a chemical industry based upon the waste liquids from the chemical pulp mills. The Mo och Domsjö Corporation of southern Norrland is one among several companies that has pointed the best way to making full use of the resources of the softwood forests [Fig. 112]. There, the waste liquids of the sulphite mills, rich in dissolved lignin from the cooking process, are fermented into alcohol. In turn this alcohol is manufactured into three basic commodities: acetaldehyde, a solvent for the paint industry; ethylene, used in anti-freeze liquids; and a group of cellulose derivatives for wallpaper glue and thickening agents.

Until 1945 the chemical industry, the last and most elaborate stage of the timber industries, was largely at an experimental and research level. In the past decade and a half, a technological revolution has brought the by-product chemicals to a commercial level of production, largely through an increase in the size of plants and a striking reduction in the ratio of man hours per ton of end product. At Mo och Domsjö, the ratio of man hours per ton has fallen from six hundred to sixty over the past fifteen years — a laboratory experiment has become a profitable industry.

In both Norway and Finland, the large vertically integrated concerns have entered the chemical industry, the logical development of the sulphite pulp processes [Plate 37]. The state-owned company of Veitsiluoto at Kemi added an alcohol plant to its industrial complex in the Second World War. At Sarpsborg on the lower Glomma, the Borregaard company leads the way in the full and rational use of softwood timber, perhaps northern Europe's greatest natural resource. There it is now claimed that through a concentration of the cooking liquors the pulp industry can become free of the use of imported fuels. As these two examples show, Finland and Norway follow Sweden closely into this latest phase of the wood-processing industries. Finland, the most richly endowed in timber resources, can look forward with high hopes into the next half-century, if the powerful and imponderable factors of European international trade, her ability to raise capital for industrial growth, and her political position in the uncertain zone of the Soviet Union's border states, permit a period of industrial expansion.

CHAPTER 13

Iron and Steel in Scandinavia

In the conventional picture of the industrial revolution, iron and steel occupy a position equal to that of coal. The products of the early blast furnaces and forges — railway lines, boilers, cast-iron pillars for factory buildings and non-conformist chapels — represent the raw materials of the industrial development of Victorian England. Geography and History determined that the countries of northern Europe should use a different blueprint in their evolution towards industrial maturity. The iron industries appeared at an early date in only one region of Scandinavia, on the forested Archaean plateau northward of Sweden's central lakes depression. Here the rich but scattered lodes of copper, silver, lead, and iron were exploited from the thirteenth century. The summit of Sweden's political power, achieved in the seventeenth century and the first years of the eighteenth century, coincided with the equally striking feat of the iron-miners and forge-masters of Bergslagen on an economic plane, when they dominated the world trade in bar-iron.

The mineral-rich hills of Bergslagen provided the only foundation for the industrial revolution in the Scandinavian world of the nineteenth century [Figs. 96 and 99]. After 1850, radical discoveries in the manufacture of iron and steel were imported into the Bergslagen region and their techniques adapted to Swedish conditions. The acid Bessemer process was introduced in 1858, and ten years later the open-hearth techniques, using a mixture of scrap and pig iron, appeared in Swedish steel-making. Perhaps the true industrial revolution in the Scandinavian iron and steel industries dates from the 1890's, when the introduction of the Thomas process opened up a fresh abundant source of phosphoric iron ore in the previously neglected ore fields of Grängesberg and Norrland.

Western Europe's industrial revolution is marked not only by its inventiveness and the vastly expanding outputs of coal, industrial raw materials, and factory products, but also by the breeding

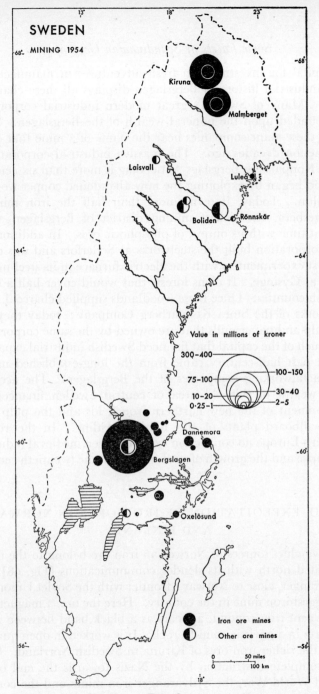

FIG. 96

Iron ores overshadow the output of all other minerals in the three mining areas of
Sweden — the Bergslagen, the Skellefte ore-field centred on Boliden, and the Norrbotten mining region at Kiruna and Malmberget. The Bergslagen ores were first
worked in the early Middle Ages, while the two northern areas have been opened up
only since the close of the nineteenth century. Since World War II Sweden's iron-ore
output has risen to 19 million tons per annum; 90 per cent of this is exported.

of capital for investment in fresh adventures in manufacturing. The industrial history of Bergslagen displays all these characteristics. Many of Sweden's great modern industrial corporations are founded upon the mineral wealth of the Bergslagen. Sometimes these giant companies bear the name of a mine that ceased to function decades ago. The massive industrial corporation of Stora Kopparberg Bergslags Aktiebolag is more than six centuries old and began by exploiting the now abandoned copper workings at Falun. Today, it owns more than half the iron mines at Grängesberg, the richest mining district of Bergslagen at the present time with its output of phosphoric ores. In addition, this vast corporation built the steelworks at Söderfors and was one of the first experimenters with the electric furnace in its steel-making plant at Gysinge. It owns forests that would cover half a dozen English counties. Once these woodlands supplied charcoal to the ironworks of the Stora Kopparberg Company; today they feed the pulp and paper mills that are owned by the same corporation.

Much of the capital that financed Swedish industrial expansion in the past half-century came from the long-established mining and metalworking companies of the Bergslagen. The accumulated wealth of this old area of central Sweden financed the development of the new northern iron fields and the pulp mills and wallboard plants of the Baltic coastline. In the rest of northern Europe no connection exists between medieval industrial enterprise and the growth of steel-making in the twentieth century.

THE EXPLOITATION OF IRON ORES IN NORWAY AND FINLAND

The two chief sources of Norwegian iron ore belong to the thinly populated north with its slender communications [Fig. 98]. At Sydvaranger, close to Norway's frontier with the Soviet Union, lies the biggest iron mine in the country. Here the ore, a magnetite of 30 per cent iron content, appears as a black band between zones of quartz in a gneissic country rock. It is worked in open quarries as are the richer iron ores of Kiruna in Swedish Norrland. Since their complete destruction by the Nazis towards the end of the Second World War, the Sydvaranger iron mines and the concentrating plant at Kirkenes have been rebuilt with the help of American dollars provided from Marshall Aid funds. They began

Iron and Steel in Scandinavia

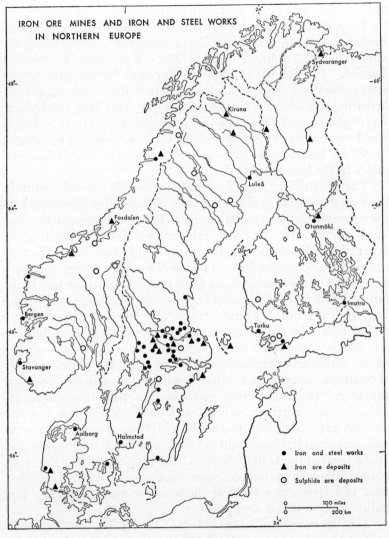

IRON ORE MINES AND IRON AND STEEL WORKS
IN NORTHERN EUROPE

Sydvaranger
Kiruna
Luleå
Fosdalen
Otanmäki
Imatra
Bergen
Turku
Stavanger
Aalborg
Halmstad

● Iron and steel works
▲ Iron ore deposits
○ Sulphide ore deposits

100 miles
200 km

Fig. 97

The pre-eminence of central Sweden, the district of Bergslagen, in the manufacture
of iron and steel is apparent. Norway's most abundant source of iron ores lies in the
remote north and her iron- and steel-making plants are scattered along the Atlantic
coastline. Finland's chief resources are in the south-west and at Otanmäki in the
Oulu valley. The bog-ores of south Jutland are negligible and contribute nothing to
Denmark's industrial economy.

379

work again in 1952 and have since reached an output of a million tons of concentrate per year with an iron content of 65 per cent.

Norway's second important source of iron ore lies in Dunderlandsdal, a site of extreme isolation among the barren, shapeless mountains of Nordland between Mo i Rana and the Swedish frontier. Despite the erection of Norway's biggest and newest state-owned iron and steel plant at Mo i Rana, the magnetite-hematite ores of this valley have not yet come into production. Up to the present, these deposits have presented severe technical problems in their extraction, although a British company managed to obtain 100,000 tons of concentrate from the Dunderlandsdal mines in the late thirties.

The intensive exploitation of Scandinavia's natural wealth in the twentieth century alone has been able to bring Norway's iron resources on to the economic stage. Before the present era they inevitably lay idle, their very remoteness a factor preventing the generation of industries on these iron fields [Fig. 97]. The new iron and steel complex laid out by the Norwegian government on a flat terrace at the head of Rana fjord perhaps points the way to the future. The Mo i Rana works consist of a smelting plant for pig iron and steel, using electric furnaces and an electrically powered rolling mill. In 1959 it produced 200,000 tons of steel, but the aim of this state-owned plant, standing only a few miles from the Arctic Circle and overshadowed by the glittering plateau-glacier of Svartisen, is an output of half a million tons of rolled products per year. It is interesting that another effort to industrialize Scandinavia's northern wilderness is the work of the Swedish government. Since the Second World War, a state-owned iron and steel plant has been built at Luleå [Fig. 101], the iron ore port at the head of the Gulf of Bothnia. In 1955 this plant, the Norrbottens Järnverk, produced more than 300,000 tons of pig iron, most of which was refined at the works to yield a quarter of a million tons of rolled steel products.

Like the state-inspired steel plant at Mo i Rana, the Norrbotten steelworks represents a radical development not only in the geography of Scandinavia's northern territories but also in the principles of industrial location for the iron and steel industry. Until recently it has been usual for iron ore to flow towards the fuels needed in the pig iron and steel-making processes. Millions of tons of the rich Kiruna ores still travel to the iron and steel mills of the Ruhr with its fat supplies of metallurgical coke. But the

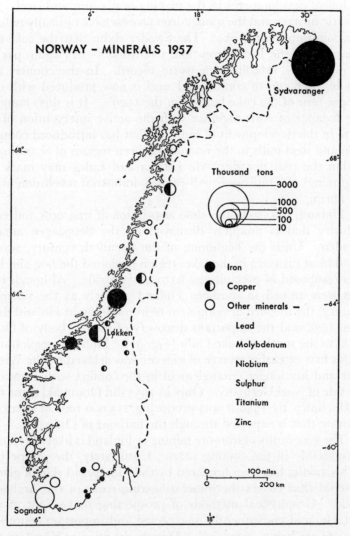

NORWAY – MINERALS 1957

Sydvaranger

Thousand tons

3000
1000
500
100
10

● Iron
◐ Copper
○ Other minerals —

Lead

Molybdenum

Niobium

Sulphur

Titanium

Zinc

Løkken

Sogndal

100 miles
200 km

FIG. 98

Norway's chief source of iron ore lies in her isolated northern territories on the shores of Varanger fjord. A secondary source of minerals — iron, copper, and sulphur — belongs to the Trondheim region. The mineral resources of southern Norway are small and scattered, though some have achieved of late a high value in the manufacture of alloys.

new giant plants at Luleå and Mo i Rana stand for the latest technical developments in the making of pig iron and steel. The electric furnace and the sponge-iron process have radically reduced the consumption of coke. The Swedes claim that the coke consumption of the Luleå iron- and steelworks — 625 kg.m. per ton of pig iron — establishes a world record. In the country as a whole, each ton of commercial steel is now produced with only 60 per cent of the coke burned in the 1920's. It is this change in the balance of costs together with the active intervention of the state in the development of industry that has introduced complex iron and steel mills to the remote northern regions of Scandinavia within the past decade. Mo i Rana and Luleå may mark the beginnings of a mid-twentieth-century industrial revolution in the far north.

Finland, too, lacks the close association of iron ores and early industry that is uniquely displayed by the Bergslagen area of Sweden. Until the beginning of the twentieth century, several small blast furnaces in the lakes region exploited the bog and lake ores composed of precipitated ferrous hydroxide. Although rock ores were mined in southern Finland as early as the sixteenth century, the modern development of iron mining in Finland dates from 1938 and the important discovery of the ore body of Otanmäki to the south of Lake Oulu [Fig. 97]. Finland's exploitation of this first extensive reserve of iron ore was delayed by the Winter War and her longer entanglement in the conflict with Russia on the side of Nazi Germany. Only in 1953 did Otanmäki come into production; by 1958 it was producing 215,000 tons of iron concentrate that is exported through the harbour of Oulu.

The geography of iron-ore mining in Finland is likely to change considerably in the coming years. Until lately, the prospecting for ore bodies has been hindered by the widespread skin of glacial material that covers the mineral-bearing rocks of the Archaean shield. Geophysical methods of prospecting make light of this obstacle, and consequently unexpected and important sources of iron ore are being uncovered. Already the mine at Kärväsvaara, eastward of the rising northern town of Rovaniemi, produces 100,000 tons of ore that finds its outlet through Oulu. At Kolari, in the far wilderness of Lapland close to the Swedish border, a body containing magnetites and hematites with a reserve of fifty million tons has been found. But Finland's most interesting prospects as an iron producer lie under the waters of the Baltic off her south-western shores. Here is a continuation of the mineral-rich leptite zone that forms the basis of Swedish Bergslagen's wealth. The submerged deposits off Jussarö probably contain 200,000,000 tons of iron ore — a reserve larger than any yet known in Finland. Lately, a similar submerged body of iron ore, long suspected from the ill-behaved compasses of ships sailing to the south of the Åland islands, has been ccurately located. Up to the present these reserves of iron have lain latent in the Finnish economy, submerged beneath the sea or else in the remote, undeveloped northern interior of the country. Already in 1960, the shape of an industry emerges that will use these considerable mineral resources. A state-owned iron and steel plant is projected at Raahe about forty miles south of Oulu to refine the ores of the north, and a similar plant is projected on the Hanko peninsula to draw on the submarine resources of the south-west.

IRON AND STEEL IN SWEDEN

A study of the metallurgical industries in northern Europe inevitably centres upon Sweden. Her Scandinavian neighbours all embarked on the advanced stages of industrialism at a late date, within the past two decades, if one takes as a measure the foundation of integrated iron and steel plants. Sweden's long and successful history in the metallurgical trades is largely due to her abundance of minerals, the high quality of her ores, and their distribution in relation to the early centres of population.

Sweden's chief sources of iron ore are concentrated in two regions — the forested hills of Bergslagen that gave birth to the metallurgical industries more than half a millennium ago, and the wastes of northern Norrland where the open-cast mines in the two-mile-long exposure of magnetite at Kiruna have been working for barely fifty years [Fig. 96].

The ore-bearing district of central Sweden occupies a band of country that stretches from the coast of the Gulf of Bothnia near Gävle across the Dal river and westward to within a few miles of the shore of Lake Vänern [Fig. 99]. The rocks of this complex tract of the Archaean shield consist of a very ancient series of volcanics and sediments, known as the leptites, that have been invaded by massive intrusions of granite. Today, the leptites contain the valuable iron ores of Bergslagen and form narrow

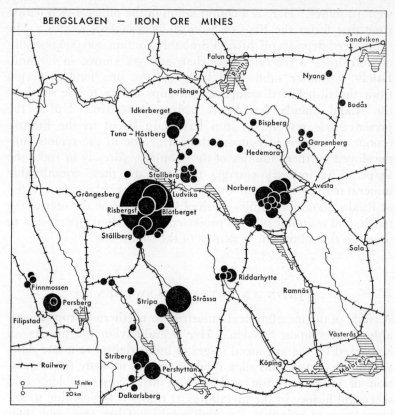

BERGSLAGEN — IRON ORE MINES

FIG. 99

The ore-bodies of this region belong to the leptites of the Archaean Shield. The long-worked non-phosphoric ores of Norberg, Stråssa, and Pershytte have been out-stripped by the phosphorus-containing mineral of Grängesberg — today the greatest producer in the region. Note the pattern of railways that evolved to serve this chief resource of the region.

steeply dipping bands between the masses of granite. The iron ores now occur as thin layers of iron minerals, magnetite or haematite, alternating with quartz. This is a feature that usually characterizes the iron deposits of the Pre-Cambrian period wherever they are found in the other continents of the world. It is believed that the ores of Bergslagen originated as sediments, perhaps deposited by thermal springs. Today, they hold out the prospect of another four hundred million tons for future mining, a quantity that might contain 150,000,000 tons of iron.

Mineralogically, the iron ores of Bergslagen divide into those with a low phosphorus content and the apatitic ores containing between 0·6 and 1·0 per cent of phosphorus. This fact deeply influenced the economic evolution of the region. The pure non-phosphoric ores formed the basis of the high-quality Swedish bar-iron industry that declined after the middle of the nineteenth century as a result of the competition of cheap iron and steel produced in quantity in western Europe by the coke-using processes. The Thomas process, discovered in 1872, permitted the use of the previously valueless phosphoric ores and brought about a technological revolution in the iron industry that deeply influenced its geography in northern Europe. The phosphoric ores of Bergslagen have been worked on an increasing scale since 1880, so that today they contribute two-thirds of the output of the region. The old tortuous mines, reaching depths of nearly three thousand feet and operating since the late Middle Ages, are eclipsed by the shallower, modern workings at Grängesberg, Blötberg, and Idkerberg, to mention only some of the chief sources of phosphoric ores whose iron content averages 60 per cent.

Apart from these important changes in the local geography of iron mining, the industry experienced a reorientation of its markets with the demand for phosphoric ores. Previously the high-quality, non-phosphoric ores were consumed entirely in Sweden. They fed an iron industry that from the end of the seventeenth century until the middle of the nineteenth century worked under decrees and state regulations whose chief effects were to deprive it of the powers of change and vigorous growth. The phosphoric ores, useless in Sweden without the new techniques of the Thomas process, were largely exported to the blast furnaces of the Ruhr and the British Isles. By the turn of the century, as the vast phosphoric iron-ore deposits of Swedish Lapland were increasingly exploited for the European ore trade, Sweden seemed to be destined for a very minor rôle among the world's producers of iron and steel. The heavy mining of the phosphoric ores of Bergslagen in the 1880's held out the prospect of reducing Sweden to the production of only the raw material of the iron and steel industry [Fig. 100]. Fortunately, the balance was redressed in the twentieth century with the establishment of large, highly efficient blast furnaces and steel mills. The electric blast furnace, electrical methods in the production of steel, and the sponge-iron process — a Swedish discovery that consumes only a quarter of the normal quantities of coke — have led to the rebirth of the ancient

2 C   385

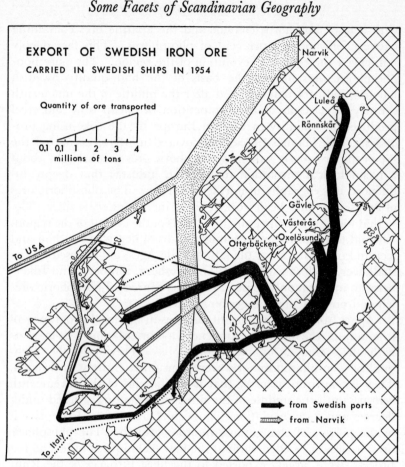

EXPORT OF SWEDISH IRON ORE

CARRIED IN SWEDISH SHIPS IN 1954

Quantity of ore transported

0.1 0.1 1 2 3 4
millions of tons

Narvik

Luleå
Rönnskär

Gävle
Västerås
Oxelösund
Otterbäcken

To USA

To Italy

➡ from Swedish ports
▦ from Narvik

FIG. 100

Despite the rapid growth of the Swedish iron and steel industry in the twentieth century, the export of iron ore to most countries of western Europe still forms one of the mainstays of the nation's economy. The ice-free Norwegian port of Narvik has a predominant rôle in this traffic. Ore boats from the Baltic play an important part in the cargoes that pass through the Kiel canal.

metallurgical industry that originated among the hills and forests of the Bergslagen.

The revival of the Swedish iron industry about the turn of the century involved no startling geographical redistribution. Today, the chief iron and steel plants nearly all lie in the eastern part of the central lakes depression, associated above all with the ancient mining region of the Bergslagen [Fig. 101]. The only iron- and steel-works outside this central area stand on the coastline. Kallinge

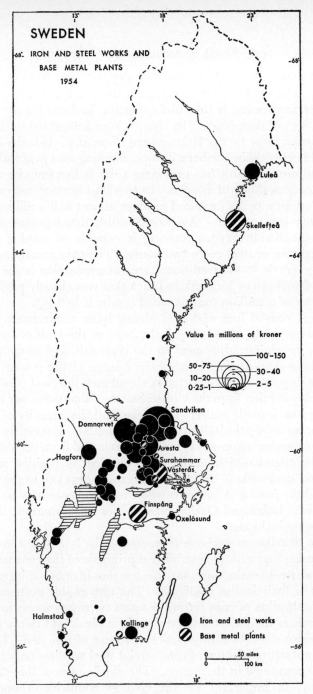

SWEDEN

IRON AND STEEL WORKS AND
BASE METAL PLANTS
1954

Luleå

Skellefteå

Value in millions of kroner

100 - 150

50 - 75
30 - 40
10 - 20
0·25 - 1
2 - 5

Sandviken

Domnarvet

Avesta

Surahammar

Hagfors

Västerås

Finspång

Oxelösund

Halmstad

Kallinge

● Iron and steel works

◐ Base metal plants

0   50 miles
0   100 km

Fig. 101

The location of iron- and steelworks and ferro-alloy plants reveals the overwhelming
importance of the Bergslagen region in Swedish industry, an inheritance from the
past when access to ore, charcoal, and water-power combined to favour this area.
Newer iron and steel plants at Luleå, Oxelösund, Kallinge, and Halmstad are sited
in ports with easy access to imported coke.

and Höganäs in southern Sweden depend largely upon scrap metal; while Oxelösund, situated on the coast a hundred miles south of Stockholm, is the chief exporting harbour for the phosphoric ores of Bergslagen. In 1961, a huge integrated steel plant was opened there by the Grängesberg Company. It is the largest coastal steelworks in northern Europe, standing on a peninsula that juts out into the Baltic Sea providing a site as free from ice as any on the eastern shores of Sweden. Its two blast furnaces use concentrated ore in a pellet form and produce almost half a million tons of sponge-iron a year. Another Swedish development at this plant, the Kaldo oxygen furnace, is capable of turning out a hundred tons of steel every two hours. The only remaining steel plant eccentric to the traditional area of production is the state-owned Norrbottens Järnverk in Luleå that was already producing a quarter of a million tons of rolled products in 1955.

These coastal iron and steel plants, lying as far apart as the north-western tip of Skåne and the head of the Gulf of Bothnia, display the closest adjustment to the economic and geographical controls in steel-making in northern Europe at the present time. Sweden depends upon imported coal and metallurgical coke, most of it today coming from the United States. Ninety-five per cent of her pig iron is made entirely with coke, and the quantity of charcoal consumed by the industry is now negligible. For nearly half a century, Sweden's iron-works have been released from the old bond with the charcoal-yielding forests. The logical position for the iron- and steelworks of the twentieth century lies close to the coast-line and the ports and harbours where coal and coke may be freely imported. Luleå and Oxelösund stand for this important change of geographical values.

The Norrbotten steel complex, among the largest in the country, breaks, too, with the established principle of the economics of iron and steel production that the ore should move towards the sources of fuels in the coalfields. The remarkable economies in the consumption of coke during the past twenty years permit this latest unit of the industry to be sited in a bleak and thinly populated region close to Europe's richest source of iron ore. Today, the manufacture of a ton of commercial steel requires only half of the fuel consumed in the 1920's. The chief causes of this striking economy, so important for the coalless countries of northern Europe, are the growing use of the electric furnace and the development of the sponge-iron technique that provides a fresh material for steel-making, equivalent to pig iron, with a remarkable economy in the consumption of coke.

If the new steel plants at Luleå and Oxelösund reflect the changing controls in the iron and steel industry in the middle of the twentieth century, the position of the bulk of Sweden's iron- and steelworks amid the forests and hills of Bergslagen illustrates the factor of inertia that affects the location of an industry even when it undergoes a thorough revolution. Today the blast furnaces, steelworks, forges, and rolling mills of east-central Sweden are mainly located between the lower valley of the Dal river and the eastern shore of Lake Vänern. Within this broad belt of ore-rich, forested country the valley of the Kolbäck river, flowing into Lake Mälaren, contains several large iron and steel plants. Westward of the canalized valley of the Kolbäck, another important centre of the iron industry belongs to the valleys that drain southward to the northern shore of Lake Vänern. Here such names as Degerfors, Bofors, and Hagfors stand for Sweden's high-quality steels and engineering products upon which her export trade in metallurgical goods largely rests.

The Rebirth of Iron- and Steel-Making in Sweden

The contemporary pattern of the iron and steel industry began to evolve in the last quarter of the nineteenth century. A small number of closely integrated iron and steel plants came to replace the hundreds of tiny blast furnaces and forges that lay scattered over Bergslagen and the adjoining regions at the beginning of the last century [Fig. 102]. Within Bergslagen there were about six hundred iron works in 1830. By 1920 the number had fallen to little more than a hundred, and in 1956 there were only fifty-six iron- and steelworks left in the whole of Sweden. The industry disappeared from most of Värmland and became extinct in the province of Södermanland to the south of Lake Mälaren. The statistics of the falling number of plants and the contracting area of iron production might suggest a waning industry. The story behind these figures is just the opposite.

The Swedish iron and steel industry was reborn at the beginning of this century, to reach in the present decade the highest levels of output in its history. The links of the present industry with the preceding stage of prosperity in the Bergslagen's metallurgical trades consist in the continued use of some long-established

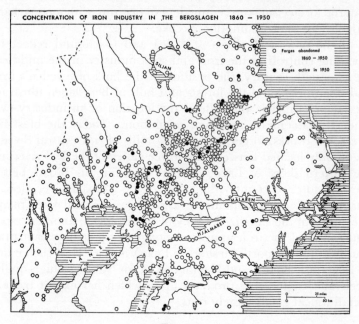

CONCENTRATION OF IRON INDUSTRY IN THE BERGSLAGEN   1860 – 1950

○ Forges abandoned
       1860 – 1950

● Forges active in 1950

Fig. 102

The disappearance of scores of small forges scattered across eastern Sweden led to the concentration of the iron and steel industry in a small number of integrated plants on sites favourable for water supply and communications in the central Bergslagen. The industry was extinguished in the forests of Värmland to the north of lake Vänern and almost eradicated from the province of Södermanland, south of lake Mälaren.

industrial sites — usually at a waterfall that has lost all its former meaning as a source of power. The past, too, is remembered in the insistence upon high quality in the products of the modern Swedish steel industry. Today she is famous for the quality of her stainless steel and the careful manufacture of ferro-alloys. In the eighteenth century, Swedish bar-iron was the best in the world, a quality that was maintained by state decree and the activities of the Jernkontoret, the Swedish Ironmasters Association.

The historic period of Swedish iron-making is perpetuated in modern times through the names of the great companies such as Uddeholm [Fig. 103] and Ramnäs whose traditions date back to the seventeenth century. These names provide a feeling of continuity that conceals the economic transformation and rebirth at the end of the last century. The old industry foundered under the impact of competition from cheap iron, produced in bulk by the

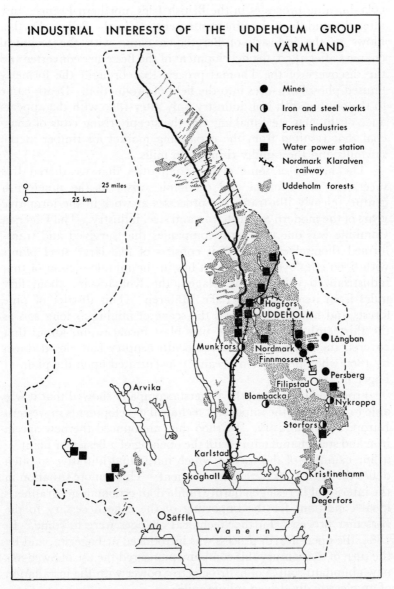

INDUSTRIAL INTERESTS OF THE UDDEHOLM GROUP IN VÄRMLAND

● Mines

◑ Iron and steel works

▲ Forest industries

■ Water power station

✕✕✕ Nordmark Klaralven railway

Uddeholm forests

25 miles

25 km

Hagfors
UDDEHOLM
Munkfors
Nordmark
Finnmossen
Långban
Persberg
Filipstad
Arvika
Blombacka
Nykroppa
Storfors
Karlstad
Skoghall
Kristinehamn
Degerfors
Säffle
Vanern

FIG. 103

Uddeholm is only one of the economic empires carved over the centuries out of the forests and mineral-rich lands of central Sweden. It is based on the northern shore of lake Vänern and stretches into the hinterland of the Klar river. Its capital interests consist of forests, iron mines, steel works, pulp mills, and railways.

coke-burning processes in the British Isles, northern France, and, after the middle of the nineteenth century, in the Ruhr. Further blows to the industry of Bergslagen came with the technical changes after 1850, the development of the Bessemer converter and the discovery of the Thomas process that brought the formerly unused phosphoric ores into the field of production. Death came to the old Swedish iron industry only after 1890 with the appearance of the new steel-making and the steeply rising costs of charcoal that resulted from the expanding market for timber at the sawmills and the rapidly rising pulp mills.

The history of some of the companies that weathered this succession of technical and economic crises in the nineteenth century clearly illustrates the processes at work in the formative years of the modern Swedish iron and steel industry. The Fagersta Combine was one of several companies that survived and transformed themselves. Today it consists of five large steel plants with 6000 employees. Fagersta lies in the middle section of that industrialized valley of Bergslagen, the Kolbäcksån, about fifty miles from its outlet into Lake Mälaren. This district of pine forests and mineral lodes was the scene of mining as long ago as the thirteenth century. The tiny blast furnaces and forges that covered the district in the seventeenth century had closed down by 1800 when production became concentrated upon the plant at Fagersta.

From 1860 onwards, the Fagersta company showed that it was able to assimilate the important technical developments in western Europe's iron industry. In 1860 they announced the new age in iron and steel manufacture with the opening of a Bessemer plant — a fine example of the way in which individual initiative so often defies the hard facts of the environment. This remote situation in the interior of Bergslagen hardly fulfilled an economic geographer's ideal conditions for the importing of the coke necessary to the Bessemer process. Further technical changes were to come. In 1884, the open-hearth process was introduced at Fagersta, and by the turn of the century this company pioneered the use of Sweden's new abundant source of hydro-electric power with the installation of an electrically-driven rolling mill.

The technical changes that secured growth and survival were accompanied by equally important changes in organization and management. The joint-stock company, Fagersta Bruks A.B., was formed in 1874. During the economic crisis that followed the

First World War, it became transformed into the Fagersta Corporation, composed of four large steelworks to which a fifth, the Forsbacka works, was added in 1929.

Since 1930 the Fagersta Corporation has carried out three long programmes of technical development. The works were enlarged in the late thirties so that output grew by 50 per cent between 1935 and 1945. The boom years since the Second World War have seen an even greater growth of the equipment and output of the Fagersta Corporation. Two seven-year plans of rationalization and re-equipment in all the company's property have been drawn up. The first plan, completed in 1952, designed afresh the metallurgical plant at Fagersta with the aim of producing a wide variety of steels. It includes three blast furnaces, two acid-lined Bessemer converters, an electric arc furnace and an open-hearth furnace, a completely new wire mill, and a hot rolling strip mill. In addition, a modern plant for the manufacture of welded tubes has been built at Fagersta. This modern steel plant largely produces the high-quality steels traditionally associated with the Bergslagen, but in its post-war development it has taken notice of Sweden's need to import ordinary commercial steels. The second seven-year plan of the Fagersta Corporation started in 1956. It aimed to remodel the four other iron- and steelworks of the company on the lines of the reorganized parent plant. The anticipated result was a doubling of the hot rolled and forged steel outputs.

The other survivors of the decline of the iron industry in the nineteenth century and the founders of the new steel industry of the twentieth century show a similar initiative in the critical years about 1900. Some ironworks survived and expanded because their owners developed special lines of manufacturing in the engineering trade. At Ramnäs, another parish on the Kolbäck river, a forge called the Kungshammaren was built in 1590 to manufacture wrought iron from pig iron. Its account books date back to the middle of the seventeenth century and a complete record of the dealings of the ironworks exists from the eighteenth century. This ancient metallurgical firm displayed a flexibility in the face of economic changes that allowed it to survive to the present day. For instance, a rolling mill was constructed at Ramnäs in 1868. The severe economic crisis that followed in western Europe during the 1870's stifled the market for the products of the Ramnäs rolling mill, and as a result the owner decided to use part of its output in the manufacture of engineering produce.

He opened a chain factory at Ramnäs in 1880 and started a line of high-quality engineering that has since come to dominate the trade of Ramnäs Bruks A.B.

The Bofors Company illustrates the changing fortunes of an ore-mining and iron-manufacturing district in the western part of Bergslagen a few miles from Lake Vänern. Here, among the charcoal-yielding forests around Karlskoga, small communities of farmers and miners erected blast furnaces and forges in the early years of the seventeenth century. Ore had been raised from such famous mines as Dalkarlsberg and the Persberg some two centuries before the widespread building of small furnaces and hammer mills. Bofors itself was constructed in 1646. By the middle of the nineteenth century this early iron industry was all but dead in the countryside around Karlskoga. The competition of the new iron-and steel-making techniques in foreign countries led the Swedish ironmaster to desert his craft, and all but two of the blast furnaces were abandoned by 1860. A few of the forges survived until the 1890's, but only two of the ironworking sites, at Bofors and Degerfors, accomplished the technological and economic resurrection that made them into powerful members of the modern steel and engineering industry in Sweden.

In 1873, the owner of Bofors, Per Lagerhjelm, founded a company, A.B. Bofors-Gullspång, that swallowed up other small ironworks, charcoal-yielding forest estates and farms, as well as shares in some of the valuable mines of the western Bergslagen. This broadly-based company achieved the first technological changes necessary to survival in the late 1870's. A blast furnace was built in 1874 and five years later the open-hearth technique was adopted along with the construction of a steel foundry. But the revolutionary event in the history of iron- and steel-making at Bofors came through an alliance with the engineering trade. A cannon factory was opened in 1884, and a decade later the association of Bofors with an expanding armaments industry became complete when Alfred Nobel gained a controlling interest over the shares of the Bofors-Gullspång Company. Today, the Bofors group is typical of some of Sweden's giant industrial concerns with an employment roll of 13,000. It produces not only war material — armour plate, artillery equipment, ammunition, and gunpowder — as a result of the corporation's monopoly in the exploitation of Alfred Nobel's patents; but the name of Bofors is also associated with high-grade steels and forgings for the car and aircraft industries. Bofors, too, is linked with the chemical industry in the form of pharmaceutical goods, plastics, and paints.

The history of Bofors repeats itself over and over again in the development of the contemporary iron and steel industry in Sweden. The continuity between the old iron industry and the modern steel plants scarcely exists. The revered and ancient names of the great metallurgical corporations conceal a far-reaching revolution in technology, industrial structure, and management that began in the closing decades of the last century. It is interesting, though perhaps idle, to speculate on what might have happened in the location of the new iron and steel industry in Sweden if the old furnaces and forges had survived another fifty years until the discovery of hydro-electric power. The technological revolution that began in a tentative fashion with the 1860's depended upon water power, charcoal, and increasing amounts of imported coke. The need for water power helped to confine the expanding iron- and steelworks to the ancient waterfall sites — hence the picturesque, topographical element of *fors* in so many names of modern steel companies. From the point of view of the import of coke, many of Bergslagen's iron and steel plants were badly placed. Likewise, these remote sites in the interior of Sweden fell far from the ideal for the development of an export trade in high-quality steel and metallurgical products. The appearance of hydro-electric power on a commercial scale in the first years of the twentieth century freed the iron and steel industry from its bonds with the directly-driven water turbine. Furthermore, charcoal resources and the forest-estates that form an important part of the assets of the great steel corporations have lost all value as siting factors in the industry. With 95 per cent of the output of the iron and steel industry produced with the help of imported coke, coal, and oil, and a high-tension grid for the transmission of electricity that extends from the power plants of Norrland to the manufacturing towns of Skåne, the logical sites for the major units of the iron and steel industry lie close to the coastline. The new state-controlled steel plant at Luleå and the new integrated works at Oxelösund foreshadow the next geographical stage in the evolution of the Swedish iron and steel industry — a movement towards the coastline that was forestalled at the beginning of the century by the grip of old and waning site factors upon the basic industry of Bergslagen in the first stage of its transformation.

Some Facets of Scandinavian Geography

Post-war Developments in the Swedish Iron and Steel Industry

The period since the Second World War is a time of great expansion in the Swedish iron and steel industry — a time as important as the last decade of the nineteenth century, when the initiative of some of her ironmasters was able to save Sweden from the prospect of becoming a mere exporter of iron ore to the metallurgical plants of Tees-side, Sheffield, and the Ruhr. The statistics of the industry abound with figures of rising industrial capacity. The year 1957 clearly records the long period of post-war prosperity, with a total output of 1,700,000 tons of iron and steel — a doubling of the output since 1945. The course of this industrial growth since the war has been shaped by an acute shortage of labour in Sweden, the rapidly rising demands of the shipbuilding, machine tool, car, and aircraft industries, a prolonged dearth of coal and coke from the traditional sources in Great Britain and Germany, and an easy world market for Swedish steel alloys and the many products of her engineering industry. Political and economic conditions outside northern Europe, as well as the natural gifts of the Swedish landscape, have determined the details of the growth of the industry in this period.

The most striking feature of steel-making in Sweden today is the emergence of two clear branches to the industry. In addition to the manufacture of high-quality steel and steel alloys, Sweden now produces a large amount of cheaper commercial steel. The figures for 1955 show that 78 per cent of her output consisted of this commoner material used by the building industry, the shipyards, and in the common tasks of the engineering trades. The expansion of this branch of the steel industry dates back to the acute shortages of the Second World War, and it has been continued by the great demands of the Swedish building and engineering trades at a time when the import of sheet metal and constructional steel from Belgium, Luxembourg, and the British Isles was greatly restricted in the years that followed the war. Nevertheless, in 1955 Sweden imported almost a million tons of iron and steel, the largest items of which were steel plate for the shipyards of Malmö and Göteborg and sheet metal for the car industry. Even in 1958 the whole of the car industry's needs of sheet metal had to be imported.

The technical trends in the iron and steel industry during the past decade were largely determined by Sweden's shortage of manpower and the cost and scarcity of metallurgical coke. Another fear that the growth of this industry might be stunted by events outside the frontiers of Sweden arose from the supply of scrap metal. This junk of an industrial civilization, together with the waste metal of the forges and rolling mills, is a necessary ingredient in modern steel-making. The steelworks of southern Sweden import scrap metal from Denmark, and a considerable amount was obtained from Germany in the years immediately after the war. The formation of the Coal and Steel Community in 1952, with its provision for a common market in scrap metal, threatened to exclude Sweden from her chief source of this ingredient in the industrial cities of western Europe. Possessing the prolific natural resource of Europe's richest iron ores, Sweden's steel industry has evolved in the 1950's under the pressure of shortages of labour and raw materials.

As we have already noticed, the commercial development of the coke-saving, sponge-iron process from a Swedish invention is one of the characteristics of the fifties. Seven plants were manufacturing sponge-iron in 1956 and they turned out 100,000 tons of this new material that rivals pig iron for the manufacture of high-grade steels. The consumption of imported fuels has been reduced through the wider installation of electric furnaces, so that today the Swedish iron and steel industry uses 10 per cent of the nation's electricity. Above all, Sweden has been forced to raise her outputs of steel without any great increase of manpower. It is claimed that over the period from 1948 to 1955 the output of steel rose by 60 per cent and that over the same period the labour force increased by only 6·6 per cent. Finally, an important discovery of the fifties in Sweden promises to bring further changes to the industry during the next decade. Since the appearance of the Thomas process three-quarters of a century ago and the radical change that it brought to the value of the phosphoric ores, Sweden has looked upon the apatites of Bergslagen and the phosphorus-holding deposits of Norrland largely as material for export. Her own iron and steel industry depended largely upon the traditional source of supply in Bergslagen's non-phosphoric iron ores. Now, by means of a process of leaching with nitric acid concentrates, iron of a very low phosphorus content can be obtained from the phosphorus-rich ores of Grängesberg and the north.

Two clear divisions exist in the Swedish steel industry. In the late 1950's commercial steels occupied three-quarters of the national output, while the other branch of the industry, the manufacture of high-quality steel and steel alloys, accounted for the rest. These two great branches of the industry seek out completely different markets. The output of commercial steel feeds Sweden's domestic demands and, as we have noticed, falls far short of satisfying her needs. On the other hand, 60 per cent of the high-quality steel is exported. It reaches its chief market in western Europe as pure carbon steel and high-alloy steel used by the machine tool industry, as cold rolled strip for saws and razor blades, as stainless steels for the equipment of the chemical industry, and in the form of wire rods for the manufacture of valve springs used in the engines of the car and aircraft industries.

Sweden's valuable high-quality steel industry almost defies logical explanation. Undoubtedly, the gifts and deficiencies of her natural environment partly account for her interest in this specialized branch of the industry. The pure ores of Bergslagen and the equally pure charcoal from her coniferous forests, with a phosphorus content only a third of that produced from deciduous trees, explain the quality of Swedish metallurgy a century and a half ago. A lack of coal and metallurgical coke prevented Sweden from competing with the British Isles, Belgium, and the Ruhr in the large-scale production of cheap iron and steel. But Sweden's perpetual interest in the finest quality of metallurgy is not only determined by the passive facts of geography. The long history of the industry reveals an obsession with quality that is part of the national psychology. The Swedish Jernkontoret — the Ironmasters Association — was formed more than two centuries ago to preserve the high standards of the industry and there is little doubt that the skill of the workers in iron- and steel-making partly explains the emphasis upon quality. As a Swedish journalist has written of the contemporary steel industry in his country — 'this preoccupation with such an onerous and complex production as high-alloy steels is in part historical, in part psychological and in part due to sheer economic necessity'.[1]

No industry remains long without change, and even the manufacture of the best Swedish steel, weighted as it is by names that are almost as old as the nation itself, seems to have entered an important period of transformation in the late fifties. Sweden appears to be turning towards a specialization in stainless steels. Ever since her experiments with chrome-nickel alloys in the manufacture of stainless steel during the early twenties, Sweden held a dominant place in this sector of the metallurgical industries. It is possible that stainless steel will come to overshadow the other types of high-quality and specialized steel. In 1958, the Uddeholm concern produced 18,000 tons of stainless steel ingots and plans to double the stainless melting capacity of its plant at Hagfors in the early sixties. Similarly, Avesta, one of the largest producers of stainless steel in Sweden, is doubling the capacity of its melt shop to 100,000 tons, and in 1958 it installed the biggest cold rolling plant in Sweden. The importance of this expansion in the stainless steel sector of Swedish industry is underlined by the fact that between 1956 and 1960 the chief corporations — Fagersta, Söderfors, Nyby Bruk, and Avesta — installed continuous cold rolling plant equivalent to a third of the capacity installed in the United States over the same period.

The rising output of stainless steel represents something more important than the ever-present minor fluctuations in the figures of industrial outputs. Behind it lie two striking changes in the organization of the Swedish iron and steel industry. Her industrial plants are turning towards larger outputs in a few specialized lines of high-quality stainless steel products. For instance, Nyby Bruk, a small steelworks that was almost bankrupt at the end of the war, replanned its operations to concentrate on two products, stainless steel sheet and stainless metal tubing. By 1958 Nyby Bruk emerged as one of the biggest steel producers in Sweden with the output of stainless sheet equal to that of the country's biggest producer, Avesta, and a quantity of tubing that represented half of the national production. Such a trend in the organization of the steel industry towards large outputs of a few selected items will transform the economics of Swedish steel-making. Until the present, she has produced special purpose steels in small quantities for individual and restricted orders. For instance, musical reed steel for the accordion trade is a Swedish speciality, but a negligible item in the vast theatre of the world's iron and steel industry. The expansion of the output and the market in a limited number of lines could return Sweden to the position of an important power in the world's iron and steel trade. Stainless steel might become the twentieth-century equivalent of the high-quality bar-iron that made Sweden the greatest power in metallurgy two centuries ago.

The growth of the stainless steel trade is also transforming the internal structure of the iron industry. Until the mid-fifties, every stage of the manufacturing process was in the hands of each firm. It was felt that the superb quality of Sweden's products owed much to the minute supervision of every industrial technique within the same company. With each decade of the twentieth century industrial equipment has become more complex, and only the largest factories can make sufficient profits for survival. Modern hot rolling mills demand for profitable working all the year round a supply of ingots larger than the output of any single steel plant. Consequently, Swedish firms are beginning to share the resources of the newest hot rolling mills. Both Avesta and Nyby Bruk, among the biggest producers of stainless steel, send their stainless steel ingots for rolling at Surahammar. The crude strip is then returned to the parent mills for the finishing process in a cold rolling plant. Söderfors, lately reorientated towards stainless steel, sends its stainless steel slabs to the hot strip mill at Domnarvet from which the 3-mm. gauge strip is returned for the final complex operations of cold rolling. This is a revolutionary development in an industry that up to the present has seen the individual firm in charge of the whole chain of the production process.

Within the next decade Sweden has the prospect of building up a large market in stainless steel, particularly in western Europe. There is a rising domestic use in kitchen sinks and refrigerators, but an even more important demand for stainless steel comes from the designers of plant for the chemical industry. The equipment of pulp mills is now largely made of stainless steel, and lately the constructors of nuclear reactors have laid heavy orders with the stainless steel firms of Sweden. In these last years, almost a quarter of the output of the stainless steel industry in Sweden has been used in the manufacture of equipment for the chemical industry. At the threshold of the sixties a fresh emphasis is apparent in one of Sweden's oldest crafts.

STEEL INDUSTRIES IN NORWAY, DENMARK, AND FINLAND

The foundation of modern iron and steel industries in Sweden's neighbour states belongs entirely to the twentieth century [Fig. 97]. Finland, always the latest among the Scandinavian states in the adoption of fresh industrial techniques, is only now completing the plans for two up-to-date, integrated iron and steel plants at

Raahe and close to Hanko. In all three countries, Norway, Denmark, and Finland, the growth of an iron and steel industry clearly illustrates the sharp trend towards industrialism in northern Europe since the end of the Second World War. All three states began to approach industrial maturity only in the fifties, and in each country the growth of the iron and steel industry arose mainly from the demands of an already well-developed and varied engineering industry. In Sweden we noticed the opposite course of evolution. There, engineering frequently appeared as a young subsidiary to a long-established ironworks, its creation arising from a period of economic depression.

The history of iron-making in Norway runs closely parallel to that of Sweden in the late eighteenth century. Its subsequent divergences underline the basic geographical differences between the two countries — the isolation of Norway's chief ore deposits in the northernmost parts of the state, and the accessibility of her Atlantic fjords to abundant hydro-electric power, imported raw materials, and overseas markets for highly specialized ferro-alloys. Two centuries ago, Norway's charcoal iron-making could challenge the timber trade as the most prosperous industry in the country. During the Napaleonic wars there were eighteen ironworks and twenty-two blast furnaces in the country, but before the end of the nineteenth century the whole industry had disappeared.

The iron and steel industry reappeared in Norway at the beginning of the twentieth century. The oldest steelworks in the country, at Oslo, was active in 1902, where the making of iron and steel in the industrial quarter of the capital city developed in response to the needs of the engineering industry.

The Oslo company of Christiania Spigerwerk illustrates the relationship between the engineering industry and the production of iron and steel. As we are told by its name, the corporation was once mainly concerned with the manufacture of nails. Today, although it owns the most complete steel-making plant in Norway, Christiania Spigerwerk possesses a wire-drawing mill, produces agricultural implements, and still manufactures wire nails. The expansion of this firm's interests in the production of steel reflects the growth of the industry in Norway as a whole. The First World War isolated neutral northern Europe from the great centres of iron- and steel-making in the Ruhr and the British Isles. This dislocation of international trade induced Christiania Spigerwerk to install two Siemens Martin furnaces and a blooming mill fed by scrap metal and imported pig iron from Sweden. In the early twenties, fresh developments at Christiania Spigerwerk reflected the orientation of Norwegian industry towards the nation's abundant supplies of hydro-electric power. Experiments with the Tysland-Hole electric furnace began in 1924, and by the close of the decade Christiania Spigerwerk was converted entirely to electric smelting. The years since the Second World War have seen a great expansion of plant at this Oslo iron and steel firm. Crude steel output multiplied six times between 1930 and 1950, a new steel rolling mill has been installed, and thus one Norwegian firm achieves the maturity that is apparent in some other sectors of the nation's industries in the post-war period.

The iron and steel industry arose in the Oslo area to serve the needs of engineering and shipbuilding. On the other hand, the making of specialized electric steels in western Norway depends upon foreign markets in countries around the North Sea basin. Two plants at lonely sites in the western fjords produce high-quality alloy steels and pig iron — Stavanger Electro-Staalverk A/S at Jørpeland, about twelve miles from Stavanger, and the A/S Bremanger Kraftselskab at Svelgen, on a remote arm of Nord fjord cut off from all communications by land [Plate 7]. Both plants illustrate the same factors in their location and development. Each company has its own hydro-electric station and most of the power output is consumed in the electric furnaces of the iron- and steelworks. At Svelgen two-thirds of the current from an 11,000-kw power station is devoured on the site by the electric pig iron plant. The second valuable element in the foundation and survival of these iron and steel plants is the sea transport to harbours that remain free of ice for the whole year. Svelgen obtains its iron ore from mines near Kristiansund and brings coke from England. Limestone is also imported by sea from quarries on the western coast of Norway. Svelgen's output of vanadium-containing pig iron — about 20,000 tons per year — is exported for the manufacture of heat resisting castings and special steels. At Jørpeland there is a fully equipped steel plant with rolling mills, a steel foundry, and departments that specialize in the production of hard cutting steels and the casting of permanent magnets. Both of these industrial plants exploit the capacities of western Norway for the refining of metals, and for their specialized commodities they find their chief markets outside the country.

A further stage in the growth of Norway's iron and steel

industry began with the end of the Second World War. Merchant steel was scarce in western Europe during the late forties and early fifties at a time when demand was very high in Norway as a result of industrial expansion, a rapid growth in the capital city, the founding of new power stations, and the rising outputs of her shipyards. To help satisfy their domestic needs the Norwegians had long thought of an integrated iron and steel plant in their northern territories. Mo i Rana began production in 1955. It differs from the other iron and steel plants of the country not only in its location in the remote, thinly populated territory of Arctic Norway and in its projected output of half a million tons per year, outstripping by far any other Norwegian works, but also in the fact that it aims to feed the home market and draws its raw materials from north Norway's iron ores, instead of importing scrap and pig iron. Mo i Rana stands as the prime example of the industrial revolution of the fifties that is evident in many parts of Norway.

The presence of an iron and steel industry in Denmark is another proof of the favourable climate for industrial growth and expansion that has prevailed in the past two decades. Geographically, she wants all the necessities for the making of iron and steel apart from limestone. Denmark lacks both coal and the rivers and lakes that provide the natural background to cheap hydro-electric power. Her bog ores in Jutland, the only iron resources of the country, are utterly inadequate as the foundation for a modern steel industry.

In Denmark, industry grew despite the dictates of geography. For nearly three centuries the economy of the country has oscillated between two ideals. At times she has shaped her economy in the image of an agricultural nation, exchanging the products of Danish farms for the industrial goods of her west European neighbours in an economic atmosphere of free trade between the North Sea countries. At other times, when wars or economic nationalism, working through tariffs, quotas, and import restrictions, have closed or reduced Denmark's markets in neighbouring countries she has turned to industrial development and the aim of an internally balanced economy.

The past quarter of a century has favoured industrial growth in this small country that lacks so many of the natural gifts for industrial development. The world economic depression of the thirties, with its drive towards economic autarchy, the isolation of the Second World War, and the boom period of the fifties forced Denmark to establish an iron and steel industry to feed the growing needs of her varied engineering works. Her largest plant, an integrated iron- and steelworks at Frederiksværk in the northeast of the island of Zealand, was founded during the Second World War. It uses Danish scrap and imported pig iron to produce almost 200,000 tons of steel products for the domestic market in the building, engineering, and shipbuilding trades. But this sum falls far short of Denmark's post-war needs. In 1957 she imported more than half a million tons of iron and steel plates and sheet, joists and hoops, strip, wire, and tubing.

The iron and steel industry of Finland is in the course of development from a rudimentary to an advanced level. At present, this industry shares some of the characteristics of her three Scandinavian neighbours. As in Denmark, the need for a substantial domestic output of iron and steel has been felt as a result of the rapid growth of the engineering industry, forced forward immediately after the Second World War by the Soviet demand for reparations. The present location of the industry is mainly close to the southern coastline, especially in the neighbourhood of Turku and Kotka [Fig. 109]. Some of these small plants date from before 1800 and the period of Swedish occupation, when ores were imported from Sweden to take advantage of Finland's internal market and the charcoal of her forests. The recent discovery of iron-ore bodies in Finland reminds one of Norway's problems in the development of a domestic iron and steel industry. They lie either in remote parts of the country or at technically inaccessible sites — at Otanmäki, to the south of Lake Oulu in the heart of central Finland, and beneath the waters of her south-western archipelago. The two ironworks planned by the Finnish government at Raahe and close to Hanko bring to mind the Norwegian state's project at Mo i Rana. Together they will go far towards supplying Finland's needs in pig iron and steel. As at Mo i Rana, they have been conceived as part of the growing national economy, and Raahe displays the same enterprise in planting a key industry in the undeveloped northlands.

CHAPTER 14

The Engineering Industries of Scandinavia

ENGINEERING has a longer history in Sweden than any other
Scandinavian state. The foundation of the modern engineering
industry dates back to the 1870's, though long before this time
there were small factories, attached to the foundries of Bergslagen
that manufactured tools for foresters and farmers. Today, engineering holds a front place among the industries of Sweden. By the
mid-fifties almost a third of Sweden's workers were employed in
this industry, and its products accounted for a quarter of the
nation's exports. Ships, cars, machine tools, dynamos, transformers, automatic lighthouses, and the equipment of hydro-
electric stations, ball bearings and refrigerators together are equal
to timber in Sweden's list of exports and closely rival pulp in her
foreign trade.

Unlike the iron and steel industry, engineering shows no
attachment to its sources of raw materials. Its chief needs are a
satisfactory supply of skilled labour and an access to the markets
for its products. Consequently, engineering is an urban industry,
belonging particularly to the capital city, the great western port
of Göteborg, and the port-towns of Skåne's western coast. In
addition, varied branches of the engineering trade have settled
in the many towns of central Sweden. It is reckoned that three-
quarters of the engineering industry is scattered through the
central lakes depression and in Sweden's two main cities, Stockholm and Göteborg [Fig. 104].

Sweden's engineering industry largely escaped the pattern
imprinted upon these trades during the first half of the nineteenth
century in Great Britain and France by the demands of coal
mining, steam power, and the textile industries. The first stage of
growth in Sweden's engineering industry accompanied the demand
for agricultural implements and tools in forestry and sawmilling
as well as the building of railways during the 1860's. Today, the
outline of this first stage in the history of the modern engineering
industry may be traced in the firms that specialize in forestry

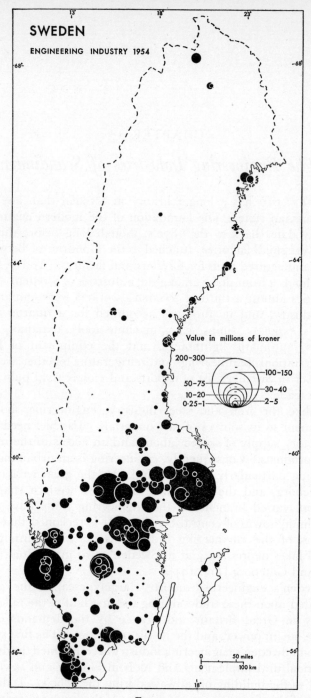

FIG. 104

The engineering industry belongs to the midlands and the south-western tip of the country. It is located in the great port cities — Stockholm, Göteborg, and Malmö — and at inland centres such as Motala, Huskvarna, and Karlskoga. The clusters around the great centres of population are partly explained by the sub-contracting system that has developed in the larger engineering industries such as shipbuilding or cars.

machinery, mainly in central Sweden, and the production of farm machinery in the south of the country. The supply of railway equipment became an important part of the industries of Bergslagen with the manufacture of rails and other heavy gear at Domnarvet. The construction of locomotives centres in two towns of the lakes depression associated with many branches of the engineering trades — Trollhättan, with its abundance of electric power on the rapids of the Göta river, and Motala at the exit to Lake Vättern. Rolling stock is built at various places in central and southern Sweden — at Arlöv, an industrial satellite of Malmö, Kalmar, Linköping, and Falun, the ancient copper-mining centre of the Bergslagen.

One of the chief tasks of the engineering industry in any country is the design and manufacture of machinery for the harnessing of power. As Sweden stood in the forefront of the development of hydro-electric power at the beginning of the twentieth century, it is not surprising that this period introduced a second stage in the growth of the engineering trades. Today, electrical engineering forms one of the strongest sectors of Swedish industry, and it has two chief branches — the production of power station equipment and transmission gear and, on the other hand, the light electrical industry that is mainly occupied with telecommunications, manufacturing telephones, automatic telephone exchanges, and radios.

The Swedish firm of A.S.E.A. (Allmänna Svenska Elektriska AB) dominates the trade in heavy electrical equipment and displays several of the characteristics of Swedish industry [Fig. 105]. For instance A.S.E.A. has exploited a Swedish gift for turning the inventiveness of her technologically minded people into commercial successes on a grand scale. This huge firm began in 1882 with only an attic room and seven workers to manufacture the dynamo designed by a young Swedish engineer, Jonas Wenström. The industry started to expand early in the 1890's after transferring its factory to Västerås on the northern shore of Lake Mälaren, a town in one of the most populated areas of east-central Sweden, possessing fine communications by railway and lake to the capital city and in close contact with the iron and steel centres of Bergslagen.

A.S.E.A. explored the difficult problems of electricity transmission. This firm achieved the first successful long-distance transmission of power in Sweden when they constructed a nine-mile-long high tension line from Hallsjön to the iron mines at

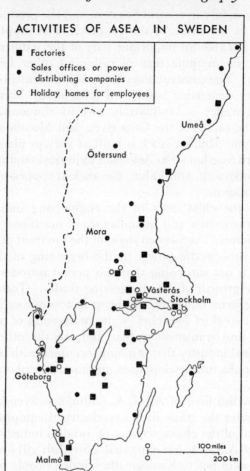

ACTIVITIES OF ASEA IN SWEDEN

- ■ Factories
- ● Sales offices or power distributing companies
- ○ Holiday homes for employees

FIG. 105

Allmänna Svenska Elektriska AB is typical of the large industrial corporations that tower over the Swedish economy. Its historic roots and controlling centre are at Västerås where much of the company's research into the problems of electricity transmission and the development of generators has been carried out. A.S.E.A. employs 30,000 people and has branches from north to south of the country.

Grängesberg, carrying 9500 volts and using the Wenström three-phase system. This was only the first of several victories in the field of power transmission that have been crowned in the 1950's with two remarkable achievements. In 1952 A.S.E.A. completed the first 400-kv. high-tension line in the world from Harsprånget in furthest Norrland to the centres of population in the south of the country, and with it one of Sweden's most difficult technical problems, the bulk transmission of electricity from the unpopulated north to the towns of the midlands and south, has been solved. Two years later A.S.E.A. brought to a conclusion a long period of research on the transmission of direct current over long distances. It has already been put to commercial use in the cable across the Baltic floor that takes electricity from the mainland to Visby in the island of Gotland. Now A.S.E.A. is providing equipment for the exchange of current across the English Channel between the grids of south-eastern England and northern France, and the firm's discoveries form the technical background to the politically barbed discussions on the laying of a submarine cable across the Skagerrak from Norway to Jutland.

A.S.E.A. has specialized with similar success in other branches of the heavy electrical engineering trade. Large generators for power stations have been an important product since the first decade of this century, when the company began to expand under the stimulus of the development of Sweden's waterfalls. The power plant at Stornorrfors on the Ume river, opened in 1959, contains three A.S.E.A. generators, each with an output of 150,000 kva., and the biggest of their kind in the world at the time of their installation. Similarly, this firm's early experiments with electricity as a motive power for railways — they built the first electrically-driven engines in the 1890's — led to the growth of one of the most important branches of the industry. They designed much of the gear for the electrification of the Swedish railway network. First, in 1910, A.S.E.A. lay behind the electrifying of the iron-ore railway from Kiruna to Narvik, and late in the 1920's they undertook the conversion to electric power of the first main line in Sweden from Stockholm to Göteborg. Since the Second World War this giant Swedish company with its subsidiaries in many other countries has supplied material for the electrification of railways in Poland and France.

In the mid-fifties, the largest sector of the electrical engineering industry was taken up by telecommunications. Here again Sweden's predilection for the large industrial unit is apparent. The manufacture of telephones, telephone exchange equipment, and radio gear for transmission and reception is largely in the hands of two giant companies that account for almost four-fifths of the national production. The main centre of this industry lies in the suburbs of Stockholm, from where the firm of Ericsson controls a dozen plants in Sweden and seventy associated companies all over the world. Both branches of Sweden's electrical industry depend upon an extensive world market, one that is maintained by the peculiar flair for sales management displayed by Swedish businessmen.

Along with the rise of the electrical industry in the first half of this century, Sweden's engineering industry grew in several other directions. This sector of engineering that includes calculating machines, low-horse-powered electric motors, refrigerators and vacuum cleaners, pneumatic drills, and dairy machinery, almost defies geographical analysis. The great passive factors of the natural environment play little part in determining the birth and success of these industries that belong to the towns and cities of central Sweden. So often the adventure of an individual, either in the realm of ideas or capital investment, is the sole reason for the appearance of an industry and its later prosperity. Perhaps this feature of engineering in Sweden stands most clearly illustrated in the history of S.K.F., the large Göteborg concern that specializes in the manufacture of ball and roller bearings.

Raw materials and sources of energy play no part in the origins and location of this industry that appeared in the suburbs of Göteborg in 1907. Svenska Kullagerfabriken owes its success above all to the ideas of Sven Wingquist, a founder who combined with his skill as an engineer revolutionary ideas upon the development of overseas markets for the products of his firm. From its beginning in the first decade of this century, S.K.F. began to build up its own export organization in the countries of western Europe, the United States, and, in later years, in almost every part of the world outside the communist bloc. Previously, Sweden's exporting industries had relied upon wholesale dealers who built up trade connections in foreign countries.

Today, S.K.F. stands for a highly specialized branch of the engineering industry, but one which places Sweden after the U.S.A. and the Soviet Union in the world production of ball and roller bearings. Over the years S.K.F. evolved into a giant corporation employing nearly 50,000 people in its Swedish nexus and world-wide subsidiaries. The process of its growth is marked by the acquisition of iron mines and steelworks at home and the purchase abroad of rivals in the manufacture of ball bearings. For instance, in 1916 S.K.F. acquired the industrial estates of Hofors Bruk that included an iron- and steelworks and iron-ore mines. In 1957, another Swedish steel plant, Hellefors Jernverk, became part of the S.K.F. corporation. Abroad, the activities of S.K.F. have been equally voracious. In a single year the firm bought up seven German ball bearing factories and rationalized production upon one centre. S.K.F. is perhaps the most perfect example of the modern engineering industry in Sweden. Its chief resource rests in the high standards of Sweden's technicians, and the continued prosperity of such a huge concern, set in a country of scarcely more than seven million people, depends upon the maintenance of markets that stretch to almost every country in the world.

SWEDISH SHIPBUILDING AND CAR INDUSTRIES

After the invention and making of equipment for the harnessing of power, engineering is perhaps most concerned with the development of means of communication. As we have seen, the building of the Swedish railways nearly a century ago sparked off the first phase in the growth of the modern engineering industry. A third stage in the evolution of the Swedish engineering industry may be identified with the development of communications in the years since the Second World War. The car industry multiplied its output ten times in a single decade between 1949 and 1959. The post-war boom in shipbuilding has brought Sweden to the fourth place among the shipbuilding nations of the world. Sweden, too, possesses the only aircraft industry among the Scandinavian states.

Shipbuilding is one of the oldest branches of Sweden's engineering industry, where in Göteborg its roots go back to the middle of the nineteenth century. Just before the First World War the Swedish shipyards constructed about 50,000 gross tons per year. At the depths of the economic depression of the inter-war years the new ships that left the slipways in 1932 reached only 44,000 tons. In 1957, a record figure of launchings was achieved with 760,200 tons, a tenth of the world's new ships in that year [Fig. 106].

Behind these dull figures of growing outputs and the fact of high prosperity in the world during the fifties lies a minor revolution in the geography of Swedish shipbuilding. New shipbuilding centres have appeared beside the long-established yards of Göteborg, Malmö, and Hälsingborg. Once more the initiative of an individual lies behind this important development in the economic

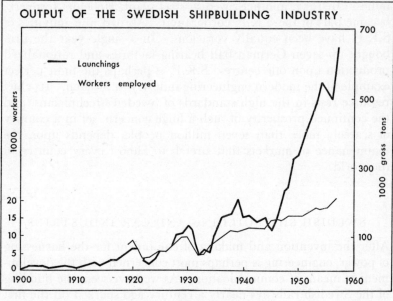

FIG. 106

Of all industries shipbuilding is one of the most sensitive to changes in world trade and prosperity. The slump of the early thirties and the economic dislocations of the Second World War are clearly marked in this graph. The post-war boom that has taken Sweden to fourth place among the world's shipbuilding nations is also a sign of the increasing industrialization of Scandinavia.

geography of Sweden. Gustav Thorden, a shipowner, turned some of his profits to shipbuilding in the post-war years, no doubt encouraged by a state whose laws, until lately, exempted from taxation industrial profits that were used for further development. Thorden built a shipyard at Uddevalla, a port lying northward of Göteborg at the head of Bohuslän's longest fjord. A hundred thousand tons of new shipping left the slipways at Uddevalla in 1955, and since then Thorden has invested in a new shipyard — cut out of the green fields of Lysekil, a few miles down the estuary from Göteborg — with the aim of building giant oil tankers of fifty thousand tons. But the fresh post-war shipbuilding centres have not changed the general location of the industry. Ninety per cent of Swedish ships still comes from the west coast harbours.

Swedish shipyards have undergone a revolution in internal equipment, organization, and methods of construction in the post-war period. Above all, the character of the industry is governed by the demands of the external market. In every year more than half of the Swedish tonnage is sold abroad, and in 1955 a half of the launchings was destined for Norwegian shipowners. As we have already noticed, the reconstructed merchant navies of the post-war period invested in larger ships and specialized designs. Above all the big oil tanker has come to dominate the shipbuilding industry in the fifties. Consequently, slipways have had to be enlarged and redesigned to take immensely larger keels.

Two internal influences also shaped the post-war development of the Swedish shipyards. High labour costs — the O.E.E.C. report of 1955 records the highest wages of Europe in Sweden — forced Swedish shipbuilders to introduce labour-saving economies. Welding, as in other countries, has largely replaced riveting, and the use of prefabricated and standardized sections has reduced the days on the slipway to a minimum. In 1956, a German trade journal, *Wirtschaftsdienst*, published statistics on the average speeds of construction in the shipyards of different European countries.[1] They showed that from the laying down of the keel it would take 808 days to complete a 32,000-ton turbine tanker in a British shipyard, while the same type of ship would require only 212 days to reach its delivery date in Sweden. This short length of construction time in Swedish shipyards is partly a measure of the amount of prefabrication that precedes the laying of the keel and therefore it is not an absolute period for the building of the ship.

During the post-war years the expansion of Swedish shipyards has been hampered by the need to import ships' plate at a time when the products of western Europe's steel mills have been both scarce and expensive. High costs of imported plate have been added to the high price of Sweden's labour. Of late, the rising capacity of Swedish iron- and steelworks, particularly in merchant steel, has opened a much needed source of ships' plate at home. For instance, the new iron and steel plant at Oxelösund, ceremonially opened by the King of Sweden in 1961, produces 300,000 tons per year of medium-heavy plate.

Shipbuilding in Sweden reached a post-war peak in 1957 with the launching of 81 hulls, divided largely between oil tankers, dry cargo ships, and large ore carriers. Although the closing months of 1958 brought the first threat of economic recession, the types of craft on the order-books of the large shipyards at the end of the decade point to the extent of the revolution in Swedish shipbuilding accomplished since the end of the war. In the spring of 1960

413

Uddevalla launched the largest tanker yet built in Europe, while Kockum's of Malmö contracted in the same year to build two 77,000-ton tankers for the American Standard Oil Company.

The making of cars and lorries began late in Sweden with the founding of the Volvo company in 1927, and the industry was of small importance until the late forties [Fig. 107]. Like the rest of

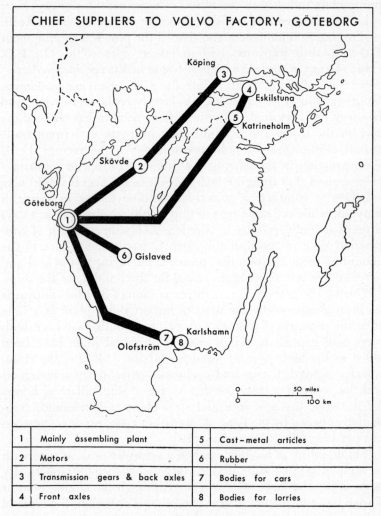

CHIEF SUPPLIERS TO VOLVO FACTORY, GÖTEBORG

1	Mainly assembling plant	5	Cast-metal articles
2	Motors	6	Rubber
3	Transmission gears & back axles	7	Bodies for cars
4	Front axles	8	Bodies for lorries

FIG. 107

Nearly a hundred different firms, scattered over central and southern Sweden, contribute to the production of Volvo cars and lorries.

the engineering industry, the manufacture of cars neglects the supply of raw materials in its siting and seems to concentrate on the supply of labour. Volvo, the biggest of the car firms, has its main assembly plant in Göteborg. Finance probably played a great part in the original siting of the company, because it was floated with the help of capital from the S.K.F. corporation, the manufacturers of ball and roller bearings with their chief factory in Sweden's western port. Its main engine plant lies inland at Skövde, but in the vast expansion of Volvo since the war nearly a hundred firms or subsidiaries in as many different places have been drawn into this large corporation's economic empire. Volvo sought out the small industrial towns of central Sweden for factories manufacturing components, because of their better labour supply and lower wages. For instance, it owns a body-building factory at Karlshamn on the coast of south-eastern Sweden in the buildings of a former sugar beet plant.

The rapid rise of the car industry in Sweden during the past decade and a half is partly explained by a widening domestic market, associated with two decades of full employment and the highest standard of living in Europe. Nevertheless, the car industry, like most branches of engineering in Sweden, could not survive at its present levels of production without a big export trade. Half the output of the industry was exported in 1959. Volvo and Saab cars found a market in the U.S.A., while buses and lorries from the same firms sold widely in Norway, Denmark, Finland, and the Benelux countries.

The Swedish engineering industry has enjoyed a long period of expansion and prosperity since 1945 — a period not to be matched at any earlier time in its history. Today, at the beginning of the sixties, the Swedish engineering shops contribute some of the chief items to the nation's export trade. In this post-war period there has been a trend away from the direct export of the products of Sweden's steel mills towards their indirect export as the more elaborate and more valuable commodities of the engineering industry. In this field of commerce Sweden is poorly placed by nature and often in open competition with the engineering industries of northern Italy, western Germany, Belgium, and the British Isles. It is hard to predict what effects would be felt in this complex and varied industry through a worsening of international trade. Already the merest ripple in the calm prosperity of the late fifties has disturbed the shipbuilding industry, the most vulnerable sector of the engineering trades. A severe contraction of international commerce might throw the Swedish engineering industry into great difficulties. The home market and the nature of its main products are insufficient to support it through a time of hardship. Sweden would be forced to turn to the surer resources of her northern environment, the timber and iron ores of Norrland. At present, however, she hopes for widening trade agreements and the lowering of customs' barriers through the 'Seven' and their possible alliance with the Common Market. With the continuance of the prosperity of the fifties and the prospect of a quasi-free-trade area in western and central Europe, Sweden could look to a further expansion of the engineering trades with their high capacities in the earning of foreign currency.

ENGINEERING IN DENMARK, NORWAY, AND FINLAND

In the rest of northern Europe the engineering industries appeared at a later date than in Sweden and without the support of a long-established iron and steel industry. Today, at the beginning of the sixties, engineering has come to occupy an important place in the economies of all the other Scandinavian states. Machinery forms the biggest item in the industrial exports of Denmark, and in the late fifties it was equal in value to the export of bacon. Finland, like Denmark, lacks the raw materials of the engineering industry; nevertheless, the construction of machinery for pulp and paper mills, the building of ships and the manufacture of cables and electrical equipment have expanded more rapidly than any other sector of the economy under the pressure of the Russian demand for reparations. Today, goods from the Finnish foundries and engineering shops form a sixth of the nation's exports. Norway's engineering industry is one of the weakest among the Scandinavian states, though during the boom period since the Second World War it has grown considerably and the most notable expansion has been in shipbuilding. During the inter-war years the annual tonnage launched from Norwegian shipyards averaged 50,000 gross registered tons, a figure that has been raised at the beginning of the sixties to more than a quarter of a million tons. In other sectors, too, the engineering industry of Norway has grown, particularly in the manufacture of water turbines and the gear for hydro-electric stations, machines for the fish-canning industry, and the varied goods of domestic electrical equipment. Apart from a few highly specialized lines, the Norwegian engineering industry turns largely towards a restricted internal market, and in this fact one discovers an important contrast with Denmark.

The engineering industries of Denmark, Norway, and Finland reveal a number of common factors in their location and origin. In each country foundries, metalworking shops, and the factories of the electrical industry belong to the capital cities and the chief centres of population. Helsinki and Turku, the semicircle of industrial suburbs around Copenhagen, and the manufacturing quarters of Oslo almost summarize the geography of engineering in these Scandinavian countries.

In each of these Scandinavian states engineering sprang from the requirements of some long-established industry. For instance, engineering in Denmark began about seventy years ago with the demands of the countryside for agricultural machinery. By the end of the nineteenth century the spread of the communal dairy in Denmark had created a flourishing and inventive engineering industry that produced milk centrifuges, pasteurization plant, and bottling machinery. In Norway, where farming plays a minor rôle in the economy, it is difficult to link the origins of the engineering industry with the countryside. There the shipyards set the pace for the expansion of engineering early in this century, and its growth in the past two decades has been governed by the development of her vast hydro-electric resources. On the other hand, engineering in Finland is centred upon the timber industries. Machinery for pulp and paper mills and the tools of forestry form one of the biggest items in the output of Finland's engineering shops. The mechanization of agriculture that brought the first stimulus to engineering in Denmark is only now beginning to affect the machine industry in Finland.

The Rise of Engineering in Denmark

Today, industry is as important in Denmark as agriculture. The new ring of industrial suburbs to the west of Copenhagen that has grown from a population of 20,000 to more than 100,000 in the past thirty years represents as valuable a part of the national economy as the golden acres of arable and the lush pastures of western Zealand. Nearly half of Denmark's exports in 1958 were taken up by industrial goods, and among these the products of the engineering industry formed the greater part. In the same year, half of the total value of the output of the engineering industry was sold abroad, a fact that underlines the limited scope of the domestic market. This industry depends upon foreign sales and its rapid growth in the fifties reflects a period of high prosperity in international trade.

It is not easy to pick out the varied parts of the Danish engineering industry. An examination of the export statistics for the late fifties shows that cement-making machinery held first place among engineering goods, an illustration of the economic rule that the engineering industry reflects the character of the primary industries of the country. The Danes specialize not only in the machinery for the manufacture of concrete pipes, but in the export of whole cement works. For instance, in 1958 cement factories were exported from Denmark for assembly in Argentine.

A second place in the list of Danish engineering goods is taken by agricultural and food-processing machinery. The equipment for slaughterhouses and dairies emerges from an agricultural economy that centres on pigs and cattle, bacon and butter. Danish farm machinery is adjusted to the needs of the small and medium-sized holding. For instance, they have developed a line of small tractors. Again, the preservation of food has brought the refrigerator industry to the front in Denmark. Two large firms at Aarhus and Copenhagen manufacture refrigerators for the domestic and wholesale food markets as well as specializing in cold storage equipment for ships and refrigerator-trucks for the railways. This branch of engineering reveals a fresh trend for Denmark, the development of ancillaries in foreign countries. The firm of Sabroe, making refrigerators at Aarhus, recently opened a subsidiary factory at Flensburg, a few miles across the Jutland frontier in western Germany. The chief purpose of this expansion is to obtain a foothold inside the wider trading area of western Europe's Common Market.

A third branch of Danish engineering has evolved around the diesel engine. The Danes pioneered this branch of motive power with the building of the first ocean-going diesel ship before the First World War. Today they manufacture diesel engines for all kinds of motor ships and fishing vessels, as well as diesel power units for factories and large thermo-electric stations. Danish inventiveness in this branch of engineering contributes much to the strength of the nation's shipbuilding industry.

Electrical engineering developed late in Denmark, reflecting the absence of hydro-electric power in the country. Today it is located chiefly in the capital city and seeks markets in the highly industrialized countries of western Europe against severe competition. High-quality transmission cables are an important product of the electrical industry. This partly results from Denmark's need for submarine cable to extend the grid to her many islands.

Among the miscellaneous products of Danish engineering, ships form the largest items. Shipbuilding yards cluster along the shore of the Sound at Copenhagen and Helsingör. Odense also is important for shipbuilding and there are construction yards at Aalborg on Jutland. This industry arose to supply the needs of the Danish merchant fleet. The link with the merchant navy becomes apparent when one notices that much of the capital for the foundation of Danish shipyards has come from her shipowners.

Since the Second World War many of the technical changes and developments that we noted in the discussion of shipbuilding in Sweden have affected the Danish industry. Prefabricated sections are widely used, and the Copenhagen shipyards have adopted the method of building in docks that are flooded on the completion of the hull so that the shell of the ship may be towed away to the fitting-out berths. Just as new shipyards appeared in western Sweden during the fifties to compete for the market in super-tankers, so two construction docks have been cut out of the muds of a flat well-farmed peninsula north of Odense. Each dock is a thousand feet long and is able to take tankers of 100,000 tons dead-weight. Close by, a new settlement has grown to house the workers of this new Lindø shipyard.

Even more than in Sweden, the Danish shipbuilding industry depends upon the import of its raw materials. Steel for heavy plates and sections must be purchased abroad, though in the post-war period the steelworks at Frederiksværk has been able to supply a quantity of rolled steel products.

Shipbuilding is one of the branches of the engineering industry most sensitive to the fluctuations of international trade. The yards of all the world's great shipbuilding nations, Japan, the U.S.A., Great Britain, and Western Germany, have responded to the demand for new ships in the fifties. Today, it is believed that the world's shipyards could replace all the ships on her seas and oceans at the present rate of construction within ten years. The turnover of such costly capital goods is inevitably slow and it seems unlikely that the demand for fresh ships will continue into the sixties at the high level of the previous decade. Small nations such as Denmark are likely to be hurt more than the bigger west European ship-builders by a slackening of demand. Already the slight recession of 1958 has made itself felt in the Danish shipyards, so much so that one Danish economist has suggested that the plant and labour of some shipbuilding firms might have to be turned towards large steel constructional jobs on land.

Engineering lies at the heart of the industrial revolution and is sensitive to the most subtle changes in the field of technology. New branches of the industry have appeared in Denmark since the end of the war, including industrial pumps and water supply plant. Ten years ago only 9 per cent of Denmark's dairies used oil heating equipment; by 1959 over 90 per cent were fitted with plant manu-factured in Denmark for the use of this fuel. The growth of electric power worked a major change in the engineering industry of Sweden; the post-war development of oil as a fuel is working a minor revolution in the structure of the engineering industry in Denmark.

Shipbuilding and the Growth of Engineering in Norway

Shipbuilding is at the crux of the engineering trades in Norway [Fig. 108]. As an industry it endured greater hardships than its neighbours in either Sweden or Denmark, but like the Swedish and Danish industries it has enjoyed a period of expansion in the prosperous post-war years. The output of the inter-war years averaged 50,000 gross registered tons; in 1957 it climbed to almost 200,000 gross registered tons. Today there are fifty ship-yards in Norway, but even so they are able to build only a fifth of the Norwegian merchant navy's yearly requirements of new vessels. Shipbuilding centres mainly around the shores of Oslo fjord, particularly in the capital city and at Fredrikstad. Elsewhere it occurs at Stavanger, Bergen, and Trondheim.

The stimulus to shipbuilding has always been present in Nor-way, the possessor of one of the world's biggest merchant fleets. The history of Norwegian shipbuilding uncovers difficulties in the supply of raw materials and even severer problems in the field of labour relations and the acquisition of capital for further growth.

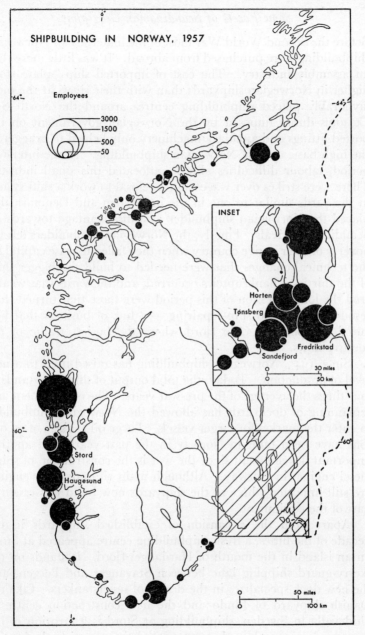

SHIPBUILDING IN NORWAY, 1957

Employees

3000
1500
500
50

INSET

Horten
Tønsberg
Fredrikstad
Sandefjord

30 miles
50 km

Stord
Haugesund

50 miles
100 km

FIG. 108

Norway has fifty shipyards among which the most important are located at Oslo, Fredrikstad, and other ports of Oslo fjord. Secondary shipbuilding centres include Bergen, Stavanger, and Trondheim. A number of minor yards serve the fishing industry of Sunnmøre and Nordmøre. Stord has developed as a shipbuilding centre since the Second World War and specializes in oil tankers.

Before the Second World War most of the materials for Norwegian shipbuilding were purchased from abroad. It was little more than an assembly industry. The cost of imported ships' plate stood higher in Norwegian shipyards than with their rivals at the more favourably placed shipbuilding centres around the North Sea. Customs duties imposed by the Norwegian government on imported fittings and auxiliary machinery only helped to exaggerate the high basic costs of Norwegian shipbuilding. In the inter-war period, labour difficulties almost suffocated this small industry. There were strikes over wages and a refusal to work a shift system in the yards similar to one in use in Sweden and Denmark that placed the Norwegian shipbuilder at a disadvantage towards his Scandinavian rivals. Finally, the Norwegian shipbuilders felt the poverty of their native country when they failed to raise capital for the technical changes that were needed to build the bigger ships of the thirties. Bankruptcies occurred, and the yards that weathered the long recession of this period were those that turned their resources chiefly to ship-repairing — a line of business that favoured the ports of Oslo fjord where the busiest traffic of the country flows.

Since 1945, Norwegian shipbuilding has raised itself to a new level of production. Today, the total output of shipping stands at four times the average of the pre-war years. The enlargement and replanning of dockyards has allowed the Norwegian shipbuilder to enter the market for larger vessels. Large oil tankers of 50,000 tons have been built in Norway in the past years, and another important development since the war is the construction of ships' diesel engines in Norway. Although main and auxiliary engines are still imported, three of the shipyards now build this essential part of the equipment.

Apart from the expansion of established shipyards in the decade of the fifties, a fresh shipbuilding centre appeared at Stord on an island in the mouth of Hardanger fjord. It stands on the skerry-guard shipping lane between Stavanger and Bergen, and the new dock specializes in the design of super-tankers. Like the Danish shipyard of Lindø and the new construction centre at Uddevalla in Sweden, shipbuilding at Stord is a creation of the post-war boom, a place that came into being to satisfy the hunger of a rapidly expanding oil trade for ever larger tankers. It will be interesting to see whether these latest additions to the shipbuilding capacity of the Scandinavian countries manage to survive a decline in the long trade boom that has characterized this industry since the war, a decline that might be foreshadowed in the slight economic recession of 1958.

Labour troubles afflicted the Norwegian shipyards in the thirties; the post-war boom of the fifties brought employment problems of quite a different kind. Full employment in Norway created a scarcity of labour that affected some industries more than others, especially forestry, foundry work, and shipbuilding. In particular, mechanics, carpenters, and electricians were drained away from the shipyards to jobs in the rapidly growing merchant navy. Norwegian shipbuilding, although it has reached the highest outputs in its history, has started the production of engines and many accessories that were formerly imported, and solved the problems of building modern large vessels, is far less firmly developed than its neighbour industries in Sweden and Denmark. This major branch of Norwegian engineering, perhaps the most sensitive to fluctuations in world trade, still remains to be tested in a period of economic depression.

The rest of the engineering industry in Norway reflects the demands of the home market. It produces heavy capital goods in the form of water turbines for hydro-electric stations, electric smelting furnaces for the manufacture of high-grade steel alloys and aluminium, machinery for herring oil and meal factories, as well as rotating blubber boilers for giant whaling ships. The tools and machinery of the forest industries — axes, saws, pulp machinery, and cardboard-making plant — are also produced in Norway along with fishhooks and net-knitting machinery. Apart from a handful of large firms in the Oslo area, this industry is composed of many small workshops, most of them with less than ten employees. Engineering is still in Norway an industry of sub-contractors. Its development in this century has been hampered by the small and scattered population of the country. The competition of imported engineering goods has always been severe and capital has been lacking for the growth of the industry. Even during the period of post-war industrial expansion, when engineering made some notable advances, a large part of Norway's slender resources for capital investment was turned to the building of hydro-electric stations, the establishment of a wider high-tension grid, the rehabilitation of the devastated lands in the far north, and the costly re-equipment of the merchant fleet.

The secondary industries, among which engineering is the

chief, play a minor rôle in the Norwegian economy. Nevertheless, a Norwegian writer, surveying the engineering industry in the early fifties, could say, 'Norway is well on the way to having the "know-how" to produce the major part of the machines, instruments, equipment and tools needed by the country'.[2] A few branches of engineering in Norway have achieved maturity in the sense that they are able to supply the needs of the home market and begin to seek wider sales abroad. This is especially true of electrical engineering. Early in the fifties Norway was able for the first time to supply her own needs in transformers. Again, by 1951 the domestic market for radio receivers was saturated and the industry was trying to develop a market abroad.

Engineering in Finland

Among Finland's industries the engineering trades have grown most rapidly in the years since the Second World War [Fig. 109]. The influence of a favourable world economic climate that largely explains the expansion of engineering in the rest of Scandinavia is masked by the effect of specific political actions in Finland. The two wars with Russia in the early forties stimulated the armaments industry. Since 1944, a heavy reparations payment to the Soviet Union that reckoned 72 per cent of the bill in the products of the engineering industry led to a further expansion of these trades. Finland's problem in the fifties has been the maintenance of a market for the products of her foundries, wire and cable works, shipyards, and machine shops. The marketing problems of Finland's engineering trades bear some resemblance to those of Norway. Its chief market lies in the home country, and a high level of manufacturing costs, partly a result of the need to import a wide range of semi-manufactured materials and accessories, almost excludes Finland from competition on the world's open markets.

Through the decade of the fifties the flow of engineering products towards the Soviet Union has been continued by two five-year trade agreements. Even so, the labour force of the engineering industry diminished by about a quarter between 1952 and 1957. Today, the metalworking industries employ about the same number of people as the timber-processing industries of Finland, and the problem that faces the country in the early sixties largely concerns the distribution of her manpower between

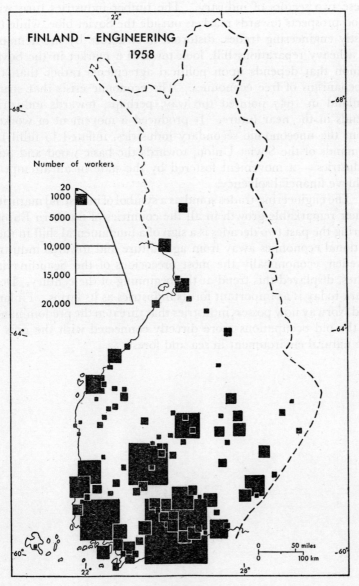

FIG. 109

This map is based on the number of workers in the chief branches of the engineering trades — metal manufacture, machinery for pulp and paper mills, railway equipment, electrical goods, and shipbuilding. Helsinki, Turku, and Tampere are outstanding as centres of the engineering industry.

these two sectors of industry. The timber industries turn with good prospects towards markets outside the Soviet bloc, while the costly engineering trades, distorted in structure by the demands of a heavy reparations bill, look towards a market in the Soviet Union that depends upon political agreements rather than the mechanisms of free economies. The economic crisis that struck Finland in 1957 pointed the way, perhaps, towards industrial trends in the near future. It produced a movement of workers from the uneconomic secondary industries, inflated to fulfil the demands of the Soviet Union, towards the basic wood and pulp industries — a movement fostered by the state in an attempt to achieve financial solvency.

The engineering trades stand as a symbol of industrial maturity. Their remarkable growth in all the countries of northern Europe during the past two decades is a sign of a fundamental shift in their national economies away from agriculture and towards industry. Sweden, economically the most precocious of the Scandinavian states, displayed this trend at the beginning of the century. Denmark today is as important for its industries as its farms. Finland and Norway now possess industries that threaten the predominance of the old occupations more directly connected with the gifts of the natural environment in sea and forest.

CHAPTER 15

The Electro-Chemical and Electro-Metallurgical Industries

THE chemical and metal-refining industries that consume vast quantities of electricity belong especially to highland Norway with its deep glaciated troughs, heavy rainfall, and rivers whose sources lie in glaciers and snowfields. The first factory for the manufacture of calcium carbide was founded in 1899. Today, the electro-chemical and electro-metallurgical industries, producing fertilizers, magnesium, zinc, aluminium, and important raw materials for the plastics trade, form one of Norway's major industries. They absorb almost half of the country's output of electricity and account for an export trade that surpassed the value of pulp and paper exports in the years of the late fifties. These giant industries, sparing in their use of labour and extravagant in their demands for power and capital equipment, took root only in Norway [Fig. 110]. Sweden and Finland have nothing to compare with this feature of Norway's economic life. In Sweden, the ever expanding output of electricity has been quickly absorbed by the towns and industries of her central lowland. The growth of hydro-electric power proceeded far more slowly in Finland until the massive power station programme began to take shape in the years after the Second World War. There electricity was harnessed mainly to sawmills and paper and pulp factories.

Among the Scandinavian states, Norway has the easiest access to the raw materials of the chemical and electro-metallurgical industries. Calcium carbide requires imported coal and coke that is fused with lime in an electric furnace. The huge aluminium plant at Årdal in a gloomy valley at the head of Sogne fjord brings its alumina from Canada, whilst the Norsk Aluminium Company's plant, Høyanger, uses bauxite from its mines in southern France. Again, the electrolytic zinc works at Eitrheim, one of the largest in Europe, imports concentrated ores from Spain, Sweden, Belgium, Luxembourg, and France. Western Norway's fjords offer sea transport for bulky raw materials all the year round to sites with a superfluity of electric energy. Only in the past two decades have similar industries made an appearance in the economic landscapes of Finland and Sweden. The Second World War encouraged the Swedes to broaden the base of their chemical industries with fertilizers and calcium carbide. In Finland this industry is even younger, dating from the early fifties when the state founded a nitrogenous fertilizer plant at Oulu. Norway's strong position in this sector of industry is perhaps illustrated by the fact that she still finds a large market for nitrogenous fertilizers in the countries of northern Europe, two-thirds of her annual export reaching Denmark and Sweden.

THE EVOLUTION OF THE ELECTRO-CHEMICAL INDUSTRIES IN NORWAY

The manufacture of calcium carbide represents the first stage in the growth of the electro-chemical industries in Norway. A small factory opened at Sarpsborg on the Glomma river in 1899. Within a decade, Norway was producing 50,000 tons of calcium carbide a year and a fifth of the world's needs at that time. The carbide plants, founded between 1900 and 1910, reveal the locational pattern of the new electro-chemical industries. With their immense hunger for electricity they chose sites in the undeveloped parts of the country possessing an abundance of cheap water power. The competition for power was too keen in the lower Glomma valley and the Oslo region, so we find that the second carbide plant appears at Meraker, a lonely site to the east of Trondheim and close to the Swedish frontier. Coal and limestone are brought by rail from a company harbour at Murviken on Trondheim fjord, and in this empty countryside the company has constructed its own power grid, fed from five hydro-electric stations.

The largest producer of calcium carbide, A/S Odda Smelteverk, came into existence in 1908 at a site that typifies the electro-chemical industries. Odda stands at the head of one of Norway's gloomiest fjords — the Sørfjord, a narrow trench enclosed by vertical rock walls more than three thousand feet high. Close by, at Tyssedal, a power station was built where the Tysso river plunges to the fjord from the vast wilderness of the Hardangervidda. Over the past half-century Odda has evolved into a complex

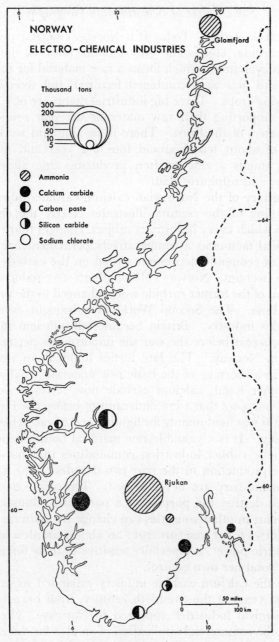

FIG. 110

The chemical industry in Norway is overshadowed by the output of Norsk Hydro, a corporation that was founded in 1905 to exploit the water-power resources of the Telemark plateau. Since the Second World War, Norsk Hydro has started the production of liquid ammonia at Glomfjord in Arctic Norway.

of chemical industries. Today it is Norway's biggest producer of
calcium carbide, and is the only manufacturer in the country
of calcium cyanamide which forms a raw material for the plastics
industry and acts as a combined fertilizer and weed-killer for
slow-growing crops. Three big industrial plants are now gathered
at Odda, importing their raw materials the year round by the
ice-free waters of the fjord. There is an alumium works with a
capacity of about ten thousand tons per year and nearby, at
Eitrheim, stands a zinc smelter, producing zinc alloys, super-
phosphate, and sulphuric acid.

The history of the Norwegian calcium carbide industry since
the beginning of the century illustrates clearly the changes of
fortune to which every industry is subject, changes that reveal the
geographical factors as a comparatively permanent background.
A period of economic depression settled on the carbide industry
in the late twenties. Norway's eleven plants were reduced to four,
and several of the former carbide works changed to the production
of ferro-alloys. The Second World War brought even greater
trials to this industry. Britain became self-sufficient in calcium
carbide, whereas before the war she imported 90 per cent of her
needs from Norway. The late forties imposed an insuperable
difficulty in a shortage of the basic raw materials, coal and coke.
On the other hand, calcium carbide now serves a number of
industrial purposes that were undreamt-of before the First World
War when it was used mainly for lighting and oxyacetylene cutting
and welding. It is a valuable raw material both for the plastics
and synthetic rubber industries, commodities that have entered
large-scale production in the past two decades. The forces that
govern an industry are never at rest. Technical changes may
increase or destroy the purpose of a particular commodity, and
developments in other countries can change the patterns of world
trade. Norway, her one sure asset an almost limitless amount of
hydro-electric power, is especially sensitive to these forces that lie
largely beyond her own control.

While the calcium carbide industry expanded its production
in the first years of the twentieth century, fresh branches of the
electro-chemical industries appeared in Norway. The chief of
these was the commercial application of an idea for the extraction
of nitrogen from the atmosphere, an idea conceived by an academic
physicist, Professor Kristian Birkeland, and an industrial engineer,
Samuel Eyde. Between them they developed the electric-arc

furnace, which combined the nitrogen and oxygen of the atmosphere into a nitrogen oxide. This substance opened the way to the manufacture of fertilizers. Its solution in water forms nitric acid, and this liquid, when neutralized with limestone, produces the valuable fertilizer, calcium nitrate. The commercial exploitation of the Birkeland-Eyde technique, voracious in its consumption of electricity, led to the foundation of Norsk Hydro — Norway's largest industrial concern.

Norsk Hydro was founded in 1905 and its factory at Notodden was the first in the world for the manufacture of synthetic fertilizers. The year of its foundation foreshadowed not only revolutionary developments in the industrial economy of the country, but this was also the beginning of Norway's new life of political independence. The founding of Norsk Hydro and the manufacture of nitrogen fertilizers ensured that the electro-chemical industry would be one of the main branches of Norway's economy. Norsk Hydro established its first plant at Notodden, an isolated inland site of Telemark province in south-eastern Norway. After only a short time, the limited power capacity of Notodden and the rising market for synthetic nitrogen fertilizers turned Norsk Hydro to search for a second industrial site more prolific in electric energy. They chose a gloomy, uninhabited valley, cut deeply into the eastern flank of the Hardanger plateau — a place where a spectacular waterfall, the Rjukanfoss, plunged hundreds of feet into this ice-carved trough.

Rjukan began to manufacture nitrate of lime by the Birkeland-Eyde process and a new town was brought into existence. Today it has a population of six thousand and serves the needs of only one industry. Rjukan is typical of several settlements brought into being by the electro-chemical and electro-metallurgical industries since the beginning of this century. They lie on the floors of deep, sunless valleys or scattered across some tiny alluvial flat at the head of a fjord, overpowered by the enclosing plateau. Odda, Høyanger, the aluminium-smelting settlement on Sogne fjord, or Mo i Rana, the new iron and steel town in Nordland — all display variations on this theme. The cloudy climate of the western fjords only emphasizes the desolate quality of these new industrial settlements whose insistence upon a surfeit of electric power leads to a rejection of so many of the golden rules of twentieth-century town planning. On many days the steep mountain-walls disappear upwards into a formless lid of grey cloud. At a lower level, a thin sheet of smoke spreads from the chimneys of an industrial plant to hang lifeless over the dark, glassy waters of the fjord. These are Norway's only examples of the 'company town'. Their recent origin, without any roots in the past, is apparent in the population structure. Most of these places have attracted immigrants from several of Norway's provinces. These colonies of factory workers settled in districts whose customs and way of life had shown little change for centuries. Zimmerman, the French geographer, noted this contrast between two strongly different economies and societies, when he wrote his description of Notodden and Rjukan. 'Two towns have arisen amid the forests and empty pastures. One does not often see expressed so strongly the differences between an unstable, rootless industrial community — steeped in socialist ideas — and the peasant groups that surround them, still faithful to their archaic techniques and customs.' [1]

Technical developments in the production of synthetic nitrates brought about a revolution in the organization of Norsk Hydro in 1928. The Birkeland-Eyde process that had given Norway a valuable lead in the electro-chemical industries was superseded by the more economical Haber-Bosch technique. The new process demanded extensive capital investment and a complete replanning of the industrial sites at Rjukan and Notodden. The chief economic reward was a vast saving of electricity, because there was only a quarter of the former consumption of power. The Haber-Bosch process is based on the manufacture of synthetic ammonia, whose raw materials — oxygen, hydrogen, and nitrogen — are extracted from water and air by electrolytic processes. The synthetic ammonia provides the basic material for the production of nitric acid and the manufacture of fertilizers.

The adoption of the Haber-Bosch technique in 1928 held out the prospect of a great increase in the output of fertilizers. By this time valuable improvements had appeared in the high voltage transmission of electricity. Norsk Hydro took the opportunity to relocate its fertilizer plant in a more accessible coastal site at Herøya on a level peninsula of Skien fjord. The liquid ammonia from Rjukan and Notodden is taken ninety miles in tank waggons to the Herøya fertilizer plant. This difficult route forms the lifeline of Norsk Hydro's economic empire. From Rjukan the railway line winds down the bleak valley of Vestfjorddal, protected here and there by windbreaks against the powerful gales that have sometimes overturned trains. At the exit of Vestfjorddal the

Måne river empties into the long lake of Tinnsjø, where the trains carrying liquid ammonia are transhipped to ferries for the twenty-five-mile journey to Tinnoset at the foot of the lake. Here a railway leads to Notodden and Herøya.

By the late 1930's the output of Norsk Hydro had tripled when compared with the years before the introduction of the Haber-Bosch technique. The decade of the fifties has witnessed an even greater growth of the synthetic fertilizer industry and an exciting territorial expansion of Norsk Hydro's empire. In 1949, Norsk Hydro decided to expand the material basis of the manufacture of nitrate of lime, the production of synthetic ammonia. A new factory was constructed at Glomfjord in remote northern Norway, a few miles north of the Arctic Circle. Its output of 50,000 tons of liquid ammonia per year is carried by a small tanker fleet on the eight-hundred-mile journey from Nordland to the synthetic fertilizer plant at Herøya in south-eastern Norway.

Today, nitrogenous fertilizers form the chief item in the products of the Norwegian electro-chemical industry, and the vast corporation of Norsk Hydro still stands alone in this sector of the nation's economic life. In 1957, Norsk Hydro produced more than a quarter of a million tons of nitrogen products, two and a half times the output of the late nineteen-thirties. Norsk Hydro owns seven major power stations and consumes a fifth of Norway's output of electricity in its industrial plants. Today the name of Norsk Hydro stands for a complex of chemical products. Besides Norwegian nitrate of lime, which still dominates the scene, Norsk Hydro produces sodium nitrate, extracting the sodium from sea water. Again one of the basic materials of the plastics industry, produced from a reaction of carbon dioxide and ammonia at high temperatures and under high pressures, increases in importance. At Herøya, during the Second World War, the Germans built a plant for the extraction of magnesium from sea water. This is now the property of Norsk Hydro and the magnesium oxide is used for the manufacture of fire-brick, insulating materials, and the production of magnesium metal by a process of fusion electrolysis. Heavy water for atomic reactors and argon, a gas used in welding, are among the forty subsidiary products of Norsk Hydro's immense output of fertilizers.

THE ELECTRO-METALLURGICAL INDUSTRIES
IN NORWAY

Norway's electro-metallurgical industries are concerned with the refining of metallic ores in electric furnaces or the extraction of metals by electrolytic processes. Iron and steel, copper, nickel, and zinc all belong to this group of industries, but as the production of nitrogen fertilizers overshadows the electro-chemical industries so the manufacture of aluminium dominates the metal refineries of Norway [Fig. 111].

The chief stages in the economic development of the Norwegian aluminium industry show some resemblance to the growth of the electro-chemical industry. In 1906, only a year after the foundation of Norsk Hydro, the British Aluminium Company obtained a concession for the development of hydro-electric power at Stangfjorden. Inside two years they were making the first aluminium in Norway, using imported aluminium oxide.

During the period between the First and Second World Wars the output of aluminium rose to 30,000 tons per year and plants had become established at Tyssedal in Hardanger fjord, using the same source of hydro-electric power as the carbide works at Odda, and on the south-east coast near Arendal. The greatest aluminium factory of this period of expanding production was opened at Høyanger by the Norsk Aluminium Company in 1915, on the tiny, mountain-enshadowed delta of one of the northern arms of Sogne fjord.

With the end of the Second World War the Norwegian aluminium industry entered the third phase of its history. By 1955, her aluminium plants produced five times the output of 1939, and it is planned that this figure of 100,000 tons should be doubled in the early sixties. This third period of development is marked by the construction of two new plants with an immense output and owned by the Norwegian state. The first stands at Årdal in a narrow, sunless valley a few miles from the head of Sogne fjord and two hundred miles from the open sea. It was planned and built by the Germans during their wartime occupation of Norway. The power station's intake, cut through solid rock, falls three thousand feet to the turbines. Årdal taps the highest fall in Norway. An additional aluminium plant is under construction at Årdal, and it is expected that this site will achieve an output of

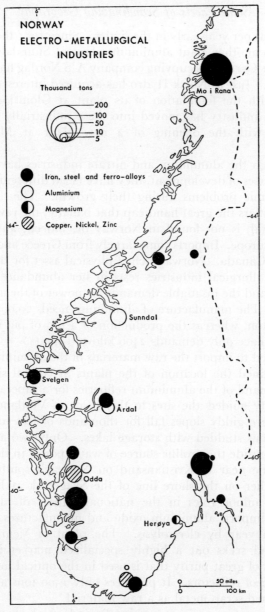

FIG. III

Three forces are at work in the location of Norway's electro-metallurgical industries. With only one exception the sites are close to the sea to allow the import of raw materials — bauxite, nickel matte, zinc ores. The abundant power resources of the western fjords are reflected by the numerous plants of this region. The overwhelming importance of Mo i Rana reveals the part played by state planning in an attempt to enrich the economy of Arctic Norway.

100,000 tons per year early in the sixties. Since 1951 the state has invested in another giant aluminium plant at Sunndalsøra, on a site that the German occupying company A/S Nordag had planned to develop. Just as Norsk Hydro has acquired interests in Arctic Norway with the foundation of its plant at Glomfjord, so the aluminium industry has moved into these industrially immature territories with the opening of a new plant at Mosjøen in 1958.

Although the aluminium and nitrate industries have pursued similar courses of development, they have faced different technical and economic problems during their growth. The aluminium industry suffers the great handicap that bauxite, the raw material of this metal, is not found in Norway or, indeed, anywhere in northern Europe. Imports come largely from Greece and southern France or Canada. Norway's chief physical asset for this branch of the metallurgical industries rests in her abundance of cheap electricity and the insatiable demands for power of the aluminium processes. The manufacture of aluminium needs 20,000 kilowatt hours per ton, whereas the production of a ton of pig iron in an electric furnace only demands 2400 kilowatt hours.

The need to import the raw materials of the aluminium industry determined the location of the plants at coastal sites. The second demand of the aluminium refineries for a superabundance of electricity guided the sites to the heads of Vestlandet's deep fjords, where giddy slopes fall for thousands of feet to sea level from plateaus studded with storage lakes. Only two aluminium plants lie outside the prolific source of water power in the western fjords — one near to Kristiansand on Norway's southern coast and the other on the shore line of the Skagerrak at Eydehavn. Both play minor rôles in the national output of aluminium. Eydehavn imports aluminium oxide and manufactures 5000 tons of metal a year by electrolysis. The plant at Vennesla near Kristiansand seeks out a highly specialized market in refined aluminium of great purity that is used in the optical industry for the making of reflectors. It produces only 1500 tons a year and uses imported scrap metal as a raw material.

There are two main stages in the industrial processes that extract the light metal, aluminium, from bauxite. First, aluminium oxide must be extracted from the bauxite clays. Then the alumina or aluminium oxide is subjected to electrolysis at temperatures of a 1000 degrees centigrade to yield the molten metal that is cast into ingots, slabs, and bars after further refining. Norwegian engineers and technicians have deeply influenced the processes of aluminium manufacture since the industry was founded half a century ago. The Pedersen process established itself in the early twenties, using an electric furnace for the fusion of bauxite with coke and limestone in the manufacture of alumina. Industrially the Pedersen technique was adopted at Høyanger in 1928. It is interesting that this is now the only Norwegian aluminium plant that imports bauxite for the production of alumina. The rest of the industry depends on imported aluminium oxide, and it is the second stage in the manufacture of the metal, a process hungry for electricity, for which Norway is so well adapted. Again in this field, the Norwegians made an important technical contribution at the end of the First World War with the development of the Søderberg electrode, a device that has become worldwide in the smelting of aluminium.

Nature's gift to Norway of the richest water power resources in Europe enabled her to develop the aluminium industry in the early years of this century at a time when the problems of the transmission of electricity over long distances had not been solved. Her metal-extracting plants arose at lonely sites in the western fjords, consuming the whole output of their power stations. By the early twenties Norway accounted for 12 per cent of the world output of aluminium. Just as her proud position in the manufacture of nitrogenous fertilizers was challenged in the thirties, so her pre-eminence in the production of aluminium found its rivals from other countries. Germany, Japan, and the states of Alpine Europe became important producers of the metal during the thirties. The Second World War and the increasing use of aluminium in the aircraft industry, for railway equipment and domestic purposes, induced a rapid expansion in the United States and Canada. Today Norway is no longer a pioneer in this particular branch of metallurgy, sought out by foreign capitalists and speculators because of the water power that runs to waste. Instead she is able to find an export market for a metal whose uses have been vastly multiplied, an expansion that is marked in Norway by an annual output in 1960 six times that of the late nineteen-thirties.

Although the aluminium industry overshadows all the other branches of electro-metallurgy in Norway, electrolytic processes and electric smelting techniques are used in the production of

437

copper, nickel, zinc, and a wide variety of high-quality ferro-alloys. The processes and equipment for the manufacture of ferro-alloys are closely related to the techniques of calcium carbide manufacture, so much so that in the period of depression after the First World War several Norwegian calcium carbide plants transformed themselves into producers of iron alloys. The chief raw materials of the industry, apart from scrap iron, are manganese, chrome, and quartz. Quartz, found in Norway, is used to make the various grades of ferro-silicon. The ores of chrome and manganese, used in the alloys of ferro-chrome and ferro-manganese, are imported from West and South Africa, the U.S.S.R., Southern Rhodesia, Turkey, India, and Pakistan. The consumption of ferro-alloys in Norway is negligible and almost the whole output enters the export market. Norway maintains its position as a producer of these important ingredients of high-quality steel-making largely because of its cheap and prolific electricity supplies. The largest ferro-alloy plant lies at the head of Saudafjord, a narrow arm of Bokn fjord in south-western Norway. Here a battery of electric furnaces specializes in the making of all kinds of manganese alloys, as well as alloys of calcium, zirconium, chromium, and niobium. Another plant close to Kristiansand concentrates on ferrosilicon, but it is interesting to note that during the spring and early summer, the driest part of the year in Scandinavia, shortages of hydro-electric power restrict the factory's output. Other ferro-alloy plants are located at Notodden, Porsgrunn, and Larvik in south-eastern Norway, as well as at Ålvik on Hardanger fjord.

Nickel and copper are closely related in the electro-metallurgical industries of Norway. The main producing centre stands close to Kristiansand in the south of the country [Plate 2]. There the history of the Falconbridge Nikkelverk A/S illustrates some of the obstacles to industrial growth in Norway. A nickel refinery started work at this coastal site in 1910, processing ores from local mines. Today, nickel is no longer mined in Norway, and the Kristiansand refinery was absorbed by a Canadian company, Falconbridge Nickel Mines, in 1929. The plant now refines nickel matte imported from Canada, using electrolytic processes for the extraction of copper and nickel. The presence of cheap electricity and a coastal site for the easy import of raw materials have exerted a powerful influence in maintaining this metallurgical plant. The only other important copper plant occupies a hostile site at

Sulitjelma, a few miles beyond the Arctic Circle in northern Norway. Here, an annual output of between 3000 and 5000 tons of copper is produced from an electric furnace.

The most important of Norway's metal refineries, after the giant aluminium plants, produces zinc at Eitrheim on a narrow branch of Hardanger fjord. Once again the history of this industry illustrates Norway's poverty in raw materials and the handicap of a shortage of capital for the floating of large companies. The Norske Zinkkompani A/S began in 1923 as a subsidiary of the Compagnie Royale Asturienne des Mines, a Belgian zinc-mining and manufacturing corporation. In 1929 this company began to develop the site at Eitrheim for the production of zinc by an electrolytic process, using hydro-electric power from the station of Tyssefaldene. Today, with an output of nearly 50,000 tons of zinc a year, it is one of the most modern metallurgical plants in Europe. Norway possesses no zinc ores and all the raw material is imported by sea in a concentrated form. The abiding Norwegian contribution, as in all branches of the metallurgical industries, is an abundance of electricity and the prospect of unrestricted power supplies for development in the future.

Eitrheim illustrates the link that may be made between metallurgical and chemical industries when they reach a mature stage of development. In 1949, a super-phosphate plant opened at Eitrheim, using the sulphuric acid that is a by-product of the manufacture of zinc. With an output of 80,000 tons per year Eitrheim helps to make up Norway's deficiencies of super-phosphate, and since 1950 she has been able to supply two-thirds of her needs in this valuable fertilizer.

The electro-chemical and metallurgical industries loom large today in Norway's industrial scene. Their commodities find scarcely any outlet in the domestic market, but since the mid-fifties nitrates, aluminium, carbide, ferro-alloys, copper, zinc, and nickel have moved into the first place among Norwegian exports. In 1958, 27 per cent of the value of Norway's exports belonged to this group, while the products of her forests took the second place with 23·1 per cent of the exports.

The rise of this important group of industries based on Norway's greatest natural resource, her water power, has not been without its political and economic difficulties. The greatest problem, particularly at the beginning of the century, centred on the provision of capital for expensive equipment that raised the ideas and techniques of the laboratory to a commercial level. When the Norwegians achieved political independence in 1905, theirs was the poorest of the Scandinavian countries after Finland. There were few industries to generate the capital for further industrial growth. Consequently Norway found that the new electro-chemical industries were financed mainly from abroad. Samuel Eyde had to attract foreign capital to raise his huge industrial complex at Notodden and Rjukan. We have noticed that Norway's first bauxite smelter was erected by the British Aluminium Company, and even in 1939 only one of her half-dozen aluminium plants was really controlled by Norwegians.

Northern Europe has long possessed something of a colonial character in relation to the rest of the continent. In the later Middle Ages, the precious commodities of the north — dried and salted cod, furs, butter, and walrus ivory — reached the markets of central Europe through the Hanseatic League and their great trading outpost at Bergen. Similarly, the electro-chemical plants and ore refineries looked like outposts of the powerful mining corporations of Europe and North America. Norwegians felt that these large industries, financed by foreign capital and often controlled from outside, might threaten her freedom and stability. As a result, between 1910 and 1920 a number of laws were passed to secure to the state the main natural resources of the kingdom — above all her great wealth of water power. Today, the concession laws limit the freedom of a company to develop a hydro-electric site to a period of fifty years. After this time the power station with all its accessories becomes the property of the state.

During the decade of the First World War, Norway passed laws to protect her greatest natural resource from encroachment by these huge alien industries that also menaced the internal balance of a rural society when they established themselves among the peasant communities of the remote western fjords. After the Second World War, the state took a much more active attitude towards the electro-chemical and metallurgical industries. The Norwegian government is no longer content to keep a watchful, passive eye over the development and use of the nation's water power resources, attempting to protect the interests of farmer and fisherman against the revolutionary changes that accompany the installation of hydro-electric plants. Today, the state promotes and owns the equipment of these industries, and it is the giant state-owned aluminium plants at Årdal and Sunndalsøra that contributed so much to the greatly increased importance of the electro-chemical and metallurgical industries in the national economy.

THE EVOLUTION OF THE CHEMICAL INDUSTRY
IN SWEDEN, DENMARK, AND FINLAND

The chemical industry displays a bewildering variety of products and processes and a few of its many variants appear in Sweden, Denmark, and Finland. In each state the structure of this industry reflects the national endowment of raw materials, the internal needs of its economy, and the level of industrial maturity achieved by the nation.

The Swedish chemical industry bears some resemblance to that of Norway [Fig. 112]. It was founded in the last decade of the nineteenth century and was based upon the newly developing sources of hydro-electric power. The manufacture of calcium carbide from imported coke began at this time. Today Sweden produces about as much calcium carbide as Norway (1956 — 73,939 tons) and is able to export a small amount. She also uses synthetic ammonia in the manufacture of nitrogenous fertilizers, but produces less than a half of the requirements of her own farms. Sweden cannot match the achievements of Norsk Hydro in this field, though her output of phosphate fertilizers is greater. Here Sweden is able to supply the demands of the home market, obtaining the raw material for the making of super-phosphates — sulphuric acid — from pyrites mined in the Skellefteå ore field of Norrland. The strongest branch of the electro-chemical industries in Sweden developed from the need of the pulp industry for chlorine and alkali. Today, Sweden's half-dozen chlorine plants are all subsidiaries of pulp mills and produce about 150,000 tons of chlorine per year, using imported salt as the raw material in the electrolysis process. It is this branch of the chemical industry that has shown the most rapid development in Sweden since the Second World War, multiplying its output five times in the space of a decade.

By the 1930's the manufacture of inorganic chemicals and fertilizers was a securely founded industry in Sweden. It lacked the spectacular character of the Norwegian electro-chemical and metallurgical industries, where new towns were created at lonely sites in gloomy western fjords by huge companies backed by foreign capital. In Sweden, the chemical industry developed within the context of the domestic economy, chiefly as a subsidiary of the wood-processing industries. Her geography, lacking the combination of deep, ice-free fjords and Europe's finest water power sites, failed to attract the industrialist who was prepared to erect his plant solely on the asset of unlimited electric energy. Since the beginning of the century, Sweden has found a hungry market for her rising outputs of hydro-electricity in the towns and industries of the midlands and Skåne, in her electrified railway network, and in the pulp and paper mills of the Bothnian coastline. Above all, her power-sites lacked the accessibility of Norway's fjords, open to sea-going ships in every month of the year. Northern Sweden, possessing the greatest reserves of hydro-electric power, lies remote from the Atlantic seaways, and a winter freeze of several weeks paralyses the harbours of the Bothnian coastline. These unalterable facts of geography largely explain the absence of the aluminium industry and a strongly developed nitrogen fertilizer industry from the Swedish economic scene.

The outbreak of the Second World War introduced a fresh stage in the growth of the chemical industry in Sweden. Her political neutrality and isolation within the Baltic Sea deprived Sweden of many chemical products that were previously imported from Germany, the British Isles, and France. In addition, Sweden was forced to turn to the elaborate transforming techniques of the chemical industry to produce substitutes for the commodities that the war and the dislocations of international trade withdrew from her economy. The most notable example is the manufacture of synthetic rubber, an industry that enjoyed a whole decade of growth before it felt the full competition of the reviving international trade in natural rubber from the tropics.

A more important development of the 1940's in Sweden was the growth of the plastics industry. Calcium carbide and calcium cyanamide produce polyvinyl chloride and melamine, two of the raw materials for the making of plastics, while chlorine and acetylene may be combined to give another valuable commodity in this industry, trichlorethylene. During the post-war years, the most valuable branch of the chemical industry has appeared as an off-shoot of the pulp mills. Sulphite alcohol yields three major raw materials with a wide range of commercial uses. From its foundation in the early years of the war, the use of sulphite alcohol

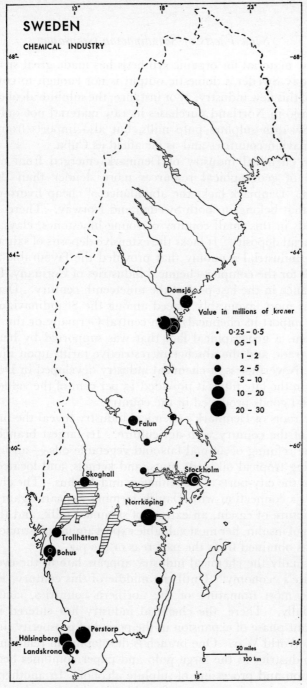

SWEDEN

CHEMICAL INDUSTRY

Domsjö

Value in millions of kroner

• 0·25 – 0·5
• 0·5 – 1
● 1 – 2
● 2 – 5
● 5 – 10
● 10 – 20
● 20 – 30

Falun

Skoghall   Stockholm

Norrköping

Trollhättan

Bohus

Perstorp

Hälsingborg
Landskrona

0   50 miles
0   100 km

FIG. 112

The chemical industry is located primarily in the ports that serve the midlands and
southern Sweden. The early abundance of hydro-electric power accounts for its
growth in the Göta valley. At Domsjö in central Norrland and at Skoghall the
chemical industry has appeared lately as a subsidiary of pulp manufacture.

as a raw material for organic synthesis has made great strides, so that today Sweden's domestic output is not enough to cover the needs of this new industry. For instance, the sulphite alcohol plant at Domsjö in Norrland purchases its raw material not only from other Swedish sulphite pulp mills, but also imports from other Scandinavian countries and as far afield as Cuba.

The chemical industry of Denmark emerged from a background of geographical resources more slender than those of Sweden. Denmark lacks the abundance of cheap hydro-electric power that belongs to both Sweden and Norway. There are not coalfields in this small country of young limestones, clays, sands, and glacial deposits. It lacks the extensive deposits of salt and the mature industrial economy that provided the favourable forcing grounds for the complex chemical industries of Germany, Britain, and France in the last part of the nineteenth century. Denmark, too, was most favourably placed among the Scandinavian countries to import its chemicals from central Germany or the United Kingdom, a geographical fact that was supported by her belief in free trade and the absence of restrictive tariffs upon imported goods. Nevertheless, a chemical industry developed in Denmark so that in the late fifties it provided 15 per cent of the value of the industrial goods produced in the country.

The roots of Denmark's chemical industry reveal the preoccupation of the country with agriculture. Its largest branch deals with the refining of animal fats and vegetable oils — an industry importing tropical oil seeds, nuts, and kernels, and located especially in the city-ports of Copenhagen and Aarhus. The chemical industry's connection with Danish farming appears again in the manufacture of casein, an extract of skimmed milk, and the production of insulin, her most valuable export among pharmaceutical products obtained from the pancreas of the pig.

Normally the chemical industry appears late in the evolution of a state's economy. Until the middle of this century, Finland was the most immature of the northern countries, considered industrially. There, the chemical industry has entered its first important phase of expansion in the period of prosperity since the Second World War. One branch is developing in relation to the forest industries as the large pulp and paper combines begin the distillation and processing of sulphite alcohol. In another direction, one notices the state as a founder of and investor in chemical plants that seem necessary to broaden the base of the nation's economy. Here the greatest step forward is the opening of the new nitrogenous fertilizer plant at Oulu.

In each of the Scandinavian states the advances of the chemical industry since the end of the Second World War are symptomatic of the achievement of industrial maturity in this part of Europe, whose resources in population and raw materials can only be described as meagre and lacking in some basic commodities. Within the space of half a decade, between 1950 and 1955, Finland doubled the labour force in her chemical industry, but such notable advances within a small nation are negligible when set against the canvas of the whole continent of Europe. Even the gigantic, lonely industrial plants of Norway with an immense capital investment in relation to the number of their workers are of small account when set beside the industrial complexes of the chemical corporations in the Ruhr, north-eastern England, Saxony, or Lorraine. Cheap hydro-electricity is no substitute in the economics of this industry for an abundance of coal, coke, salt, lignite, and the presence of capital and markets generated by neighbouring industries.

CHAPTER 16

Scandinavia Today

In the foregoing chapters much has been written about the unity of Scandinavia, a unity that may be discerned in the climates, landforms, rock types, languages, industries, and social forms of this large area of the European continent. One is tempted to recognize a search for political unity as one of the strands in Scandinavian history. In the past, political unity seemed possible only at the price of the aggrandizement of one of the northern powers. For instance, the Union of Kalmar of 1389, the first general gathering of Scandinavians for political purposes, marked the extinction of Norway as an independent state and the late medieval ascent to power of the Danish kingdom. Again, in the middle of the seventeenth century a fleeting political unity of the Baltic area was achieved at the peak of Sweden's career as an aggressive militaristic power, when Finland, Estonia, the mouths of the north German rivers, Bornholm, and parts of south-eastern Norway were all under her control.

During the nineteenth century, the political relationships between the states of northern Europe changed from national rivalry to one of international tolerance and co-operation. In 1905, after almost a century of attachment to Sweden, the Norwegian parliament could vote for a dissolution of the union with her Scandinavian neighbour and the establishment of an independent Norway. Only a tiny ultra-nationalistic minority in Sweden made a call for war against the new nation — a call that went unheeded by the Swedish government.

The political history of the Åland archipelago clearly displays the working of policies that follow the ideal of excluding conflict from the area of northern Europe. These rocky islands that stretch across the mouth of the Gulf of Bothnia from the south-western coast of Finland are inhabited almost entirely by Swedish-speaking people. At the end of the First World War, when Finland was the youngest among the Scandinavian states and freed from the rule of Russia, the question of the political

446

status of this archipelago remained to be settled. Political groups in both Sweden and the Åland islands agitated for its attachment to Sweden. An appeal was made to the peace conference of the powers at Versailles that determined so many of the new frontiers in Europe, but the question was passed on to the newly-created international body, the League of Nations, for investigation. In 1920, the Council of the League of Nations recognized Finnish sovereignty in the Åland islands and Sweden accepted this decision. Once again, the same archipelago came under discussion at the close of the Second World War. A movement among the islanders agitated for its transfer to Swedish rule. The cultural benefits of union with Sweden were now powerfully reinforced by the advantages of inclusion within a state that had remained neutral in Europe's wars for a century and a half and whose standard of life was among the highest in the world. Sweden again remained passive to the prospect of a political change that could have brought her great strategic advantages in a Baltic Sea whose power relationships were so deeply changed by Russia's absorption of the republics of Estonia, Latvia, and Lithuania and her acquisition of military bases on the Finnish mainland. One is reminded of Switzerland's passivity at the same time towards the movement in Vorarlberg — a movement in this westernmost province of Austria on the upper Rhine that voluntarily asked for union with the Swiss Confederation in the difficult period after the Second World War.

The four nation-states of the Scandinavian world now seem to be firmly established. The old struggles for power that impart an heroic quality to the history of this most northern part of Europe are over, and it is only the relationship of the region as a whole with the world beyond the formal limits of Scandinavia that holds out the prospect of danger and future change. As the Scandinavians act together, they reflect the physical unity and common interests of this northern region. In their constitutions as separate nations, they underline the physical contrasts that exist within the Scandinavian world. Despite the preponderance of immensely old Archaean rocks over much of this territory, despite the high latitudinal position that adds such a strong flavour to all the climates of these north European countries, there are vivid physical differences within the area — differences that form part of the distinctiveness of each Scandinavian nation. The grey fjords of western Norway, washed by the warm Atlantic, are an utterly

447

different world from the still, dark forests of Finnish Karelia. One is able to sense these differences at every stage of their history. Karelia has remained one of the remotest corners of the European continent. Even today, a first generation of settlers may be seen making clearings in her forests where the wilderness slowly gives way to farmland — a process that recedes into the depths of prehistory in western and central Europe. In contrast, western Norway was a dynamic centre of European history a thousand years ago, when the robber-lords of her fjords established transitory kingdoms that ranged from Sicily to Iceland.

The unity of the Scandinavian area expresses itself at a political level in the desire for neutrality, the wish to be left out of the entanglements of European politics that has been a part of northern policies since the end of the Napoleonic wars. Just as differences of physique underlie national differentiations within the area, so the space relationships of northern Europe interfere with the growth of common policies towards the rest of the continent. Norway and Denmark, whether they wish it or not, are deeply interested in the areas of the North Sea basin and the Atlantic Ocean. On the other hand, Finland occupies the rôle of a marchland state, overshadowed by the continental power of the Soviet Union across her eastern frontier. Swedish policies express her central position within the Scandinavian area. There is a cool friendliness, without participation, towards the alliances and defence arrangements of the western nations. Towards the east, Swedish policies pursue a line of proper neutrality guarded by one of the world's most efficient armies.

Never was the influence of Scandinavia's space relationships so clear as in the past two decades that contained the Second World War and the years that followed. Norway was deeply involved in the conflict for power in the North Atlantic. For instance, the strategic value of her long Atlantic coastline and the ice-free port of Narvik — chief outlet for northern Sweden's iron ore — deprived her of neutrality. In the same war Denmark was occupied by German armies. Geographically, she is a peninsula of central Europe, forming an island-crossing into Scandinavia and controlling the sea passages into the Baltic. Sweden alone, centrally placed in the Baltic, was able to maintain a neutral position, while Finland became a battlefield on Germany's eastern front.

Since 1945, power relationships on the border of the Scandinavian world have suffered drastic changes. Finland's Arctic corridor to the port of Petsamo has disappeared and the Soviet Union and Norway now meet along a common frontier in the northern tundra lands. The eastern boundary of Finland now nearly follows a line that was formerly established by the Treaty of Uusikaupunki between Sweden and Russia in 1721 — a change that deprives Finland of some valuable Karelian territory. Within the Baltic Sea the balance of political power is totally transformed. At the end of the war the U.S.S.R. absorbed the republics of Latvia, Estonia, and Lithuania, proclaiming a twelve-mile margin of territorial waters. Poland gained a long stretch of the Baltic coastline at the expense of Germany and the full control of the mouth of the Vistula. Westward of the mouth of the Oder, two hundred miles of the Baltic coast are in the hands of communist Eastern Germany, while the West German Federal Republic touches the sea at the end of the narrow corridor between Lübeck Bay and the Danish frontier.

Before 1939 the states of northern Europe felt themselves remote from the conflicts that raged at the heart of the continent. Today they lie on the frontier between the Atlantic nations and the Soviet Union and her satellites, poised on the edge of the great political rift that cuts across the continent from the Barents Sea to the head of the Adriatic and the eastern Mediterranean. This new position is clearly reflected in the international relationships of the Scandinavian states since the end of the war. Norway and Denmark both entered the North Atlantic Treaty Organization in 1949. From the beginning, Norway was convinced that her interests lay with the larger defensive alliance of the Atlantic powers. Denmark, the guardian of the entrance to the Baltic, was persuaded with some reluctance to the Norwegian point of view. Sweden, on the other hand, hoped that Scandinavian unity would be found in an alliance of the Nordic countries with a neutralist outlook to the rest of the world. Sweden's part in the debate of the late forties over the creation of N.A.T.O. seems to follow from her central position in the Baltic area. Public opinion, particularly as expressed in the columns of her liberal newspapers, leaned towards the alliance of the western powers. Her government, though representing the same liberal opinion, placed the traditional national policy of neutrality first. The Swedish government feared that entry into a military alliance of the west would only draw a clearer and more hostile frontier between east and west through the Baltic. Finland, surviving in the twilight world of the states on the Soviet Union's eastern border, might be drawn irrevocably into the Russian sphere if Sweden joined herself officially with the policies of the west.

It is not for the geographer to follow in detail the changing political relationships between the nations through the decade of the fifties. It is enough to say that the demands among the western powers for effective military unity have given rise to neutralist feelings in Scandinavia. Norway and Denmark have both rejected the stationing of foreign troops in their countries during peace-time. Even greater arguments have raged around the establishment of rocket bases and the equipping of their national armies with atomic weapons. The revelation in 1960 that flights by light, high-flying American military aircraft over the Soviet Union were based on airfields in northern Norway only helped to swing this country back towards Scandinavia's traditional neutrality. By 1954 the Swedish public had ceased to argue about the entry of the country into the N.A.T.O. group. Liberal opinion generally granted that the government had acted correctly in affirming the country's neutrality, and the debate began to move to the difficult question of the equipping of Swedish forces with atomic weapons.

Of all the Scandinavian states Finland is the most deeply influenced by the changes in Baltic power relationships since the end of the war. Since making peace with the Soviet Union in 1944, she has moved in a political twilight, unable to formulate foreign policies without considering the attitudes of her powerful eastern neighbour. At times, Finland is able to move towards collaboration with the other Scandinavian countries; on other occasions she is brought up sharply with the unpleasant knowledge that her internal prosperity and the stability of her governments depend partly upon the attitude of the Soviet Union.

In 1955 Finland was able to join the Nordic Council, a body of ministers from the Scandinavian countries that discusses the common problems of northern Europe with the exclusion of defence and foreign policy. Between 1958 and 1960 the Russian government was able to display both its tolerance and hostility towards Finnish independence. 1958 was a year of economic depression and unemployment in Finland. At the general elections in that summer, the party of the People's Democrats, belonging to the extreme left and favouring Soviet policies, gained fifty seats and became the biggest body in Parliament. A coalition government of the Social Democrats and Agrarians took office and was forced to resign after a few months, mainly as a result of a brief period of difficulties with the Soviet Union. The Russians withdrew their ambassador from Helsinki, refused to take delivery of Finnish goods, and cancelled discussions on a future trade agreement between the two countries. The strain imposed upon Finland's economy by the loss of Russian trade and the precarious structure of parliamentary government in the country caused the government to fall in this crisis that was precipitated from beyond her frontier.

Within two years Russo-Finnish relations had moved to the other extreme. A minority government of the Agrarian party under Premier Sukselainen was acceptable to the U.S.S.R. Meanwhile, international trade improved, and Finland moved out of the economic crisis that afflicted the country in 1957 and 1958. Late in 1960, Russia's attitude to Finland softened further. In September of that year, the Soviet Union found no objection to Finland's approach towards the European Free Trade Association, the discussions of the Seven that aimed at the creation of a free trade area among 85 million people in Britain, Switzerland, Portugal, Austria, and the Scandinavian countries. Russia was willing to discuss the effect of membership in the European Free Trade Association upon the 'most-favoured-nation' clause in her own treaty with Finland. Two months later, in November 1960, Russia went further in the establishment of better relationships when she told Finland that she was prepared to lease the Saimaa Canal, an act that would restore water communications between the Finnish eastern lake-system and the sea.

In adjusting itself to the realities of power politics the Nordic world is split into three spheres. Apart from the partly veiled propositions of naked political power, the Scandinavian countries have had to define their attitude to the various economic organizations that have grown up in Europe since the end of the war. As we have already noticed on several occasions, the post-war period has been one of expanding industries and a growing volume of trade in manufactured goods. Trade in industrial products expanded during the decade of the fifties at twice the rate, in relation to the growth of manufacturing, of the expansion of trade in the pre-war decade. Above all, the chief features of the fifties are a great rise in the trading of manufactured goods between industrial countries and the appearance of hundreds of new items in the trading lists each year with the quickening of the technological revolution. The political background to this expansion of international trade in the prosperous decade of the fifties is formed by the creation of bodies to discuss the lowering of tariffs, the abolition of trade restrictions, and to debate multilateral trade agreements. The Soviet Union and the communist countries of eastern Europe have stood apart from these efforts to make a wider economic unit out of Europe.

The first part of the decade of the fifties is marked by the work of two bodies in western Europe. The European Payments Union was created to deal with the transfer of currency in a time of great exchange difficulties. The Organization for European Economic Co-operation (O.E.E.C.), with eleven member states, has its headquarters in Paris, where national representatives meet daily to discuss the trade and economy of the continent. This organization has sponsored many surveys of the industries and resources in the territories of its membership. The second half of the fifties saw the creation of new and more limited international bodies in western Europe. The European Economic Community (E.E.C.) came into being at the beginning of 1958. Its member states — France, Western Germany, Belgium, the Netherlands, Luxembourg, and Italy — pass under the collective title of 'the Six'. This body arose out of the European Coal and Steel Community that began to operate in the six countries at the start of 1953. In a space of five years the steel industries of the European Coal and Steel Community made remarkable progress. Steel production rose faster than in the rest of the world, and over the same period trade in iron and steel between the member countries rose by 160 per cent. When the Six set up the European Economic Community in 1958, they proposed the creation of a common market. By 1970 it was planned to demolish all internal tariffs and quotas, to apply a common external tariff, and to introduce uniform transport rules for an area stretching from Naples to Hamburg and from Bordeaux to Munich.

The plans for the establishment of the European Economic Community involve more than the creation of a uniform trading area stretching between the Mediterranean and the North Sea and from the Bay of Biscay to the banks of the Elbe. It aims to maintain its authority through several supra-national bodies that include a Council of Ministers to decide all major issues of policy, an executive organ in the nine-member European Commission, and an Assembly composed of 142 members drawn from the national parliaments of the Six. In addition, there will be a Court of Justice to resolve disagreements that arise in the organization and running of the Common Market.

As the plans for the creation of this large economic unit in western Europe have evolved since the summer of 1955, so the nations on the edge of the Six who wish for the creation of a free trade area have felt a strong revulsion against the political aspects of E.E.C. Switzerland and Sweden both believe that membership of the Common Market would clash with their traditional policies of neutrality. Austria, too, following a policy of strict neutrality, since the withdrawal of occupation forces, finds herself excluded from the terms of the Common Market. Britain found objections to the supra-national bodies with political powers that are proposed for E.E.C. and even greater difficulties in reconciling her trade agreements with the Commonwealth and entry into the economy of the Common Market.

In 1959, the states of western Europe moved towards the formation of two economic blocs. The nations outside the Common Market gathered together in the creation of the European Free Trade Association (E.F.T.A.). It is composed of Great Britain, Sweden, Norway, Denmark, Switzerland, Austria, and Portugal, otherwise known as the Seven. E.F.T.A. began operations in the summer of 1960 with the cautious application of lower tariffs towards each other.

It is important now to discover the attitudes of the Scandinavian countries towards the two trading areas that are arising in western Europe. All the northern countries favour the reduction of tariff barriers and the abolition of quota systems in international trade. The easy exchange of raw materials, manufactured goods, and services between the world's nations inevitably brings the greatest benefits to the small states. Denmark has scarcely swerved from the liberal ideal of free trade over the past two centuries, and she would profit greatly from an unhampered international market in agricultural commodities. Norway's huge merchant navy depends upon the freedom to collect cargoes at almost any port in the world; she regards nothing with greater distaste than the growing trend towards flag discrimination. The prosperity of Finland and the stability of her domestic politics depend upon overseas markets, especially in western Europe, for timber products. Likewise,

Sweden rests upon her massive exports of iron ore and pulp and hopes for an increasing trade in paper and the high-quality products of her engineering industry and shipyards.

Scandinavian policies favour free trade and, above all, a freedom of trade in western Europe. It is with a mixture of hope and dismay that the northern nations have greeted the creation of the Six and the Seven in the past two years. The political elements in the apparatus of the Common Market and the links of the northern currencies with the sterling area carried Sweden, Denmark, and Norway into the group of the Seven and the plans for the European Free Trade Area. But in the many speeches of foreign ministers and commercial attachés on occasions of trade fairs and commercial agreements there is uncovered the hope that this division of Europe will give way to the creation of a bigger free trade area in western Europe, involving both the Six and the Seven. The Scandinavian states have looked upon the Seven as an instrument for negotiating a greater freedom of commerce with the Six. In the jargon of the world of the commercial diplomat 'E.F.T.A. is regarded as a stepping-stone towards the wider economic community in Europe'.[1]

For Sweden the splitting of Europe into two trading blocs seems most harmful, an attitude that reflects the division of her commerce in almost equally large proportions between the countries of the Common Market and the United Kingdom. One of the notable features of Swedish export trade in the decade of the fifties is the rising share of the Common Market countries. After an almost total eclipse in the period that followed the end of the Second World War, Germany has returned to play an important part in Swedish trade. The figures for 1957 show that western Germany took 14 per cent of Swedish exports. The Benelux countries, too, have almost doubled their share of imports from Sweden as compared with the years before the Second World War. In 1957, a third of Sweden's exports went to the Common Market countries and an even greater proportion of her imports, 40 per cent, came from the same trading area.

It is the political collaboration proposed by the Six that excludes Sweden from an active membership of the Common Market. In the sphere of trade she has much to lose through exclusion from the Six. It is this unpleasant prospect that explains Sweden's opposition to the proposed uniform tariff wall that France has advertised for the Common Market countries. Swedish iron ore might find itself in severer competition with the ores of Lorraine and Luxembourg. In 1957, Germany and Belgium together consumed the largest proportion of Swedish iron ore exports, taking nine million tons as compared with the three million tons imported into the United Kingdom. With the high-quality products of the engineering industry Sweden is likely to find herself in a contracting market in the Common Market countries, if she is faced by a uniform tariff barrier.

As the Swedes review their prospects in relation to the free trade association of the Seven, they see little hope of expanding the total volume of their exports. The best prospect that member-ship of the Seven holds out to the Scandinavian countries is the easier movement of capital for investment. They hope that the economic unit of the Seven, as it emerges, might attract capital from the United States. In the post-war years the chief currents of American investment have been set towards western Germany and the United Kingdom. Sweden's import trade might readjust itself partially towards the Seven, but it seems more than likely that the bulk of industrial imports in the next decade will still be drawn from western Germany. German firms have built up efficient sales and distribution arrangements in Sweden since the war and these are likely to secure the continued flow of trade between the two countries.

Denmark's attitude to the threatened rift in European trade between the blocs of the Six and the Seven is different from Sweden's. The geography of this small agricultural state, poor in the natural resources of industry, determines her views on Europe's international politics. Agricultural products hold a dominant position in her exports, and three-quarters of her export market lies in western Europe. Denmark has consistently aimed at the creation of a large free trade area in Europe, ideally one that would be coincident with the eleven member states of O.E.E.C., and that would therefore include her two biggest customers, the United Kingdom and Western Germany. It was with some dismay that Denmark greeted the breakdown in 1958 of the negotiations for a wide Common Market including the United Kingdom and the northern countries. She was sceptical about the scheme of the Seven and put forward the view that in the trade arrangements of this new group of countries there should be no kind of discrimination against the six. Denmark could not suffer a severe contraction of her market for agricultural products in Germany, and she remembers that the Common Market contains her chief rival in this sector of trade, the Netherlands.

Denmark, too, found herself dissatisfied with the preliminary discussions over the creation of E.F.T.A. The first plans for the widening of trade among the Seven only applied to industrial goods. One writer, F. V. Mayer, described the Convention of Stockholm that set the seal on the first stage of the economic organization of the Seven as 'a scheme for filling the pockets of those who work by manufacturing'.² The exclusion of agricultural products from the liberation of trade among the Seven only promised to damage the Danish economy. The Danes could imagine a restriction of their exports of butter, bacon, and eggs through the many devices of quotas, tariffs, and farmers' subsidies that subtly control the volume of international trade. On the other hand, the reduction of tariffs within the trading area of the Seven would probably lead to harsher competition on the home market for Denmark's industries.

Among the northern countries, Denmark is especially sensitive to discriminations in trade, particularly as farm products are so often subject to protective measures by the importing states of western Europe, measures that do not affect the basic raw materials of industry such as iron ore and timber. At length, in the negotiations between the Seven notice was taken of Denmark's interests, and it was decided that the Treaty of the Seven should contain a general agreement upon agriculture. Of greater importance, perhaps, is the fact that within the agreements of the Free Trade Area Denmark was able to arrange a bilateral treaty with the United Kingdom which gave a reduction of tariffs on two-thirds of her exports to the British Isles. It also provided that Denmark should benefit by any increases of consumption in the British Isles in future years. Nevertheless, Denmark is acutely conscious of the dual outlook of her export traders upon a Europe that promises to be split between the Common Market countries and the outer ring of the Free Trade Area. On examining her trade statistics for 1958 she cannot fail to note that two of the Common Market countries — Western Germany and Italy — were together buying more from her than the United Kingdom.

The coolness that characterizes the attitude of the Nordic countries to the politics of the rest of the continent has its counterpart in the efforts to create some supra-national organization among themselves. The past half-century has thrown up several suggestions of economic union between the Scandinavian states. The latest of these belongs to the early 1950's, when the Americans pleaded for some form of economic union between the Marshall Aid countries or, at least, between members of regional groups in Europe, among which the Scandinavian nations seemed the most obvious.

In 1950, a joint committee studied the question of economic union for Norway, Sweden, and Denmark, but concluded that there were no strong reasons for merging their economies. The harsh truth is that the states of this area are not economically complementary, but in several activities they stand as severe competitors in the world's markets. The fiercest competition arises in the timber industries — the dominating occupation in Sweden, Norway, and Finland. In another sphere, the Scandinavian states appear as competitors between each other for the merchant traffic of the world's oceans. Both Finland and Sweden compete with Denmark, though on a small scale, in the western European market for dairy produce. The internal industrial patterns of the Scandinavian states also possess certain similarities. For instance, all four of northern Europe's nations contain textile industries of a size sufficient to supply their own internal markets. The fear that a stronger member, in this case Sweden, might grow at the expense of the weaker provided further arguments against economic union.

The main hope and expression of collaboration in northern Europe has appeared since the war in the meetings of the Nordic Council, a body composed of ministers from the governments of the Scandinavian states that makes recommendations to the individual parliaments. Its first meeting took place in 1953, but Finland, her initiative at first quelled by the attitude of the Soviet Union, was not able to join the Nordic Council's activities until 1955.

At its annual meetings the Nordic Council discusses social, cultural, and political problems belonging to the whole area of Scandinavian Europe. So far its greatest achievement is the creation of a uniform passport area covering the Norden countries — Denmark, Finland, Norway, and Sweden. Its discussions, too, have led to a greater mobility of labour between the Scandinavian states — a fact shown in the statistics of foreign workers in Sweden whose chronic labour shortage and high wages have attracted immigrants in the fifties. There were 124,328 foreign workers in Sweden in 1956, but almost 70,000 of this number were drawn from her three Scandinavian neighbours. The largest proportion, nearly 50,000, came from Finland to find work in her northern forest communities and the iron-mining towns of Norrland, where the legislation of the welfare state does much to mitigate the rigorous Arctic winter.

At its second meeting in 1954, the Nordic Council returned to the century-old question of a customs union between the states of northern Europe. In these discussions Norway clearly revealed her fears of a close economic union between the Scandinavian states. Her strictly planned economy includes heavy state subsidies for farm products and she sees the danger of Danish competition in an open Scandinavian market. On the other hand, her comparatively backward industrial development invites the predominance of Swedish manufactures in the Norwegian market if a customs union created a common trading area in the Scandinavian countries. The main aim of economic planning in Norway is to expand her power resources and elaborate the structure of her industry, but to accomplish this change Norway needs to attract investment from beyond her frontiers. Economic union would make it easier for Denmark and Sweden to invest in Norway, but it might change the nature of her economic problems at the same time.

The long debate over the creation of a customs union in northern Europe has not yet achieved any results. Even if the Scandinavian countries have failed to create grand supra-national bodies, for a long time they have been conscious of their common way of life. In so many branches of commerce and industry organizations exist that transgress the national boundaries. Already we have noticed that Swedish capital has helped to build a new Norwegian power plant near Trondheim that contributes some of its output to Sweden's grid. Perhaps the most striking instance of the growing unity of northern Europe, at a practical rather than a political level, is the union since the Second World War of the national airlines of Norway, Sweden, and Denmark into the big international company of S.A.S. — the Scandinavian airlines system.

Since its creation, the Nordic Council has discussed ideas that can only lead to the closer union of this vast tract of cold-temperate Europe. For example, at its meeting in 1954 it recommended the bridging of the Sound — the traditional water barrier between the Scandinavian peninsula and central Europe, a frontier between

Denmark and Sweden, a corridor of sea whose coastal towns and cities promise to form the largest conurbation in these northern countries. The Nordic Council suggested the construction of a four-carriage roadway for eleven and a half miles between Malmö and Copenhagen, a task that would require close financial and technical co-operation between neighbour states. If this comes into existence it will stand as a memorial to the changing political relationships between the northern countries, for only three centuries ago the armies of Sweden marched across the ice of the frozen Sound to burn and plunder Copenhagen.

NOTES

CHAPTER I

1. Shetelig, H., and Falk, H., *Scandinavian Archaeology*, 1937, p. 201
2. Zimmerman, M., 'États scandinaves', *Géog. Univ.*, 3 (1933), p. 68
3. Coon, C. S., *The Races of Europe*, 1939, pp. 337-343

CHAPTER II

1. Brøgger, A. W., *Det Norske Folk i Oldtiden*, Oslo, 1925

CHAPTER III

1. Aagesen, A., 'The Copenhagen district and its population', *Guide-Book Denmark*, Int. Geog. Cong., Norden (1960), pp. 358-359

CHAPTER VI

1. Sømme, A., *A Geography of Norden*, Oslo, 1960, p. 29
2. Rudberg, S., and Bylund, E., 'From the Bothnian Gulf through Southern and Central Lapland to the Norwegian fjords', *Geog. Ann.*, 41 (1959), pp. 261-288
3. Sømme, A., *A Geography of Norden*, p. 90
4. Strøm, K. M., 'The geomorphology of Norway', *Geog. J.*, 112 (1948), p. 20
5. Ahlmann, H. W : son, 'Geomorphological studies in Norway', *Geog. Ann.*, 1 (1919)
6. de Geer, G., 'A geochronology of the last 12,000 years', *Int. Geol. Cong.*, Sess. II, Stockholm, 1910. *Transactions*, Vol. I, Stockholm, 1912
7. Strøm, K. M., *ibid.*, p. 22
   Strøm, K. M., 'The Norwegian coast', *Norsk Geog. Tidsskrift*, 17 (1959), p. 136
8. Tietze, W., 'Ein Beitrag zum geomorphologischen Problem der Strandflate', *Petermanns Geog. Mitt.*, 106 (1962), pp. 1-20
9. Manley, G., 'The range of variation of the British climate', *Geog. J.*, 117 (1951), pp. 43-68
   Kraus, E. B., 'Synoptic and dynamic aspects of climatic change', *Q. J. R. Met. Soc.*, 86 (1960), pp. 1-15
   Longley, R. W., 'Temperature trends in Canada', *Proc. Toronto Met. Conf.* (1953), p. 207

CHAPTER VII

1. Klindt-Jensen, O., *Denmark before the Vikings*, London, 1957, pp. 34-57
2. Shetelig, H., and Falk, H., *Scandinavian Archaeology*, 1937, p. 315

3. Derry, T. K., *A Short History of Norway*, 1957, pp. 70-73
4. Keilhau, W., *Norway in World History*, 1944, pp. 112-115
5. Ahlmann, H. W: son, 'The economic geography of Swedish Norrland', *Geog. Ann.*, 3 (1921), p. 98
6. Montelius, S., 'The burning of forest land for the cultivation of crops: "svedjebruk" in Central Sweden', *Geog. Ann.*, 35 (1953), pp. 49-50
7. Huntington, E., *Mainsprings of Civilization*, New York, 1945, pp. 604-605
8. Teal, J. J., 'The rebirth of North Norway', *For. Aff.*, 32 (1953-54), p. 128
9. Bosi, R., *The Lapps*, London, 1960, pp. 167-176
   Vorren, Ø., *Norway North of 65*, 1960, pp. 100-147
10. Teal, J. J., *ibid.*, pp. 132-133
11. Äyräpää, A., 'The settlement of prehistoric age', *Suomi — a general handbook on the Geography of Finland*, 1952, pp. 285-299
12. Äyräpää, A., *ibid.*, p. 292
13. Granö, J. G., 'Geographic regions', *Suomi*, pp. 408-438
14. Tunkelo, A., 'Population', *Suomi*, p. 315
15. Jutikkala, E., 'Die Bevölkerung Finlands in den Jahren 1721–1749', *Ann. Acad. Sc. Fennicae B.*, 55 (1945)

CHAPTER VIII

1. Jensen, E., *Danish Agriculture: its economic development*, Copenhagen, 1937
2. Lambert, A. M., 'Farm consolidation and improvement in the Netherlands: an example from the Land van Maas en Waal', *Econ. Geog.*, 37 (1961), p. 116
3. Sømme, A., 'The physical background of Norwegian agriculture', *Geog.*, 35 (1950), pp. 141-154
4. *Economic Survey of Europe* (annually since 1948), United Nations, Secretariat of the Economic Commission for Europe, Geneva
5. Smeds, H., Finland, p. 180 (in Sømme, *A Geography of Norden*)

CHAPTER IX

1. Häggström, E., 'Shipbuilding, a major export', *The Financial Times Survey of Sweden* (1958), p. 31
2. 'Finns face inflation', *The Economist* (October 1956)

CHAPTER XI

1. Sømme, A., *A Geography of Norden*, p. 65
2. Landmark, K., Løkse, E., Vikingstad, J., and Vorren, Ø., 'Northern Norway: nature and livelihood', *Norsk Geog. Tidsskrift*, 17 (1959–60), pp. 149-161

CHAPTER XII

1. Ohlson, B., 'Settlement and economic life in Enontekiö — a parish in the extreme north of Finland', *Fennia*, 84 (1960), pp. 23-27
2. Adamson, O. J., *Industries of Norway*, Oslo, 1952, pp. 130-148
   Sømme, A., *A Geography of Norden*, pp. 248-251

Notes

3. Arnborg, T., 'The forests from the tree limit to the coastline', *A Geographical Excursion through Central Norrland*, edited by C. M : son Mannerfelt, pp. 66-76
4. Smeds, H., 'Finland', *A Geography of Norden*, p. 181
5. Sømme, A., *A Geography of Norden*, p. 80

CHAPTER XIII

1. Sandström, G., 'New deal in steel', *Industria International*, Stockholm, 1959-60, p. 3

CHAPTER XIV

1. *Wirtschaftsdienst*, April 1956 (Hamburg)
2. Adamson, O. J. (editor), *Industries of Norway*, Oslo, 1952, p. 248

CHAPTER XV

1. Zimmerman, M., 'États scandinaves', *Géog. Univ.*, 3 (1933), p. 121

CHAPTER XVI

1. Danielsen, N., 'Swedish exports today', special issue of the *Svenska Dagbladet* (April 1960), p. 4
2. Mayer, F. V., *The Seven: a provisional appraisal of E.F.T.A.*, London, 1960

BIBLIOGRAPHY

AAGESEN, Aa., 'Die Bevölkerung Dänemarks', *Geographische Rundschau*, 8 (1956), pp. 424-431

AARIO, L., 'The inner differentiation of the large cities in Finland', *Fennia*, 74 (1951), pp. 1-67

ADAMSON, O. J. (Editor), *Industries of Norway*, Oslo, 1952

AHLMANN, H. W: son, 'Geomorphological studies in Norway', *Geografiska Annaler*, 1 (1919), pp. 3-148, 193-252

AHLMANN, H. W: son, 'The economic geography of Swedish Norrland', *Geografiska Annaler*, 3 (1921), pp. 97-164

AHLMANN, H. W: son, 'Glaciers in Jotunheim and the physiography', *Geografiska Annaler*, 4 (1922), pp. 1-57

AHLMANN, H. W: son, *Glaciological Research on the North Atlantic Coasts*, R.G.S. Research Series, No. 1 (1948), London, The Royal Geographical Society

AHLMANN, H. W: son, 'The present climatic fluctuation', *Geographical Journal*, 112 (1948), pp. 165-195

ALDSKOGIUS, H., 'Changing land use and settlement development in the Siljan region', *Geografiska Annaler*, 42 (1960), pp. 250-261

AMÉEN, L., 'Die Verkehrsverhältnisse des Nordens', *Sonderdruck aus Geographische Rundschau*, 1960, pp. 38-47

ÅNGSTRÖM, A., *Sveriges Klimat*, Stockholm, 1958

ARNBORG, L., 'The delta of the Ångermanälven', *Geografiska Annaler*, 30 (1948), pp. 673-690

ARPI, G., 'The supply with charcoal of the Swedish iron industry from 1830–1950', *Geografiska Annaler*, 35 (1953), pp. 11-27

Atlas of Finland (Suomen Kartasto; Atlas över Finland), Helsinki, 1925–28

Atlas of Sweden. Svenska Sällskapet för Antropologi och Geografi. Kartografiska Institutet, Generalstabens Litografiska Anstalt, Stockholm, 1953

BEHREN, S., BERGSTEN, K. E., NORDSTRÖM, O., AMÉEN, L., *Regional Geography of Southern Sweden*, Guidebook to Excursion E.Sw5 A-B, International Geographical Congress, Norden, 1960

BERGSTEN, F., 'The land uplift in Sweden from the evidence of the old water marks', *Geografiska Annaler*, 36 (1954), pp. 81-111

BLACHE, J., 'Dans les montagnes norvégiennes. Paysages et problèmes', *Revue de Géographie Alpine*, Grenoble, 1930, pp. 697-730

BRAEKHUS, K., 'Norwegens Schiffahrt aus geographischer Sicht', *Sonderdruck aus Geographische Rundschau*, 1960, pp. 83-87

BRØNDSTED, J., *Danmarks Oldtid*, Gyldendalske Boghandel, Nordisk Forlag A/S., Copenhagen, 1957

BODVALL, G., 'Bodland i norra Hälsingland', (Bodland in north Hälsingland; studies of the part played by land clearance in the expansion of the permanently settled area up to 1850), English summary, *Geographica*, 36, Uppsala, 1959

BODVALL, G., 'Expansion of the permanently settled area in northern Hälsingland', *Geografiska Annaler*, 42 (1960), pp. 244-249

BODVALL, G., 'Periodic settlement, land clearing and cultivation', *Geografiska Annaler*, 39, 1957, pp. 213-256

BOSAEUS, B., *Uppsala City*, Uppsala, 1960

BOSI, R., *The Lapps*, London, 1960

BYLUND, E., 'Koloniseringen av Pite Lappmark t.o.m. ar 1867' (The colonization of Pite Lappmark until 1867), English summary, *Geographica*, 30, Uppsala, 1956

CASTELLI, A., 'La Vallée de l'Ångermanälven entre Åsele et la mer', *Geografiska Annaler*, 30 (1948), pp. 708-727

CASTELLI, A., 'Les Industries suédoises des plaques isolantes en fibre', *Annales de Géographie*, 57 (1948), p. 184

CHABOT, G., 'La Naissance d'un Karst : l'Île de Gotland dans la mer Baltique', *Annales de Géographie*, 52 (1943), pp. 98-104

CHABOT, G., 'Le Commerce extérieur de la Suède', *Annales de Géographie*, 57 (1948), pp. 185-186

CHABOT, G., 'Problèmes de l'économie scandinave', *Annales de Géographie*, 55 (1946), pp. 259-81

CHABOT, G., 'Un Aspect du paysage nordique : les ôs', *Mélanges Zimmermann*, 1950

CHABOT, G., GUILCHER, A., BEAUJEU-GARNIER, J., *L'Europe du Nord et du Nord-Ouest*, Collection Orbis, 2 vols., Paris, 1958

CHILDS, M. W., *Sweden: the middle way*, New Haven, 1938

COLLINDER, B., *The Lapps*, Princeton, N.J., 1949

Conference on rural life, *Norway*, League of Nations, Geneva, 1939

Conference on rural life, *Sweden*, League of Nations, Geneva, 1939

CORNISH, R. T., 'The influence of physical features on rural settlement in east-central Sweden', *Trans. Institute of British Geographers*, Publication No. 16 (1950), pp. 125-135

DAHL, E., 'Biogeographic and geologic indications of unglaciated areas in Scandinavia during the glacial ages', *Bulletin of the American Geological Society*, 66 (1955), pp. 1499-1520

DANNSTEDT, G., 'Bottentopografien i Södra Kalmarsund', *Geografiska Annaler*, 29 (1947), pp. 1-19

DE GEER, S., 'Greater Stockholm : a geographical interpretation', *Geographical Review*, 13 (1923), pp. 497-506

DE GEER, S., 'Das geologische Fennoscandia und das geographische Balto-scandia', *Geografiska Annaler*, 10 (1928), pp. 119-139

Denmark Exports, 1959/60, special annual publication of Børsen

DERRY, T. K., *A Short History of Norway*, London, 1957

Economic Survey of Europe in 1953, United Nations, Geneva, 1954

Economic Survey of Europe since the War, United Nations, Geneva, 1953

ENQUIST, Fr., *Die glaziale Entwicklungsgeschichte Nordwestskandinaviens*, Sveriges Geol. Undersökning, Section C. No. 285, Stockholm, 1918

ENEQUIST, G., *Geographical Changes of Rural Settlement in North-western Sweden since 1523*, Uppsala Universitets Årsskrift, 8 (1959)

ENEQUIST, G., 'Advance and retreat of rural settlement in north-western Sweden', *Geografiska Annaler*, 42 (1960), pp. 211-219

ERIKSSON, G. A., 'The decay of blast furnaces and ironworks in Väster Bergslagen in Central Sweden, 1860–1940', *Geografiska Annaler*, 35 (1953), pp.1-10

Bibliography

ERIKSSON, G. A., 'The decline of the small blast furnaces and forges in Bergslagen after 1850', *Geografiska Annaler*, 39 (1957), pp. 257-275

ERIKSSON, G. A., 'Advance and retreat of charcoal iron industry and rural settlement in Bergslagen', *Geografiska Annaler*, 42 (1960), pp. 267-284

ERIKSSON, G. A., 'Der Bergbau, die Eisen- und Stahlindustrie im Norden', *Sonderdruck aus Geographische Rundschau*, 12 (1960), pp. 48-58

European Steel Trends in the Setting of the World Market, Steel Division, Economic Commission for Europe, Geneva, 1949

Europe's Growing Needs of Energy: How can they be met? O.E.E.C., 1956

FABER, H., *Co-operation in Danish Agriculture*, London, 1918

Finland: a survey 1957-60, *The World Today*, 17 (1961), pp. 12-24

FRIIS, H., *Scandinavia between East and West*, New York, 1950

GEIJER, P., and MAGNUSSON, N. H., 'The iron ores of Sweden', Vol. 2, *Symposium sur les gisements de fer du monde* (Editors: Blondel, F., and Marvier, L.), Algiers, 1952

GJESSING, G., *Changing Lapps: a study in culture relations in northernmost Norway*, London School of Economics and Political Science, Monographs on Social Anthropology, 13 (1954)

Guide-book Denmark, I.G.U. Congress, 1960, *Geogr. Tidsskr.* 59 (1960)

Guide-book Norway, I.G.U. Congress, 1960, *Norsk geogr. Tidsskr.*, 17 (1959-60)

HAMPDEN-JACKSON, J., 'Finland since the Armistice', *International Affairs*, 24 (1948), pp. 505-514

HANSEN, J. Chr., 'Nordnorwegen, ein Land am Rande der Ökumene', *Sonderdruck aus Geographische Rundschau*, 1960, pp. 69-77

HAURWITZ, B., and AUSTIN, J. M., *Climatology*, New York, 1944

HECKSCHER, E. F., *An Economic History of Sweden* (translated by G. Ohlin), Harvard Univ. Press, 1954

HEDENSTIERNA, B., 'Stockholms Skärgård. Kulturgeografiska studier i Värmdö gamla skeppslag', *Geografiska Annaler*, 30 (1948), pp. 1-444

HEDENSTIERNA, B., *Geographic Features of Stockholm's Skärgård*, International Geographical Congress, Norden, 1960

HEDENSTIERNA, D., 'Näringslivet i Sotholms härad under 1600 -talet', *Geografiska Annaler*, 32 (1950), pp. 85-163

HEIDEN, N. R., 'Odda and Rjukan — two industrialized areas of Norway', *Annals of the Association of American Geographers*, 42 (1952), pp. 108-128

HILDEBRAND, K. G., 'Sweden', *Stockholm 1960*: First International Conference of Economic History

HILL, R. G. P. (Editor), *The Lapps Today*. Publication du Centre d'Études Arctiques et Antarctiques, Paris, 1960

HOLDAR, C. G., 'The inland ice in the Abisko area', *Geografiska Annaler*, 41 (1959), pp. 231-235

HOLTEDAHL, O., 'The structural history of Norway and its relation to Great Britain', *Quarterly Journal of the Geological Society*, 108 (1952), pp. 65-98

HOLTEDAHL, H., 'On the Norwegian continental terrace, primarily outside Møre — Romsdal: its geomorphology and sediments', *Universitet Bergen Årbok*, 1955

HÖÖK, E., ELSHULT, A., and RISBERG, H., *The Economic Life of Sweden*, The Swedish Institute, Stockholm, 1956

HOPPE, G., 'Hummocky moraine regions with special reference to the interior of Norrbotten', *Geografiska Annaler*, 34 (1952), pp. 1-72

Scandinavian Lands

HOPPE, G., 'Problems of glacial morphology and the Ice Age', *Geografiska Annaler*, 39 (1957), 1-18

HOPPE, G., 'Glacial morphology and inland ice recession in northern Sweden', *Geografiska Annaler*, 41 (1959), pp. 193-211

HUBBARD, G. D., 'The geography of residence in Norway fjord areas', *Annals of the Association of American Geographers*, 22 (1932), pp. 109-118

Industria International, Annual publication of the Swedish Employers' Federation

Industrial Denmark, The Federation of Danish Industries, Copenhagen, 1958

JAATINEN, S., and MEAD, W. R., 'The intensification of Finnish farming', *Economic Geography*, 33 (1957), pp. 31-40

JAATINEN, S., DE GEER, E., and WELANDER, K., *The coast and archipelago of south-western Finland*, International Geographical Congress, Norden, 1960

JENSEN, E., *Danish Agriculture, its Economic Development*, Copenhagen, 1937

JENSEN, K. M., 'An outline of the climate of Denmark', *Geogr. Tidsskr.*, 59 (1960)

JOEDEN, U. von, 'Die mittlere Vereisung der Ostsee', *Zeitschrift der Gesellschaft für Erdkunde zu Berlin*, 7-8 (1918), pp. 316-324

JOHANSSON, O. H., 'The distribution of precipitation in Norway', *Geografiska Annaler*, 19 (1937), pp. 104-117

JONASSON, O., 'The relation between the distribution of population and of cultivated land in the Scandinavian countries', *Economic Geography*, 1 (1925), pp. 107-123

JONASSON, O., *Economic Geographical Excursion to Middle Sweden*, I.G.U. Congress. Norden, 1960

JUTIKKALA, E., *Suomen Historian Kartasto (Atlas of Finnish History)*, Helsinki, 1949

KÄÄRIARNEN, E., 'On the recent uplift of the Earth's crust in Finland', *Fennia*, 76 (1953)

KAMPP, Aa. H., 'The agricultural geography of Møn', *Erdkunde*, 16 (1962), pp. 173-190

KARJALAINEN, A., *A National Economy based on Wood*, Helsinki, 1957

KEILHAU, W., *Norway in World History*, London, 1944

KENDREW, W. G., *The Climates of the Continents*, Third Edition, Oxford, 1942

KIRK, W., and SYNGE, F. M., 'Farms of Verdal, Norway', *Scottish Geographical Magazine*, 70 (1954), pp. 106-123

KLEPPE, P., *Main Aspects of Economic Policy in Norway since the War*, Oslo, 1960

KLINDT-JENSEN, O., *Denmark before the Vikings*, London, 1957

KRISTIANSSON, A. L., 'Kulturgeografiska studier i Stockholms norra skärgård', *Geografiska Annaler*, 29 (1947), pp. 48-127

Kulturhistoriskt lexikon för nordisk medeltid, Malmö, 1960

LEISTIKOW, G., 'Denmark's creeping crisis', *Foreign Affairs*, 33 (1954-55), pp. 473-483

LILJEQUIST, G., 'Winter temperatures and ice conditions of Lake Vetter with special regard to the winter 1939-40', *Geografiska Annaler*, 23 (1941), pp. 24-52

LINDBERG, E., 'Seasonal migration of labour from the Siljan area and its economic background', *Geografiska Annaler*, 42 (1960), pp. 262-266

LINDBERG, O., 'An economic-geographical study of the localization of the Swedish paper industry', *Geografiska Annaler*, 35 (1953), pp. 28-40

LJUNGBERG, G., *Swedish Technology and the Attendant Factors*, The Swedish Institute, 1959

Bibliography

LLOYD, T., 'Iron-ore production at Kirkenes (Norway)', *Economic Geography*, 31 (1955), pp. 211-233

LOWEGREN, G., *Swedish Iron and Steel*, Stockholm, 1948

LUND, D. H., 'Revival of Northern Norway', *Geographical Journal*, 112 (1947), pp. 185-197

MÄKINEN, E., 'Outokumpu copper mine and smelter in Finland', *Mining and Metallurgy*, 1938

MANNERFELT, C. M : son, *A Geographical Excursion through Central Norrland*, I.G.U. Conference, Stockholm, 1960

MARMO, V., 'Iron ores of Finland', Vol. 2, *Symposium sur les gisements de fer du monde* (Editors: Blondel, F. and Marvier, L.), Algiers, 1952

MAYER, F. V., *The Seven: a provisional appraisal of E.F.T.A.*, London, 1960

MEAD, W. R., 'Esbjerg', *Economic Geography*, 16 (1940), pp. 250-259

MEAD, W. R., 'Finland in the sixteenth century', *Geographical Review*, 30 (1940), pp. 400-411

MEAD, W. R., 'Ribe', *Economic Geography*, 17 (1941), pp. 195-203

MEAD, W. R., 'Three city ports of Denmark', *Economic Geography*, 18 (1942), pp. 41-56

MEAD, W. R., 'Sogn and Fjordane in the fjord economy of western Norway', *Economic Geography*, 23 (1947), pp. 155-166

MEAD, W. R., 'The Finnish outlook, east and west', *Geographical Journal*, 113 (1948), pp. 9-20

MEAD, W. R., 'The cold farm in Finland, resettlement of Finland's displaced farmers', *Geographical Review*, 41 (1951), pp. 529-543

MEAD, W. R., *Farming in Finland*, London, 1953

MEAD, W. R., 'The margin of transference in Finland's rural resettlement', *Tijdschrift voor Economische en Sociale Geografie*, 48 (1957), pp. 178-183

MEAD, W. R., *An Economic Geography of the Scandinavian States and Finland*, London, 1958

MEAD, W. R., 'The seasonal round. A study of adjustment on Finland's pioneer fringe', *Tijdschrift voor Economische en Sociale Geografie*, 49 (1958), pp. 157-162

MEAD, W. R., 'Frontier Themes in Finland', *Geography*, 44 (1959), pp. 145-156

MONTELIUS, S., 'The burning of forest land for the cultivation of crops — "svedjebruk" in central Sweden', *Geografiska Annaler*, 35 (1953), pp. 41-54

MONTELIUS, S., 'Finn settlement in central Sweden', *Geografiska Annaler*, 42 (1960), pp. 285-293

MUSSET, L., 'Les Villes du Danemark', *Annales de Géographie*, 57 (1948), pp. 308-321

MUTTON, A. F. A., 'Hydro-electric power development in Norway', *Trans. Inst. British Geogr.*, 19 (1953), pp. 123-130

MYKLEBOST, H., 'Die Wasserkräfte in Norwegen', *Sonderdruck aus Geographische Rundschau* (1960), pp. 64-68

NELSON, H., 'Dalarna', *Svensk Geografisk Årsbok*, 34 (1958), pp. 99-120

NIELSEN, N. (Editor), *Atlas of Denmark*, Vols. I and II, Copenhagen, 1949 and 1961

NORDSTROM, O., 'Die Landwirtschaft des Nordens', *Sonderdruck aus Geographische Rundschau*, 1960, pp. 30-37

NORLING, G., 'Abandonment of rural settlement in Västerbotten Lappmark, North Sweden, 1930–1960', *Geografiska Annaler*, 42 (1960), pp. 232-243

Scandinavian Lands

Norway's Industry, Federation of Norwegian Industries, Oslo, 1958

O'DELL, A. C., *The Scandinavian World*, London, 1957

OHLSON, B., OKKO, V., NIIRANEN, E., *Physical and Human Geography of Finnish Lapland*, Guidebook to Excursion E.F.2, IGU Congress, Norden, 1960, Helsinki, 1960

OSVALD, H., *Swedish Agriculture*, Swedish Institute, Stockholm, 1952

OUREN, T., *The Port Traffic of the Oslofjord Region*, Oslo, 1958

Overseas Economic Surveys, *Norway*, London, 1949

PETERSEN, M., 'Oslo', Sonderdruck aus Geographische Rundschau, 1960, pp. 94-96

PICKARD, J. P., 'Manufacturing regions of Norway', *Annals of the Association of American Geographers*, 42 (1952), p. 254

PLATT, R. R., *Finland and its Geography*, New York, 1955

'Political and Social trends in Sweden', *The World Today*, 12 (1956), pp. 503-511

PORENIUS, P., 'Comments on the development of rural regions in Norrland', *Geografiska Annaler*, 42 (1960), pp. 221-224

POULSEN, A. O., 'The iron ore resources of Norway', Vol. 2, *Symposium sur les gisements de fer du monde* (Ed. Blondel, F., and Marvier, L.), Algiers, 1952

Power Supply in Sweden, Swedish State Power Board, 1956

PRESSNELL, L. S., *Studies in the Industrial Revolution*, London, 1960

PRIOU, C., 'Le Commerce extérieur du Danemark', *Annales de Géographie*, 57 (1948), pp. 187-188

PUGH, J. C., 'The floating power stations of Scandinavia, 1959-61', *Geography*, 47 (1962), pp. 270-277

RAITT, W. L., 'The changing pattern of Norwegian hydro-electric development', *Economic Geography*, 34 (1958), pp. 127-144

REBEYROL, P., 'Les Industries de Stockholm', *Annales de Géographie*, 49 (1940), pp. 35-43

REDDAWAY, W. F., *Problems of the Baltic*, Cambridge, 1940

REPO, R., VARJO, V., and PALOMÄKI, M., *Regional Geography of the Finnish Lake Plateau and of Eastern Finland*, Guidebook to excursion E.F.3, IGU Congress, Norden, 1960

RUDBERG, S., and BYLUND, E., 'From the Bothnian Gulf through southern and central Lapland to the Norwegian fjords', *Geografiska Annaler*, 41 (1959), pp. 261-288

RUGE, S., *Norwegen, Land und Leute*, Leipzig, 1926

SAVORY, H. J., 'Farming in the North Trøndelag', *Geography*, 39 (1954), pp. 272-282

SCHACKE, E., 'The Danish Heath Society', *Scottish Geographical Magazine*, 67 (1951), pp. 45-54

SCHOU, A., 'Danish coastal cliffs in glacial deposits', *Geografiska Annaler*, 31 (1949), pp. 357-364

SCHOVE, D. J., 'Summer temperatures and tree-ring analysis in north Scandinavia. A.D. 1461–1950', *Geografiska Annaler*, 36 (1954), pp. 40-80

SCHYTT, V., 'The glaciers of the Kebnekajse massif', *Geografiska Annaler*, 41 (1959), pp. 213-227

SHAW, E., 'Swine industry of Denmark', *Economic Geography*, 14 (1938), pp. 23-37

SHETELIG, H., and FALK, H., *Scandinavian Archaeology* (translated by E. V. Gordon), Oxford, 1937

Bibliography

SKRUBBELTRANG, F., *Agricultural Development and Rural Reform in Denmark*, F.A.O., Agricultural Studies, 22, Rome, 1953

SMEDS, H., 'The cultural landscape of Swedish Ostrobothnia', *Geographical Review*, 27 (1937), pp. 156-157

SMEDS, H., and MATTILA, J., 'Om utvecklingen av tätorter och landsbygd i Finland, 1880–1930' (on the development of urban and rural areas in Finland since 1880. A study in the geography of population.) *Geografiska Annaler*, 23 (1941), pp. 210-238

SMEDS, H., 'The Replot Skerry Guard: emerging islands in the Northern Baltic', *Geographical Review*, 40 (1950), pp. 103-133

SMEDS, H., 'The distribution of urban and rural population in southern Finland, 1950', *Fennia*, 81 (1958), pp. 1-21

SMEDS, H., 'Post-war land clearance and pioneering activities in Finland', *Fennia*, 83 (1960), pp. 1-31

SØMME, A., 'The physical background of Norwegian agriculture', *Geography*, 35 (1950), pp. 141-154

SØMME, A., 'Norwegian agriculture and food supply', *Geography*, 35 (1950), pp. 215-227

SØMME, A., *Geography of Norwegian Agriculture*, A, Text-volume (1954), B, Atlas (1949), Bergen

STAGG, F. N., *North Norway: a history*, London, 1952

STRØM, K. M., 'The geomorphology of Norway', *Geographical Journal*, 112 (1948), pp. 19-27

SUND, T., and SØMME, A., *Norway in Maps*, Bergen, 1947

SUNDBORG, Å., 'The River Klarälven: a study of fluvial processes', *Geografiska Annaler*, 38 (1956), pp. 125-316

Suomi: a General Handbook on the Geography of Finland, The Geographical Society of Finland, Helsinki, 1952

'Sweden's mineral wealth', *The World Today*, 15 (1959), pp. 78-88

TAMMEKAN, A., 'Salpausselkä', *Geographische Rundschau*, 7 (1955), pp. 94-100

TANNER, V., 'On the nature of the Salpausselkä ridge in Finland', *Fennia*, 58 (1933), pp. 1-36

TEAL, J. J., 'The rebirth of North Norway', *Foreign Affairs*, 32 (1953–54), pp. 123-135

'The future of Finland', *Geographical Review*, 40 (1950), pp. 141-142

The Iron and Steel Industry in Europe, O.E.E.C., 1957

The Northern Countries in the World Economy, Copenhagen, 1937

'The Norwegian Iron and Steel Industry', *British Iron and Steel Federation, Monthly Statistical Bulletin*, 24 (1949)

'The outlook for European trade, after the Free Trade Area negotiations', *The World Today*, 15 (1959), pp. 114-123

'The political scene in Finland', *The World Today*, 11 (1955), pp. 210-216

The Scandinavian States and Finland: a political and economic survey, Royal Institute of International Affairs, 1951

'The U.S.S.R. and her northern neighbours', *The World Today*, 15 (1959), pp. 387-394

THOMSON, C., 'Norway's Industrialization', *Economic Geography*, 14 (1938), pp. 372-380

THORMODSAETER, A., 'Die Nutzung der Fjellgebiete in Norwegen', *Sonderdruck aus Geographische Rundschau*, 1960, pp. 78-82

471

THORPE, H., 'The influence of inclosure on the form and pattern of rural settlement in Denmark', *Transactions of the Institute of British Geographers*, 17 (1951), pp. 113-129

THORPE, H., 'A special case of heath reclamation in the Alheden district of Jutland, 1700-1955', *Trans. Inst. Brit. Geog.*, 23 (1957), pp. 87-121

TIETZE, G., and W., 'Ein Beitrag zur Geographie der Landwirtschaft Schwedens', *Geographische Rundschau*, 1955, pp. 168-173

TIETZE, W., 'Grundzüge der norwegischen Landschaften', *Sonderdruck aus Geographische Rundschau*, 1960, pp. 96-98

TIETZE, W., 'Ein Beitrag zum geomorphologischen Problem der Strandflate', *Petermanns Geographische Mitteilungen*, 106 (1962), pp. 1-20

TINGSTEN, H., 'Issues in Swedish foreign policy', *Foreign Affairs*, 37 (1958-59), pp. 474-485

TSCHUDI, A. B., 'Norwegens Außenhandel', *Sonderdruck aus Geographische Rundschau*, 1960, pp. 87-94

VALLAUX, C., *La Norvège*, Paris, 1913

VEIRULF, O. (Editor), *Dalarna*, Stockholm, 1951

VORREN, Ø., *Norway north of 65*, Oslo, 1960

WALLÉN, C. C., 'Glacial-meteorological investigations on the Kårsa Glacier in Swedish Lapland, 1942-48', *Geografiska Annaler*, 30 (1948), pp. 451-672

WALLÉN, C. C., 'The shrinkage of the Kårsa glacier and its probable meterological causes', *Geografiska Annaler*, 31 (1949)

WALLÉN, C. C., 'The Kårsa glacier and its relation to the climate of the Torne Träsk region', *Geografiska Annaler*, 41 (1959), pp. 236-244

WERENSKIOLD, W., 'Glacial measurements in the Jotunheim', *Geografiska Annaler*, 31 (1949)

WESTERMARCK, N., *Finnish Agriculture*, Pellervo Society, Helsinki, 1954

WIKLUND, K. B., 'The Lapps in Sweden', *Geographical Review*, 8 (1923), pp. 223-242

WILLIAM-OLSSON, W., 'Stockholm : its structure and development', *Geographical Review*, 30 (1940), pp. 420-438

WILLIAM-OLSSON, W., *Stockholm — Structure and Development*, I.G.U. Congress, Norden, 1960. Uppsala, 1960

WOODS, E. G., *The Baltic Region*, London, 1932

ZIMMERMAN, M., 'États scandinaves', 3, *Géographie Universelle* (ed. Vidal de la Blache, P., and Gallois, L.), Paris, 1933

INDEX

Aalborg, 98, 103, 104, 149, 419
Aarhus, 91, 101, 104, 418, 444; population of, 101
Absalon, archbishop, 88
Accordion trade, 399
Acetaldehyde, 374
Acetylene, 442
Adding machines, 261
Aerø, 86, 96
Aga, 248
Agrarian Party (Finland), 451
Agricola, Michael, 125
Agricultural implements, 401, 405
Agricultural labour, decline in Denmark, 235; lack in Finland, 253-4; lack in Sweden, 246, 262
Agricultural machinery, 88, 225-6, 235, 241, 247, 249, 254, 407, 417, 418
Agricultural Revolution in Denmark, 221-5, 236; in Finland, 221, 236, 247, 251-9; in Norway, 236, 247-51, 252; in Sweden, 221, 236-46
Ahlmann, H. W : son, 149, 157
Ähtävänjoki, 215
Aircraft, 394-5, 396, 398, 411, 437
Åkerselv, 23, 35, 37
Åland (Ahvenanmaa) archipelago, 121-124, 446; agriculture of, 123-4; iron ores, 383
Alcohol, 354, 362, 374, 375, 442-4
Alder, 336
Ålesund, 32, 294, 331
Alexander, Tsar, 115, 135
Alitari, 215
Alkali, 363, 441
Allmänna Svenska Elektriska AB, 407
Aluminium, 20, 31, 263, 275, 292, 423, 427, 430, 431, 434-7, 439; cans, 329; oxide, 434, 436; scrap, 436
Ålvik, 438
Ammonia, 432-3, 441
Ancylus Lake, 71, 156
Ångermanland, 76, 188, 338
Ångerman River, 284, 300, 338, 353, 354, 356, 366, 367
Animal fats, 444
Antarctic continent, 158; whaling in, 308, 315, 320-2, 330
Apatite, 397
Apples, 19, 29, 35, 123, 248

Archaean period, 1, 143; mountain building in, 145; rocks of, 4, 383, 447
Arctic, 13, 192; climatic influence of, 166, 168
Arctic air, 168
Arctic Circle, 1, 11, 197, 315
Arctic corridor, 220
Arctic fisheries, 315
Arctic Norway, 276, 290, 316, 329, 403, 423, 433
Arctic railway, 273
Arctic Stone Age, 182, 198, 206, 322
Årdal, 31, 275, 292, 427, 434, 440
Arendal, 22, 434
Areskutan, 73
Argon, 433
Arlöv, 70, 407
Armaments, 44, 79, 394, 424
Arnborg Tore, 349
Artesian water, 149
Artificial fibres, 133, 135, 354
Artificial insemination, 234
Artificial pearls, 322
A/S Bremanger Kraftselskab, 402
A/S Nordag, 275
A/S Odda Smelteverke, 428
Atlantic Ocean, 13, 308; climatic influence of, 165-6, 167, 169
Atomic energy, 262, 264, 266, 304
Atomic reactor, 261, 433
Atomic weapons, 450
Ätran River, 64
Automatic lighthouses, 405
Automatic telephone exchanges, 407
Avaviken, 186
Avesta, 399, 400
Axes, 423
Axles, 61
Azores anticyclone, 108

Bacon, 44, 100, 222, 226, 234, 278, 416, 418
Ball bearings, 66, 405, 410-11
Baltic area, 2, 169, 181, 211, 311, 446
Baltic herring, 308, 325, 326
Baltic Republics, 4, 7, 192, 447, 449
Baltic Sea, 2, 4, 165, 169, 170, 214, 308, 326, 342, 382
Baltic Shield, 1, 50, 51, 109, 143-4, 146
Bardu River, 200, 201

Barents Sea, 319, 449
Barley, 25, 35, 40, 55, 69, 87, 100, 127, 161, 173, 183, 196, 202, 225, 228, 230, 231, 234, 235, 239, 241, 244, 246, 247, 259
Bauxite, 263, 427, 436
Bears, 107
Beech, 19, 63, 86, 87, 90, 93
Beef, 233
Bergen, 14, 16, 20, 22, 24, 27, 28, 33-5, 165, 171, 192, 193-5, 199, 249, 267, 294, 296, 330, 420, 422, 440
Bergen, industries of, 34, 260, 268
Bergen-Oslo railway, 41, 43
Bergkulland, 145
Bergslagen, 50, 51, 54, 60-2, 65, 145, 180 236, 270, 353, 376, 378, 382-8, 389, 392, 394, 395, 397, 398, 405, 407
Bessemer process, 61, 376, 392, 393
Bicycles, 79
Bilberry, 136
Birch, 26, 43, 185, 220, 335, 338, 340, 363
Birch-bark flour, 198
Birch forest belt, 26, 339-40, 349, 364
Birger Jarl, 170, 212
Birka, 215
Birkeland, Professor Kristian, 430
Birkeland-Eyde technique, 431, 432
Blaavands Huk, 105
Black Death, 179, 199
Black Sea, 2
Blast furnaces, 376, 382, 385, 388, 389, 393, 394, 461
Blekinge, 48, 70, 345
Blötberg, 385
Blubber boiler, 423
Boat Axe Culture, 207, 210
Bodø, 260, 273, 291
Bofors, 389, 394; A.B. Bofors-Gullspång, 394
Bog and lake ores, 382, 463
Bohuslän, 7, 51, 62, 181, 323, 325, 331, 412
Boilers, 376
Bokn fjord, 29-30, 34, 296, 438
Book publishing, 365
Boots and shoes, 55, 135, 278
Borlange, 365
Bornholm, 80, 82, 93
Borregaard Company, 354, 375
Bottling machinery, 417
Boulder clay, 4, 68, 71, 105, 110, 340, 382
Brass, 269
Braviken, 178
Brevik, 20
Breweries, 70, 103
Bricks, 149

Brisling, 264
British Aluminium Co., 434, 440
Brøgger, A. W., 14, 179
Bronze Age, 6, 28, 36, 43, 86, 87, 88, 96, 103, 147, 156, 160, 169, 172-3, 175, 200, 209, 214, 338; settlement and glacial features, 154
Building industry, 396, 404
Burmeister and Wain, 309
Buses, 415
Butter, 25, 44, 56, 69, 71, 119, 222, 226, 228, 234, 247-8, 259, 278, 418, 440

Cable works, 424
Calcareous sandstone, 196
Calcium alloys, 438
Calcium bisulphate, 360
Calcium carbide, 278, 427, 428-30, 438, 441, 442
Calcium cyanamide, 430, 442
Calcium nitrate, 431, 433
Calculating machines, 410
Caledonian structures, 4, 25, 29, 30, 38, 73, 143, 145, 146-7
Cambrian Period, 19, 25, 29, 40, 55, 67, 71, 146, 196
Cameras, 44
Canning industry, 244
Cannons, 394
Cardboard, 361; cardboard-making plant, 423
Cargo liners, 312, 313; ships, 413
Carlsberg Brewery, 92
Cars, 66, 178, 261, 262, 264, 276, 394, 396, 398, 405, 411, 414-15
Casein, 444
Cash registers, 261
Cattle, 35, 40, 42, 56, 112, 131, 183, 202, 206, 222, 228, 230, 231, 233, 241, 248, 253, 257, 418
Cattle food, 233, 249, 259, 322, 330
Cellulose, 16, 46, 76, 133, 190, 265, 351, 354, 356, 358, 361, 362, 367, 375; cellulose wool, 190
Cement, 72, 83, 98, 124, 149, 363, 368; cement - making machinery, 418; cement factories, 103, 418
Charcoal, 61, 269, 345, 353, 366, 378, 388, 392, 395, 398, 401, 405
Charles IX of Sweden, 51
Charles Gustavus X of Sweden, 167
Cheese, 25, 56, 222, 234, 247, 248, 259
Chemicals, 16, 114, 116, 261, 354, 374, 395, 398, 400, 427; electro-chemical industry, 27, 266, 274, 362, 363; chemical industry in Denmark, 428, 441, 444; chemical industry in Finland, 427, 428, 441, 444-5; location

Index

of, 428; chemical industry in Norway, 427, 428-33; chemical pulp, 360-1, 367, 370, 373, 374; settlements based on chemical industry, 431-2; chemical industry in Sweden, 427, 428-33
Cherries, 19, 35, 96, 248
China, 92, 116
Chlorine, 363, 441, 442
Christian era, 2, 6, 173
Christian missionaries, 211
Christian IV, King of Denmark, 92
Christiania Spigerwerk, 401-2
Christianity, 2, 125, 160, 265
Christiansborg, 88
Chrome, 438; alloys, 438
Climate, 1, 2, 5, 13, 32, 56, 67, 75, 76-7, 78, 80-2, 93, 102, 107-8, 112, 127, 137, 240, 244, 252-3, 294, 338, 447; Atlantic influence in Scandinavian climate, 165-6, 167, 169; climate and character, 163; local climates, 230, 246, 248, 333; local climate and settlement, 162; climatic fluctuations, 161-9, 170-171, 180, 199, 251, 331, 349, 370; post-glacial climates, 156, 157, 200
Clothing, 91, 116, 278
Clover, 239
Coal, 101, 103, 114, 200, 263-8 pass., 278, 282, 298, 309, 310, 353, 388, 395, 427, 428, 430
Cod, 32, 121, 194, 307, 308, 315-19, 322-330 pass., 440
Cod liver oil, 322
Coke, 204, 263-5 pass., 380-8 pass., 392, 395, 397, 402, 427, 430, 437, 441
Comb Ceramic Culture, 209
Common lands, 221, 223
Common Market, 416, 418, 452-3, 454
Communications, 21, 22, 36, 41, 56, 57, 75, 79, 88, 96, 103, 118, 121-9 pass., 130, 133, 134, 137, 163, 177, 186, 193, 265, 270-6 pass., 323, 363-6 pass., 407-411 pass., 442; changes in twentieth century, 27; effect of glacial deposits on, 53, 154; and forest industries, 342-343; of Göteborg, 64-5; of Helsinki, 115-16; and freezing of ports, 118, 120, 125, 126, 162, 367-70; medieval, 43; in the North Norway Plan, 204; of Oslo, 23; prehistoric, 36, 154, 175
Compagnie Royale Asturienne des Mines, 439
Company towns, 431-2
Compressed air drilling, 299
Concentrating plants, 378
Condensed milk, 222
Constitutional monarchy, 5
Conurbation, 70

Co-operatives, 227, 243; bacon co-operatives, 100, 227; dairies, 100, 119, 226, 227, 248, 417; fishing co-operatives, 329
Copenhagen, 33, 57, 83, 87, 88-93, 149, 223, 272, 315, 417, 418, 419, 450; history of, 175-6; industries of, 91-2, 444
Copper, 26, 37, 40, 44, 50, 180, 267, 376, 378, 467, 434, 438, 439
Cotton, 24, 34, 64, 66, 127, 135, 268, 269, 360
Cream separator, 226
Cretaceous period, 4 67, 83, 87, 93, 98, 103, 149
Customs Union, 458
Cutlery, 44, 79

Dairy farming, 5, 25, 49, 69, 71, 87, 92, 100, 124, 127, 196, 257-9; export of products, 101, 119; machinery, 44, 410
Dala sandstone, 145
Dalecarlia, 53
Dalkarlsberg, 394
Dal River, 46, 48, 60, 179, 185, 284, 383, 389
Danian limestone, 149
Danish archipelago, 1, 4, 69, 80
Danish Heathland Society, 177, 225
Danish-Prussian War of 1864, 105
Deal, 188
Deciduous woodland, 335-6, 339; uses of, 342, 363
Deep freeze, 244
de Geer, Louis, 178, 269
de Geer, Sten, 154
Degerfors, 389
Denmark, 4, 5, 8, 11, 51, 62, 63, 69, 70, 78, 80-106, 166, 169, 196, 197, 243, 265, 275, 415, 448, 449, 450-57 pass., agricultural revolution in, 221, 223, 239; agriculture of Denmark compared with the British Isles, 228-30; agriculture of, 222-35, 236, 241-9 pass.; agriculture regions, 230-3; area of, 80; chemical industry in, 428, 441, 444; climate of, 166, 169; Danes in Sweden, 192; Danish history, 173-7; Denmark and Norway, 196-7, 199; economy of, 84, 249, 278; electricity, 281, 298, 302; engineering, 88, 91, 263, 401, 404, 416, 417-20; exports of, 222-3, 234, 243, 278; fishing, 307, 322-3, 325, 326; forests, 335, 336; German minority in, 99-100; glaciation in, 153; heaths, 83-4, 96, 98, 104, 177, 224, 233, 240; industrial maturity

475

of, 262; Industrial Revolution in, 223, 260; industry, 263-5; iron ores in, 397, 401, 403-4; merchant navy of, 306-7, 309-15 *pass.*, 326; population of, 80; post-war trends in agriculture, 233-5; railways, 272, 273; scrap iron, 397

'Diamonds', 182

Diesel engines, 309, 326, 422

Diesel fuel, 305

Diesel ships, 109, 418

Distilling, 103

Dnieper valley, 2, 7

Dolomitic limestone, 146

Domestic electrical equipment, 417

Domnarvet, 400, 407

Domsjö, 444

Douglas Fir, 339

Dovrefjell, 13, 16, 23, 27, 31, 149, 150

Drammen, 19-23 *pass.*, 297, 353, 373

Dramselv, 20, 373

Dunderlandsdal, 203, 380

Dutch timber trade, 351

Dynamos, 116, 405, 407

Dyrehavn, 90

East Germany, 449

Echo sounders, 261, 320, 327

Economic depressions, 277-8, 354, 369, 393, 403, 411, 413, 423, 426, 430, 451

Economic Union, 457-8

Eels, 103, 325

Egersund, 319

Eggs, 222

Eidsvoll, 23, 272

Eitrheim, 30, 263, 427, 430, 439

Ejer, Mt, 83

Ekman, Carl, 360

Electric locomotives, 44, 409

Electric motors, 66, 116, 261, 410

Electricity: in Denmark, 281, 298, 302; distribution and uses of, 281, 282, 286, 289, 290, 294, 296, 427; electrical engineering, 261, 276, 369; in Finland, 280-2, 283, 286-9, 294-300 *pass.*, 302, 427; electric furnaces, 378, 380, 383, 385, 388, 393, 397, 402, 423, 427, 434, 436, 437, 438, 439; hydro-electricity, 14, 18, 20, 60-1, 66, 79, 84, 119, 133, 177, 190, 195, 204, 262, 264, 266, 274, 275, 342, 353, 395, 401, 402, 407, 419, 423, 434; international transmission of, 302-4; in North Norway Plan, 204; in Norway, 280-3, 290-7, 299, 300, 302, 304; oil tanker electric generators, 297; potential hydro-electric power, 75, 139, 266, 282,

284, 286; power stations, 31, 128, 134, 266, 284, 296; power station equipment, 109, 276, 405, 407-16; electric railways, 284, 409, 442; electric smelting, 275; in Sweden, 280, 281, 282, 283-6, 290, 294, 296, 297-304 *pass.*; seasonal variations of, 292-4, 297; thermo-electric plant, 298; transformers, 276, 424; transmission of electricity, 190, 276, 281-90 *pass.*, 292, 294, 296, 300-2, 393, 407-9, 423, 428, 432, 437, 458; underground power stations, 294, 299, 300

Emigration, 67, 72, 92, 99, 100, 233, 268; Finnish emigration to Sweden, 17, 62, 458; Swedish emigrants to Finland, 114, 121, 126; Viking emigrants, 28, 46, 198

Enclosure of open fields, 223-4

Engelbrektsson, Engelbrekt, 181

Engel, Ludvig, 117

Engineering, 23, 34; in Denmark, 88, 91, 263, 401, 404, 416, 417-20; in Finland, 109, 116, 124, 135, 254, 263, 277, 401, 404, 416, 417, 424-6; in Norway, 401, 402, 416-17, 420-4; in Sweden, 44, 54, 55, 60, 61, 177-8, 243, 306, 396, 405, 426; origins of engineering industry, 416-17

England and industry in Scandinavia, 268, 269, 274-7, 351, 368, 392

Ericson, Nils, 272

Ericsson Coy., 409

Eric the Holy, 181

Esbjerg, 91, 99, 100, 101, 105-6, 272, 323

Eskers, 53, 71, 78, 110, 128, 130, 135, 154, 178, 215, 286

Eskilstuna, 48, 177

Estates, 56, 87, 238, 254; of Rosendal, 30

Ethylene, 374

Eurasia, high pressure system of, 165

European Coal and Steel Community, 452

European Economic Community, 416, 418, 452-3

European Free Trade Association, 416, 451, 453-4, 456

European Payments Union, 452

Eydehavn, 436

Eyde, Samuel, 430, 440

Faaborg, 97

Fäbod, 183, 222

Faeroes, 4

Fagersta, 392

Fagersta Bruks A.B., 392, 393, 399

Faggot, Jacob, 236

Falconbridge Nikkelverk A/S, 438
Fallow, 221, 239
Falster, 86, 93, 169, 176, 230
Falun, 60, 267, 378, 467
Famine, 198, 219
Farm buildings, 69, 213-14, 224
Farm implements, 116
Farm size, 233, 241, 242, 246, 249
Farmers, 11, 14, 40, 182, 220, 223, 242
Farming, 87, 96, 260-1, 266; archaic
    methods of, 222, 247; and climate,
    162, 170; in Denmark, 173, 222-35;
    in Finland, 110, 112, 120, 124, 127,
    130-1, 136, 138, 215-18 *pass.*, 251-59;
    and government policy, 243, 246, 458;
    in Norway, 25, 35, 195, 202, 203, 247-
    251; in Sweden, 61, 63, 69, 190, 236-
    246
Farmland, 18, 29, 49, 161, 190, 200, 251;
    abandoned 200, 235, 246, 248, 366;
    marginal, 40, 75, 180, 190, 235, 251;
    potential, 188; reclaimed, 72, 83, 98,
    105
Farsta, 262
Faxe, 149
Femunden Lake, 26
Fenno-Scandia, 143
Ferro-alloys, 261, 438, 439
Ferro-chrome, 438
Ferro-manganese, 438
Ferro-silicon, 438
Fertilizers, 18, 20, 101, 103, 149, 224, 225,
    233, 253, 259, 305, 322, 427-39 *pass.*,
    441, 445
Field drains, 131, 224-5, 241
Filjefell, 27
Finland, 4-11 *pass.*, 80-1, 265, 275, 276,
    300, 415, 449, 450, 451, 453, 457;
    agricultural revolution, 221, 247;
    charcoal, 404; climate, 169; chemical
    industry, 427, 428, 441, 444-5; eco-
    nomic self-sufficiency, 251; economic
    trend, 254; electricity and industry,
    266, 280, 283, 286-9, 294, 296, 298,
    300, 302, 427; engineering in, 109,
    116, 124, 135, 254, 263, 277, 401, 404,
    416, 417, 424-6 farming in, 110, 112,
    120, 124, 127, 130-1, 136, 138, 215,
    216, 218, 236, 251-9; farm subsidies,
    257, 259; Finns in Sweden, 62, 183-5;
    192; Finns, origin of, 208; fishing,
    118, 170, 307-8, 317, 322; forest
    ownership, 344, 345, 351, 356; forests
    in, 333-5, 338, 341-9 *pass.*; 364;
    glaciation in, 153-6; growth of com-
    munications, 115-16; heaths, 112;
    industry, 260, 261, 263-9 *pass.*, 277;
    iron in, 382-3, 400, 401, 404; mer-

chant navy of, 306, 307, 309; popula-
    tion of, 107, 219; railways, 272, 273;
    space relationships of, 107-9, 206, 211,
    220, 448; Swedes in Finland, 117, 125,
    181, 206, 212, 218, 404, 446-7; trade
    and industry, 358-61 *pass.*, 369-73, 374,
    375; tribal areas, 211, 218
Finlayson, James, 135, 269
Finnmark, 40, 198, 202-6 *pass.*, 290, 315,
    317-19
Finse, 41
Firebrick, 433
Firn-line, 171
First crusade, 125, 181, 211, 212
Fish: canneries, 197, 264, 320, 322, 330,
    417; dried fish, 317, 329, 330; freez-
    ing of, 261, 317, 319, 322, 323, 329,
    330; hooks, 423; machinery for fac-
    tories, 423; meal, 329, 330; and the
    North Norway Plan, 204; offal, 249;
    oil, 329, 330; processing of, 319, 320,
    322, 323, 325-9 *pass.*; trade in, 193-4,
    196, 199
Fishing, 11, 20, 37, 40, 44, 105, 175, 202,
    203, 260-1, 266, 267, 305, 315, 359;
    archaic techniques, 317, 325, 327-9;
    Baltic herring, 308, 325, 326; brisling,
    264; cod, 32, 121, 194, 307, 308, 315-
    319, 322-32 *pass.*; in Denmark, 307,
    322-3, 325, 326; echo sounding in,
    320, 327; eels, 103, 325; environ-
    mental changes, 331-2; in Finland,
    118, 170, 307-8, 317, 322; flounder,
    121; fishing grounds, 5, 305, 316-17,
    319-25 *pass.*; halibut, 323; herring,
    88, 121, 175, 194, 197, 307, 308, 319,
    320-31 *pass.*; mackerel, 320, 329; in
    Norway, 305, 307, 315-22, 325, 326-9,
    330, 331; oysters, 103; plaice, 323;
    purse seine nets in, 320; salmon, 304,
    308, 325; sealing, 32, 200, 326, 331;
    sprats, 320; in Sweden, 322, 323-25,
    326, 331, 332; trout, 308; whale, 200,
    308, 315, 320-22
Fjäll, 73, 236
Fjell, 23, 192, 195
Flackarp, 239
Flensburg, 99, 418
Flour mills, 23, 88, 91, 127, 135
Fodder, 40, 112, 127, 221, 228, 230, 235,
    239, 251, 259
Fodder beet, 235
Folgefonni plateau, 248
Folk High Schools, 226, 243
Food processing machinery, 418
Forestry tools and machinery, 405-7, 417,
    423
Forests, 16, 75, 110, 138, 160-1, 188, 198,

241, 260-1, 266, 308, 378, 439; afforestation, 105, 177, 233, 246, 335, 339, 366; burning, 131, 171, 179, 183, 340, 349; clearance and grazing, 42, 43, 127, 179, 194; company forests, 345, 347; conservation of, 342, 347, 353, 358; in Denmark, 335; evolution in post-glacial times, 156, 157; farming in, 241-2; in Finland, 333-5, 338, 341, 342, 343, 349, 364; individual ownership of, 343, 347, 348, 358; location of forest industries, 353, 362, 369, 371; management of, 347, 348, 356, 358, 370; in Norway, 333, 336, 338, 343, 348; parish ownership, 343; rate of growth, 132, 138, 277, 341-2; state ownership of forests, 343, 344, 345, 358; in Sweden, 333, 337-43 *pass.*, 349; types of, 60, 71, 102, 123, 132, 136, 333-39 *pass.*; uses of, 347, 350-1, 356; vertical zonation of, 336

Forest industries: in Finland, 358, 359, 360, 361, 369-73, 374, 375; in Norway, 351, 354-6, 359, 360, 361, 369-74, 375; in Sweden, 351-8, 359, 361, 362-3, 364-369

Forest ownership: in Finland, 344, 345, 351, 356; in Norway, 343, 348, 356; in Sweden, 345-7

Forest Tree Breeding Association, 349

Forges, 376, 389, 394

Forsbacka works, 393

Foundries, 416, 417, 424

Frederikshavn, 104, 323

Frederikstad, 18, 420

Frederiksværk, 275, 404, 419

Free trade, 243, 268, 369, 444, 453-4, 455

Frisians, 100, 214, 215, 233

Fröding, Gustav, 62

Frogner, 24

Frognerseter, 24

Funen, 83, 86, 95, 153, 176; Alps of, 153; population of, 96

Furniture, 79, 129, 133, 278, 335, 351

Furs, 37, 126, 196, 206, 210, 214, 267, 440; fur traders, 182, 215; fur trappers' trails, 216

Gabbro, 73, 145

Gällivare, 186, 188, 284

Gamla Uppsala, 54

gard, 247

Gaula River, 36

Gävle, 50, 60, 65, 270, 383

Gävleån, 179

Gedser, 88

Geophysical prospecting, 382

Germany, relations with, 274-7, 279, 312

Gestrikland, 60

Gibson, Alexander, 269

Glass, 20, 79, 116, 190

Glint line, 144, 190

Glomfjord, 292, 433, 436

Glomma River, 16, 18, 20, 22, 23-6 *pass.*, 353, 372, 373, 375, 428

Gneiss, 18, 40, 49, 61, 75, 77, 94, 121, 146

Goats, 40, 42

Gold, 60, 180

Göta canal, 55, 178

Göta River, 51, 62, 64, 156, 266, 269, 363, 407

Götaverken, 269

Göteborg, 23, 44, 48, 56, 64-7, 72, 269, 270, 272, 302, 306, 315, 323, 363, 365, 366, 396, 405, 409, 410; manufacture of cars at, 415; population of, 66; shipbuilding in, 411

Goths, 2, 50, 177, 211

Gotland, 2, 71, 236, 409

Götland, 51, 55-6, 160

Graadyb, 105

Grängesberg, 60, 272, 376, 378, 385, 397, 408

Grängesberg Coy., 313, 388

Granite, 7, 18, 19, 40, 62, 75, 77, 82, 94, 110, 121, 145, 146, 147, 383; industry, 95

Granö, J. G., 210

Gravehalsen tunnel, 43

Great Belt, 86, 87, 96; glaciation of, 153, 156

Great Death, 219

Great Northern War, 219

Greek Orthodox Church, 198, 211-12

Greenland, 4

Grimstad, 22

Grundtvig, N. F. S., 226

Guanin, 322

Gudbrandsdal, 26, 27, 296

Gulf of Bothnia, 110, 112, 121, 126, 138, 163, 182, 210, 215, 325, 326, 342, 345, 351, 354, 365, 366, 367, 370, 388; emergence of land from, 127, 154, 170, 182

Gulf of Finland, 110, 112, 129, 147, 181, 253, 325, 340, 370

Gustavus Adolphus of Sweden, 4, 51, 59, 64-66, 178, 186

Gustavus Vasa of Sweden, 50, 54, 59, 114, 181, 218

Gysinge, 61, 378

Haarfarge, Harald, 28

Haber-Bosch process, 432, 433

Hagfors, 389, 399

Halden, 261, 373

Index

Halibut, 323
Halland, 48, 51, 63-4, 78, 345
Hallingdal, 20-8 *pass.*, 296, 373
Hallingskarvet, 41
Hallsberg, 302
Hallsjön, 407
Hallsta, 365
Hälsingborg, 69, 70, 88, 265, 302, 411
Hamar, 25, 147
Häme, 211, 212
Hamina, 120
Hammarö island, 362
Hammerfest, 200, 266
Hammer mills, 394
Han, 102
Hanko, 110, 112, 115, 118-21, 154, 383, 404
Hanseatic League, 28, 33, 58, 72, 89, 106, 170, 193-4, 196, 199, 267, 329, 330, 440
Hantsholm, 323
Hardanger fjord, 29-30, 193, 248, 263, 422, 434, 438, 439
Hardangervidda, 13, 16, 23, 27, 41, 146, 151
Hardboard, 46, 76, 128, 364, 374
Härjedalen, 76
Härnösand, 76
Harsprånget, 285, 286, 302, 408
hartkorn valuation, 174
Haus, 34
Hay, 40, 75, 112, 124, 127, 131, 137, 222, 241, 247
Heaths: in Denmark, 83-4, 96, 98, 104, 177, 224, 233, 240; in Finland, 112; in Sweden, 71, 77
Heat resisting castings, 402
Heavy water, 433
Hede, 87, 96, 153, 173, 174
Helgeland, 291
Helsingør, 87, 419
Helsinki, 1, 112, 114-18, 120, 170, 451; industries of, 116, 417; population of, 116; replanning of, 117; site of, 114
Hematite, 380, 382, 384
Hemp, 131
Henningsvaer, 317
Henry, Bishop of Uppsala, 211
Herning, 177
Herøya, 20, 432, 433
Herring, 88, 104, 121, 175, 194, 197, 307, 308, 319, 320, 322-31 *pass.*
Himmelberg, 83, 153
Himmerland, 102
Historical geography: of Denmark, 172, 173-7; of Finland, 172, 206-20; of Norway, 179, 180, 192-205; of Sweden 177-92

Hjälmaren Lake, 53, 54
Hjedding, 227
Hofors Bruk, 410
Höganäs, 388
Højer, 99
Holbæk, 88
Holmestrand, 20
Hønefoss, 25, 361, 372, 373
Hönö Klova, 323
Hordaland, 34, 294, 296
Hops, 96, 230
Horses, 71, 226
Høyanger, 31, 427, 431, 434, 437
Huskvarna, 79
Hyndevads River, 177
hyttan, 61

Ice Age, 1, 2, 11, 18, 25, 143, 148, 150-61, 169, 338; in Archaean period, 145; in Denmark, 83, 94, 98, 99, 104, 153; in Norway, 32, 151; in Sweden, 53, 153
Iceland, 4, 28, 448
Idkerberg, 385
Ii River, 127
Iisalmi, 134
Imatra, 133, 289
Inari Lake, 138
Indals River, 275, 284, 300, 356
Industrial growth: supply of capital for, 264-5, 269-70, 376-8, 420-22, 423, 439-440
Industrial location, 380, 388-95 *pass.*, 428, 431-2, 438
Industrial Revolution, 23, 103, 188, 221, 223, 260, 264, 273, 309, 353, 354, 358-364, 376, 382, 420; in Denmark, 265; in Finland, 265, 269; in Norway, 265, 268; in Sweden, 265-8, 383-400
inmark, 247
Insulating material, 433
Insulin, 444
Iron Age, 2, 7, 14, 157, 171, 173, 200, 208-14 *pass.*, 222, 247
Iron industry, 44, 54, 180, 264, 267, 275, 276, 292, 345, 353, 359, 366, 376, 410, 434; bar-iron, 376, 385, 390, 399; Bessemer process, 376, 392, 393; decline of iron industry in the nineteenth century, 61, 269, 385, 389-92, 461; in Denmark, 397, 401, 403-4 electric furnace in, 378, 380, 382, 385, 393, 397; in Finland, 382-3, 400, 401, 404; Kaldo oxygen furnace, 388; in Norway, 378-82, 401-3; open-hearth process, 376, 393, 394; rolled strip mills, 393, 399, 400; Siemens Martin furnace, 461; sponge iron, 382, 385, 388,

479

397; in Sweden, 376, 378, 380-2, 383-400, 402; Thomas process, 376, 385, 392, 397; Tysland-Hole electric furnace, 402
Iron ore, 5, 37, 40, 44, 50, 60, 73, 75, 145, 180, 186, 188-9, 197, 203, 243, 263, 264, 270, 284, 306, 376, 378, 380, 382, 383-5, 401, 404, 416, 455
Isefjord, 88
Isohaara, 288

Jæren, 124, 193
Jammer Bugt, 102
Jämtland, 36, 73, 76, 147, 182, 183, 222, 241, 242, 338, 340, 343, 345, 349
Jänniskoski, 138
Jernkontoret, The Swedish Ironmasters Association, 390, 398
Johnson Line, 66
Jokkmokk, 186
Jönköping, 78, 79
Jørpeland, 402
Jotnian sandstone, 145
Jotunheimen, 13, 16, 26, 41, 149, 150, 292
Jurassic period, 149
Jussarö, 383
Jutland, 4, 80, 83, 86, 93, 96, 98-106, 149, 153, 166, 169, 173, 176-7, 199, 225-35 *pass.*, 282, 323, 409, 419
Jyväskylä, 134, 374

Kainu, 136
Kajaani, 137
Kaldo oxygen furnace, 388
Kalevala, 131, 209
Kalix River, 289
Kallavesi Lake, 134
Kallinge, 386-88
Kalmar, 48, 71, 72, 78, 407
Karasjok, 203
Karelia, 107, 109, 136-38 *pass.*, 169, 172, 209, 210-20 *pass.*, 287, 302, 448, 449
Karjala, 211
Karlshamn, 415
Karlskoga, 394
Karlstad, 64
Kärväsvaara, 382
Kaskinen, 127
Kassefors, 64
Kattegat, 165
Kautokeino, 203
Keiller, Alexander, 269
Kemi, 138, 358, 361, 375
Kemijoki Corporation, 289
Kemiö, 124
Kemi River, 127, 138, 286, 287-9, 294, 300, 302, 340, 341-2, 345, 353
Kernels, 444

Kinna, 64
Kirkenes, 13, 290, 378
Kiruna, 284, 378, 380, 383, 409
Kirunavaara, 188-9
Kitchen middens, 182, 326
Kitchen sinks, 400
Klar River, 50, 60, 61, 362-3
klipfisk, 32, 194, 329, 330
Knitted goods, 135
Kockum, 70, 414
Køge, 87
Kohlrabi, 235
Kokemäenjoki, 125, 126, 210, 211, 212, 215
Kokkola, 127, 212, 215
Kola peninsula, 198
Kolari, 382
Kolbäcksån, 179, 389, 392, 393
Kolmärden, 53
Kolsaas, 19
Komsa culture, 206
Kongsberg, 27
Kongsvinger, 23
Kopparberg, 60
Korean War, 277
Kotka, 118-21, 404
Kraft paper, 363, 368
Kramfors, 188
Kristiansand, 22, 263, 296, 402, 436, 438
Kristiansund, 32, 319
Kristinehamn, 64
Krylbo, 61
Kungshammaren, 393
Kuopio, 134
Kymi River, 112, 118, 119, 130, 212, 361, 370
Kyrönsalmi strait, 134

Labour: in fisheries, 325, 326, 332; in forestry, 347-8, 354, 356, 423; industrial, 191, 396-7, 405, 413, 420-3, 424-6, 427, 445; mobility between Scandinavian states, 457
Labrador, 4
Ladoga Lake, 119, 128, 134, 144, 210, 211, 253
Lagan River, 64
Lagerhjelm, Per, 394
Lagerlöf, Selma, 62
Lahti, 115, 129, 133
Lakes Plateau, Finland, 128-35; communications, 129; industrial centres, 133-5; origin of lakes, 129; postglacial uplift and drainage changes, 130
Land: clearance, 172, 179, 183-6; reclamation, 177, 200, 239, 240-1; reform, 124, 224, 248

Index

Langeland, 86, 96
Langerak, 103
Langesund, 20
Language: Danish, 5, 102; Finnish, 7, 117-18, 128, 131, 208-9, 212; Norwegian, 24-5, 31; Swedish, 5, 7
Lapland, 77, 107, 135, 136-9 *pass.*, 165, 166, 168, 189, 257, 276, 286, 287, 294, 336, 342, 364, 382, 385
Lappeenranta, 133
Lapps, 6, 40, 76, 188, 202-3
Larvik, 19, 20, 320, 438
Lauritsala, 133
Lava, 19, 147-48
Lead, 60, 145, 180, 376
League of Nations, 447
Leptite, 144, 145, 383
Lichens, 136
Lidköping, 178
Lilla Edet, 66
Lillehammer, 25, 373
Lillesand, 22
Lillestrøm, 23, 25
Lille Vildmose, 102
Lime, 19, 72, 124, 225, 230, 240, 427
Limestone, 19, 25, 56, 67, 72, 83, 149, 402, 437
Limfjorden, 98, 103
Lindø, 419, 422
Linen, 66, 104
Linköping, 407
Linseed, 233, 244
Little Belt, 86, 96, 99; glaciation of, 153
Littorina Sea, 71, 98, 103, 156-7, 170, 181, 209
Liverwort, 136
Ljungan River, 284, 300, 353, 356, 366
Lofoten Islands, 196-200 *pass.*, fishing, 315, 317, 327-32 *pass.*; local glaciation of, 151; strandflat, 158
Løgumkloster, 99
Loimaa, 121, 124-6, 210
Lolland, 86, 93, 176, 230, 231
Lom, 43
Longyearbyen, 171
Lönnrot, Elias, 209
Lorries, 4, 14, 415
Lübeck, 95, 449
Ludvika, 270
Luleå, 186, 380, 382, 388, 389, 395
Lule River, 284, 285
Lund, 67, 70
Lutheran missionaries, 202, 203
Lyngby, 92
Lyngenfjord, 146
Lysefjord, 30
Lysekil, 412

Maarianhamma, 122-3
Machine tools, 116, 178, 294, 396, 398, 405
Mackerel, 320, 329
Magnesium, 427, 433
Magnetite, 378, 380, 382, 383
Magnets, 402
Mälaren Lake, 50-7 *pass.*, 72, 156, 160, 169, 170, 177, 180, 236, 239, 298
Malmö, 56, 68-70 *pass.*, 298, 306, 396, 407, 411, 414, 459
Måls River, 200, 201
Måne River, 433
Manganese, 438
Mangolds, 235
Manor farms: in Denmark, 224, 226
Margarine, 70, 91, 101, 103, 330
Mariager fjord, 98, 100
Market gardening, 71, 87, 235, 244
Marling, 225
Marshall Aid, 204, 225, 276, 378, 457
Marstal, 97
Marstrand, 63
Matches, 79, 134, 178
Mayer, F. V., 456
Mechanical pulp, 359, 360, 373
Melamine, 442
Meraker, 428
Merchant navies: change from sail to steam, 309-10; of Denmark, 306, 310-311, 419; of Finland, 307; of Norway, 194-5, 268, 276, 310, 420, 423; of Sweden, 306, 311
Mesolithic fisheries, 326
Mesozoic Age, 83, 98, 148-9, 173
Metallurgical-electro industries, 266, 274, 275, 281, 431; in Norway, 434-41; Scandinavian states compared, 427-8
Metallurgical coke, 380, 382, 385, 388, 392, 395, 396-402 *pass.*
Middle Ages, 2, 5, 24, 58, 63, 76, 79, 222, 440; Bergen in, 33, 193-4; Copenhagen in, 88-9, 175; deforestation, 333; Denmark in, 86, 93-9 *pass.*, 106, 153, 233, 446; Finland in, 114, 118, 121, 125, 126, 134, 135, 206, 214, 218; fishing techniques of, 317, 329; Norrland settlement in, 182-5; Norway settlement in, 161, 198; Stockholm in, 59, 170; Swedish industry of, 44, 180, 270, 376, 393
Midskog, 275
Mikkeli, 114
Milk centrifuges, 417
Mining: copper, 26, 50, 60, 180, 267; gold, 60, 180; iron, 50, 60, 180, 188, 197, 378-84, 402, 407; lead, 60, 180; silver, 27, 60, 180; zinc, 60

Mink, 249
Miocene period, 157
Mixed forests, 335-6
Mjøsa Lake, 25, 147, 250, 373
Mo i Rana, 204, 292, 380, 382, 403, 404, 431
Møn, 86, 93, 149, 169, 176, 230
Mo och Domsjö Corporation, 374, 375
Moraines, 25, 75, 87, 95, 100, 101, 153, 185
Møre, 33
Moscow Agreement (1944), 253
Mosjøen, 292, 436
Moskensøy, 158
Motala, 55, 178, 407
Motala River, 55, 178
Motor ships, 305, 307, 309-11, 323, 418
Mullavesi, 133
Muoni River, 289
Murviken, 428
Mustard, 244

Næstved, 88
Nails, 401
Namdal, 35
Napoleonic Wars, 5, 7, 89, 96, 176, 206, 224, 230, 274, 401, 448
Nappes (Caledonian), 144
Närke, 53
Narvik, 284, 306, 409, 448
Näsijärvi Lake, 135, 210, 215
Nationalism, 192-3, 251
N.A.T.O. (North Atlantic Treaty Organization), 449, 450
Navigation Act (1849), 268
Nea River, 302
Neolithic period, 28, 67, 72, 143, 153, 158, 160, 169, 170-73 *pass.*, 177, 193, 196, 200, 210, 336
Netherlands, 312, 368, 456
Newsprint, 361-8 *pass.*, 373
Nickel, 263, 434, 438, 439
Nid River, 36, 37
Niobium, 438
Nissan River, 64
Nitrates, 439
Nitrogenous fertilizers, 428, 437, 442, 445
Nobel, Alfred, 394
Nordag A/S, 436
Nord fjord, 30-1, 248, 294, 402
Nordic Council, 450, 457-9
Nordic Race, 5
Nordland (province of Norway), 203, 273, 291, 292, 320, 380, 431, 433
Nordmarka, 19, 22
Nordmøre, 31-3, 294
Normandy, 4

Norrbotten, 76, 183, 188, 244
Norrbottens Järnverk, 380, 388
Norrköping, 53, 55, 178, 365
Norrland, 46, 48, 50, 59, 73-7, 110, 136, 147, 161, 163, 179, 192, 197, 202, 242, 337, 342-5 *pass.*, 353, 358, 374, 408-9, 441, 444, 458; agriculture, 246; climate of, 76-7, 168; economy in the nineteenth century, 188-91; Finns in, 183, 185; hydro-electricity, 266, 284-6, 289, 292, 294, 300; iron ores of, 376, 378, 397; pulp and paper industries in, 360, 365, 366, 367-9 *pass.*; settlement of, 181-6; towns, foundation of, 186
Norrmalm, 57, 59
Norsemen, 4
Norsk Aluminium Co., 427
Norsk Hydro, 20, 431, 432-3, 434-41 *pass.*
Norske Zinkkompani A/S, 439
North Atlantic Drift, 319
North Cape, 13
North Norway Plan, 203-4
North Sea Trade, 311-12
Norway, 4-8 *pass.*, 51, 62, 63, 236, 260, 448, 450, 453; abandonment of farms, 179-80; agriculture of, 221, 247-51; area of, 13; chemical industry in, 375, 428-33, 445; climate of, 165, 167-8, 294; colonization of Arctic Norway in the eighteenth century, 200-1; cores of, 18-23 *pass.*; dual outlook, 192-3; and economic union in Scandinavia, 458; electro-metallurgical industries, 434-41; engineering industries, 416, 417, 423-4; fisheries, 308, 315-22, 325, 326-32; forestry, 333, 338-9, 343, 348; forest ownership, 343-4; forests, 336-337; historical geography of, 192-204; hydro-electricity, 266, 274, 280-3, 290-297, 299, 302; Ice Age in, 150-1; independence of, 431, 440, 446; industries of, 261-5, 276; iron and steel in, 378-80, 401-3; iron mining in the north of, 203-4; isolation in, 13, 14; Lapps in, 202-3; merchant navy, 305-306, 313; population of, 14, 16; pulp industry in, 360, 361, 370, 372-3; railways, 272-3; rise of industry in twentieth century, 260; relations with Russia, 198-200; sawmills in, 354-6, 359; sea, relationship to, 28, 305, 308; shipbuilding, 420-3; trade, 24, 278, 439; underground power stations, 294
Norwegian Channel, 147
'Norwegian Riviera', 19
Norwegian Sea, 305, 316, 319

Index

Notodden, 431-40 *pass.*
Novgorod, 211, 212
Nuclear reactors, 400
Numedal, 27
Nyborg, 96
Nyby Bruk, 399, 400

Oak, 156, 335
Oats, 25, 49, 56, 63, 69, 100, 105, 183, 202, 225, 228, 234, 239, 244, 259
Odda, 30, 428-34 *pass.*
Odda Smelteverk A/S, 428
Odense, 95-6, 419
O.E.E.C. (Organization for European Economic Co-operation), 413, 452, 455
Ofoten fjord, 146
Oil, 263, 264, 278, 282, 313, 395, 420; oil dock, 114; oil-filled high voltage cables, 276; oil-heating equipment, 420; oil pipe-lines, 313; oil tankers, 305-7 *pass.*, 313-14, 412, 413, 422
Oilseeds, 91, 244
Öland, 71
Olav II, of Norway, 36
Olav V, of Denmark, 199
Olav Kyrre, 193
Olav Tryggveson, 37, 196
Olavinlinna, 134
Onega Lake, 144
Open fields: in Denmark, 221, 223; in Sweden, 236, 239
Open-hearth technique, 376, 392, 393, 394
Optical industry, 436
Orchards, 93, 124, 230, 248
Ordovician period, 146
Örebro, 48, 54-5, 272
Ore carriers, 413
Orkla, 36
Orkney, 28
Oslo, 1, 14, 16, 19, 20, 22-4, 25, 34, 193-197 *pass.*, 260, 262, 268, 272, 296, 315, 359, 373, 401, 402, 417, 423, 428
Oslo fjord, 13-24 *pass.*, 145, 161, 195, 290, 292, 320, 336, 351, 361, 373, 420, 422
Osnes family, 30
Östterbotten, 126-8, 131, 206, 219, 308; Swedish colonization of, 127
Öster Dal, 185
Østerdal, 26
Östergötland, 55, 177, 178
Östersund, 75
Østfold, 18, 19, 20, 195
Østlandet, 41
Otanmäki, 382, 404
Otta, 43
Oulu, 126, 127, 382, 383, 428, 445
Oulu River, 127, 137, 139, 215, 286,

302; hydro-electric schemes in, 287, 289, 345, 370
Oulujärvi, 210, 215-19 *pass.*, 287, 382, 404
Ounas River, 340
Outfield, 247
Oxelösund, 270, 388, 389, 395, 413
Oysters, 103

Päijänne, Lake, 129-33 *pass.*, 210, 211
Paint industry, 374, 395
Pajusaari island, 361
Palaeozoic period, 38, 73, 143
Paper, 16, 18, 20, 61, 109, 119, 127, 137, 190, 192, 243, 269, 335, 345, 351-58 *pass.*, 358-73, 378, 427
Parainen, 124
Parish woodlands, 343, 345
Pasvik River, 289
Pears, 248
Peasant culture and society, 7, 14, 16, 24, 195, 440; building in wood, 27-8; in Finland, 106, 128, 131-2, 209, 212-13; 334; folk museums, 92-3; in Norway, 247, 348, 432
Peat, 57, 240-1, 264, 338
Pedersen Process, 437
People's Democratic Party (Finland), 450
Permian period, 19, 22, 143, 147-8
Persberg, 394
Petäjäskoski, 289
Petsamo, 138, 206, 220, 308, 449
Pharmaceutical goods, 395
Phosphates, 441
Phosphoric ores, 376, 378, 385, 388, 392, 397
Pielisjärvi, 210, 215, 218
Pig iron, 376, 380, 382, 388, 397, 402, 404, 436
Pigs, 100, 225-35 *pass.*, 244, 418, 444
Pine, 26, 48, 136, 138, 185, 333, 335, 339, 340, 363
Pirkkala, 135, 215
Pirttikoski, 300
Piteå, 186
Place-names, *bo* element, 179; early elements in Östergötland, 178; *inge* element, 173; *rud* element, 179; *ryd* element, 179; *seter* element, 179
Plaice, 323
Plankton, 307, 308, 319
Plant breeding, 225, 239, 240
Plastics, 190, 395, 427, 428, 430, 433, 442
Pliocene period, 83, 149, 157
Plums, 35, 96, 123, 248
Plywood, 133, 134, 335, 340, 351, 374
Pneumatic drills, 410
Pohjanmaa, 220

Polar continental air, 165, 167
Polderlands, 233
Political unity of Scandinavia, 446, 447, 448
Polyvinyl chloride, 442
Porcelain, 20, 88
Pori, 125, 370
Porjus, 284-5
Porkkala peninsula, 253, 257
Porphyries, 144
Porsgrunn, 20, 438
Porvoo, 118
Porvoonjoki, 118
Post-glacial seas, 34, 35, 53, 55, 63, 68, 71, 75, 98, 110-11, 123, 154, 157, 158, 160, 181, 186, 209, 249, 252-3; marine deposits of, 161, 170, 196, 201-2; post-glacial emergence and history, 169-70
Potatoes, 35, 40, 75, 105, 131, 137, 161, 168, 202, 225, 239, 241, 246
Poultry, 235
Pre-Cambrian period, 18, 126, 149, 384
Precision instruments, 44
Prefabricated houses, 335
Prefabricated sections in shipbuilding, 413, 419
Printing, 23, 116
Protestantism, 4
Pulp, 16, 18, 20, 46, 60, 61, 66, 76, 79, 109, 119, 127, 132, 137, 138, 192, 261, 277, 298, 335, 340, 342, 345, 347, 351, 354, 356, 358-73, 378, 427; mechanical pulp, 360-1, 363, 370; chemical pulp, 360-1, 363, 370, 373-4, 441
Pulp machinery, 44, 400, 416, 417, 423
Pumps, 420
Purse seine net, 320, 327-8
Pyhäjärvi, Lake, 129
Pyrites, 264, 441
Pyynikki, esker, 135

Quarries, 378, 402
Quartz, 378, 384, 438

Raahe, 383, 401, 404
Radios, 261, 276, 407, 409, 424
Radio-telephones, 261, 320, 327, 409
Ragunda, 242
Railways, 14, 20, 23, 27, 36, 41, 43, 56, 57, 79, 96, 98, 103, 105, 134, 193, 270-274, 405; electrification, 409; equipment, 44, 55, 267, 407, 437; in Finland, 115, 118, 119, 130, 132, 137, 273; in Norway, 272-3; in Sweden, 64-5, 75, 186, 284
Raised beaches, 160-1
Ramnäs, 390, 393
Rana fjord, 380

Ranstad, 264
Rapakivi granite, 121, 122
Rape, 244
Rauma, 370
Rayon, 190, 354, 361
Razor blades, 398
Reclamation, 54, 56
Redistribution Act (1827), Sweden, 236
Refrigerators, 261, 276, 400, 405, 410, 418
Reindeer, 137, 188, 204; herders, 6, 40, 202-3; moss, 136
Reparations, 277, 286, 307, 369, 404, 416, 424, 426
Replot archipelago, 163, 170, 325
Research and industry, 363-4
Ribe, 99, 100, 106
Ringerike, 25
Ringkøping, 106
Ringsted, 88
Riss glaciation, 104
Rjukan, 296, 431-3, 440
Rjukan foss, 431
Roads, 20, 343, 347, 364, 370
Rocket bases, 450
Rogaland, 296
Roller bearings, 410
Rolled products, 380, 388
Rolling mills, 380, 392, 393, 397, 399, 400, 402
Romele Åsen, 70
Romerike, 25
Romsdal, 31, 32, 43
Romsdalsfjord, 294
Rondane, 41
Rønne, 95
Røros, 26
Rosenborg Castle, Copenhagen, 92
Rosendal, Barony of, 30
Roskilde, 86, 88, 175, 272
Røssäge power station, 292
Round timber, 270
Rovaniemi, 138, 382
Rubber, 116, 135
rud, place-name element, 62
Rudberg, Sten, 150
Russo-Finnish relations, 7, 108, 114, 115, 119, 206, 219, 251, 253, 263, 286-7, 307, 308, 424, 447, 449, 450-1
Rye, 55, 69, 105, 131, 183, 185, 221, 225, 228, 239, 240, 250, 253

Saab, 415
Sabroe Coy., 418
Sailing ships, 309
Saimaa Lake, 119, 128-33 *pass.*, 218, 219, 370, 451
St Botolph, 103

Index

St Petersburg, 115, 134, 154
Salmon fisheries, 304, 308, 325
Salpausselkä, 110, 114-18 *pass.*, 130, 133, 134, 154, 169, 257
Salt trade, 43, 441, 444
Saltfjord, 273, 291, 292
Sandefjord, 20
Sandviken, 61
Sarek massif, 73, 182
Sarpsborg, 18, 20, 373, 375, 428
Sarpsfossen, 18, 354
S.A.S., 458
Saudafjord, 438
Savo, 212-19 *pass.*
Savonlinna, 114, 115, 134
Savons, 218, 219
'Sawmill black death', 354
Sawmills, 16, 18, 61, 76, 119, 128, 133-38 *pass.*, 185, 188, 192, 268, 354-6, 361, 427; waste of, 373
Sawn timber, 20, 268, 277, 335, 350-8, 362
Saws, 61, 178, 398, 423
Scandinavian anticyclone, 167
Schleswig-Holstein, 100, 175-7
Schlusselburg Treaty, 214
Scorched-earth policy, 203, 253, 276
Scrap aluminium, 436
Scrap iron, 376, 388, 397, 402-4 *pass.*, 438
Seal fishing, 32, 163, 182, 200, 326, 331
Second crusade, 212
Senja, 198
Senonian limestone, 149
Seter, 162, 247, 248
Settlement: in Arctic Norway, 197-8; medieval colonization, 61-2; medieval settlement in Finland, 218; post-war colonization in Finland, 254-7; in pre-historic Finland, 210-11; types in Finland, 254-7
'Seven', The, 416, 453-6 *pass.*
Sheep, 40, 42, 71, 104
Sheet metal, 396, 399, 404
Shetland, 28, 63
Shifting settlement, 173
Ship building, 20, 24, 66, 67, 70, 88, 101, 116, 126, 243, 254, 261, 263, 269, 277, 369, 396, 402, 403, 416; in Denmark, 419-20; in Norway, 420-3; recession, 419-20; in Sweden, 411-14, 415, 416, 419-22 *pass.*
Ship burials, 173
Ship repairing, 24, 66, 70, 103, 116, 422
Ships, 58, 254, 274, 405
Siberia, 342
Siemens Martin furnace, 401
Siljan Lake, 50

Silurian period, 19, 25, 29, 40, 55, 56, 67, 71, 73, 75, 143, 146, 182, 186, 196
Silver, 27, 60, 145, 376
Silver fox, 249
Simo River, 127
Sitka spruce, 339
Skagen, 104
Skagerrak, 14, 20, 165, 302, 305, 320, 323, 409
Skåne, 11, 46, 48, 63, 67-70, 79, 88, 124, 143, 163, 181, 236-44 *pass.*, 284, 298, 388, 405; agriculture, 244, 246; climate, 67; Danish influences in, 69; forests, 342, 345; population of, 67
Skara, 160
Skellefteå, 76, 441
Skerry-guard, 32, 62, 146, 281, 320, 422
Skien, 19, 20, 266, 361
Skien fjord, 16, 20, 373, 432
Skog, place-name element, 62
Skoghall, 362-3
Skövde, 415
Slesvig, 99, 105, 153, 226
Slotsholm, 88
Småland, 48, 51, 55, 63-4, 68, 69, 77-9, 172, 175, 179, 236, 241, 336; climate of, 78
Small Holdings Acts (Denmark), 224
Smallholdings, 224, 235, 241-2, 418
Smögen, 323
Snåsa Lake, 35
Snowy Mountains project, 262
Soap, 70
Social Democratic Party (Finland), 451
Søderberg electrode, 437
Söderfors, 61, 378, 399, 400
Södermanland, 56-7, 389
Sodium nitrate, 433
Sogn, 292
Sogne fjord, 27, 30-1, 43, 193, 248, 275, 294, 427, 431, 434
Sognfjell, 43
Sømme, Axel, 251, 354
Sørfjord, 30, 248, 428
Sørlandet, 320, 343
Sorø, 88
Sound, The, 70, 87-90 *pass.*, 156, 167, 175, 315, 419, 458
South-eastern valleys (Norway), 24-8
Space relationships, 448
Specialized ships, 312
Sphagnum moss, 136
Spitsbergen, 146, 171, 200, 265-6, 331
Sponge iron, 261, 382, 385, 388, 397
Sprats, 320
Spring wheat, 221, 240, 259
Spruce, 26, 48, 335, 338-9, 340, 349, 363

485

Stabbur, 27
Staden, 170
Stamsund, 317
State control of industry, 385, 440
State forests, 343, 344-5, 348
State ownership of industry, 380, 383, 388, 404, 434, 440
Stathelle, 20
Stavanger, 20, 22, 193, 296, 329, 420
Stavanger Electro-Staalverk A/S, 402
Stavkirken, 27
Steam-driven sawmills, 35-54 *pass.*
Steamships, 309-10
Steel, 54, 204, 263, 275, 376, 378-89 *pass.*, 393-5, 396-404, 415, 434, 452; carbon steel, 398; commercial steel, 396, 397-398; ferro-alloys, 299, 396, 398, 401, 402, 423, 430, 438; mills, 385, 388, 392-5, 400, 401, 402, 404; musical reed steel, 399; steel plate, 396, 404; stainless steel, 390, 398-400; ship's plate, 413, 419, 422
Stensele, 186
Sterling area, 454
Stevns Klint, 87
Stiklestad, 36
Stjördal, 35, 36
Stockholm, 1, 23, 44, 48, 56, 57-9, 61, 71, 72, 73, 170, 177, 192, 262, 297, 298, 306, 315, 365, 405; archipelago, 48-9, 57, 222; convention of, 456; growth of, 59; industries of, 409-10; monopoly in Norrland, 59; population of, 48, 57; site of, 55, 57-8
Stokkfisk, 194
Stor Lake, 76, 182
Stora Kopparberg Bergslags Aktiebolag, 267, 378
Stord, 422
Stornorrfors, 286, 300, 409
Storsjön, 345
Strandflat, 34, 40, 157-8, 194-201 *pass.*, 236, 315, 317, 333
Strip mills, 393
Studsvik, 262
Sub-Atlantic period, 200
Sub-boreal period, 200
Sub-Cambrian peneplain, 41, 53, 56, 77, 109, 110, 145-6
Sub-Norwegian trench, 319
Submarine electric cables, 281, 282, 290, 419
Sugar beet, 55, 63, 69, 87, 93, 96, 112, 124, 225, 230, 231, 235, 239, 244
Sukselainen, Premier of Finland, 451
Sulitjelma, 439
Sulphate process, 360, 361, 375
Sulphite alcohol, 362, 374, 442, 444

Sulphite pulpmills, 360, 361, 374, 444
Sulphuric acid, 133, 428, 439, 441
Sundsvall, 76, 186, 188, 190
Sunndal, 275
Sunndalsør, 436, 440
Sunnmøre, 31-3, 157, 167, 320
Suomenlinna, 117
Suomenselkä, 253
Suomi, 211
Super-phosphate, 103, 119, 428, 439, 441
Super tankers, 422
Surahammar, 400
Svartisen, 380
Svea, 50, 54, 177, 179
Svealand, 51
svedjebruk, 185
Svelgen, 402
Svendborg, 97
Svenska Cellulosa A.B., 190, 345
Svenska Kullagerfabriken (S.K.F.), 410-411
Sverige-Nord Amerika Line, 66
Svolvær, 317, 327
Sweden, 2, 4, 5, 8, 11, 18, 44-79, 177-92, 236-46, 284-6, 383-400, 407-16, 441-4, 446-7, 448, 454; agrarian revolution in, 221, 236-9; agriculture, 236-46; area of, 13; chemical industry of, 374-375, 428, 441-4; climate, 166-7; coal, 265; comparison with Danish agriculture, 240-3; decline of population engaged in agriculture, 266-7; economy of, 44-6; engineering, 405-16; fisheries, 323-5, 326-32 *pass.*, forest ownership, 345-7; forestry, 333, 336, 342, 347-8, 349, 353; frontier of, 13, 23; growth of national territory, 50-1, 62, 64, 70, 76, 175, 446; historical geography of, 177-92; hydro-electricity, 266, 275, 280-82, 284-6, 300-2, 304; Ice Age in, 153-4; industrial revolution in, 188-90, 208-9, 359, 376, 378; industries, 261-2, 265, 276-7; merchant navy, 306, 313, 315; nationalism, 180-1; neutrality, 442, 447, 449-50, 453; population, 44; pulp and paper industry, 361, 362-3, 364-9; railways, 272, 273; sawn timber, 268, 354, 356-8; shipbuilding, 422, 411-14; Swedes in Finland, 117-18, 120-6 *pass.*, 181, 206, 211, 212, 218, 219, 446-7; towns, earliest in, 160, 178
Sydvaranger, 276, 378
Syenite, 145, 147
Synthetic fertilizers, 431, 433
Synthetic fibres, 190
Synthetic nitrates, 432, 441
Synthetic rubber, 430, 432

Index

Taasinge, 86, 96
Taberg, 78
Tallin, 114
Tammerkoski, 135
Tampere, 116, 134-5, 210, 215, 260, 269; industries of, 135; population of, 134
Tane River, 289
Tape recorders, 261, 276
Tar, 220, 267, 351-3
Telecommunications, 409
Telemark, 25, 27, 280, 296, 431
Telephones, 49, 276, 407, 409
Territorial waters, 331, 449
Tertiary period, 4, 11, 41, 51, 56, 78, 83, 87, 95, 98, 110, 129, 137, 143, 148-50, 205
Textiles, 24, 34, 64, 66, 91, 101, 116, 134, 178, 267, 278, 405, 457
Thermal power stations, 290, 297, 298, 418
Third crusade, 212, 214
Thomas process, 376, 385, 392, 397
Thorden, Gustav, 412
Thralls, 179
Three-field system, 236
Tidaholm, 178
Tietze, Wolf, 158
Timber, 5, 44, 61, 264, 267, 405, 453; cutters, 14; floating, 304, 353, 364; industries, recent trends of, 373-5, 424, 426, 457; trade in, 23
Tin, 269
Tinglev, 99
Tinnoset, 433
Tinnsjø, 433
Tithe accounts, 185
Tobacco, 96, 126, 230
Tokke, 280, 296
Tønder, 99
Tønning, 105, 106
Tønsberg, 20
Topelius, Zachris, 210, 214
Torne River, 75, 138, 139, 216, 289
Tornio, 218
Torridonian sandstone, 145
Tourism, 29, 43, 63, 87, 95, 118, 134, 178, 304, 337
Trade: of Denmark, 84, 90, 278, 306-7, 323, 416, 417, 455-6; of Finland, 109, 335, 358, 364, 416; medieval trade of Gotland, 72; of Norway, 305, 322, 330, 351, 439; post-war trade, 276; of Sweden, 364, 368, 400, 405, 410, 413, 415, 454-6; in World Wars I and II, 274-5
Tramp steamers, 44, 312
Transformers, 276, 405, 424
Transhumance, 24, 26, 29, 41-2, 183, 222, 248

Trawlers, 323, 325, 328-9
Treaty of Moscow (1944), 119
Treaty of Uusikaupunki (1721), 219, 449
Trelleborg, 69, 70
Trichlorethylene, 442
Trollhättan, 66, 266, 275, 407
Trollhättan canal, 64
Troms, 290
Tromsø, 162, 198, 200
Trøndelag, 31, 35-7, 41, 294, 297
Trondheim, 13, 14, 16, 20, 23, 36-7, 193, 196-7, 265, 302, 420; fjord, 16, 195-7, 292, 294, 296; population, 37
Tubes, 393, 399, 404
Tundra, 1, 6, 26, 73, 107, 136, 157, 168, 188, 202
Turbines, 44, 416
Turku, 110, 115, 121, 124-6, 211, 212, 404; population, 125
Turnips, 34
Two-field system, 236
Tyin Lake, 292
Tyrifjord, 25, 373
Tysland-Hole electric furnace, 402
Tyssedal, 30, 34, 428, 434
Tyssefaldene, 439
Tysso River, 428

Uddeholm, 362, 390, 399
Uddevalla, 412, 414, 422
Ulriken gneiss, 193
Ume River, 285, 286, 300, 409
Umeå, 186
Union of Kalmar (1389), 446
Uppland, 50, 53-4, 57, 146, 158, 245
Uppsala, 53, 54, 158, 177, 211
Uranium, 264
Utmark, 247
Uusikaupunki, Treaty of, 219, 449

Vääksy canal, 129
Vaasa, 115, 125, 127, 134
Vacuum cleaners, 276, 410
Väja, 368
Valdres, 27
Valkeakoski, 133
Valve springs, 398
Vanadium, 402
Vanajavesi, 133
Vantaa River, 115
Varanger fjord, 198, 203, 204, 290, 319
Vardø, 319
Vardøhus, 198
Värmland, 61-2, 219, 353, 366, 389
Vasa, House of, 58

Väster Dal, 75, 185
Västerås, 48, 54, 298, 407
Västerbotten, 76, 183
Västervik, 302
Västmanland, 54
Vättern Lake, 55, 79, 167, 177
Vegetable oils, 444
Veitsiluoto Coy., 358, 375
Vendsyssel, 102
Vennesla, 436
Verdal, 35, 36
Versailles Conference, 447
Vertical integration, 371, 375
Vertical zonation of forests, 336
Vesijärvi Lake, 129
Vestebro Park, 102
Vesterälen, 200, 290
Vestergötland, 55-6, 177, 178, 244
Vestfjord, 315-28 *pass.*, 330, 332
Vestfjorddal, 432
Vestfold, 18, 19, 20, 22, 25, 195
Vestlandet, 32, 41, 193, 247, 336, 338, 436; changes in farming, 248; fisheries of, 315, 319-20, 331, 336
V.H.F. transmitters and receivers, 261
Viborg, 104
Vidda, 333
Vigeland, Gustav, 24
Viipuri, 120, 134, 181, 211, 219
Vikings, 3, 14, 28, 34, 46, 158, 172, 173, 198; and forest clearance, 179-180
vin, 198
Visby, 72, 302, 409
Viskan, 64
Vistula River, 209, 211, 449
Vivsta varv, 188
Volvo Coy., 414-15
Vuoksi River, 119, 129, 134, 286, 289

Wage rates, 413, 415
Wallboard, 335, 342, 351, 367, 373-4
Wallpaper glue, 375
Walrus ivory, 440
Washing machines, 261, 276
Watercourse Regulation Act (1917), Norway, 304

Water-driven sawmills, 351
Welfare state, 281, 305, 332, 348, 458
Wenström, Jonas, 407, 408
West German Federal Republic, 276-7, 368, 449
Western fjords, 28-35
Whalebone, 37
Whaling, 20, 198, 200, 264, 320-2, 330; factories, 5, 330, 423; international convention on, 321-2
Wheat, 25, 49, 55, 60, 63, 69, 87, 100, 112, 124, 163, 172, 173, 221, 225-229 *pass.*, 230-1, 239, 249, 250, 253, 259
White Sea, 331
Wingquist, Sven, 410
Winter War, 119, 253, 308, 382, 424
Winter wheat, 163, 225, 239, 244, 259
Wire, 269, 404
Wire mills, 393, 401, 424
Wire rods, 298
Wirtschaftsdienst, 413
Wisconsin glaciation, 151
Wolves, 107
Wood processing, 333, 348, 354, 359, 362-363, 369, 374, 442
Woollen industry, 34, 64
World War I, 99, 115, 124, 191, 233, 274, 401, 440, 442
World War II, 95, 100, 108, 109, 203, 204, 210, 233, 243, 253-4, 273, 274-6, 284, 286, 297, 310, 375, 396, 404, 430, 433, 437, 447
Würm glaciation, 150, 151, 158

Yoldia Sea, 156, 206
yt Arna, 34

Zealand, 83, 86-8, 92, 93, 169, 173-5, 176, 230, 404, 418
Zimmerman, Maurice, 432
Zinc, 60, 145, 263, 427, 428, 434, 438, 439
Zirconium, 438
Zuider Zee, 102

THE END

PRINTED BY R. & R. CLARK LTD., EDINBURGH